W9-APO-225

# THE IDEA

CARL BENSON · TAYLOR LITTLETON · *Auburn University*

# OF TRAGEDY

*Scott, Foresman and Company*

Library of Congress Catalog Card No. 66-14838

Copyright © 1966 by Scott, Foresman and Company, Glenview, Illinois 60025

All rights reserved. Printed in the United States of America.

Regional offices of Scott, Foresman and Company are located in

Atlanta, Dallas, Glenview, Palo Alto, and Oakland, N.J.

The authors are grateful to two of their colleagues, Professors Norman Brittin and Ward Allen, who offered helpful advice during the preparation of this book.

The authors also gratefully acknowledge the following publishers for permission to reprint the selections in this book:

**George Allen & Unwin Ltd.** for excerpts from *The Paradox of Tragedy* by D. D. Raphael.

**Anderson House** for excerpts from "The Essence of Tragedy" by Maxwell Anderson. Copyright 1939 by Maxwell Anderson. All rights reserved. Reprinted by permission of Anderson House.

**Ashley Famous Agency, Inc.** for "Tragedy and the Common Man" by Arthur Miller. Reprinted by permission of Ashley Famous Agency, Inc. Copyright © 1949 by The New York Times Company.

**Cambridge University Press** for excerpts from *The Origin of Attic Comedy* by Francis M. Cornford.

**The Clarendon Press** for excerpts from *Hamlet, Father and Son* by Peter Alexander. Reprinted by permission of The Clarendon Press, Oxford.

**Cornell University Press** for excerpts from *Tragedy: A View of Life* by Henry A. Myers. © 1956 by Cornell University Press. Used by permission of Cornell University Press.

**Hardin Craig** for his text of Shakespeare's *King Lear*.

**Crown Publishers, Inc.** for excerpts from "Catharsis and The Modern Theater" by John Gassner. From *European Theories of the Drama* by Barret H. Clark. Copyright 1947 by Crown Publishers, Inc. Used by permission of the publishers.

**Dover Publications, Inc.** for excerpts from *Aristotle's Theory of Poetry and Fine Art* by S. H. Butcher, translator. Published by Dover Publications, Inc., New York 14, New York, at $2.00, and reprinted through permission of the publisher.

**Harcourt, Brace, & World, Inc.** for excerpts from *The Modern Temper,* copyright 1929, 1957 by Joseph Wood Krutch. Reprinted by permission of Harcourt, Brace, & World, Inc.

**Harvard University Press** for excerpts from *The Classical Tradition in Poetry* by Gilbert Murray. Copyright 1927 by the President and Fellows of Harvard College and 1955 by Gilbert Murray. Reprinted by permission of the publishers.

**Hogarth Press Ltd.** for excerpts from *Tragedy* by F. L. Lucas.

**Indiana University Press** for excerpts from *The Paradox of Tragedy* by D. D. Raphael.

**The Macmillan Company** for excerpts from *Tragedy* by F. L. Lucas. Copyright © 1957, 1962 by F. L. Lucas. Reprinted with permission of The Macmillan Company.

**Macmillan & Company Ltd., St. Martin's Press, Inc.,** and **The Macmillan Company of Canada, Ltd.** for excerpts from *Shakespearean Tragedy* by A. C. Bradley.

**Methuen & Company Ltd.** for excerpts from *The Frontiers of Drama* by Una Ellis-Fermor. Published in the United States by Barnes & Noble, Inc. Reprinted by permission of Methuen & Company Ltd.

**The New York Times** for "Tragedy and the Common Man" by Arthur Miller. © 1949 by The New York Times Company. Reprinted by permission of Ashley Famous Agency, Inc.

**Oxford University Press**, London, for excerpts from *Archetypal Patterns in Poetry* by Maud Bodkin.

**Penguin Books, Ltd.** for E. F. Watling's translation of *King Oedipus* from *The Theban Plays* and for Philip Vellacott's translation of *Agamemnon* from *The Oresteian Trilogy*.

**Routledge & Kegan Paul Ltd.** for excerpt from *The Story of the Night* by John Holloway.

**University of Nebraska Press** for excerpts from *Romance and Tragedy* by Prosser Hall Frye. Reprinted by permission of the University of Nebraska Press. Copyright 1961 by the University of Nebraska Press.

# INTRODUCTION

What is tragedy? Oedipus himself might quail at this sphinx-like question, and this book proposes no final answer to it. But it does seek to present evidence that Western man's traditional conception of himself as a tragic figure and his artistic expression of this awareness in drama is full of meaning for the student in the twentieth century. It is hoped that the contents and arrangement of this book will aid the student who sets out seriously to search for that meaning.

"Idea," the opening section of essays, has a beginning, a middle, and an end. It opens with Aristotle's classic statement of the theory of tragedy (to which a detailed modern commentary is appended), a definition that all subsequent writers on the subject have either developed, explicated, or rejected. The middle is comprised of a dozen essays that attempt less to define the tragic mystery as a whole than to make complete statements on one aspect of it — the nature of the tragic hero, the ritual element in the tragic structure, *catharsis*, and so on. Although Gilbert Murray and Maud Bodkin may seem to offer specialized points of view, although the A. C. Bradley and Peter Alexander selections are, in a sense, companion pieces, and although many of the essays complement each other, nevertheless each one is a self-contained statement. The section closes with the two best-known arguments concerning possibilities for tragic expression in the modern world. All sixteen essays have been selected to provide the student with a diverse set of judgments with which he may widen his critical approach to the meaning of the tragedies in Part Two.

Four of the six tragedies — *Agamemnon, King Oedipus, King Lear,* and *The Duchess of Malfi* — have been selected from what are generally regarded as the two great ages of tragic composition: fifth-century Athens and Renaissance England. That these two periods in history also mark high tides in the Western World's confidence in human possibilities perhaps makes valid Nietzsche's observation — which the student will doubtless wish to ponder carefully — that tragedy becomes possible only in an age of optimism. But whereas these four dramas take a hard — and perhaps hopeful — look at man's prospects for victory over the gods, destiny, and himself, the late nineteenth-century plays of Ibsen and Chekhov contain elements that are hardly present in the Greek and Elizabethan works but that are nevertheless strongly pervasive in twentieth-century literature. *Rosmersholm* shows the uncertain direction of modern life by presenting a man caught between loyalty to a religious and heroic tradition that has lost its vitality and the doubtful promise of social ideals. Chekhov's sensitively naturalistic *Uncle Vanya* is not fully tragic, of course, but it is included to allow the student to ask questions about where tragedy begins and leaves off. Although Chekhov's characters do not confront the fearful symmetry of a mechanistic universe, as do many representative figures in contemporary literature, they face what is perhaps the more central problem of how to retain humanity in the midst of an aimless and cluttered existence.

Part Two, "Tragedy," is arranged in a slightly unorthodox manner. Two sets of three plays are presented, each set containing a Greek, an Elizabethan, and a modern play. Although the plays within each triad are quite different in form and social context, they are to some extent unified in theme and situation. *King Oedipus, King Lear,* and *Rosmersholm* are tragedies in which the hero suffers the pains of self-discovery and is forced to attain a new awareness of himself. *Agamemnon, The Duchess of Malfi,* and *Uncle Vanya* show figures unhappily imprisoned by circumstances seemingly beyond their control; in addition, both *Agamemnon* and *Uncle Vanya* (and *Rosmersholm*) reflect the age-old theme of the burdens laid by the past on the present.

This arrangement of the plays is not intended to suggest that the assumption in Greek tragedy of a grand design in the universe, which encloses the apparent chaos in the lives of men, is necessarily found also in the work of Ibsen and Chekhov. Nor should this organizational scheme prevent the student's perceiving that there are striking differences in method, material, and dramatic statement among the dramas written for the theaters of fifth-century Athens, Elizabethan England, and nineteenth-century Europe. But despite all the differences and despite the fact that each play is unique in presenting a particular action, the student doubtless will also discover that there is an astonishing likeness at the root of all genuine expressions of tragic experience.

Thus, if the plays are read and discussed in the order presented, the student will move twice through the historical sequence of Greek, Elizabethan, and modern tragic insight on a common theme. It is hoped that this repeated progression will help enforce the understanding that although the lofty, ethic, mythological generalizations upon which Greek tragedy rests may not fit either the psychological involvements of the romanticized Elizabethan hero or the frustrations of the narrowly circumscribed and diminished characters of Chekhov, *tragedy* is nonetheless a term that transcends time and place. Of course, the plays are also adaptable to the more traditional approach, which explores chronologically the tragic consciousness of classic, Renaissance, and modern drama.

The questions at the end of each play are largely conceptual and seek to correlate the critical appraisals of tragedy with the plays themselves rather than to pose the kind of restricted, analytic, textual problems that are best conceived by the individual instructor. Many of the questions may serve as essay assignments, and more elaborate papers may result from the student's measuring carefully one of the six plays in this book (or some other play) against one of the critical theories in Part One. To that end, the original pagination of the essays is provided between diagonals, e.g., /14/. Questions on certain twentieth-century plays comprise the last section of the book; thus, the student may add an extra dimension to his study by assaying the possibility of tragedy in the contemporary world, by brooding over the implications of such essays as those of Joseph Wood Krutch and Arthur Miller, or by trying to apply to modern drama Prosser Hall Frye's notion of the "tragic qualm."

The editors hope that the student will be challenged to provide thoughtful and discriminating answers to the many questions that the plays, critical opinions, and aids to study will raise for him. He may, in fact, decide upon reflection that several of the dramas in this book should not be called tragedies at all. Surely *Uncle Vanya* hovers between the tragic, the comic, and the pathetic. What, then, distinguishes tragedy from other dramatic forms? Lear behaves irrationally at the very beginning, to say nothing of when he is mad, or near-mad, on the heath. Can such a man be a tragic hero? If Oedipus is truly a tragic figure, where do the causes of his tragedy lie — in his unwitting fulfillment of an irrational prophecy, in his human and inescapable will to know, or in his pride? Is there such a thing as a "tragic flaw"? If so, can the tragic flaw of the classics be represented in the same sense in a modern context?

Do ritualistic interpretations, in terms of which Oedipus and Lear may be viewed as scapegoats, modify significantly our criteria for tragedy? To what extent is *catharsis* (if that is always a pertinent term) dependent upon suffering that results from a choice freely made between seriously demanding alternatives? Is it always characteristic of tragedy that the free choice and subsequent suffering are accompanied by heroic assumption of responsibility? Is the *catharsis* effected through our realization of the ascending grandeur of the hero, even in his fall?

If there is some validity in Nietzsche's observation that tragedy is possible only in an age of optimism, something very like the reverse is probably true as well. A meaningful optimism is possible only in terms of a serious realization of the evil in the world and of the inescapable disproportion in rewards and punishments, which fall mysteriously to the deserving and the undeserving. Recognizing that tragedy is in certain necessary ways related to the contemporary social context, is it not reasonable to think that it is also in some way beyond the contemporary and in an arena where, in Yeats' terms, contradictions are never resolved, where man feels at the same time "predestinate and free"? Is not this what Shakespeare suggests when he has Hamlet exclaim, "What a piece of work is Man" — man who can reason like a god but who also can fall prey to the most bestial appetites? In short, are not pessimism and optimism the necessary twin and opposite poles of total realization of man's potentiality, a potentiality that becomes tragic in proportion as the tragic artist dramatizes the immense range between aspiring pride and wisdom learned through suffering? Are not these terms forever relevant — from Aeschylus to Sartre?

Thus, here are many problems and issues to consider. But as the student analyzes these dramas and begins to sense the nature and range of the tragic emotion, to sense the evolvement — or perhaps the rise and fall — of the idea of tragedy in Western culture, he may well pose to himself the ultimate question of whether the ordinary twentieth-century man, minus an Apollo and minus the Renaissance hero's conviction that one can effect his destiny by applying the virtues of his own mind, may still discover in himself those certain qualities of dignity, heroism, and confidence that make possible a response to the high call of tragic experience. One of the important purposes of this book is to stimulate such an inquiry and, if the student's answer to the question is negative, to perform an equally significant function by reminding him of what he and his age have lost.

# CONTENTS

# PART TWO : TRAGEDY

# PART ONE

✻

# IDEA

※

# ARISTOTLE: *The Poetics*

Tragedy, then, is an imitation of an action that is serious, complete, and of a certain magnitude; in language embellished with each kind of artistic ornament, the several kinds being found in separate parts of the play; in the form of action, not of narrative; through pity and fear effecting the proper purgation of these emotions. By 'language embellished,' I mean language into which rhythm, 'harmony,' and song enter. By 'the several kinds in separate parts,' I mean, that some parts are rendered through the medium of verse alone, others again with the aid of song.

Now as tragic imitation implies persons acting, it necessarily follows, in the first place, that Spectacular equipment will be a part of Tragedy. Next, Song and Diction, for these are the medium of imitation. By 'Diction' /23/ I mean the mere metrical arrangement of the words: as for 'Song,' it is a term whose sense every one understands.

Again, Tragedy is the imitation of an action; and an action implies personal agents, who necessarily possess certain distinctive qualities both of character and thought; for it is by these that we qualify actions themselves, and these — thought and character — are the two natural causes from which actions spring, and on actions again all success or failure depends. Hence, the Plot is the imitation of the action: — for by plot I here mean the arrangement of the incidents. By Character I mean that in virtue of which we ascribe certain qualities to the agents. Thought is required wherever a statement is proved, or, it may be, a general truth enunciated. Every Tragedy, therefore, must have six parts, which parts determine its quality — namely, Plot, Character, Diction, Thought, Spectacle, Song. Two of the parts constitute the medium of imitation, one the manner, and three the objects of imitation. And these complete the list. These elements have been employed, we may say, by the poets to a man; in fact, every play contains Spectacular elements as well as Character, Plot, Diction, Song, and Thought.

But most important of all is the structure of the /25/ incidents. For Tragedy is an imitation, not of men, but of an action and of life, and life consists in action, and its end is a mode of action, not a quality. Now character determines men's qualities, but it is by their actions that they are happy or the reverse. Dramatic action, therefore, is not with a view to the representation of character: character comes in as subsidiary to the actions. Hence the incidents and the plot are the end of a tragedy; and the end is the chief thing of all. Again, without action there cannot be a tragedy; there may be without character. The tragedies of most of our modern poets fail in the rendering of character; and of poets in general this is often true. It is the same in painting; and here lies the difference between Zeuxis and Polygnotus. Polygnotus delineates character well: the style of Zeuxis is devoid of ethical quality. Again, if you string together a set of speeches expressive of character, and well finished in point of diction and thought, you will not produce the essential tragic effect nearly so well as with a play which, however deficient in these respects, yet has a plot and artistically constructed incidents. Besides which, the most power-

From "The Poetics," in Aristotle's Theory of Poetry and Fine Art, *trans. S. H. Butcher, 4th ed. (New York: Dover Publications, Inc., 1951). Translation originally published in 1894.*

ful elements of emotional interest in Tragedy — Peripeteia or Reversal of the Situation, and Recognition scenes — are parts of the plot. A further proof is, that novices in the art attain to finish of diction and precision of portraiture before they can construct the plot. It is the same with almost all the early poets.

The Plot, then, is the first principle, and, as it were, /27/ the soul of a tragedy: Character holds the second place. A similar fact is seen in painting. The most beautiful colours, laid on confusedly, will not give as much pleasure as the chalk outline of a portrait. Thus Tragedy is the imitation of an action, and of the agents mainly with a view to the action.

Third in order is Thought, — that is, the faculty of saying what is possible and pertinent in given circumstances. In the case of oratory, this is the function of the political art and of the art of rhetoric: and so indeed the older poets make their characters speak the language of civic life; the poets of our time, the language of the rhetoricians. Character is that which reveals moral purpose, showing what kind of things a man chooses or avoids. Speeches, therefore, which do not make this manifest, or in which the speaker does not choose or avoid anything whatever, are not expressive of character. Thought, on the other hand, is found where something is proved to be or not to be, or a general maxim is enunciated.

Fourth among the elements enumerated comes Diction; by which I mean, as has been already said, the expression of the meaning in words; and its essence is the same both in verse and prose.

Of the remaining elements Song holds the chief place among the embellishments.

The Spectacle has, indeed, an emotional attraction of its own, but, of all the parts, it is the least artistic, and connected least with the art of poetry. For the power of Tragedy, we may be sure, is felt even apart from representation and actors. Besides, the production of /29/ spectacular effects depends more on the art of the stage machinist than on that of the poet.

These principles being established, let us now discuss the proper structure of the Plot, since this is the first and most important thing in Tragedy.

Now, according to our definition, Tragedy is an imitation of an action that is complete, and whole, and of a certain magnitude; for there may be a whole that is wanting in magnitude. A whole is that which has a beginning, a middle, and an end. A beginning is that which does not itself follow anything by causal necessity, but after which something naturally is or comes to be. An end, on the contrary, is that which itself naturally follows some other thing, either by necessity, or as a rule, but has nothing following it. A middle is that which follows something as some other thing follows it. A well constructed plot, therefore, must neither begin nor end at haphazard, but conform to these principles.

Again, a beautiful object, whether it be a living organism or any whole composed of parts, must not only have an orderly arrangement of parts, but must also be of a certain magnitude; for beauty depends on magnitude and order. Hence a very small animal organism cannot be beautiful; for the view of it is confused, the object being seen in an almost imperceptible moment of time. Nor, again, can one of vast size be beautiful; for as the eye cannot take it all in at once, the unity and sense of the whole is lost for the spectator; as for instance if there were one a thousand miles long. As, therefore, in the case of animate bodies and organisms a certain magnitude is necessary, and a magni- /31/ tude which may be easily embraced in one view; so in the plot, a certain length is necessary, and a length which can be easily embraced by the memory. The limit of length in relation to dramatic competition and sensuous presentment, is no part of artistic theory. For had it been the rule for a hundred tragedies to compete together, the performance would have been regulated by the water-clock, — as indeed we are told was formerly done. But the limit as fixed by the nature of the drama itself is this: — the greater the length, the more beautiful will the piece be by reason of its size, provided that the whole be perspicuous. And to define the matter roughly, we may say that the proper magnitude is comprised within such limits, that the sequence of events, according to the law of probability or necessity, will admit of a change from bad fortune to good, or from good fortune to bad.

Unity of plot does not, as some persons think, consist in the unity of the hero. For infinitely various are the incidents in one man's life which cannot be reduced to unity; and so, too, there are many actions of one man out of which we cannot make one action. Hence the error, as it appears, of all poets who have composed a Heracleid, a Theseid, or other poems of the kind. They imagine that as Heracles was one man, the story of Heracles must also be a unity. But Homer, as in all else he is of surpassing merit, here too — whether from art or natural genius — seems to have happily discerned the truth. In composing the Odyssey he did not include all the adventures of Odysseus — such as his wound on Parnassus, or his feigned madness at the mustering of /33/ the host — incidents between which there was no necessary or probable connexion: but he made the Odyssey, and likewise the Iliad, to centre round an action that in our sense of the word is one. As therefore, in the other imitative arts, the imitation is one when the object imitated is one, so the plot, being an imitation of an action, must imitate one action and that a whole, the structural union of the parts being such that, if any one of them is displaced or removed, the whole will be disjointed and disturbed. For a thing whose presence or absence makes no visible difference, is not an organic part of the whole.

It is, moreover, evident from what has been said, that it is not the function of the poet to relate what has happened, but what may happen, — what is possible according to the law of probability or necessity. The poet and the historian differ not by writing in verse or in prose. The work of Herodotus might be put into verse, and it would still be a species of history, with metre no less than without it. The true difference is that one relates what has happened, the other what may happen. Poetry, therefore, is a more philosophical and a higher thing than history: for poetry tends to express the universal, history the particular. By the universal I mean how a person of a certain type will on occasion speak or act, according to the law of probability or necessity; and it is this universality at which poetry aims in the names she attaches to the personages. The particular is — for example — what Alcibiades did or suffered. In Comedy this is already apparent: for here the poet first constructs the plot on the lines of prob- /35/ ability, and then inserts characteristic names; — unlike the lampooners who write about particular individuals. But tragedians still keep to real names, the reason being that what is possible is credible: what has not happened we do not at once feel sure to be possible: but what has happened is manifestly possible: otherwise it would not have happened. Still there are even some tragedies in which there are only one or two well known names, the rest being fictitious. In others, none are well known, — as in Agathon's Antheus, where incidents and names alike are fictitious, and yet they give none the less pleasure. We must not, therefore, at all costs keep to the received legends, which are the usual subjects of Tragedy. Indeed, it would be absurd to attempt it; for even subjects that are known are known only to a few, and yet give pleasure to all. It clearly follows that the poet or 'maker' should be the maker of plots rather than of verses; since he is a poet because he imitates, and what he imitates are actions. And even if he chances to take an historical subject, he is none the less a poet; for there is no reason why some events that have actually happened should not conform to the law of the probable and possible, and in virtue of that quality in them he is their poet or maker.

Of all plots and actions the epeisodic are the worst. /37/ I call a plot 'epeisodic' in which the episodes or acts succeed one another without probable or necessary sequence. Bad poets compose such pieces by their own fault, good poets, to please the players; for, as they write show pieces for competition, they stretch the plot beyond its capacity, and are often forced to break the natural continuity.

But again, Tragedy is an imitation not only of a complete action, but of events inspiring fear or pity. Such an effect is best produced when the events come on us by surprise; and the effect is heightened when, at the same time, they follow as cause and effect. The tragic wonder will then be greater than if they happened of themselves or by accident; for even coincidences are most striking when they have an air of design. We may instance the statue of Mitys at Argos, which fell upon his murderer while he was a spectator at a festival, and killed him. Such events seem not to be due to mere chance. Plots, therefore, constructed on these principles are necessarily the best.

Plots are either Simple or Complex, for the actions in real life, of which the plots are an imitation, obviously show a similar distinction. An action which is one and continuous in the sense above defined, I call Simple, when the change of fortune takes place without Reversal of the Situation and without Recognition.

A Complex action is one in which the change is accompanied by such Reversal, or by Recognition, or by both. These last should arise from the internal structure of the plot, so that what follows should be the /39/ necessary or probable result of the preceding action. It makes all the difference whether any given event is a case of *propter hoc* or *post hoc*.

Reversal of the Situation is a change by which the action veers round to its opposite, subject always to our rule of probability or necessity. Thus in the Oedipus, the messenger comes to cheer Oedipus and free him from his alarms about his mother, but by revealing who he is, he produces the opposite effect. Again in the Lynceus, Lynceus is being led away to his death, and Danaus goes with him, meaning to slay him; but the outcome of the preceding incidents is that Danaus is killed and Lynceus saved.

Recognition, as the name indicates, is a change from ignorance to knowledge, producing love or hate between the persons destined by the poet for good or bad fortune. The best form of recognition is coincident with a Reversal of the Situation, as in the Oedipus. There are indeed other forms. Even inanimate things of the most trivial kind may in a sense be objects of recognition. Again, we may recognise or discover whether a person has done a thing or not. But the recognition which is most intimately connected with the plot and action is, as we have said, the recognition of persons. This recognition, combined with Reversal, will produce either pity or fear; and actions producing these effects are those which, by our definition, Tragedy represents. Moreover, it is upon such situations that the issues of good or bad fortune will depend. /41/ Recognition, then, being between persons, it may happen that one person only is recognised by the other — when the latter is already known — or it may be necessary that the recognition should be on both sides. Thus Iphigenia is revealed to Orestes by the sending of the letter; but another act of recognition is required to make Orestes known to Iphigenia.

Two parts, then, of the Plot — Reversal of the Situation and Recognition — turn upon surprises. A third part is the Scene of Suffering. The Scene of Suffering is a destructive or painful action, such as death on the stage, bodily agony, wounds and the like. . . . /43/

As the sequel to what has already been said, we must proceed to consider what the poet should aim at, and what he should avoid, in constructing his plots; and by what means the specific effect of Tragedy will be produced.

A perfect tragedy should, as we have seen, be arranged not on the simple but on the complex plan. It should, moreover, imitate actions which excite pity and fear, this being the distinctive mark of tragic imitation. It follows plainly, in the first place, that the change of fortune presented must not be the spectacle of a virtuous man brought from prosperity to adversity: for this moves neither pity nor fear; it merely shocks us. Nor, again, that of a bad man passing from adversity to prosperity: for nothing can be more alien to the spirit of Tragedy; it possesses no single tragic quality; it neither satisfies the moral sense nor calls forth pity or fear. Nor, again, should the downfall of the utter villain be exhibited. A plot of this kind would, doubtless, satisfy the moral sense, but it would inspire neither pity nor fear; for pity is aroused by unmerited misfortune, fear by the misfortune of a man like ourselves. Such an event, therefore, will be neither pitiful nor terrible. There remains, then, the character between these two extremes, — that of a man who is not eminently good and just, yet whose misfortune is brought about not by vice or depravity, but by some error or frailty. He must be one who is highly renowned and prosperous, — a /45/ personage like Oedipus, Thyestes, or other illustrious men of such families.

A well constructed plot should, therefore, be single in its issue, rather than double as some maintain. The change of fortune should be not from bad to good, but, reversely, from good to bad. It should come about as the result not of vice, but of some great error or frailty, in a character either such as we have described, or better rather than worse. The practice of the stage bears out our view. At first the poets recounted any legend that came in their way. Now, the best tragedies are founded on the story of a few houses, — on the fortunes of Alcmaeon, Oedipus, Orestes, Meleager, Thyestes, Telephus, and those others who have done or suffered something terrible. A tragedy, then, to be perfect according to the rules of art should be of this construction. Hence they are in error who censure Euripides just because he follows this principle in his plays, many of which end unhappily. It is, as we have said, the right ending. The best proof is that on the stage and in dramatic competition, such plays, if well worked out, are the most tragic in effect; and Euripides, faulty though he may be in the general management of his subject, yet is felt to be the most tragic of the poets.

In the second rank comes the kind of tragedy which some place first. Like the Odyssey, it has a double thread of plot, and also an opposite catastrophe for the good and for the bad. It is accounted the best because of the weakness of the spectators; for the poet is guided in what he writes by the wishes of his audience. The pleasure, however, thence derived is not the true tragic /47/ pleasure. It is proper rather to Comedy, where those who, in the piece, are the deadliest enemies — like Orestes and Aegisthus — quit the stage as friends at the close, and no one slays or is slain.

Fear and pity may be aroused by spectacular means; but they may also result from the inner structure of the piece, which is the better way, and indicates a superior poet. For the plot ought to be so constructed that, even without the aid of the eye, he who hears the tale told will thrill with horror and melt to pity at what takes place. This is the impression we should receive from hearing the story of the Oedipus. But to produce this effect by the mere spectacle is a less artistic method, and dependent on extraneous aids. Those who employ spectacular means to create a sense not of the terrible but only of the monstrous, are strangers to the purpose of Tragedy; for we must not demand of Tragedy any and every kind of pleasure, but only that which is proper to it. And since the pleasure which the poet should afford is that which comes from pity and fear through imitation, it is evident that this quality must be impressed upon the incidents.

Let us then determine what are the circumstances which strike us as terrible or pitiful.

Actions capable of this effect must happen between persons who are either friends or enemies or indifferent to one another. If an enemy kills an enemy, there is nothing to excite pity either in the act or the intention, — except so far as the suffering in itself is pitiful. So again with indifferent persons. But when the tragic incident occurs between those who are near or dear to /49/ one another — if, for example, a brother kills, or intends to kill, a brother, a son his father, a mother her son, a son his mother, or any other deed of the kind is done — these are the situations to be looked for by the poet. He may not indeed destroy the framework of the received legends — the fact, for instance, that Clytemnestra was slain by Orestes and Eriphyle by Alcmaeon — but he ought to show invention of his own, and skilfully handle the traditional material. Let us explain more clearly what is meant by skilful handling.

The action may be done consciously and with knowledge of the persons, in the manner of the older poets. It is thus too that Euripides makes Medea slay her children. Or, again, the deed of horror may be done, but done in ignorance, and the tie of kinship or friendship be discovered afterwards. The Oedipus of Sophocles is an example. Here, indeed, the incident is outside the drama proper; but cases occur where it falls within the action of the play: one may cite the Alcmaeon of Astydamas, or Telegonus in the Wounded Odysseus. Again, there is a third case, — to be about to act with knowledge of the persons and then not to act. The fourth case is when some one is about to do an irreparable deed through ignorance, and makes the discovery before it is done. These are the only possible ways. For the deed must either be done or not done, — and that wittingly or unwittingly. But of all these ways, to be about to act knowing the persons, and then not to act, is the worst. It is shocking without being tragic, for no disaster follows. It is, therefore, never, or very rarely, found in poetry. One instance, however, is in the Antigone, where Haemon threatens to kill Creon. The next and better way is that the deed /51/ should be perpetrated. Still better, that it should be perpetrated in ignorance, and the discovery made afterwards. There is then nothing to shock us, while the discovery produces a startling effect. The last case is the best, as when in the Cresphontes Merope is about to slay her son, but, recognising who he is, spares his life. So in the Iphigenia, the sister recognises the brother just in time. Again in the Helle, the son recognises the mother when on the point of giving her up. This, then, is why a few families only, as has been already observed, furnish the subjects of tragedy. It was not art, but happy chance, that led the poets in search of subjects to impress the tragic quality upon their plots. They are compelled, therefore, to have recourse to those houses whose history contains moving incidents like these.

Enough has now been said concerning the structure of the incidents, and the right kind of plot.

In respect of Character there are four things to be aimed at. First, and most important, it must be good. Now any speech or action that manifests moral purpose of any kind will be expressive of character: the character will be good if the purpose is good. This rule is relative to each class. Even a woman may be good, and also a slave; though the woman may be said to be an inferior being, and the slave quite worthless. The second thing to aim at is propriety. There is a type of manly valour; but valour in a woman, or unscrupulous cleverness, is inappropriate. Thirdly, character must be true to life: for /53/ this is a distinct thing from goodness and propriety, as here described.

The fourth point is consistency: for though the subject of the imitation, who suggested the type, be inconsistent, still he must be consistently inconsistent. As an example of motiveless degradation of character, we have Menelaus in the Orestes: of character indecorous and inappropriate, the lament of Odysseus in the Scylla, and the speech of Melanippe: of inconsistency, the Iphigenia at Aulis, — for Iphigenia the suppliant in no way resembles her later self.

As in the structure of the plot, so too in the portraiture of character, the poet should always aim either at the necessary or the probable. Thus a person of a given character should speak or act in a given way, by the rule either of necessity or of probability; just as this event should follow that by necessary or probable sequence. It is therefore evident that the unravelling of the plot, no less than the complication, must arise out of the plot itself, it must not be brought about by the *Deus ex Machina* — as in the Medea, or in the Return of the Greeks in the Iliad. The *Deus ex Machina* should be employed only for events external to the drama, — for antecedent or subsequent events, which lie beyond the range of human knowledge, and which require to be /55/ reported or foretold; for to the gods we ascribe the power of seeing all things. Within the action there must be nothing irrational. If the irrational cannot be excluded, it should be outside the scope of the tragedy. Such is the irrational element in the Oedipus of Sophocles.

Again, since Tragedy is an imitation of persons who are above the common level, the example of good portrait-painters should be followed. They, while reproducing the distinctive form of the original, make a likeness which is true to life and yet more beautiful. So too the poet, in representing men who are irascible or indolent, or have other defects of character, should preserve the type and yet ennoble it. In this way Achilles is portrayed by Agathon and Homer.

These then are rules the poet should observe. Nor should he neglect those appeals to the senses, which, though not among the essentials, are the concomitants of poetry; for here too there is much room for error. But of this enough has been said in our published treatises.

What Recognition is has been already explained. We will now enumerate its kinds.

First, the least artistic form, which, from poverty of wit, is most commonly employed — recognition by signs. Of these some are congenital, — such as 'the spear which the earth-born race bear on their bodies,' or the stars introduced by Carcinus in his Thyestes. Others are acquired after birth; and of these some are bodily marks, as scars; some external tokens, as necklaces, or the little ark in the Tyro by which the discovery is effected. Even these admit of more or less skilful treatment. Thus in the recognition of Odysseus by his scar, the discovery is /57/ made in one way by the nurse, in another by the swineherds. The use of tokens for the express purpose of proof — and, indeed, any formal proof with or without tokens — is a less artistic mode of recognition. A better kind is that which comes about by a turn of incident, as in the Bath Scene in the Odyssey.

Next come the recognitions invented at will by the poet, and on that account wanting in art. For example, Orestes in the Iphigenia reveals the fact that he is Orestes. She, indeed, makes herself known by the letter; but he, by speaking himself, and saying what the poet, not what the plot requires. This, therefore, is nearly allied to the fault above mentioned: — for Orestes might as well have brought tokens with him. Another similar instance is the 'voice of the shuttle' in the Tereus of Sophocles.

The third kind depends on memory when the sight of some object awakens a feeling: as in the Cyprians of Dicaeogenes, where the hero breaks into tears on seeing the picture; or again in the 'Lay of Alcinous,' where

Odysseus, hearing the minstrel play the lyre, recalls the past and weeps; and hence the recognition.

The fourth kind is by process of reasoning. Thus in the Choëphori: — 'Some one resembling me has come: no one resembles me but Orestes: therefore Orestes has come.' Such too is the discovery made by Iphigenia in the play of Polyidus the Sophist. It was a natural reflexion for Orestes to make, 'So I too must die at the altar like my sister.' So, again, in the Tydeus of Theodectes, the father says, 'I came to find my son, and I lose my own life.' So too in the Phineidae: the women, on seeing the place, inferred their fate: — 'Here /59/ we are doomed to die, for here we were cast forth.' Again, there is a composite kind of recognition involving false inference on the part of one of the characters, as in the Odysseus Disguised as a Messenger. A said that no one else was able to bend the bow; . . . hence B (the disguised Odysseus) imagined that A would recognise the bow which, in fact, he had not seen; and to bring about a recognition by this means — the expectation that A would recognise the bow — is false inference.

But, of all recognitions, the best is that which arises from the incidents themselves, where the startling discovery is made by natural means. Such is that in the Oedipus of Sophocles, and in the Iphigenia; for it was natural that Iphigenia should wish to dispatch a letter. These recognitions alone dispense with the artificial aid of tokens or amulets. Next come the recognitions by process of reasoning.

In constructing the plot and working it out with the proper diction, the poet should place the scene, as far as possible, before his eyes. In this way, seeing everything with the utmost vividness, as if he were a spectator of the action, he will discover what is in keeping with it, and be most unlikely to overlook inconsistencies. The need of such a rule is shown by the fault found in Carcinus. Amphiaraus was on his way from the temple. This fact escaped the observation of one who did not see the situation. On the stage, however, the piece failed, the audience being offended at the oversight.

Again, the poet should work out his play, to the best of his power, with appropriate gestures; for /61/ those who feel emotion are most convincing through natural sympathy with the characters they represent; and one who is agitated storms, one who is angry rages, with the most life-like reality. Hence poetry implies either a happy gift of nature or a strain of madness. In the one case a man can take the mould of any character; in the other, he is lifted out of his proper self.

As for the story, whether the poet takes it ready made or constructs it for himself, he should first sketch its general outline, and then fill in the episodes and amplify in detail. The general plan may be illustrated by the Iphigenia. A young girl is sacrificed; she disappears mysteriously from the eyes of those who sacrificed her; she is transported to another country, where the custom is to offer up all strangers to the goddess. To this ministry she is appointed. Some time later her own brother chances to arrive. The fact that the oracle for some reason ordered him to go there, is outside the general plan of the play. The purpose, again, of his coming is outside the action proper. However, he comes, he is seized, and, when on the point of being sacrificed, reveals who he is. The mode of recognition may be either that of Euripides or of Polyidus, in whose play he exclaims very naturally: — 'So it was not my sister only, but I too, who was doomed to be sacrificed'; and by that remark he is saved.

After this, the names being once given, it remains to fill in the episodes. We must see that they are relevant to the action. In the case of Orestes, for example, there is the madness which led to his capture, and his deliverance by means of the purificatory rite. In the drama, the episodes are short, but it is these that /63/ give extension to Epic poetry. Thus the story of the Odyssey can be stated briefly. A certain man is absent from home for many years; he is jealously watched by Poseidon, and left desolate. Meanwhile his home is in a wretched plight — suitors are wasting his substance and plotting against his son. At length, tempest-tost, he himself arrives; he makes certain persons acquainted with him; he attacks the suitors with his own hand, and is himself preserved while he destroys them. This is the essence of the plot; the rest is episode. /65/

---

## s. h. BULCHER : *The Function of Tragedy*

Bernays,[1] with equal learning and literary skill, maintained that *katharsis*[2] here is a medical metaphor, 'purgation,' and denotes a pathological effect on the soul analogous to the effect of medicine on the body. The thought, as he interpreted it, may be expressed thus. Tragedy excites the emotions of pity and fear — kindred emotions that are in the breasts of all men — and by the act of excitation affords a pleasurable relief. The feelings called forth by the tragic spectacle are not indeed permanently removed, but are quieted for the time, so that the system can fall back upon its normal course. The stage, in fact, provides a harmless and pleasurable outlet for instincts which demand satisfaction, and which can be indulged here more fearlessly than in real life.

Plato, it must be remembered, in his attack upon the drama had said that 'the natural hunger after sorrow and weeping' which is kept under /245/ control in our own calamities, is satisfied and delighted by the poets. 'Poetry feeds and waters the passions instead of starving them.' Through its tearful moods it enfeebles the manly temper; it makes anarchy in the soul by exalting the lower elements over the higher, and by dethroning reason in favour of feeling. Aristotle held that it is not desirable to kill or to starve the emotional part of the soul, and that the regulated indulgence of the feelings serves to maintain the balance of our nature. Tragedy, he would say, is a vent for the particular emotions of pity and fear. In the first instance, it is true, its effect is not to tranquillise but to excite. It excites emotion, however, only to allay it. Pity and fear, artificially stirred, expel the latent pity and fear which we bring with us from real life, or at least, such elements in them as are disquieting. In the pleasurable calm which follows when the passion is spent, an emotional cure has been wrought. . . . /246/

Aristotle, it would seem, was led to this remarkable theory by observing the effect of certain melodies upon a form of religious ecstasy, or, as the Greeks said, 'enthusiasm,' such as is rarely seen in this country, and whose proper home is in the East. The persons subject to such transports were regarded as men possessed by a god, and were taken under the care of the priesthood. The treatment prescribed for them was so far homoeopathic in character, that it consisted in applying movement to cure movement, in soothing the internal trouble of the mind by a wild and restless music. The passage in the *Politics*

From "The Function of Tragedy," *an essay appended to* Aristotle's Theory of Poetry and Fine Art, *4th ed. (New York: Dover Publications, Inc., 1951).*

[1] *Jakob Bernays, author of a treatise in German (published 1857) on Aristotle's theory of tragedy in which he defines* catharsis *in medical terms* — Eds.
[2] katharsis, *the Greek word for the emotional effect of tragedy described by Aristotle in his famous short definition (see the first sentence of the excerpt from* The Poetics, *p. 1). The exact meaning of the term has been much debated* — Eds.

in which Aristotle de- /248/ scribes the operation of these tumultuous melodies is the key to the meaning of *katharsis* in the *Poetics*. Such music is expressly distinguished by Aristotle from the music which has a moral effect or educational value. It differs, again, from those forms of music whose end is either relaxation or the higher aesthetic enjoyment. Its object is *katharsis*. It is a physical stimulus which provides an outlet for religious fervour. Patients, who have been subjected to this process, 'fall back,' to quote Aristotle's phrase, 'into their normal state, as if they had undergone a medical or purgative treatment.' The emotional result is a 'harmless joy.' ... /249/

The whole passage of the *Politics* here referred to is introduced by certain important prefatory words: 'What we mean by *katharsis* we will now state in general terms; hereafter we will explain it more clearly in our treatise on Poetry.' But in the *Poetics*, as we have it, the much desired explanation is wanting; /251/ there appears to be a gap in the text at this most critical point. We are therefore driven back upon the *Politics* itself as our primary authority. The tone of the passage and particular expressions show two things plainly — first, that there the term is consciously metaphorical; secondly, that though its technical use in medicine was familiar, the metaphorical application of it was novel and needed elucidation. Moreover, in the words last quoted, — 'all undergo a *katharsis* of some kind,' — it is pretty plainly implied that the *katharsis* of pity and fear in tragedy is analogous to, but not identical with, the *katharsis* of 'enthusiasm.'

Now, Bernays transferred the *katharsis* of the *Politics* almost without modification of meaning to the definition of tragedy. He limited its reference to the simple idea of an emotional relief, a pleasurable vent for overcharged feeling. This idea, no doubt, almost exhausts the meaning of the phrase as it is used in the *Politics*. It also expresses, as /252/ has been above explained, one important aspect of the tragic *katharsis*. But the word, as taken up by Aristotle into his terminology of art, has probably a further meaning. It expresses not only a fact of psychology or of pathology, but a principle of art. The original metaphor is in itself a guide to the full aesthetic significance of the term. In the medical language of the school of Hippocrates it strictly denotes the removal of a painful or disturbing element from the organism, and hence the purifying of what remains, by the elimination of alien matter. Applying this to tragedy we observe /253/ that the feelings of pity and fear in real life contain a morbid and disturbing element. In the process of tragic excitation they find relief, and the morbid element is thrown off. As the tragic action progresses, when the tumult of the mind, first roused, has afterwards subsided, the lower forms of emotion are found to have been transmuted into higher and more refined forms. The painful element in the pity and fear of reality is purged away; the emotions themselves are purged. The curative and tranquillising influence that tragedy exercises follows as an immediate accompaniment of the transformation of feeling. Tragedy, then, does /254/ more than effect the homoeopathic cure of certain passions. Its function on this view is not merely to provide an outlet for pity and fear, but to provide for them a distinctively aesthetic satisfaction, to purify and clarify them by passing them through the medium of art.

But what is the nature of this clarifying process? Here we have no direct reply from Aristotle. He has, however, left us some few hints, some materials, out of which we may perhaps reconstruct the outlines of his thought.

The idea of *katharsis* implies, as we have seen, the expulsion of a painful and disquieting element. Now pity and fear in their relation to real life are by Aristotle reckoned among [this painful and disquieting element]. Each of them is, according to the /255/ definition in the *Rhetoric*, a form of pain. Fear Aristotle defines to be 'a species of pain or disturbance arising from an impression of impending evil which is destructive or painful in its nature.' Moreover, the evil is near not remote, and the persons threatened are ourselves. Similarly, pity is 'a sort of pain at an evident evil of a destructive or painful kind in the case of somebody who does not deserve it, the evil being one which we might expect to happen to ourselves or to some of our friends, and this at a time when it is seen to be near at hand.' Pity, however, turns into fear where the object is so nearly related to us that the suffering seems to be our own. Thus pity and fear in Aristotle are strictly correlated feelings. We pity others where under like circumstances we should fear for ourselves. /256/ Those who are incapable of fear are incapable also of pity.

Thus in psychological analysis fear is the primary emotion from which pity derives its meaning. Its basis is a self-regarding instinct; it springs from the feeling that a similar suffering may happen to ourselves. It has in it a latent and potential fear. But it is a wrong inference to say, as Lessing does,[3] that fear is always an ingredient in pity, — that we fear for ourselves whenever we feel pity for another. The Aristotelian idea simply is that we would fear for our-selves if we were in the position of him who is the object of our pity. The possible fear may never become actual, but the strength of the pity is not thereby impaired. Still the tacit reference to self makes pity, as generally described in the *Rhetoric,* sensibly different from the pure instinct of com-passion, the unselfish sympathy with others' /257/ distress, which most modern writers understand by pity.

The conditions of dramatic representation, and above all the combined appeal which tragedy makes to both feelings, will considerably modify the emotions as they are known in actual reality. Pity in itself undergoes no essential change. It has still for its object the misfortunes of 'one who is undeserving'; which phrase, as interpreted by Aristotle (*Poet.* ch. xiii), means not a wholly innocent sufferer, but rather a man who meets with sufferings beyond his deserts. The emotion of fear is profoundly altered when it is trans-ferred from the real to the imaginative world. It is no longer the direct appre-hension of misfortune impending over our own life. It is not caused by the actual approach of danger. It /258/ is the sympathetic shudder we feel for a hero whose character in its essentials resembles our own. /259/

The tragic sufferer is a man like ourselves; and on this inner likeness the effect of tragedy, as described in the *Poetics,* mainly hinges. Without it our complete sympathy would not be enlisted. The resemblance on which Aristotle insists is one of moral character. His hero (*Poet.* ch. xiii) is not a man of flawless perfection, nor yet one of consummate villainy; by which we must not understand that he has merely average or mediocre qualities. He rises, indeed, above the common level in moral elevation and dignity, but he is not free from frailties and imperfections. His must be a rich and full humanity, composed of elements which other men possess, but blended more harmoniously or of more potent quality. So much human nature must there be in him that we are able in /260/ some sense to identify ourselves with him, to make his misfortunes our own. At the same time he is raised above us in external dignity and station. He is a prince or famous man who falls from a height of greatness. Apart from the impressive effect of the contrast so presented, there is a gain in the hero being placed at an ideal distance from the spec-tator. We are not confronted with outward conditions of life too like our own. The pressure of immediate reality is removed; we are not painfully reminded of the cares of our own material existence. We have here part of the refining

---

[3] *Ephraim Lessing (1729-1781), German dramatist and critic. Lessing's principal critical work was* New Laokoon *(1766); he discussed Aristotle's* Poetics *in a series of critical articles called* Hamburgische Dramaturgie *(1767-1768)* — Eds.

process which the tragic emotions undergo within the region of art. They are disengaged from the petty interests of self, and are on the way to being universalised.

The tragic fear, though modified in passing under the conditions of art, is not any languid emotion. It differs, indeed, from the crushing apprehension of personal disaster. In reading or witnessing the *Oedipus Tyrannus* we are not possessed with a fear that we may be placed in circumstances similar to those of Oedipus, or be overtaken by the same calamities. Yet a thrill runs through us, a shudder of horror or of vague /261/ foreboding. The feeling is immediate and unreflective. The tension of mind, the agonised expectation with which we await the impending catastrophe, springs from our sympathy with the hero in whose existence we have for the time merged our own. The events as they pass before us seem almost as if we were directly concerned. We are brought into a mood in which we feel that we too are liable to suffering. Yet the object of dread is not a definite evil threatening us at close quarters. In the spectacle of another's errors or misfortunes, in the shocks and blows of circumstance, we read the 'doubtful doom of human kind.' The vividness with which the imagination pictures unrealised calamity produces the same intensity of impression as if the danger were at hand. The true tragic fear becomes an almost /262/ impersonal emotion, attaching itself not so much to this or that particular incident, as to the general course of the action which is for us an image of human destiny. We are thrilled with awe at the greatness of the issues thus unfolded, and with the moral inevitableness of the result. In this sense of awe the emotions of fear and pity are blended.

We can now see that the essential tragic effect depends on maintaining the intimate alliance between pity and fear. According to Aristotle, not pity alone should be evoked by tragedy, as many moderns have held; not pity *or* fear, for which Corneille argued;[4] not pity and 'admiration,' which is the modification under which the Aristotelian /263/ phrase finds currency in the Elizabethan writers. The requirement of Aristotle is pity *and* fear. He would no doubt allow that in some tragedies the primary and predominant impression is fear, in others pity. He would probably go farther and say that an inferior tragedy may excite one only of the two emotions generally called tragic. But the full tragic effect requires the union of the two, nor can /264/ the distinctive function of tragedy as *katharsis* be discharged otherwise.

In the phrase of the anonymous fragment, 'On Comedy,' which appears to contain some genuine Aristotelian tradition, 'tragedy seeks to blend fear with pity in due proportion.' Pity, as Bernays explains, through its kinship with fear, is preserved from eccentricity and sentimentalism. Fear, through its alliance with pity, is divested of a narrow selfishness, of the vulgar terror which is inspired by personal danger. A self-absorbed anxiety or alarm makes us incapable of sympathy with others. In this sense 'fear casts out pity.' Tragic fear, though it may send an inward shudder through the blood, does not paralyse the mind or stun the /265/ sense, as does the direct vision of some impending calamity. And the reason is that this fear, unlike the fear of common reality, is based on an imaginative union with another's life. The spectator is lifted out of himself. He becomes one with the tragic sufferer, and through him with humanity at large. One effect of the drama, said Plato, is that through it a man becomes many, instead of one; it makes him lose his proper personality in a pantomimic instinct, and so prove false to himself. Aristotle might reply: True; he passes out of himself, but it is through the enlarging power of sympathy. He forgets his own petty sufferings. He quits the

---

[4] *Pierre Corneille (1606-1684), great French dramatist. It is frequently said that French classical tragedy begins with his* Le Cid *(1636)* – Eds.

narrow sphere of the individual. He identifies himself with the fate of mankind.

We are here brought back to Aristotle's theory of poetry as a representation of the universal. Tragedy exemplifies with concentrated power this highest function of the poetic art. The characters it depicts, the actions and fortunes of the persons with whom it acquaints us, possess a typical and universal value. The artistic unity of plot, binding together the several parts of the play in close inward coherence, reveals the law of human destiny, the causes and effects of suffering. The incidents which thrill us are intensified in their effect, when to the shock of surprise is added the discovery that each thing as it has happened could /266/ not be otherwise; it stands in organic relation to what has gone before. There is a combination of the inevitable and the unexpected. Pity and fear awakened in connexion with these larger aspects of human suffering, and kept in close alliance with one another, become universalised emotions. What is purely personal and self-regarding drops away. The spectator who is brought face to face with grander sufferings than his own experiences a sympathetic ecstasy, or lifting out of himself. It is precisely in this transport of feeling, which carries a man beyond his individual self, that the distinctive tragic pleasure resides. Pity and fear are purged of the impure element which clings to them in life. In the glow of tragic excitement these feelings are so transformed that the net result is a noble emotional satisfaction.

The *katharsis,* viewed as a refining process, may have primarily implied no more to Aristotle than the expulsion of the disturbing element, namely, the pain, which enters into pity and fear when aroused by real objects. The mere fact of such an expulsion would have supplied him with /267/ a point of argument against Plato, in addition to the main line of reply above indicated. In the *Philebus* Plato had described the mixed or impure pleasures as those which have in them an alloy of pain; and the pleasure of tragedy was stated to be of the mixed order. The Aristotelian theory asserts that the emotions on which tragedy works do indeed in real life contain a large admixture of pain, but that by artistic treatment the painful element is expelled or overpowered.

In the foregoing pages, however, we have carried the analysis a step farther, and shown how and why the pain gives way to pleasure. The sting of the pain, the disquiet and unrest, arise from the selfish element which in the world of reality clings to these emotions. The pain is expelled when the taint of egoism is removed. If it is objected that the notion of universalising the emotions and ridding them of an intrusive element that belongs to the sphere of the accidental and individual, is a modern conception, which we have no warrant for attributing to Aristotle, we may reply that if this is not what Aristotle meant, it is at least the /268/ natural outcome of his doctrine; to this conclusion his general theory of poetry points.

Let us assume, then, that the tragic *katharsis* involves not only the idea of an emotional relief, but the further idea of the purifying of the emotions so relieved. In accepting this interpretation we do not ascribe to tragedy a direct moral purpose and influence. Tragedy, according to the definition, acts on the feelings, not on the will. It does not make men better, though it removes certain hindrances to virtue. The refining of passion under temporary and artificial excitement is still far distant from moral improvement. Aristotle would probably admit that indirectly the drama has a moral influence in enabling the emotional system to throw off some perilous stuff, certain elements of feeling, which, if left to themselves, might develop dangerous energy and impede the free play of those vital functions on which the exercise of virtue depends. The excitation of noble emotions will probably in time exert an effect upon the will. But whatever may be the indirect effect of the repeated operation of the *katharsis,* we may confidently say that Aristotle in his definition of tragedy is thinking, not of any such remote result, but of the immediate end of the art, of the aesthetic function it fulfils.

It is only under certain conditions of art that /269/ the homoeopathic cure of pity and fear by similar emotions is possible. Fear cannot be combined with the proper measure of pity unless the subject-matter admits of being universalised. The dramatic action must be so significant, and its meaning capable of such extension, that through it we can discern the higher laws which rule the world. The private life of an individual, tragic as it may be in its inner quality, has never been made the subject of the highest tragedy. Its consequences are not of far-reaching importance; it does not move the imagination with sufficient power. Within the limited circle of a *bourgeois* society a great action is hardly capable of being unfolded. A parochial drama, like that of Ibsen, where the hero struggles against the cramping conditions of his normal life, sometimes with all the ardour of aspiring hope, more often in the spirit of egoistic self-assertion which mistakes the measure of the individual's powers, can hardly rise to tragic dignity. We are conscious of a too narrow stage, of a confined outlook, and of squalid motives underlying even conduct which is invested with a certain air of grandeur. The play moves on the flat levels of existence. The characters are unequal to the task imposed on them; and though we may find room for human pity in witnessing failure and foiled hopes, still it is commonplace and gloomy failure. No one can question the skill in dramatic /270/ construction and the stirring interest of Ibsen's plays, but the depressing sense of the trivial cannot be shaken off, and the action always retains traces of an inherent littleness which hinders the awakening of tragic fear, — still more of that solemnity and awe which is the final feeling left by genuine tragedy. Some quality of greatness in the situation as well as in the characters appears to be all but indispensable, if we are to be raised above the individual suffering and experience a calming instead of a disquieting feeling at the close. The tragic *katharsis* requires that suffering shall be exhibited in one of its comprehensive aspects; that the deeds and fortunes of the actors shall attach themselves to larger issues, and the spectator himself be lifted above the special case and brought face to face with universal law and the divine plan of the world.

In order that an emotion may be not only excited but also allayed, — that the tumult of the mind may be resolved into a pleasurable calm, — the emotion stirred by a fictitious representation must divest itself of its purely selfish and material elements, and become part of a new order of things. It is perhaps for this reason that love in itself is hardly a tragic motive. The more exclusive and self-absorbed a passion is, the more does it resist *kathartic* treatment. The feelings excited must have their basis in the permanent and objective /271/ realities of life, and be independent of individual caprice or sentiment. In the ordinary novel the passion of love in its egoistic and self-centred interest does not admit of being generalised, or its story enlarged into a typical and independent action. The rare cases where a love story is truly tragic go to prove the point which is here enforced. In *Romeo and Juliet* the tragedy does not lie merely in the unhappy ending of a tale of true love. Certain other conditions, beyond those which contribute to give a dramatic interest, are required to produce the tragic effect. There is the feud of the two houses, whose high place in the commonwealth makes their enmity an affair of public concern. The lovers in their new-found rapture act in defiance of all external obligations. The elemental force and depth of their passion bring them into collision with the fabric of the society to which they belong. Their tragic doom quickly closes in upon them. Yet even in death the consequences of their act extend beyond the sphere of the individual. Over the grave of their love the two houses are reconciled.

Tragedy, as it has been here explained, satisfies a universal human need. The fear and pity on and through which it operates are not, as some have maintained, rare and abnormal emotions. All men, as Aristotle says, are susceptible to them, /272/ some persons in an overpowering measure. For the modern, as for the ancient world, they are still among the primary instincts; always present, if below the surface, and ready to be called into activity. The Greeks, from temperament, circumstances, and religious beliefs, may have been more sensitive to their influence than we are, and more likely to suffer from them in a morbid form. Greek tragedy, indeed, in its beginnings was but a wild religious excitement, a bacchic ecstasy. This aimless ecstasy was brought under artistic law. It was ennobled by objects worthy of an ideal emotion. The poets found out how the transport of human pity and human fear might, under the excitation of art, be dissolved in joy, and the pain escape in the purified tide of human sympathy. /273/

---

GILBERT **MURRAY**: *The Classical Tradition in Poetry*

Drama was held by Aristotle to spring spontaneously from the needs of human nature, which loves imitating and loves rhythm and therefore is pretty sure to indulge in rhythmic imitations. And it seems to be found, in one form or another, among most peoples in the world who are not debarred from it by some religious scruple. Yet it is well to remember that all the things that we habitually do seem to us to spring from human nature, while a great many of them in reality owe their present form to a quite complicated and fortuitous historical process. The drama that we know in Europe is historically derived from Greek sources; and the same may perhaps be true of Indian and Chinese drama as well. The dates at any rate permit of it.

Now the peculiar characteristic of classical Greek drama is the sharp and untransgressed division between tragedy and comedy. The two styles are separate and never combined. No classical author is known to have written in both. At the end of a rather voluminous literature which has appeared recently about the origin of the Greek drama, I think we may accept the general conclusions reached in the preceding chapter: that both forms of drama have their origin in ritual; that the ritual was connected with the cult of what is sometimes /52/ called a Year-Daemon, or a Vegetation God, or a Life Spirit, which everywhere forms the heart of Mediterranean religion; and, lastly, that we can find a sort of degraded survival of the original form of drama in the Mummers' Play, which still survives among the peasantry of Europe. In that play there are two main elements. The hero, like the typical Year-Daemon, appears as a child who grows tall and strong with surpassing swiftness and is married amid a revel or *Comos* of rejoicing. Secondly, he fights various enemies and eventually meets some dark antagonist, by whom he is killed, though he shows a tendency to come to life afterwards. We know from Herodotus that tragedy represented the sufferings of Dionysus, and that these were, except for certain details, identical with those of Osiris. And Osiris, we know, was slain by his enemy, the burning Set; torn in pieces as a corn sheaf is torn and scattered over the fields; bewailed and sought for in vain during many months, and rediscovered in fresh life when the new corn began to shoot in spring. Tragedy is the enactment of the death of the Year-Spirit; and comedy is the

*From* The Classical Tradition in Poetry *(Cambridge, Mass.: Harvard University Press, 1927).*

enactment of his marriage, or rather of the *Comos* which accompanies his marriage. . . .

Thus Greek drama starts, not as a mere picture of ordinary life, or even of ordinary adventure, but as a re-creation, or *mimesis,* of the two most intense experiences that life affords; a re-creation of life at its highest power. The purpose of the drama was — it is generally agreed — originally magical. The marriage *Comos* was intended actually to produce fertility; the death-celebration was the expulsion of evil from the community, /53/ the casting out of the Old Year with its burden of decay, of the polluted, the Scapegoat, the Sin-Bearer. It is well to remember that dramatic performances were introduced into Rome *inter alia caelestis irae placamina*[1] in order to cure a pestilence. This occurred actually during the lifetime of Aristotle. But Aristotle himself has forgotten as completely as we have that tragedy was ever a magical rite: he treats it simply as an artistic performance, and judges it, not for any concrete effect it may have on the public health, but simply on aesthetic grounds. And this shows us that, for whatever reason it was created, drama persisted and increased because it answered to some constant need in human nature.

It was a *mimesis,* — what we call an "imitation," — and the word always disappoints us. We feel that art must be more than mere imitation, and modern critics tend to deny that it contains any element of imitation at all. I think myself that Aristotle is right. Art is a *mimesis*; and we quarrel with the statement only because we do not see the exact meaning of the term. If you fought with a wolf yesterday, you go over the fight in your mind. You re-create the fight; but it is not the same fight: it is an imitation fight, a fight in your imagination. If you are to fight the beast to-morrow, you go over the coming fight beforehand, and very likely feel it intensely. But this also is not the real fight: it is an imagined or an imitated fight. And Aristotle tells us expressly that the characteristic of poetry and drama is that it imitates, not the particular thing that is or was, but the sort of thing that might, or would under certain conditions, be. /54/

In the particular case we are considering, drama takes the two most intense experiences, for good or evil, that normal life affords; it goes over in imagination the great obvious joy, the great obvious terror. It intensifies experience. And also, by emphasizing one part of the thing experienced and ignoring or belittling another, it transfigures experience. It selects its facts and details. It practices that art so much praised by ancient orators, of making things small or great at will. It provides the blessed, the indispensable, element of illusion. In the *Comos* it provides not merely the suggestion that love will endure: that may quite possibly be true; but the more thrilling illusion that the intense joy of the moment when love is won will continue as a permanent element in life. It is like the illusion which a study of the various apocalyptic writings has revealed in their descriptions of Heaven. The heavenly life, as described in most of them, is conceived on the model of the crowning moment of the Mysteries, the topmost hallelujah of inspiration, prolonged through all eternity.

Tragedy in the same way, facing a still more pressing need, hides or adorns the "coming bulk of death," magnifies the glory of courage, the power of endurance, the splendour of self-sacrifice and self-forgetfulness, so as to make us feel, at least for the fleeting moment, that nothing is here for tears, and that death is conquered.

Thus drama does not merely select the most intense experiences of life; in those experiences it intensifies the elements that it desires to have increased and belittles or ignores those that it does not want. It exercises the ordinary

[1] *Livy, VII, 2: "among other means of conciliation of divine wrath"* — Eds.

selective power of art. And this explains one of the most striking judgements of Aristotle. To him the fundamental difference between tragedy /55/ and comedy is not that between tears and laughter; it is that between high and low. Tragedy, he says, deals with those better than ourselves, people whom we must needs look up to; comedy, with those lower, whom we can patronize and laugh at. Now why should people at a funeral be nobler in nature than people at a wedding-breakfast? Only because, if tragedy is to get the full artistic value and beauty out of death, the death must be met and faced and somehow or other, amid all its terrors, conquered on its own ground; if comedy is to get full value out of its revel, it must be a revel enjoyed to the full and not spoilt by any tiresome temperance or prudential considerations of the morrow. Death, to yield its full value in art, demands heroism. A frolic, to yield its full value, demands a complete surrender to frolic. . . . /56/

. . . Why is it that people should find not merely enjoyment, but a very high kind of enjoyment, in scenes of death and anguish, the disappointment of human hopes, the terrific punishment of slight errors, and generally the overthrow of the great? Aristotle, in his abrupt style, like the style of a telegram, speaks of "pity and terror," and then says that tragedy affords a purgation of "affections of that sort." Perhaps, if we possessed his explanation of what he meant by "affections of that sort," we should understand this better. In default of that, /59/ let us try to conjecture what elements of primitive instinct, ordinarily repressed by our sense of duty and the needs of social intercourse, can possibly find release, or *katharsis,* in the spectacle of *Oedipus* or *Macbeth* or *Hamlet* or *Athalie.*

First, let us remember how Greek tragedy dwells on the danger of greatness and the envy of the gods. Sometimes the poets are at pains to explain that it is not greatness in itself that brings on disaster, but only the pride or cruelty that is often associated with greatness. But in the main popular conception there is no such subtlety: life is seen in the tragic pattern. As the Sun every year and every morning begins weak and lovely, then grows strong and fierce, then excessive and intolerable, and then, by reason of that excess, is doomed to die, so runs the story with trees, beasts, and men, with kings and heroes and cities. Herodotus sees the history of the Persian War in the same tragic pattern: Xerxes, tall, strong, beautiful, lord of a vast empire, became proud and desired too much, was led into Atê and stricken down. Thucydides sees the history of Athens in the same pattern: incredible achievements, beauty, splendour; then pride, battle, determination to win at all costs; crime, brutality, dishonour, and defeat after all. That is the essential tragic idea, however we translate it into modern language, climax followed by decline, or pride by judgement. Why do we enjoy it?

It may perhaps be suggested that the envy in question is perfectly real, only it is the envy of our own hearts and not of the gods. It is a pleasure, everyone knows it, to hear anecdotes telling how proud people were "scored off," or made to look small. There was a great Spanish nobleman in *Candide,* whose mien — as /60/ Voltaire puts it — was so distinguished, whose bearing so magnificent, whose blood so blue, that no ordinary man could be ushered into his presence without immediately conceiving a desire to kick him. There is a pleasure in hearing of the defeat of the great Spanish armies by the Dutch, or the great Burgundian armies by the Swiss, and, generally, in the downfall of the proud. At every fight the sympathy of the onlookers tends to back the little 'un. We identify ourselves with the under dog, just as we always think of ourselves as more oppressed than oppressing. Such little injuries as we may have done to other people are really so pardonable and easily forgotten and even, if looked at in the right spirit, humorous; but the wrongs done by others to us are different and do demand some imaginative satisfaction.

It is worth while remembering that it is to sects and nations that have suffered persecution that we are indebted for almost all our information about Hell. It is thus quite conceivable that there is in the mass of mankind a subconscious sense of unredressed injury. Still, I doubt if such a feeling goes far in accounting for tragedy. As a rule, such a sentiment is more comic than tragic; it is amused by small mishaps to the unduly dignified, but it is no longer amused if the mishaps become painful.

However, if we have faced that unamiable element in our instinctive sub-terranean nature, let us also face something worse: man, differing herein from most other carnivores, takes pleasure in torture and cruelty. Savages torture their prisoners; children in most countries torture animals. The Roman games, the sports of the Middle Ages and even of the eighteenth century, the records of the burning of martyrs and of public execu- /61/ tions, not to speak of certain elements in the late war and the succeeding revolutions, are more than suf-ficient to show that there is in man an element which lusts for the infliction and the sight of pain. It enables us to understand many extant forms of sport, and I think also part of the fascination of certain scenes in such plays as Flecker's *Hassan*, Sardou's *Théodora*, and the stamping on Gloucester's eye-balls in *King Lear*. . . .

. . . I think we shall agree that the emotion with which we regard the fate of Oedipus or Macbeth or Othello consists genuinely of "pity and fear," and not in the least of *Schadenfreude*.[2] Pity for the great man overcast; fear, because we partially identify him with ourselves and realize through his fate the precariousness of our own. We feel, as we /62/ look on the overthrow of the tragic hero, that man himself has here no abiding city.

I would suggest that there is perhaps one further element in the tragic emotion besides this pity and fear. There is a curious suspicion that the brutal and meaningless disasters inflicted by Fortune are, in some mystical way, not quite unjust. We are almost like dogs who feel that they must have been naughty if they are accidentally trodden upon.

Aristotle makes an acute remark on this subject. He points out that, while tragedy demands the fall of the great, the hero must not be absolutely wicked, nor yet utterly innocent. If he is merely wicked — like an Elizabethan villain — the theme loses grandeur as well as interest and reality. If he is entirely inno-cent, the story becomes what Aristotle calls . . . "revolting." He must commit some offence, he must show some flaw — not enough, by human standards, to justify his punishment, but enough to let us feel that Nature or Fortune or the gods are, after all, according to their own inhuman rules, playing the game. Such a conception makes these powers less blind and dead, but all the more terrible.

We see the hero doing exactly the things calculated to get him into trouble, and feel that he can hardly complain of the consequences. We all know how Fortune is apt to behave; and the hero who boasts, or shows pride, or forgets proper precautions, with that knowledge in front of him, is like a man who carelessly drinks the water in his bedroom in a town where there is known to be typhoid. He is not exactly a wicked man, but really he almost deserves what he gets. /63/

But let us look further, and we may find an explanation of these curiously divergent impressions.

Two recent writers — Dr. Janet Spens in 1916 and Mr. Cornford in 1922[3] — have independently brought out a most significant fact about ancient tragedy

[2] Schadenfreude, *malicious joy* — Eds.
[3] Shakespeare and Tradition, *by Janet Spens, 1916; Lecture on* The Origin of the Drama, *by F. M. Cornford, Conference on New Ideals in Education, Stratford, 1922.*

toward which I also was groping. It is that the tragic hero (embodying as he does the good Vegetation Spirit torn and scattered, and at the same time the evil Old Year cast out) presents a curious combination of contradictory qualities. It is quite in accord with the strange but well-known confusion which exists in the Bacchic ritual and the sacramental feast. Is it the god himself who is torn and devoured, or is it the god's enemy? To avoid the horror of murdering your god, you can say that the figure you tear is the enemy Pentheus and not the god Dionysus; but you know in your heart that it is only the life of Dionysus himself that will have any true magical effect, and you show your knowledge of this by arranging that the image which you call Pentheus shall be shaped and dressed in every detail so as to be like Dionysus. In later ages we have distinguished the hero and the villain, but there are no villains in Greek tragedy and the villain's fate is normally suffered by the hero.

Put briefly, it seems that historically the tragic hero is derived both from the Life Spirit — call him Dionysus or what you will — who comes to save the community with the fruits of the New Year, and from the polluted Old Year, the *Pharmakos* or Scapegoat, who is cast out to die or to wander in the wilderness, bearing with him the sins of the community. Every Year- /64/ Spirit is first new and then old, first pure and then polluted; and both phases tend to be combined in the tragic hero. Oedipus is the saviour of Thebes, the being whose advent delivered Thebes from death; Oedipus is also the abomination, the polluter of Thebes, the thing which must be cast out, if Thebes is to live and be clean. Orestes is the saviour who comes to redeem the House of Atreus from the rule of murderers; Orestes is also the murderer, the matricide, whose polluting presence must be removed from all human society. Pentheus, the stricken blasphemer, is, as we have seen, identical with Dionysus, the sacrificed god. The conflict between two rights or two commands of conscience, which is said by Hegel to be the essence of tragedy, is already present in the tragic hero himself.

The emotion which the striving and the death of such a hero rouses in the normal man must be far from simple. We feel love for him because he is a saviour and a champion, a brave man fighting and suffering to redeem those who without him would be lost; we feel horror toward him because of his sins and pollutions, and their awful expiation. And both feelings must have been intensified in ancient tragedy by the subconscious memory that the sins he expiates are really ours. The Greek hero, when he suffers, almost always suffers in order to save others.[4] And the artist knows how to /65/ make us feel that such suffering is a better thing than success.

It is only through sacrifice and suffering that courage and greatness of soul can be made visible, and the dramatist who knows his business knows how to make the beauty of such sacrifice resplendent while hiding away the ugliness of the mere pain and humiliation. He shows the beauty of human character fighting against fate and circumstance; he conceals the heavy toll of defeats and weaknesses and infidelities which fate and circumstance generally levy on the way.

If this analysis is historically correct, and I believe it is, it goes far toward answering our whole problem about "the pleasure of tragedy." First, no doubt, tragedy implies the contemplation, not of mere suffering and disaster, but of the triumph of the human soul over suffering and disaster. So much seems certain, but it is not very characteristic. That pleasure one might receive from any

---

[4] *This point has not been sufficiently realized. Thus Oedipus suffers for Thebes, Orestes for his father, Alcestis for her husband, Prometheus for mankind, Eteocles for Thebes, Menoikeus for Thebes, Antigone for her brother, Iphigenia in Aulis for Hellas, Macaria for her brethren, etc. Some suffer for the Gods or for duty, but nearly all suffer* for *somebody or something. The tragic hero is thus affiliated to the Suffering God and the Babylonian "Faithful Son." Cf. Langdon,* Tammuz and Ishtar.

exciting drama or story of adventure in which the bad people seem to hold all the cards but the good people eventually win. What is really characteristic is that, from the very beginning, the tragic conflict has in it an element of mystery derived ultimately from the ancient religious conceptions of *katharsis* and atonement. The contest takes place on a deeper level of reality. It is not to be estimated in terms of ordinary success or failure, ordinary justice and injustice, but in those of some profounder scheme of values in which suffering is not the worst of things nor happiness the best. A tragedy is true to type when one can sincerely say at the end of it, "Nothing is here for tears," as one does at the end of *Samson Agonistes* or *Othello* or *Lear* or *Oedipus* or *Antigone* or *The Trojan Women*. Only one /66/ can never say such words except under the inspiration of some more or less mystical faith or some high artistic illusion. /67/

---

M A U D  **B O D K I N** : *Archetypal Patterns in Poetry*

Perhaps the most important contribution that has been made by the Freudian theory of dream interpretation to the understanding of the emotional symbolism of poetic themes is that concerned with the 'splitting' of type figures. In comparing the Hamlet story with the story of Oedipus, Dr. Jones asserts that both are variants of the same *motif*, but in one the father figure remains single, while in the other it is 'split into two' — the father loved and revered, and the hated tyrannical usurper.

This assertion involves two elements of hypothesis:

1. The fundamental assumption — implied also in the statements of Jung and Gilbert Murray . . . — that these ancient stories owe their persistence, as traditional material of art, to their power of expressing or symbolizing, and so relieving, typical human emotions.

2. That the emotion relieved is in this case the two-sided — ambivalent — attitude of the son towards the father. Let us examine this latter hypothesis more closely.

It appears to be characteristic of the relation between father and son that the father should excite in the son both feelings of admiration, love, and loyalty, and also impulses of anger, jealousy, and self-assertion. The more the son learns to 'idolize' his father, developing what Shand has called the 'conscience of the sentiment', so that any muttering of jealousy or hostile criticism is suppressed as disloyal, the more acute will become the tension of the /13/ inner attitude. It is such an attitude that can find relief in imaginative activity wherein both the love and the repressed hostility have play. In the story of Oedipus, according to the Freudian hypothesis, a repressed persistent impulse to supplant the father and enjoy the mother finds expression in the first part of the action; then in the latter part, in the hero's remorse and suffering, appears the expression of the sentiment of respect and loyalty. In the Hamlet legend — as it appears, e.g. in the Amleth Saga — combined fear and hostile self-assertion against the father find expression through all the incidents of simulated stupidity, and secret bitter word-play, and at last in the achievement of the plotted slaying of the usurper; while at the same time the sentiment of love and loyalty is triumphantly expressed in that same act of filial vengeance.

From Archetypal Patterns in Poetry *(New York: Oxford University Press, 1934).*

It is Shakespeare only who appears to have brought into the rendering of the ancient story the subtle factor of the division and paralysis of the will of the hero, by the intuitive apprehension that the impulse that drove his uncle against his father was one with that present in himself.

The story of Orestes may be considered as another example of the imaginative expression of the ambivalent attitude of child toward parent. In this story, as presented by the three great Attic tragedians, there is a wealth of material illustrating the manner in which inner forces of emotion may, through shapes created by imagination, become palpable to sense. But we must be content here to consider briefly only the outline of the story.

Considered as a variant of the Hamlet theme, its distinctive note is that the usurper upon whom the son's fierce self-assertion and craving for vengeance strike is not alone the male kinsman, but also the queen-mother, who has betrayed, and with her own hands murdered the father. Therefore the moment of triumphant self-assertion, when the son has proved his manhood, and vindicated his loyalty upon his father's enemies, is also the moment when there awakens the palpable, pursuing horror of the outraged /14/ filial relation – since this enemy was also a parent, the mother of the slayer.

The conflict presented in the Orestes dramas is plainly concerned not directly with sex, but with combined love and hate of either son or daughter converging upon a parent figure which may be either father or mother. It is the enduring conflict between the generations which continues to find expression in the story, when more temporary questions – such as that between patriarchy and mother-right, which may have been present in Athenian minds – are no longer urgent. That this theme of conflict between the generations had great significance within the sensibility that found expression in Shakespeare's plays, is evident from the tragedy of *King Lear*.

In this drama the emotional conflict between the generations is communicated from the standpoint of the old man, the father who encounters in separate embodiment in his natural successors, the extremes of bestial self-seeking, and of filial devotion. Bradley has noted how the play illustrates 'the tendency of imagination to analyse and subtract, to decompose human nature into its constituent factors'.[1] This mode of thought, he suggests,[2] is responsible for 'the incessant references to the lower animals' which occur throughout the play. Thus Goneril is likened to a kite, a serpent, a boar, a dog, a wolf, a tiger. This analysing work of the imagination, separating the bestial and the angelic in human nature and giving them distinct embodiment, in the wicked daughters and Cordelia (and again in Edmund and Edgar, the cruel and the loyal sons of Gloucester), presents another instance of what we have already observed in the 'splitting' of the father figure. The splitting in this play is from the point of view of the parent; as, in the Orestes or Hamlet story, it is from the point of view of the child. As, to the feeling of the child, the parent may be both loved protector and unjustly obstructing tyrant, and these two aspects find their emotional symbolism in separate figures in the play; so, to the feeling /15/ of the parent, the child may be both loving support of age and ruthless usurper and rival, and these two aspects find expression in separate figures, such as the tender and the wicked daughters of Lear. . . . /16/

According to Bradley, the tragic exultation that we feel at the close of *Hamlet* is connected with our sense that the spiritual power of which Hamlet is in some manner the expression or product, is receiving him to itself. It would /20/ be this same sense that, as Bradley observes,[3] demands, and is

---

[1] *Shakespearean Tragedy, p. 264.*
[2] *Ibid., p. 266.*
[3] *Shakespearean Tragedy, p. 147.*

satisfied by, the words of Horatio, introducing, against Shakespeare's custom, the reference to another life: 'flights of angels sing thee to thy rest'. If, as I suggest, the spiritual power, which the philosopher analysing his poetic experience is constrained to represent, be conceived psychologically as the awakened sense of our common nature in its active emotional phase, then our exultation in the death of Hamlet is related in direct line of descent to the religious exultation felt by the primitive group that made sacrifice of the divine king or sacred animal, the representative of the tribal life, and, by the communion of its shed blood, felt that life strengthened and renewed. Hamlet, though he dies, is immortal, because he is the representative and creature of the immortal life of the race. He lives, as he desired to live, in the story with which he charged Horatio — and us who, having participated in that story, descend from the poetic ecstasy to draw breath again in the harsh world of our straitened separate personalities.

The insight of Nietzsche, who knew at once the intoxication of the artist and the analytic urge of the philosopher, discerned the essential nature of tragedy as a vision generated by a dance.[4] The dance of rhythmical speech, like the dance of the ancient chorus, excites the Dionysian ecstasy wherein arises, serene and clear, the Apollonian vision of the imaged meanings the dancing words convey.

The painful images within the vision are at once intimately known and felt, and also 'distanced' like the objects in a far stretching landscape, 'estranged by beauty'. So far as the memory material used by the imaginative activity comes from personal experience, it has undergone 'separation ... from the concrete personality of the experiencer' and 'extrusion of its personal aspects';[5] but experience is also used which has never been connected with the /21/ personal self — as when, in *King Lear*, Shakespeare causes the actor to 'impersonate Lear and the storm together',[6] and in the storm 'it is the powers of the tormented soul that we hear and see'.[7] Here, dramatist, actor, and spectator are using experience which was never personal, but shaped through previous apprehension of physical storms into which was imaginatively projected that same impersonal emotional energy from which the daemonic figure of the hero is now fashioned.

To the impersonal, 'distanced', vision corresponds, in Schopenhauer's phrase, 'a Will-free subject', one indifferent to the aims and fears of the ego — not held to its private perspective.[8]

This felt release, and Dionysian union with a larger whole, would seem to constitute that element of religious mystery — of purgation and atonement — traditionally connected with the idea of tragedy.

If now, summing up our results, we recur to the question: what determining emotional pattern corresponds to the form of tragedy? we may answer first, in accordance with our earlier discussion, that the pattern consists of emotional tendencies of opposite character which are liable to be excited by the same object or situation, and, thus conflicting, produce an inner tension that seeks

[4] *See* The Birth of Tragedy, *Section 8.*
[5] *E. Bullough, 'Distance as an aesthetic principle',* Brit. J. of Psychol., V., part 2, p. 116.
[6] *Granville-Barker,* Prefaces to Shakespeare, p. 142.
[7] *A. C. Bradley,* Shakespearian Tragedy, p. 270.
[8] *This character of the aesthetic experience is vividly expressed, in imaginative form, in the lines of de la Mare:*

> *When music sounds, all that I was I am*
> *Ere to this haunt of brooding dust I came.*

*Here we have the felt contrast between the subject of the aesthetic experience — 'all that I was I am' — and the self that is bounded in space and time by the bodily organism — 'this haunt of brooding dust'.*

relief in the activity either of fantasy, or of poetic imagination, either originally or receptively creative. The nature of the opposed tendencies that find relief through diverse renderings of the essential tragic theme, the death or fall of a hero, it is not easy to describe at once with conciseness /22/ and adequacy. But we may attempt this through the concept of an ambivalent attitude toward the self.

In the gradual fashioning and transforming, through the experience of life, of an idea of the self, every individual must in some degree experience the contrast between a personal self — a limited ego, one among many — and a self that is free to range imaginatively through all human achievement. In infancy and in the later years of those who remain childish, a comparatively feeble imaginative activity together with an undisciplined instinct of self-assertion may present a fantasy self — the image of an infantile personality — in conflict with the chastened image which social contacts, arousing the instinct of submission, tend to enforce. In the more mature mind that has soberly taken the measure of the personal self as revealed in practical life, there remains the contrast between this and the self revealed in imaginative thought — wellnigh limitless in sympathy and aspiration.

Within what McDougall calls the self-regarding sentiment these contrasting images, and the impulses that sustain and respond to them, may bring about persistent tension. The experience of tragic drama both gives in the figure of the hero an objective form to the self of imaginative aspiration, or to the power-craving, and also, through the hero's death, satisfies the counter movement of feeling toward the surrender of personal claims and the merging of the ego within a greater power — the 'community consciousness'.

Thus the archetypal pattern corresponding to tragedy may be said to be a certain organization of the tendencies of self-assertion and submission. The self which is asserted is magnified by that same collective force to which finally submission is made; and from the tension of the two impulses and their reaction upon each other, under the conditions of poetic exaltation, the distinctive tragic attitude and emotion appears to arise.

The theme of the conflict between the generations — considered earlier, in relation to Hamlet and Orestes, as /23/ corresponding to an ambivalent attitude toward a parent figure — is plainly related to this more general theme and pattern; since, as we saw, the same underlying emotional associations cling to the images of father and of king. In experiencing imaginatively the conflict of the generations, the spectator is identified with the hero both as son, in his felt solidarity with the father and revolt against him, and again, when, making reparation for the 'injustice' against his predecessor, he gives place to a successor, and is reunited with that whole of life whence he emerged.

One or two points in regard to the argument may be briefly reviewed.

The question is sometimes asked whether the creative activity of the poet and the imaginative response of the reader are sufficiently alike, psychologically, to be considered together. Here I have been concerned primarily with imaginative response, and have not attempted to consider the distinctive activity of original composition. In so far, however, as the poet's work, e.g. a play of Shakespeare, does reveal his imaginative response to material communicated to him by others and by him to us, I have of course been concerned with the poet's experience.

The concept of racial experience enters the present essay in two ways: (1) all those systems or tendencies which appear to be inherited in the constitution of mind and brain may be said to be due to racial experience in the past. It is not necessary for our purpose to determine exactly the method of this 'biological inheritance' from our ancestors. Of more importance for our purpose is the question concerning (2) the racial experience which we may 'enjoy' in responding to that 'social inheritance' of meanings stored in language which also comes to us from our ancestors, and wakens into activity the potentialities of our inherited /24/ nature. In such racial or collective experience as we have discussed in relation to tragic poetry, so far as there is reference to an experiencer, this seems to be not an individual, but rather that larger whole from which what we know as the individual, or personal, self has been differentiated, and which remains with us as the sense, either latent or active, of a greater power.

In the present paper it is maintained that racial experience in this sense is an important factor in the total experience of tragic drama, at the present day, as in the ritual dance from which drama arose. In regard to this question further examination of the imaginative experience can alone be decisive. /25/

---

FRANCIS M. **CORNFORD**: *The Origin of Attic Comedy*

Tragedy must represent the way of the world, the movement of life, the workings of destiny, the end that grows inevitably out of a given beginning, as a plant or animal grows out of its germ. The sense of internal structural necessity seems indispensable to the /196/ tragic effect. It is not really absent even where the fatal moment is a clash between the unaccountable spontaneity of will and the stroke of blind chance. There is still the feeling that such things must be; and chance itself no sooner ceased to be a power of malignant purpose than it was resolved into inexorable law. There is no room for accidents that are insignificant, in other words, *particular* accidents, without what Aristotle calls a 'universal' meaning.

Among such particular accidents we must reckon all the richness of individuality which any real person has, in so far as it is irrelevant to the action. The weaker a tragedian is, the more he will be tempted to make his characters look real and life-like, by admitting these casual traits. The stronger he is, the more his characters will possess the inner coherence, or rather the indivisible unity, which belongs, not to the life-like, but to the living; and, by virtue of this unity, his characters may be indefinitely rich without irrelevance, or any sacrifice of the sense of necessity. Still, it remains true that the character is dominated and dictated by the action or 'experience'. . . . /197/

Turning from plot to character, we find again that Comedy alike enjoys a greater freedom than Tragedy, and, as a consequence, departs less from the old tradition. In Tragedy, as Aristotle says, 'the persons in the play do not go through their action (or 'experience') in order to give a representation of their characters; they include a representation of character for the sake of the action.' The tragic poet starts with a given action, the experience of a certain group of legendary persons. These persons generally have only that one context, in which their whole being moves: they are the people who went through just that great and significant experience. Their very names — Agamemnon, Clytaemnestra, Aegisthus, Cassandra — bring that action at once before us, and nothing else. They come (so to say) as supporting this action, which is itself the primary thing. It dictates their characters, demanding that these shall be moulded to fit the experience they must carry through to its traditional end. Hence, the tragedians were forced to create characters capable of doing and

*From* The Origin of Attic Comedy, *2nd ed. (Cambridge, Eng.: Cambridge University Press, 1934).*

suffering what the story relates. The action requires certain /200/ motives; the characters must be such as can have those motives, and, further, such that those motives will be the characteristic motives. So the tragic poet must work from action to motive, and from motive to character. These causes led to the creation of types which had never before appeared in literature, and could not have been conceived except by a man of genius working under these stern necessities. We may instance the heroic maiden, Antigone, and a whole gallery of women in Euripides. These are not taken from the Epic, still less from ordinary Athenian life; for we know from Aristophanes how they startled and scandalised Athenian society. Once invented, these characters, of course, became types for the imitation of inferior artists. But originally they were imaginative creations. The effect was to enlarge and deepen knowledge of human nature, by discovering possibilities of character and motive that lie within its compass, but are rarely shown in common life, and are beyond the power of observation of ordinary men, who, indeed, not seldom remain unable to conceive them, even when the artist has put them before their eyes. . . . /201/

The persons in Greek tragedy are royal . . . because at one time to be a King was to be half a God, and these divine princes can therefore tread the same stage with the higher Gods, whose will directs the course of human life and is itself immediately overshadowed by the ultimate power of Destiny.

Here the argument connects with our previous point — the primacy of the plot in Tragedy. Tragedy does not seek to ape the manners or portray the characters of everyday society; its function is to represent the destiny of man, the turning wheel of Time and Fate. To accomplish this, it must roll away the particoloured screen, the motley surface of social custom, the fashions and accidents of the place and the hour, and open to our sight a vision of man's life and death, which the bravest can hardly endure to contemplate until it is redeemed by art. Greek Tragedy, thanks to the peculiar genius of Greek religion, had the great advantage of being able to bring upon its stage in visible form the divine powers at work behind the screen. Only the innermost mystery is never unveiled, whether it be called 'Zeus, whoever he be,' or Destiny, Moira, to whom Zeus himself had once been subject. With this reservation, however, we can be allowed to see the figures of the /206/ Gods themselves; and the human actors, whose experience we read in the awful light thrown upon it from those supernatural forms, must be magnified to the scale of those heroes who held converse with Gods and fought with them on the plains of Troy and Thebes. /207/

---

PROSSER HALL **FRYE**: *Romance and Tragedy*

Like every other work of literature a tragedy is the product of two factors. There is, first, the crude stuff or substance, fact or invention — the "myth" or "fable," as it used to be called, the "story," as it is called nowadays — which serves as the foundation of the action; and second, the handling or treatment, the "art," which gives this raw material its literary value. It is only by a kind of license that we can speak of an event, whether real or imaginary, as a tragedy. In such a case we are merely availing ourselves of a handy theatrical

*From* Romance and Tragedy, *rev. ed. (Lincoln: University of Nebraska Press, 1961). Originally published in 1922.*

/94/ figure. Literally, we are justified in saying at most that such an oc-currence might possibly yield a tragedy if properly worked up and presented. Even in the common manner of speaking the force of the figure depends on a recognition of the necessity of dramatic elaboration for genuinely tragic effect. In other words, a tragedy is not a work of nature but of art.

Like the treatment, however, the myth or story itself, upon which the tragedy is founded, should have a special character of its own. It is probably a vague recognition of the circumstance that every transaction indifferently is not proper material for tragic handling, which confines the popular applica-tion of the term to certain occurrences in real life, however capricious and inexact this application of the word is likely to be. In short, tragedy is not wholly an affair of manner any more than it is wholly an affair of matter. The substance must be suitable; and it can be so only when it is of a sort to violate our feeling of moral congruity or fitness. That is to say, the tragic story or fable should involve a discrepancy between our sense of fact, as illustrated in the incidents of the action, on the one hand, and on the other, our concep-tion of justice and right reason. And it is just this disheartening consciousness of inconsistency, implicit in the perception of the dramatic data, as between our knowledge of things as they are or seem to be and our vision of them as they should be, which it is one of the duties of the tragic dramatist to reinforce and deepen by his treatment.

At first sight it may seem something of a paradox /95/ to rest tragedy upon the same general basis, the appreciation of incongruity, as that upon which it has become usual to rest comedy. And yet it has been observed again and again that as far as the mere dramatic substratum is concerned, there is no essential difference between tragedy and comedy: the same premises may serve for either according to circumstances. . . . The truth is, incongruity may stir very different emotions under different circumstances.

In the case of comedy it is the sense of decorum and convention, rather than any graver feeling, which is offended. A violation of the proprieties, an inconsistency of character, a contrariety of circumstances — of such is the fabric of comedy. In spite of its tragic possibilities *Le Misanthrope* arouses, as a matter of fact, no profound distrust, it stirs no serious misgivings. That a prig of Alceste's stamp should so far belie his professions as to fall in love with a trifling flirt like Célimène, arouses much the same feeling, under Molière's management, as that a man in irreproachable evening clothes, to borrow an example from Professor Sully, should slip and fall into the mud. To the intelligent observer the one experience is, of course, much more /96/ interesting than the other. The latter is wholly superficial and fortuitous. The former is rooted in human nature and furnishes a better pasturage for that sort of intellectual curiosity and amusement which it is the business of the comic poet to elicit from his themes as it is the business of the tragic poet to elicit from his the motifs proper to his own *genre*.

In the case of tragedy, on the contrary, the incongruity is such as to shock profoundly the moral prepossessions of the race — to shake, if not to unsettle, confidence in the moral order, in the moral reality of the universe. The sacrifice of a girl so innocent and ingenuous as Iphigenia to the indirections of her father's ambitious policy or that of a woman so elevated and disinterested as Antigone to state's reason and municipal convenience, is in itself a direct attack upon the observer's faith in a supreme equity, in a just apportionment of human lots. . . .

It is this sort of thing that I should like to call the tragic qualm — this feeling of insecurity and confusion, as it were a sort of moral dizziness and nausea, due to the vivid realization, in the dramatic fable, of a suspicion which is always lurking un- /97/ comfortably near the threshold of consciousness, that the world is somehow out of plumb. Herein lies the genuine "clash" of tragedy, as it has been called — not in a mere collision of persons or interests or even of ideas within the confines of the play itself, but rather in the contradiction life is perpetually opposing to our human values and standards.

To be sure, our sensibility for this sort of thing is rather blunt at present. This is not a tragic age. Nor is it essentially a moral one. But for all that there are times when the tragic qualm, inherent as it is in the nature of things rather than of art, obtrudes itself irresistibly. The wanton assassination of the most inoffensive of our presidents is a case in point — as is the senseless obliteration of an entire population by earthquake, volcanic upheaval, or other cataclysm. I grant that even these tremendous catastrophes are beginning to lose their terrors for the popular imagination in the rapid extension of a civilization preponderantly material. But at the same time, though such matters are not of themselves proper for tragedy for a reason that I shall assign in a few minutes, yet they do still stir in thoughtful natures the kind of feeling peculiar to the tragic fact as such; they raise again the horrifying old distrust of nature and her dealings with her creature. Like every lapse of reason, like every intrusion or irruption of the irrational or the unintelligible into the sphere of human interests, they threaten again the security of man's dearest illusions, they trouble his spirit and fill him with nameless apprehensions for the sanity and good faith of that order in which humanity with its quivering /98/ and importunate conscience is helplessly and irrevocably involved. For after all the tragic qualm is perhaps nothing more or less than a sudden and appalling recognition of our desperate plight in a universe apparently indiscriminate of good and evil as of happiness and misery.

Without the tragic qualm, then, in the dramatic data there is no tragedy. But this is not enough; it is but preliminary — in Plato's words, "The things before a tragedy." It is necessary that the qualm should be allayed, that the quarrel between the certainties of experience and the exactions of conscience should be composed, and that confidence should be restored. In addition to making sure of the emotions proper to his stuff in itself, the poet must also manage in such a way as to answer the question mutely propounded by his fable: if such things can be, what becomes of the law of eternal righteousness as given in the heart of man? Such is the question which the drama, as "the imitation of an action," forces relentlessly upon the attention of the audience. And the whole function of tragedy, as a literary *genre,* is to resolve this doubt, in one way or another, through the medium of the action but of the action as a dramatic, not as an actual, performance. Otherwise, there is no art — nothing but a dull dead stereotype of reality with all its contradictions, incoherences, and inconsequences — and with all its resultant incredibility. Senseless assassination or aimless annihilation may indeed present a problem, but the problem is insoluble. And where there is no solution, either by fault of the circumstances or by fault of the poet, there is no genuine tragedy. /99/

If I may venture for a little while into the thicket of critical exegesis, this or something very like it seems to me to be what Aristotle had in mind in speaking of the "purgation of the passions" as the end of tragic poetry. The eventual relaxation of the emotions of pity and horror, which were characteristic of the tragic qualm as it affected the sensibilities of the Greek by reason of certain conditions ... — the eventual relaxation and alleviation of these emotions by some adjustment or other, after their violent excitation by the representation of the action, appears to satisfy the Aristotelian definition of tragedy, as ... accomplishing through pity and horror the purgation of these selfsame passions. But in any case — and this is the point after all — what is indisputable is the sharp distinction drawn by the *Poetics* between the myth and its handling, between the action as an imitation and an initiation — or in other words, between life and literature. And in the light of the distinction it can hardly be denied that Aristotle regarded as indispensable some such final accommodation as I have tried to indicate. Without some such reconciliation of experience with conscience, without some adjustment of the course of events to the principles of human nature he could not have conceived of a tragedy in the proper sense.

It is through this solution, as I have called it in customary fashion, that tragedy acquires its significance, as it acquires its poignant sense of reality through its presentation of the tragic problem im- /100/ plicit in its imitation of an action. While it is by the latter avenue that life enters tragedy, ideas enter it through the former. In this manner verisimilitude on the one part and moral consistency on the other become necessary attributes of the tragic poem. But even in the first case, in the case of the fable itself, it is as much the dramatist's vision which is involved as his observation. The success of his action, even as imitation, depends mainly upon his eye for the problem. What affects the audience is his fidelity, not so much to a certain order of phenomena, as to a certain order of emotions. In a word, the verisimilitude of his drama, and hence its reality, is measured, in the last resort, not by the exactitude with which he is seen to reproduce the spectators' own sensations, but by the justice with which he is felt to have voiced the tragic qualm. /101/

---

F. L. **LUCAS**: *Tragedy*

Life is fascinating to watch, whatever it may be to experience. In *Iliad VII*, when Hector is about to challenge the Achaeans to single combat, Apollo and Athene perch in the shape of eagles on a great oak in the Trojan Plain, "delighting in the deeds of men" — the first of Greek tragic audiences. And so we too go to tragedies not in the least to get rid of emotions, but to have them more abundantly; to banquet, not to purge. Our lives are often dull; they are always brief in duration and confined in scope; but in drama or fiction, even the being "whose dull morrow cometh and is as to-day is" can experience, vicariously, something more. To be "tragic", however, the experience must have in addition a certain peculiar quality — "must", not for moral or philosophic reasons, but because if the experience were not of that kind, we should use a different word for it. Some other forms of art may be merely beautiful; by /73/ Tragedy, I think, we imply also something fundamentally true to life. It need not be the whole truth, but it must be true. Twice at the theatre I can remember having felt in the midst of a play, "Yes, this is the very essence of Tragedy": once, in Turgenev's *A Month in the Country*, where the slow disillusionment of years is crowded into one agonized scene, and a girl frozen into a woman before our eyes. Were the truth and the beauty of it less perfect, we should feel it less keenly; were they less perfect, we might feel it more keenly than we could bear. As it is, we mutter, "How unbearable! — and yet, yes, that is how it happens, the inevitable change that comes on all of us, made visible here as never before. This is life. This is growing up. How appallingly — how fascinatingly true!" And so again in the work of another Russian, *The Three Sisters* of Chekhov. A series of petty, futile disasters has passed across these women's lives; and now nothing is left them, not even (it might seem) any-

*From* Tragedy, rev. ed. (New York: The Macmillan Co., 1958). Originally published in 1928.

thing tragic, only a monotony of hopelessness, like the flapping of burnt paper in an empty grate, as all that had lent meaning to their existence passes away from them with the music of the departing regiment — that music which goes marching on so gaily, so confidently, as if it at least had no part in these weary doubts, and knew whither it was going and why men are born. There is, for me, no more really tragic ending in all drama; for as we see these wasted figures stand before us, as we hear fife and bugle go dancing so light-heartedly upon their way, in that contrast seems embodied, for /74/ one eternal moment, the paradox of the tragedy of life, its hopefulness and its despair, its calling trumpets and its after silences. And here too the only consolation is the utter truthfulness: we have seen for an instant through its mists the sheer mountain-face of life.

So the essence of Tragedy reduces itself to this — the pleasure we take in a rendering of life both serious and true. It must be serious, whether or no it has incidentally comic relief. It must seem to matter, or else the experience would belong to a different category and need a different name. And it must also seem true, or it will not move us. This is all. It may be good for us, but that is not why we go to it. And watching scenes like those of Turgenev, the mind revolts with a sudden anger at the thought of the besetting narrowness of philosophers, who can so seldom be disinterested, who so often make life a reformatory, and beauty useful, and art a pill. Tragedy may teach us to live more wisely; but that is not why we go to it; we go to have the experience, not to use it.

But is there, beyond this, no definite attitude to life in general which we may call tragic, something in fact common to *The Oresteia* and *Othello, The Bacchœ* and *The Master Builder,* some common impression which they leave? Is there in tragedy something corresponding to that fundamental paradox of comedy, which men have seen supremely embodied in Falstaff — the eternal incongruity between the divine wit and the animal grossness of man? The /75/ answer is, I think, "Yes." And this paradox of Hamlet which answers that of Falstaff? It is the very same. "What a piece of work is a man!" cries the Tragic Muse; and Comedy echoes with a laugh, "What a piece of work!" Nietzsche's tragic antithesis seems nearer to the truth than his predecessors' simpler answers. For in Tragedy is embodied the eternal contradiction between man's weakness and his courage, his stupidity and his magnificence, his frailty and his strength. It is the transcendent commonplace of Pope:

> *Placed on this isthmus of a middle state,*
> *A being darkly wise, and rudely great:*
> *With too much knowledge for the Sceptic side,*
> *With too much weakness for the Stoic's pride,*
> *He hangs between; in doubt to act, or rest,*
> *In doubt to deem himself a God, or Beast;*
> *In doubt his Mind or Body to prefer,*
> *Born but to die, and reas'ning but to err . . .*
> *Created half to rise, and half to fall:*
> *Great lord of all things, yet a prey to all;*
> *Sole judge of Truth, in endless Error hurl'd:*
> *The glory, jest, and riddle of the world!*

That is the essential theme of Tragedy. The dramatist may be a pessimist like Euripides, or a Jansenist like Racine, or we know not what, like Shakespeare. There may be a god out of a machine to come hereafter, a happy epilogue; but *Hamlet* or *Phèdre* call for neither of these; they need nothing to perfect them. They stand alone and we forget the rest — the after-life with its readjustments, the /76/ martyr's crown, the lost in their livery of flame. Here is a mirror held up to the fashion of this world; we can look in it and bear to look, without being turned to stone. Here the problem of evil and of suffering is set before us; often it is not answered, but always there is something that makes it endurable. It may be the thought that the hero, like Oedipus or Hamlet or Samson, has at last got nobly off the stage, away from the fitful fever of life.

> *Vex not his ghost, O let him passe, he hates him*
> *That would upon the wracke of this tough world*
> *Stretch him out longer.*

It may be simply the consolation of perfect language, as when Antigone passes with that last great cry down to her living tomb:

> *O tomb, O bridal-chamber, prison-house*
> *Deep-delved, sure-guarded ever; whither I*
> *Pass and am gathered to my kin, all those*
> *Persephone has numbered with her dead!*

It may be the sense that human splendour is greater and finer even in defeat than the blind universe that crushes it; as in the last cry of Synge's Deirdre — "It's a pitiful thing, Conchubor, you have done this night in Emain; yet a thing will be a joy and triumph to the ends of life and time."[1] /77/

Or it may be simply the consolation of the sheer integrity which faces life as it is. The characters may no longer be heroes sublime even in their fall, they may be the ordinary men and women of Ibsen and Chekhov, over whose lack of tragic splendour critics have mourned so needlessly. Complaining of the want of great personalities in this play or that, they forgot the author. For the characters may be poor in spirit and feeble in desire, and the play remain tragic in spite of it, if we feel that the author is himself none of these things and has never cheated or paltered in his picture of men as they are. Tragedy, then, is a representation of human unhappiness which pleases us notwithstanding, by the truth with which it is seen and the fineness with which it is communicated.... /78/

---

## MAXWELL **ANDERSON**: *The Essence of Tragedy*

Anybody who dares to discuss the making of tragedy lays himself open to critical assault and general barrage, for the theorists have been hunting for the essence of tragedy since Aristotle without entire success. There is no doubt that playwrights have occasionally written tragedy successfully, from Aeschylus on, and there is no doubt that Aristotle came very close to a definition of what

---

[1] *Cf. the words of Hecuba at the close of the* Trojan Women *of Euripides:*

> *Had not God*
> *Turned upside-down the happiness of Troy,*
> *We should have lain forgot, instead of giving*
> *Songs to the poets of the after-time.*

*From "The Essence of Tragedy," in "The Essence of Tragedy" and Other Footnotes and Papers (Washington, D.C.: Anderson House, 1939).*

tragedy is in his famous passage on catharsis. But why the performance of a tragedy should have a cleansing effect on the audience, why an audience is willing to listen to tragedy, why tragedy has a place in the education of men, has never, to my knowledge, been convincingly stated. I must begin by saying that I have not solved the Sphinx's riddle which fifty generations of skillful brains have left in shadow. But I have one suggestion which I think might lead to a solution if it were put to laboratory tests by those who know something about philosophical analysis and dialectic.

There seems no way to get at this suggestion except through a reference to my own adventures in playwriting, so I ask your tolerance while I use myself as an instance. A man who has written successful plays is usually supposed to know something about the theory of playwriting, and perhaps he usually does. In my own case, however, I must confess that I /3/ came into the theatre unexpectedly, without preparation, and stayed in it because I had a certain amount of rather accidental success. It was not until after I had fumbled my way through a good many successes and an appalling number of failures that I began to doubt the sufficiency of dramatic instinct and to wonder whether or not there were general laws governing dramatic structure which so poor a head for theory as my own might grasp and use. I had read the *Poetics* long before I tried playwriting, and I had looked doubtfully into a few well-known handbooks on dramatic structure, but the maxims and theories propounded always drifted by me in a luminous haze — brilliant, true, profound in context, yet quite without meaning for me when I considered the plan for a play or tried to clarify an emotion in dialogue. So far as I could make out every play was a new problem, and the old rules were inapplicable. There were so many rules, so many landmarks, so many pitfalls, so many essential reckonings, that it seemed impossible to find your way through the jungle except by plunging ahead, trusting to your sense of direction and keeping your wits about you as you went.

But as the seasons went by and my failures fell as regularly as the leaves in autumn I began to search again among the theorists of the past for a word of wisdom that might take some of the gamble out of playwriting. What I needed most of all, I felt, was a working definition of what a play is, or perhaps a /4/ formula which would include all the elements necessary to a play structure. A play is almost always, probably, an attempt to recapture a vision for the stage. But when you are working in the theatre it's most unsatisfactory to follow the gleam without a compass, quite risky to trust "the light that never was on sea or land" without making sure beforehand that you are not being led straight into a slough of despond. In other words you must make a choice among visions, and you must check your chosen vision carefully before assuming that it will make a play. But by what rules, what maps, what fields of reference can you check so intangible a substance as a revelation, a dream, an inspiration, or any similar nudge from the subconscious mind?

I shan't trouble you with the details of my search for a criterion, partly because I can't remember it in detail. But I re-read Aristotle's *Poetics* in the light of some bitter experience, and one of his observations led me to a comparison of ancient and modern playwriting methods. In discussing construction he made a point of the recognition scene as essential to tragedy. The recognition scene, as Aristotle isolated it in the tragedies of the Greeks, was generally an artificial device, a central scene in which the leading character saw through a disguise, recognized as a friend or as an enemy, perhaps as a lover or a member of his own family, some person whose identity had been hidden. Iphigeneia, for example, acting as priestess in an alien country, receives a victim for /5/ sacrifice and then recognizes her own brother in this victim. There is an instant and profound emotional reaction, instantly her direction in the play is altered. But occasionally, in the greatest of the plays, the recognition turned on a situation far more convincing, though no less contrived. Oedipus, hunting savagely for the criminal who has brought the plague upon Thebes, discovers that he is himself that criminal — and since this is a discovery that affects not only the physical well-being and happiness of the hero, but the whole structure of his life, the effect on him and on the direction of the story is incalculably greater than could result from the more superficial revelation made to Iphigeneia.

Now scenes of exactly this sort are rare in the modern drama except in detective stories adapted for the stage. But when I probed a little more deeply into the memorable pieces of Shakespeare's theatre and our own I began to see that though modern recognition scenes are subtler and harder to find, they are none the less present in the plays we choose to remember. They seldom have to do with anything so naïve as disguise or the unveiling of a personal identity. But the element of discovery is just as important as ever. For the mainspring in the mechanism of a modern play is almost invariably a discovery by the hero of some element in his environment or in his own soul of which he has not been aware — or which he has not taken sufficiently into account. Moreover, nearly every teacher of playwriting has had some /6/ inkling of this, though it was not until after I had worked out my own theory that what they said on this point took on accurate meaning for me. I still think that the rule which I formulated for my own guidance is more concise than any other, and so I give it here: A play should lead up to and away from a central crisis, and this crisis should consist in a discovery by the leading character which has an indelible effect on his thought and emotion and completely alters his course of action. The leading character, let me say again, must make the discovery; it must affect him emotionally; and it must alter his direction in the play.

Try that formula on any play you think worthy of study, and you will find that, with few exceptions, it follows this pattern or some variation of this pattern. The turning point of *The Green Pastures,* for example, is the discovery of God, who is the leading character, that even he must learn and grow, that a God who is to endure must conform to the laws of change. The turning point of *Hamlet* is Hamlet's discovery, in the play-scene, that his uncle was unquestionably the murderer of his father. In *Abe Lincoln in Illinois* Lincoln's discovery is that he has been a coward, that he has stayed out of the fight for the Union because he was afraid. In each case, you will note, the discovery has a profound emotional effect on the hero, and gives an entirely new direction to his action in the play.

I'm not writing a disquisition on playwriting and /7/ wouldn't be competent to write one, but I do want to make a point of the superlative usefulness of this one touchstone for play-structure. When a man sets out to write a play his first problem is his subject and the possibilities of that subject as a story to be projected from the stage. His choice of subject matter is his personal problem, and one that takes its answer from his personal relation to his times. But if he wants to know a possible play subject when he finds it, if he wants to know how to mould the subject into play form after he has found it, I doubt that he'll ever discover another standard as satisfactory as the modern version of Aristotle which I have suggested. If the plot he has in mind does not contain a playable episode in which the hero or heroine makes an emotional discovery, a discovery that practically dictates the end of the story, then such an episode must be inserted — and if no place can be found for it the subject is almost certainly a poor one for the theatre. If this emotional discovery is contained in the story, but is not central, then it must be made central, and the whole action must revolve around it. In a three-act play it should fall near the end of the second act, though it may be delayed till the last; in a five-act play it will usually be found near the end of the third, though here also it can be delayed. Everything else in the play should be subordinated to this one episode — should lead up to or away from it.

Now this prime rule has a corollary which is just as important as the rule itself. The hero who is to /8/ make the central discovery in a play must not be a perfect man. He must have some variation of what Aristotle calls a tragic fault — and the reason he must have it is that when he makes his discovery he must change both in himself and in his action — and he must change for the better. The fault can be a very simple one — a mere unawareness, for example — but if he has no fault he cannot change for the better, but only for the worse, and for a reason which I shall discuss later, it is necessary that he must become more admirable, and not less so, at the end of the play. In other words, a hero must pass through an experience which opens his eyes to an error of his own. He must learn through suffering. In a tragedy he suffers death itself as a consequence of his fault or his attempt to correct it, but before he dies he has become a nobler person because of his recognition of his fault and the consequent alteration of his course of action. In a serious play which does not end in death he suffers a lesser punishment, but the pattern remains the same. In both forms he has a fault to begin with, he discovers that fault during the course of the action, and he does what he can to rectify it at the end. In *The Green Pastures* God's fault was that he believed himself perfect. He discovered that he was not perfect, and he resolved to change and grow. Hamlet's fault was that he could not make up his mind to act. He offers many excuses for his indecision until he discovers that there is no real reason for hesitation and that he has delayed out of coward- /9/ ice. Lincoln, in *Abe Lincoln in Illinois,* has exactly the same difficulty. In the climactic scene it is revealed to him that he had hesitated to take sides through fear of the consequences to himself, and he then chooses to go ahead without regard for what may be in store for him. From the point of view of the playwright, then, the essence of a tragedy, or even of a serious play, is the spiritual awakening, or regeneration, of his hero.

When a playwright attempts to reverse the formula, when his hero makes a discovery which has an evil effect, or one which the audience interprets as evil, on his character, the play is inevitably a failure on the stage. In *Troilus and Cressida* Troilus discovers that Cressida is a light woman. He draws from her defection the inference that all women are faithless — that faith in woman is the possession of fools. As a consequence he turns away from life and seeks death in a cause as empty as the love he has given up, the cause of the strumpet Helen. All the glory of Shakespeare's verse cannot rescue the play for an audience, and save in *Macbeth* Shakespeare nowhere wrote so richly, so wisely, or with such a flow of brilliant metaphor.

For the audience will always insist that the alteration in the hero be for the better — or for what it believes to be the better. As audiences change the standards of good and evil change, though slowly and unpredictably, and the meanings of plays change with the centuries. One thing only is certain: that an /10/ audience watching a play will go along with it only when the leading character responds in the end to what it considers a higher moral impulse than moved him at the beginning of the story, though the audience will of course define morality as it pleases and in the terms of its own day. It may be that there is no absolute up or down in this world, but the race believes that there is, and will not hear of any denial.

And now at last I come to the point toward which I've been struggling so laboriously. Why does the audience come to the theatre to look on while an imaginary hero is put to an imaginary trial and comes out of it with credit to the race and to himself? It was this question that prompted my essay, and unless I've been led astray by my own predilections there is a very possible answer in the rules for playwriting which I have just cited. The theatre originated in two complementary religious ceremonies, one celebrating the animal in man and one celebrating the god. Old Greek Comedy was dedicated to the spirits of lust and riot and earth, spirits which are certainly necessary to the health and continuance of the race. Greek tragedy was dedicated to man's aspiration, to his kinship with the gods, to his unending, blind attempt to lift himself above his lusts and his pure animalism into a world where there are other values than pleasure and survival. However unaware of it we may be, our theatre has followed the Greek patterns with no change in essence, from Aristophanes and Euripides to our own day. Our more ribald /11/ musical comedies are simply our approximation of the Bacchic rites of Old Comedy. In the rest of our theatre we sometimes follow Sophocles, whose tragedy is always an exaltation of the human spirit, sometimes Euripides, whose tragi-comedy follows the same pattern of an excellence achieved through suffering. The forms of both tragedy and comedy have changed a good deal in non-essentials, but in essentials — and especially in the core of meaning which they must have for audiences — they are in the main the same religious rites which grew up around the altars of Attica long ago.

It is for this reason that when you write for the theatre you must choose between your version of a phallic revel and your vision of what mankind may or should become. Your vision may be faulty, or shallow, or sentimental, but it must conform to some aspiration in the audience, or the audience will reject it. Old Comedy, the celebration of the animal in us, still has a place in our theatre, as it had in Athens, but here, as there, that part of the theatre which celebrated man's virtue and his regeneration in hours of crisis is accepted as having the more important function. Our comedy is largely the Greek New Comedy, which grew out of Euripides' tragi-comedy, and is separated from tragedy only in that it presents a happier scene and puts its protagonist through an ordeal which is less than lethal.

And since our plays, aside from those which are basically Old Comedy, are exaltations of the human /12/ spirit, since that is what an audience expects when it comes to the theatre, the playwright gradually discovers, as he puts plays before audiences, that he must follow the ancient Aristotelian rule: he must build his plot around a scene wherein his hero discovers some mortal frailty or stupidity in himself and faces life armed with a new wisdom. He must so arrange his story that it will prove to the audience that men pass through suffering purified, that, animal though we are, despicable though we are in many ways, there is in us all some divine, incalculable fire that urges us to be better than we are.

It could be argued that what the audience demands of a hero is only conformity to race morality, to the code which seems to the spectators most likely to make for race survival. In many cases, especially in comedy, and obviously in the comedy of Molière, this is true. But in the majority of ancient and modern plays it seems to me that what the audience wants to believe is that men have a desire to break the moulds of earth which encase them and claim a kinship with a higher morality than that which hems them in. The rebellion of Antigone, who breaks the laws of men through adherence to a higher law of affection, the rebellion of Prometheus, who breaks the law of the gods to bring fire to men, the rebellion of God in *The Green Pastures* against the rigid doctrine of the Old Testament, the rebellion of Tony in *They Knew What They Wanted* against the convention that called on him to repudiate his cuck- /13/ old child, the rebellion of Liliom against the heavenly law which asked him to betray his own integrity and make a hypocrisy of his affection, even the repudiation of the old forms and the affirmation of new by the heroes of Ibsen and Shaw, these are all instances to me of the groping of men toward an excellence dimly apprehended, seldom possible of definition. They are evidence to me that the theatre at its best is a religious affirmation, an age-old rite restating and reassuring man's belief in his own destiny and his ultimate hope. The theatre is much older than the doctrine of evolution, but its one faith, asseverated again and again for every age and every year, is a faith in evolution, in the reaching and the climb of men toward distant goals, glimpsed but never seen, perhaps never achieved, or achieved only to be passed impatiently on the way to a more distant horizon. /14/

---

UNA **ELLIS-FERMOR:** *The Frontiers of Drama*

... [I]n great tragedy there is an element common to the individual plays, though differing in form and theme, an element which marks both the treatment of the material and the nature of the resulting interpretation: it is the presence of . . . conflict . . . between two impressions made by his experience upon the poet's mind.

The part of this experience which is most clearly revealed is the intense awareness of evil and pain. But in conflict with this specific response to fact and event is another of a wholly different kind; the intuitive and often undefined apprehension of another universe implying other values. Beyond the realization of evil and pain (and the work of art will be great in proportion as this is profound), beyond the apprehension of an alien destiny that appears to shape man's action, there is the perception, at once more comprehensive and less explicit, of a possible resolution, of some reconciliation with or interpretation in terms of good. The impressions in conflict may be of various kinds; of a malevolent and a beneficent world-order; of apparent lawlessness against underlying law, a casual against a causal, a chaotic against a patterned universe. And the unresolved conflict between them will at first give rise to a sense of mystery; to the assumption that evil can never be sounded, however thoroughly it be analysed, that its causes will never fully reveal themselves, even to the most passionate questioning.

It is here that, in the finest tragic writing, there is equilibrium. The reality of evil and pain is not denied; if it /128/ were, tragedy would not speak to man's condition as it has done from the time of Aeschylus to the present day. Nevertheless, something is revealed which makes possible the transvaluation of the values upon which this rests; the works of art which we call tragedies are distinguished from others, not only by technical characteristics of subject-matter or form, but also by the balance maintained between conflicting readings of the universe and of man's condition and destiny. The supreme works in this kind reveal that balance in the highest degree, thus satisfying most nearly man's need to find his complex and contradictory experience transmuted unto the enduring form of art. Certain tragedies, it is true, fail to maintain complete balance, some lessening their hold on the imagination by presenting irremediable evil and a satanic universe, and some, with similar consequences, indicating remedies so immediate or so easily defined that men's judgement and innate sanity mistrust them. Both kinds may nevertheless remain within the category

*From* The Frontiers of Drama, *2nd ed. (London: Methuen and Company, 1946).*

of tragedy, provided they do not destroy either of the elements in whose conflict the average man recognizes an essential part of his own dual experience.

The characteristic balance thus obtained results, as we have said, in a play
of a certain quality. In content and in thought tragedy is, like all great art, an
interpretation of some part of the universe of man's experience, but inasmuch
as it is dramatic it is primarily an interpretation by implication, by the emphasis
it lays on certain parts of that experience, the significance with which it invests
them, rather than by explicit or direct commentary. The part of this experience
which it selects involves suffering and some kind of catastrophe, and these
significant of something more than the bare facts actually present. Balance is
thus maintained in all great tragedy; suffering and catastrophe upon the one
hand and upon the other a relation (often unspecified and undefined) with some
fundamental or universal law whose operation justifies or compensates them.
From this arises the conflict of impressions; evident evil against partially hidden
yet immanent and overruling good. Thus far all tragedy is akin. /129/

---

HENRY A. **MYERS**: *Tragedy: A View of Life*

Aristotle's definition of tragedy epitomizes the virtues of his method and the
weakness of his aim in the study of poetry. Since the definition appears in the
*Poetics* near the beginning of the discussion of tragedy and is followed by
generalizations which seem to depend upon its acceptance, an unwary reader
might mistakenly infer that these generalizations are consequences deduced from
supposedly self-evident assumptions. The answer to such a misunderstanding of
the Aristotelian method is to be found in the difference between the order of
investigation /47/ and the order of demonstration. In his investigation of
tragedy, Aristotle started by analyzing the available specimens into their dis-
tinguishable parts, proceeded by generalizing concerning the constituent elements
of tragedy, and ended by synthesizing his findings in the definition. In demonstrating his results, however, he reverses the steps of investigation: in the
*Poetics* he starts with his definition, proceeds by discussing the generalizations
which it summarizes, and ends by supporting each generalization with examples
chosen from particular tragedies. Properly understood, then, the definition
marks the end of the investigation of tragedy and the beginning of the
demonstration of its nature. But although the definition is the culmination of
an admirable scientific method, its ending in a puzzling metaphor signalizes
the inadequacy of Aristotle's attempt to explain tragedy by treating it as though
it were charged with feeling but lacking in meaning.

"Tragedy," says Aristotle, "is an imitation of an action that is serious,
complete, and of adequate magnitude — in language embellished in different
ways in different parts — in the form of action, not of narration — through pity
and terror effecting the purgation of these emotions." Here we have the kind of
logical definition, invented by Socrates and perfected by Aristotle, which first
places the object to be defined in its proximate genus and then distinguishes
it as a species by listing its specific differences. Like all other forms of poetry,
tragedy is an imitation of an action: imitation is the genus to which tragedy,
as one of the imitative arts, belongs. The action represented in a tragedy, however, has qualities which distinguish it from the actions represented in other /48/
arts and other kinds of poetry. It is serious, complete, and of adequate magni-

*From* Tragedy: A View of Life *(Ithaca, N.Y.: Cornell University Press, 1956).*

tude. A single incident of suffering or enjoying may serve as material for a lyric poem or a dramatic episode, but the action of a tragedy cannot be less than the series of incidents, in probable or necessary sequence, of a change of fortune. Unlike the little ups and downs of comedy, which can be laughable because they are trivial, the change of fortune of a tragedy is serious, with great and grave consequences; therefore, a tragedy loses effectiveness if its action is too brief to make a serious impression or too long for its incidents, which reveal the probability or necessity of the change of fortune, to be easily retained in memory. A (Greek) tragedy is composed of choral odes and dramatic episodes, and each of these is embellished in its own way, one with melody, the other with meter — a point which further distinguishes (Greek) tragedy from other kinds of (Greek) poetry. Tragedy is distinguished from epic and narrative poetry by its dramatic form: its main incidents are in the form of action taking place at the moment they are seen or read. And since (presumably) each kind of poetry is most clearly distinguished by the particular pleasure derived from its special emotional effects, a poem which meets the other tests may be positively identified as a tragedy by the pleasure it affords while purging us of the emotions of pity and terror.

Interest in Aristotle's definition has always centered on his concluding phrase — "through pity and terror effecting the purgation of these emotions" — on the famous metaphor which brings to an anticlimax a study which, had it been guided only by a scientific method, should have resulted in a clear, literal, and objective definition of trag- /49/ edy. When we remember that Aristotle is necessarily defining only Greek tragedy in relation to Greek art and poetry, we must admit that the early parts of his definition possess the qualities of scientific description. The concluding phrase manifests, however, a sharp break with his method. From a consideration of those qualities of tragedy which may be objectively observed and analyzed, he turns suddenly to the effects of tragedy as they are subjectively experienced by the spectator. At the end of a series of generalizations, literally applicable to the individual tragedies from which they have been derived by induction, he falls back upon a metaphor suggested by the science and art of medicine.

Though it does not take us far, probably the only safe guide to the meaning of Aristotle's medical metaphor is the passage in the *Politics* in which he discusses the place of music in education. Many benefits, he tells us, are derived from music: some melodies are valuable aids in education; others offer relaxation and recreation after exertion; and still others offer a restoring and healing purgation to those who are troubled by an excess of such feelings as religious enthusiasm. This purgation, he goes on to say, is an important function of art; through catharsis those who are especially susceptible to pity, fear, and enthusiasm, and all others in a lesser degree of intensity, find a pleasurable relief. That is all we find in the passage, except the promise that he will provide a fuller explanation of catharsis in his study of poetry.

Since the *Poetics,* as we know it, fails to keep this promise, some scholars have assumed that the part of the text containing the explanation has been lost. Several considerations suggest reasonable doubts concerning this /50/ possibility. Although parts of the *Poetics* may be missing, is it likely that the most important part should be lost and completely forgotten? And since Aristotle's promised explanation of catharsis would necessarily trace this mysterious effect to its causes, making possible a consideration of the relative effectiveness of these causes as they appear in particular tragedies, is it likely that Aristotle had worked out an explanation of how pity and terror are pleasurably purged and yet failed to use it or to refer to it in any of the many scattered passages in which he discusses how these emotions are effectively excited? It seems more likely that Aristotle, realizing that an explanation would raise the question of the meaning of tragedy, decided that his metaphor was by itself sufficiently clear to serve its purpose.

Although a metaphor is anticlimactic at the end of a scientific investigation, Aristotle's theory of catharsis, as it is explained in the passage in the *Politics,* admirably suits his purposes in the study of poetry. It answers Plato's extreme criticisms of poets and poetry. Poetry, Plato had charged, feeds the passions, which should be starved. Poetry, Aristotle seems to reply, provides a healthful emotional outlet, a beneficial mean between the dangerous extremes of surrender to passion and suppression of feeling. The poets, Plato had charged, are untrustworthy teachers. The poets, Aristotle seems to reply, are to be judged, not as teachers, but as contributors to the emotional well-being of mankind. Indeed, the theory of catharsis is Aristotle's solution to the ancient quarrel between poetry and philosophy: the poet is granted an honored function in the realm of the feelings, but the philosopher remains king in the realm of meaning. /51/

If Aristotle's metaphor were altogether clear and illuminating, we might accept it as proof that philosophy and science must end, as they so often begin, in poetry. Instead of a clear and full illumination, however, it provides an intriguing and tantalizing partial illumination: in it we find the question to be answered rather than the answer to the question. This question presents an apparent paradox. The misfortunes of men like ourselves excite such unpleasant feelings as pity and terror, and yet the total effect of tragedy is pleasing. Aristotle recognizes this apparent paradox but fails to explain it. Although he discusses in detail the objective causes of the spectator's pity and terror, judging the suitability of heroes, of plots, and of the parts of plots by their effectiveness in exciting these emotions, he *nowhere* points out the cause or causes of the catharsis which supposedly transforms pity and terror into pleasure. His metaphor merely asserts that this transformation takes place; it contains no hint as to why it takes place. For this reason, scholars who accept Aristotle's metaphorical definition of tragedy are obliged to furnish their own explanations of its meaning, with the result that there are said to be now available more than sixty interpretations of the theory of catharsis.

The theory of catharsis, as Aristotle presents it, ignores the manifest intention of the Greek tragic poets to demonstrate the fundamental conditions of human destiny. Aeschylus, the inventor of tragedy, obviously regarded himself as a teacher of personal freedom and responsibility and his tragedies as striking illustrations of the divine justice which finally prevails in human affairs. Sophocles, by stressing the dignity and beauty of the heroic human spirit, taught a religious acceptance of ordained events, however /52/ terrible they may be. Euripides, the rebel and skeptic, was torn between a desire to equal the triumphs of his predecessors in demonstrating the justice of strange dooms and a desire to surpass them by using drama to expose the injustices of the *status quo* in society. Each poet developed a distinctive attitude or solution, but all aimed at the solution of one and the same problem, the problem of justice; and it would be ridiculous to say of any one of them that as an artist in tragedy his purpose was merely to play upon the emotions of the spectator or to afford the spectator a healthful but inexplicable pleasure.

Aristotle's preoccupation with the emotional effect of poetry obliged him to ignore the plain and obvious fact that every true tragedy is a demonstration of the justice of the unalterable conditions of human experience. If he had been willing to admit that the reason that tragedy leaves us at the end with a sense of reconciliation rather than with one of horror is that it affects both the mind and the feelings by presenting a view of life in which the idea of justice is central, he might have avoided his puzzling and unsatisfactory metaphor and concluded his definition with a clear, literal, and objective statement of its essential quality. "Tragedy," *he might then have said,* "is an imitation of an action that is serious, complete, and of adequate magnitude — in language embellished in different ways in different parts — in the form of action, not of narration" — *revealing a just relation between good and evil in the life of a representative man.* /53/

---

D. D. **RAPHAEL**: *The Paradox of Tragedy*

Tragedy always presents a conflict. This proposition needs no defence. It is familiar enough. But a conflict between what? I suggest that it is a conflict between inevitable power, which we may call necessity, and the reaction to necessity of self-conscious effort. Tragic conflict differs from the conflicts presented by other forms of drama in that the victory always goes to necessity. The hero is crushed.

I have spoken of necessity, not fate. Writers on this subject often draw a distinction between classical Tragedy, which attributes human disaster to fate, and modern Tragedy, which attributes it to human character. For my purpose the distinction is irrelevant. In both cases, the cause of the disaster is necessity, whether external to the hero or inherent in his own character. For that matter, external necessity is not exhausted by fate or non-human powers. Antigone is in conflict with, and is crushed by, political power. (It is true that, in the same play, Creon /25/ opposes, and is in a different way struck down by, supernatural ordinance; but Antigone and her ordeal form the centre of interest.) In any event it is superficial to make the difference between classical and, say, Shakespearean Tragedy turn on a distinction between supernatural and psychological causes. Is Aeschylus' portrayal of Clytemnestra in the *Agamemnon* a study of the workings of supernatural fate or of human psychology? It is either or both. And the same is true of Shakespeare's treatment of Macbeth. You may choose, if you wish, to regard the workings of character as embodying dark forces that transcend the individual. Or you may regard myths, that speak of supernatural forces, as vivid expressions of the effects of psychological traits. *King Lear* is agreed to be the most nearly classical of Shakespeare's Tragedies; yet it can be treated as a study of pride and ingratitude. On the other side, is the psychological interest of Euripides' *Medea* any less than that of *Othello* or *Phèdre*?

The conflict, then, is with necessity, inevitable power that is bound to defeat any opposition. The tragic hero, even though he be a villain like Macbeth, attracts our admiration because of some *grandeur d'âme,* a greatness in his effort to resist, and our pity for his defeat. Although he must be crushed in his conflict, since his adversary is necessity, yet he does not yield the victory on all counts. . . . His *grandeur d'âme* is sublime and wins our admiration. Herein lies the satisfaction, the elevation, produced by Tragedy.

So far, I have not said anything particularly novel. Let /26/ me now proceed to characterize further the aesthetic satisfaction of Tragedy. Tragic beauty is a species of the sublime. What is felt to be sublime is something surpassingly great. It may be physically great or spiritually great, 'the starry heavens above' or 'the moral law within'. Both these, said Kant, fill us with wonder and awe. Now I want to suggest that the reaction to the sublime need not always be

*From* The Paradox of Tragedy *(Bloomington: Indiana University Press, 1960).*

wonder *and awe*. It may be admiration alone. The works of God or Nature, 'the chains of the Pleiades, the bands of Orion' — when we feel these to be sublime, we feel wonder and awe. As A. C. Bradley says, our rapture goes along with self-surrender, with feelings of abasement no less than those of elevation. But what of the sublimity of human effort? When we see this, does our admiration include feelings of abasement? We may feel that we ordinary mortals could not rise to the heights of the tragic hero if we were in his place — though I shall try to show that the dramatist deliberately counters this by raising us in other ways above the characters in his play. At any rate, we do not feel that *man* is lowly, is dust and ashes, when confronted by the greatness of that which he opposes and by which he is crushed. He is defeated, but he remains great, sublime, in his fall. The greatness of his opponent is greatness of physical power. His own greatness is greatness of spirit. I suggest that at least some of the peculiar satisfaction of tragic drama comes from a feeling that the sublimity of the hero's spirit is superior to the sublimity of the power which overwhelms him. The dramatist stirs in us more admiration for the human spirit than awe for the powers of necessity.

Both Tragedy and Epic, as Aristotle says, elevate man /27/ in their representation of human action, while Comedy abases him. Both Tragedy and Epic achieve the elevation of a hero through triumph in a conflict. Tragedy differs from Epic in that the tragic conflict and its issue are complicated and paradoxical. On the natural plane, the hero is worsted by the strength of his adversary, which thus appears great and, in the necessity of its conquest, sublime in the sense of awe-inspiring. On the spiritual plane, the hero appears great in his necessarily futile struggle. The inevitability of his defeat on the natural plane is what gives sublimity to his reaction. The inner conflict of Tragedy is between the two forms of the sublime, the awe-inspiring strength of necessity and the *grandeur d'âme* which inspires admiration. Each triumphs on its own plane, but the triumph of the human spirit is the more elevating. And that is why the tragic fate of the hero gives us satisfaction.

Because Tragedy snatches a spiritual victory out of a natural defeat, it is nearer to the religious attitude than is Epic. In another way, however, Tragedy tends to be inimical to religion. It elevates man in his struggle with necessity, while the religious attitude is one of abasement before that which is greater than man, before the awe-inspiring sublime. This corollary of the sense of the tragic invites further discussion. Before pursuing it, we must return to pick up a thread left loose a short while ago.

The tragic hero, like the epic hero, Aristotle remarks, is given a nobility greater than that of life. As Anouilh says in his *Antigone,* futile reaction against necessity has no place in the life of ordinary men. 'It's a luxury (*C'est gratuit*). It's for kings.' Does it then follow that the audience of ordinary men feel themselves small before the grandeur of the superhuman heroes on the stage? No, /28/ it does not follow, for the dramatist employs his arts on the audience, too. He cannot give them superhuman nobility, such as he gives his hero, but in another way he raises them above his hero. A mark of the tragic hero is his limited knowledge, and the mark of tragic irony is the contrast between the hero's ignorance and the audience's knowledge, whereby statements that mean one thing to him have a *double entendre* for them. In his ignorance the tragic hero displays the finitude of man. The audience are free from this limitation. Within the universe of the play, they have the omniscience of the gods. A former colleague of mine, Mr. D. H. Monro, in his book *Argument of Laughter,* speaks of the 'God's-eye view' of humanity presented in the Comedy of character. It is given in Tragedy, too. Indeed, in Greek Tragedy it is sometimes a view superior to that of a god. For if a god is brought upon the stage, the audience has a view embracing both the outlook of the god and that of the other characters. Even in *Prometheus Vinctus*, where Zeus never actually appears as a character on the stage, Aeschylus sets the audience above Zeus and Prometheus alike, for his aim is to seek a superior theology in which power and benevolence shall be combined, and in so far as he grasps and communicates such a 'God's-eye view' he places his audience at the vantage point from which that view may be obtained.

Tragedy is a form of art, and its pleasure is an aesthetic pleasure. We rarely, if ever, obtain from the so-called tragedies[1] of life the satisfaction that we gain from tragic /29/ drama. In life, we are on the same level as those who suffer, we are fellow human beings. Our sympathy for their disaster is usually too strong for feelings of satisfaction at any sublimity they may display. In the theatre, the way is cleared for the appreciation of sublimity by giving us the 'God's-eye view'. The scene is set in the past, so that we know what is going to happen; or, if not in the past, in a distant clime, so that we shall not be too disposed to identify ourselves in sympathy with the characters on the stage. The dramatist fails in his purpose if, like Phrynichus with *The Capture of Miletus,* he represents life close to his audience and inhibits admiration by excessive pity.

Yet the separation must not go too far; for we shall be able to admire the human quality of the characters only if we feel sympathy for them as human beings ourselves. The author of Comedy, especially of satiric Comedy, can sometimes allow the distance between audience and stage to cross the boundary separating the human from the non-human. For instance, by de-humanizing his characters, as Karel Čapek does in *The Insect Play,* he completes the temporary deification of the audience — for he does not want them to sympathize. When the play is done, and they are brought back from divinity to humanity, they will see the beasts in themselves. The tragedian must raise his audience to the level of the God's-eye view, yet at the same time he must be careful not to deprive them of fellow-feeling with the characters on the stage.

He can succeed in this double purpose because the tragic hero is himself larger than life. The hero lacks the omniscience of his audience, but the gods who watch him, like the powers against whom he strives, fall below him in *grandeur d'âme*. Hero and adversary are balanced /30/ by their respective superiority in spiritual grandeur on the one side and natural power on the other. *Vis-à-vis* the audience, the spiritual grandeur of the hero is balanced by their godlike omniscience. Thus we can at the same time sympathize and admire. The hero is a man like us, showing human weaknesses from which the devices of art free us for the nonce; but though an object of our sympathy, he also seems sublime, for he outstrips us, and the superior powers whom he opposes, in greatness of spirit. And our sympathy for him as a fellow human being gives to his sublimity a stronger appeal than that exerted by the sublimity of the alien power with which he contends. By such devices Tragedy exalts man in our eyes. Its creed is humanistic. /31/

---

[1] *It is important to bear in mind the distinction between tragic drama and 'tragedy' in a looser sense. I mark it by writing the word with a capital initial letter when it has the first meaning, and not when it has the second.*

ANDREW CECIL **BRADLEY**: *Shakespearean Tragedy*

Let us now turn from the 'action' to the central figure in it; and, ignoring the characteristics which distinguish the heroes from one another, let us ask whether they have any common qualities which appear to be essential to the tragic effect.

One they certainly have. They are exceptional beings. We have seen already that the hero, with Shakespeare, is a person of high degree or of public importance, and that his actions or sufferings are of an unusual kind. But this is not all. His nature also is exceptional, and generally raises him /19/ in some respect much above the average level of humanity. This does not mean that he is an eccentric or a paragon. Shakespeare never drew monstrosities of virtue; some of his heroes are far from being 'good'; and if he drew eccentrics he gave them a subordinate position in the plot. His tragic characters are made of the stuff we find within ourselves and within the persons who surround them. But, by an intensification of the life which they share with others, they are raised above them; and the greatest are raised so far that, if we fully realise all that is implied in their words and actions, we become conscious that in real life we have known scarcely any one resembling them. Some, like Hamlet and Cleopatra, have genius. Others, like Othello, Lear, Macbeth, Coriolanus, are built on the grand scale; and desire, passion, or will attains in them a terrible force. In almost all we observe a marked one-sidedness, a predisposition in some particular direction; a total incapacity, in certain circumstances, of resisting the force which draws in this direction; a fatal tendency to identify the whole being with one interest, object, passion, or habit of mind. This, it would seem, is, for Shakespeare, the fundamental tragic trait. It is present in his early heroes, Romeo and Richard II., infatuated men, who otherwise rise comparatively little above the ordinary level. It is a fatal gift, but it carries with it a touch of greatness; and when there is joined to it nobility of mind, or genius, or immense force, we realise the full power and reach of the soul, and the conflict in which it engages acquires that magnitude which stirs not only sympathy and pity, but admiration, terror, and awe.

The easiest way to bring home to oneself the nature of the tragic character is to compare it with a character of another kind. Dramas like *Cymbeline* and the *Winter's Tale*, which might seem destined /20/ to end tragically, but actually end otherwise, owe their happy ending largely to the fact that the principal characters fail to reach tragic dimensions. And, conversely, if these persons were put in the place of the tragic heroes, the dramas in which they appeared would cease to be tragedies. Posthumus would never have acted as Othello did; Othello, on his side, would have met Iachimo's challenge with something more than words. If, like Posthumus, he had remained convinced of his wife's infidelity, he would not have repented her execution; if, like Leontes, he had come to believe that by an unjust accusation he had caused her death, he would never have lived on, like Leontes. In the same way the villain Iachimo has no touch of tragic greatness. But Iago comes nearer to it, and if Iago had slandered Imogen and had supposed his slanders to have led to her death, he certainly would not have turned melancholy and wished to die. One reason why

*From* Shakespearean Tragedy, *2nd ed. (London: The Macmillan Co., 1950). Originally published in 1905.*

the end of the *Merchant of Venice* fails to satisfy us is that Shylock is a tragic character, and that we cannot believe in his accepting his defeat and the conditions imposed on him. This was a case where Shakespeare's imagination ran away with him, so that he drew a figure with which the destined pleasant ending would not harmonise.

In the circumstances where we see the hero placed, his tragic trait, which is also his greatness, is fatal to him. To meet these circumstances something is required which a smaller man might have given, but which the hero cannot give. He errs, by action or omission; and his error, joining with other causes, brings on him ruin. This is always so with Shakespeare. As we have seen, the idea of the tragic hero as a being destroyed simply and solely by external forces is quite alien to him; and not less so is the idea of the hero as contributing to his destruction only by acts in which we see no /21/ flaw. But the fatal imperfection or error, which is never absent, is of different kinds and degrees. At one extreme stands the excess and precipitancy of Romeo, which scarcely, if at all, diminish our regard for him; at the other the murderous ambition of Richard III. In most cases the tragic error involves no conscious breach of right; in some (*e.g.* that of Brutus or Othello) it is accompanied by a full conviction of right. In Hamlet there is a painful consciousness that duty is being neglected; in Antony a clear knowledge that the worse of two courses is being pursued; but Richard and Macbeth are the only heroes who do what they themselves recognise to be villainous. It is important to observe that Shakespeare does admit such heroes,[1] and also that he appears to feel, and exerts himself to meet, the difficulty that arises from their admission. The difficulty is that the spectator must desire their defeat and even their destruction; and yet this desire, and the satisfaction of it, are not tragic feelings. Shakespeare gives to Richard therefore a power which excites astonishment, and a courage which extorts admiration. He gives to Macbeth a similar, though less extraordinary, greatness, and adds to it a conscience so terrifying in its warnings and so maddening in its reproaches that the spectacle of inward torment compels a horrified sympathy and awe which balance, at the least, the desire for the hero's ruin.

The tragic hero with Shakespeare, then, need not be 'good,' though generally he is 'good' and therefore at once wins sympathy in his error. But it is necessary that he should have so much of greatness that in his error and fall we may be vividly conscious of the possibilities of human nature. Hence, in the first place, a Shakespearean /22/ tragedy is never, like some miscalled tragedies, depressing. No one ever closes the book with the feeling that man is a poor mean creature. He may be wretched and he may be awful, but he is not small. His lot may be heart-rending and mysterious, but it is not contemptible. The most confirmed of cynics ceases to be a cynic while he reads these plays. And with this greatness of the tragic hero (which is not always confined to him) is connected, secondly, what I venture to describe as the centre of the tragic impression. This central feeling is the impression of waste. With Shakespeare, at any rate, the pity and fear which are stirred by the tragic story seem to unite with, and even to merge in, a profound sense of sadness and mystery, which is due to this impression of waste. 'What a piece of work is man,' we cry; 'so much more beautiful and so much more terrible than we knew! Why should he be so if this beauty and greatness only tortures itself and throws itself away?' We seem to have before us a type of the mystery of the whole world, the tragic fact which extends far beyond the limits of tragedy. Everywhere, from the crushed rocks beneath our feet to the soul of man, we see power, intelligence, life and glory, which astound us and seem to call for our worship. And everywhere we see them perishing, devouring one another and destroying themselves,

---

[1] *Aristotle apparently would exclude them.*

often with dreadful pain, as though they came into being for no other end. Tragedy is the typical form of this mystery, because that greatness of soul which it exhibits oppressed, conflicting and destroyed, is the highest existence in our view. It forces the mystery upon us, and it makes us realise so vividly the worth of that which is wasted that we cannot possibly seek comfort in the reflection that all is vanity. . . . /23/

Let us attempt then to re-state the idea that the ultimate power in the tragic world is a moral order. Let us put aside the ideas of justice and merit, and speak simply of good and evil. Let us understand by these words, primarily, moral good and evil, but also everything else in human beings which we take to be excellent or the reverse. Let us understand the statement that the ultimate power or order is 'moral' to mean that it does not show itself indifferent to good and evil, or equally favourable or unfavourable to both, but shows itself akin to good and alien from evil. And, /33/ understanding the statement thus, let us ask what grounds it has in the tragic fact as presented by Shakespeare.

Here, as in dealing with the grounds on which the idea of fate rests, I choose only two or three out of many. And the most important is this. In Shakespearean tragedy the main source of the convulsion which produces suffering and death is never good: good contributes to this convulsion only from its tragic implication with its opposite in one and the same character. The main source, on the contrary, is in every case evil; and, what is more (though this seems to have been little noticed), it is in almost every case evil in the fullest sense, not mere imperfection but plain moral evil. The love of Romeo and Juliet conducts them to death only because of the senseless hatred of their houses. Guilty ambition, seconded by diabolic malice and issuing in murder, opens the action in *Macbeth*. Iago is the main source of the convulsion in *Othello*; Goneril, Regan and Edmund in *King Lear*. Even when this plain moral evil is not the obviously prime source within the play, it lies behind it: the situation with which Hamlet has to deal has been formed by adultery and murder. *Julius Caesar* is the only tragedy in which one is even tempted to find an exception to this rule. And the inference is obvious. If it is chiefly evil that violently disturbs the order of the world, this order cannot be friendly to evil or indifferent between evil and good, any more than a body which is convulsed by poison is friendly to it or indifferent to the distinction between poison and food.

Again, if we confine our attention to the hero, and to those cases where the gross and palpable evil is not in him but elsewhere, we find that the comparatively innocent hero still shows some marked imperfection or defect, — irresolution, pre- /34/ cipitancy, pride, credulousness, excessive simplicity, excessive susceptibility to sexual emotions, and the like. These defects or imperfections are certainly, in the wide sense of the word, evil, and they contribute decisively to the conflict and catastrophe. And the inference is again obvious. The ultimate power which shows itself disturbed by this evil and reacts against it, must have a nature alien to it. Indeed its reaction is so vehement and 'relentless' that it would seem to be bent on nothing short of good in perfection, and to be ruthless in its demand for it.

To this must be added another fact, or another aspect of the same fact. Evil exhibits itself everywhere as something negative, barren, weakening, destructive, a principle of death. It isolates, disunites, and tends to annihilate not only its opposite but itself. That which keeps the evil man[2] prosperous, makes him

---

[2] *It is most essential to remember that an evil man is much more than the evil in him. I may add that in this paragraph I have, for the sake of clearness, considered evil in its most pronounced form; but what is said would apply,* mutatis mutandis, *to evil as imperfection, etc.*

succeed, even permits him to exist, is the good in him (I do not mean only the obviously 'moral' good). When the evil in him masters the good and has its way, it destroys other people through him, but it also destroys *him*. At the close of the struggle he has vanished, and has left behind him nothing that can stand. What remains is a family, a city, a country, exhausted, pale and feeble, but alive through the principle of good which animates it; and, within it, individuals who, if they have not the brilliance or greatness of the tragic character, still have won our respect and confidence. And the inference would seem clear. If existence in an order depends on good, and if the presence of evil is hostile to such existence, the inner being or soul of this order must be akin to good. /35/

These are aspects of the tragic world at least as clearly marked as those which, taken alone, suggest the idea of fate. And the idea which they in their turn, when taken alone, may suggest, is that of an order which does not indeed award 'poetic justice,' but which reacts through the necessity of its own 'moral' nature both against attacks made upon it and against failure to conform to it. Tragedy, on this view, is the exhibition of that convulsive reaction; and the fact that the spectacle does not leave us rebellious or desperate is due to a more or less distinct perception that the tragic suffering and death arise from collision, not with a fate or blank power, but with a moral power, a power akin to all that we admire and revere in the characters themselves. This perception produces something like a feeling of acquiescence in the catastrophe, though it neither leads us to pass judgment on the characters nor diminishes the pity, the fear, and the sense of waste, which their struggle, suffering and fall evoke. And, finally, this view seems quite able to do justice to those aspects of the tragic fact which give rise to the idea of fate. They would appear as various expressions of the fact that the moral order acts not capriciously or like a human being, but from the necessity of its nature, or, if we prefer the phrase, by general laws, — a necessity or law which of course knows no exception and is as 'ruthless' as fate.

It is impossible to deny to this view a large measure of truth. And yet without some amendment it can hardly satisfy. For it does not include the whole of the facts, and therefore does not wholly correspond with the impressions they produce. Let it be granted that the system or order which shows itself omnipotent against individuals is, in the sense explained, moral. Still — at any rate for the eye of sight — the evil against which it asserts itself, and /36/ the persons whom this evil inhabits, are not really something outside the order, so that they can attack it or fail to conform to it; they are within it and a part of it. It itself produces them, — produces Iago as well as Desdemona, Iago's cruelty as well as Iago's courage. It is not poisoned, it poisons itself. Doubtless it shows by its violent reaction that the poison *is* poison, and that its health lies in good. But one significant fact cannot remove another, and the spectacle we witness scarcely warrants the assertion that the order is responsible for the good in Desdemona, but Iago for the evil in Iago. If we make this assertion we make it on grounds other than the facts as presented in Shakespeare's tragedies.

Nor does the idea of a moral order asserting itself against attack or want of conformity answer in full to our feelings regarding the tragic character. We do not think of Hamlet merely as failing to meet its demand, of Antony as merely sinning against it, or even of Macbeth as simply attacking it. What we feel corresponds quite as much to the idea that they are *its* parts, expressions, products; that in their defect or evil *it* is untrue to its soul of goodness, and falls into conflict and collision with itself; that, in making them suffer and waste themselves, *it* suffers and wastes itself; and that when, to save its life and regain peace from this intestinal struggle, it casts them out, it has lost a part of its own substance, — a part more dangerous and unquiet, but far more valuable and nearer to its heart, than that which remains, — a Fortinbras, a Malcolm, an

Octavius. There is no tragedy in its expulsion of evil: the tragedy is that this involves the waste of good.

Thus we are left at last with an idea showing two sides or aspects which we can neither separate nor reconcile. The whole or order against which the individual part shows itself powerless seems /37/ to be animated by a passion for perfection: we cannot otherwise explain its behaviour towards evil. Yet it appears to engender this evil within itself, and in its effort to overcome and expel it it is agonised with pain, and driven to mutilate its own substance and to lose not only evil but priceless good. That this idea, though very different from the idea of a blank fate, is no solution of the riddle of life is obvious; but why should we expect it to be such a solution? Shakespeare was not attempting to justify the ways of God to men, or to show the universe as a Divine Comedy. He was writing tragedy, and tragedy would not be tragedy if it were not a painful mystery. Nor can he be said even to point distinctly, like some writers of tragedy, in any direction where a solution might lie. We find a few references to gods or God, to the influence of the stars, to another life: some of them certainly, all of them perhaps, merely dramatic — appropriate to the person from whose lips they fall. A ghost comes from Purgatory to impart a secret out of the reach of its hearer — who presently meditates on the question whether the sleep of death is dreamless. Accidents once or twice remind us strangely of the words, 'There's a divinity that shapes our ends.' More important are other impressions. Sometimes from the very furnace of affliction a conviction seems borne to us that somehow, if we could see it, this agony counts as nothing against the heroism and love which appear in it and thrill our hearts. Sometimes we are driven to cry out that these mighty or heavenly spirits who perish are too great for the little space in which they move, and that they vanish not into nothingness but into freedom. Sometimes from these sources and from others comes a presentiment, formless but haunting and even profound, that all the fury of conflict, with its waste and woe, is less than half the truth, even /38/ an illusion, 'such stuff as dreams are made on.' But these faint and scattered intimations that the tragic world, being but a fragment of a whole beyond our vision, must needs be a contradiction and no ultimate truth, avail nothing to interpret the mystery. We remain confronted with the inexplicable fact, or the no less inexplicable appearance, of a world travailing for perfection, but bringing to birth, together with glorious good, an evil which it is able to overcome only by self-torture and self-waste. And this fact or appearance is tragedy. /39/

---

### PETER **ALEXANDER**: *Hamlet, Father and Son*

... Bradley like Aristotle and Hegel insists that tragedy effects a reconciliation or produces a sense of redemption; how then does he overcome the difficulty about the lack of correspondence between the flaw and the catastrophe? It is a fault /50/ not to look both ways, but such omissions though they may explain do not reconcile us to the death of the pedestrian. Has Bradley isolated the factor in tragedy that allows us to look upon the conclusion with other eyes than those with which we so regularly contemplate the brutalities of existence?

*From* Hamlet, Father and Son *(Oxford: The Clarendon Press, 1955).*

Bradley begins by insisting that the hero always contributes in some measure to the disaster in which he perishes. A man or girl, let us say, becomes a soldier and is killed in the course of duty — have they contributed in some measure to their fate because they did not stay at home? But Bradley does not mean contribute in this sense. The tragic figure must show a fatal tendency to identify his whole being with one interest, object, passion, or habit of mind. Suppose then our soldier had a tendency in action to identify his whole being with winning the battle, a tendency that proved fatal. Has he contributed to his own destruction? Again the answer must be no, for there are these further qualifications:

> The critical action is, in a greater or less degree, wrong or bad. The catastrophe is the return of the action on the head of the agent. It is an example of Justice.

Of poetical justice there is no account, and of human justice hardly any, for there is no pretence that the punishment fits the crime. We should be back where we started, were it not for a further assumption. /51/

We are, Hegel and Bradley urge, to regard the Cosmos as an ethical substance — so ethical that it can tolerate nothing short of perfection. This substance finds the tragic hero identifying himself in a whole-hearted way with some particular object or passion. Antigone is determined to give her brother the rites of burial; Romeo and Juliet are devoted lovers. Such determinations and devotions the ethical substance judges too narrow and imperfect and wipes them out. No plea for mitigation of sentence on the score of merit or loyalty will serve: the more devoted the more culpable. At the end, however, we have, so we are told, a sense of reconciliation because what is denied is, so it is asserted, the exclusive and wrongful assertion of some right. The total right has engulfed the divided rights.

Bradley's elaboration of the Hegelian thesis has had a strong attraction for scholars and men of letters. Yet it shows no respect for the virtues of men; the best are doomed because not wholly perfect. This Cosmos that sentences the good and the true to death with as little compunction as it shows to the wicked resembles in one important respect the imaginings of the arch-pessimist among the great historians. Tacitus lays it down at the beginning of his *History,* as the thesis his account of affairs will sustain, that the gods care not for the happiness of /52/ mortals, only for their punishment. . . . Bradley's Cosmos resembles in its passion for retribution the gods of Tacitus: it cares only for the punishment of men. Bradley in his zeal to reconcile us to the facts of tragedy offers us a conclusion to which only a profound pessimism could possibly reconcile us. . . . /53/

It would be tedious to illustrate in detail the contradictory aspects of Bradley's doctrine; I must, however, draw your attention to one feature in the arrangement of his argument that may help to explain to you how the contradictions arise. The chapter in *Shakespearean Tragedy* dealing with *The Substance of Tragedy* concludes with this note:

> Partly in order not to anticipate later passages, I abstained from treating fully here the question why we feel, at the death of the tragic hero, not only pain but reconciliation and sometimes even exultation. As I cannot at present make good this defect, I would ask the reader to refer to the word Reconciliation *in the Index.*

Turning to the index you will find that the references are neither numerous nor extensive; but they provide the corrective to the scheme Bradley has tried /55/ to construct for us. At times they cancel out much of what he has already said, for we come on sentences of this tenor:

> The impression [*at the end of a tragedy is*] *that the heroic being, though in one sense and outwardly he has failed, is yet in another sense superior to the world in which he appears.*

Further, anyone who asserts that Shakespeare's tragedies are un-Christian in their outlook should consider carefully Bradley's observation that the feeling of the hero's having risen superior to the demands of a merely mundane morality seems to imply an idea which if developed would transform the tragic view of things. In short the chapter on *The Substance of Tragedy* does not deal with its real substance or the essential being of the form; this is only dealt with later; the chapter that claims to deal with the substance merely describes certain accidental features whose significance depends on the substance to which they belong. . . . /56/

Bradley gave only a subordinate place in his exposition of tragedy to 'reconciliation' or what Aristotle calls *catharsis*. This word Aristotle himself uses once only in the *Poetics,* but it is the key to his defence of the drama against Plato's attack. The notion of *hamartia* or the tragic flaw is of secondary importance, being introduced to serve as an explanation of *catharsis*. The terms are not on a par with one another: *catharsis* is the name given to a variety of experience; *hamartia* is a form of hypothesis put forward to account for the phenomenon. Till we get this distinction clear we can hardly hope to escape the tangle in which Bradley finds himself. His difficulties come from his putting the cart before the horse. We must first examine the phenomenon, and then we may be in a position to judge the value of the explanation that is offered us. In *The Substance of Tragedy* Bradley deals only with *hamartia; catharsis* is added in a footnote. If we are to get the elements /57/ of the problem in their proper order we must begin with *catharsis,* and I shall now venture on this difficult topic, for, however inadequate the treatment, on some such ground all reasonable interpretations of tragedy must rest.

The first and major difficulty in this inquiry, you may point out to me, is the precise meaning we are to give the word *catharsis*. On whose authority do I keep translating it as 'reconciliation' or 'redemption'? For are there not almost as many meanings to this word as there are scholars? 'A great historical discussion has centred round the phrase', says Butcher, and he adds, 'No passage, probably, in ancient literature has been so frequently handled by commentators.'

Like the search for the origins of tragedy the tracking of *catharsis* to its primal significance can take us back into a mysterious world where the golden bough still hung in the sacred grove. The word may have had reference to some ritual purification; and as Professor Gilbert Murray has insisted again and again the Dionysus ritual was a *catharsis* — a purification of the community from the taints and poisons of the old year. Such scholarly exploration is exciting and may be instructive, but it must be left to those properly equipped for the difficulties of the journey, especially if we can come by some /58/ understanding of Aristotle's use of the word by a more direct approach. . . .

. . . Certain subsidiary features Butcher and others do make clear to us: that Aristotle was deliberately using the word in a metaphorical sense (which he promised in the *Politics* to explain in his treatise on Poetry); that its technical use in medicine was familiar, yet this was not the sense in which Aristotle employed it or he would not have had to promise to elaborate his meaning later. After a close and learned analysis Butcher concludes:

> *Let us assume, then, that the tragic Katharsis involves not only the idea of emotional relief, but the further idea of the purifying of the emotions so relieved.*

Butcher after all feels he can do no more than assume; and it must be confessed that his assumption is not easily understood. Earlier he had said: /59/

> *Pity and fear are purged of the impure element which clings to them in life.*

The results of the inquiry about the various meanings of *catharsis* are, it must be admitted, disappointing.

Turning to examine *hamartia* Butcher emphasizes its subordinate place to *catharsis* in Aristotle's argument:

> *With the exception of the definition of tragedy itself, probably no passage in the* Poetics *has given rise to so much criticism as the description of the tragic hero in ch. xiii. The qualities requisite to such a character are here deduced from the primary fact that the function of tragedy is to produce the* katharsis *of pity and fear; pity being felt for a person who, if not wholly innocent, meets with suffering beyond his deserts; fear being awakened when the sufferer is a man of like nature with ourselves.*

Butcher arranges the elements of the problem in their significant order: we must start from the primary fact — *catharsis*. The scholar, however, soon finds himself confronted by the difficulty we have already encountered — the nature of the tragic flaw. 'A moral error', Butcher observes,

> *A moral error easily shades off into a mere defect of judgment. But that mere defect may work as potently as crime. Good intentions do not make actions right. The lofty disinterestedness of Brutus cannot atone for his want of practical insight.* /60/

And having arrived at the old problem of the lack of correspondence between cause and catastrophe the Greek scholar takes refuge in the Bradleian remark:

> *In the scheme of the universe a wholly unconscious error violates the law of perfection; it disturbs the moral order of the world. Distinctions of motive — the moral guilt or purity of the agent — are not here in question. So too in tragedy those are doomed who innocently err no less than those who sin consciously.*

We have here a moral order that recognizes no moral distinctions . . . yet at the end the same ambiguity that we find in Bradley:

> *The tragic irony sometimes lies precisely herein, that owing to some inherent frailty or flaw — it may be human short-sightedness, it may be some error of blood or judgment — the very virtues of a man hurry him forward to his ruin.*

We have again reached the point from which we wished to return to make a fresh start: faults are once more turning into virtues. Butcher in his study of *catharsis* and *hamartia* gets their relation to each other right, but he still leaves us in the tangle of Bradley's doctrine.

In our difficulty over *catharsis* there seems open to us only one promising resource, and this may be /61/ illustrated from that part of Aristotle's writings that deal with his biological interests. One of the most admired of his studies in this field is his examination of the development of the embryo in the egg. His method was simple but effective. Taking a gathering of eggs whose dates he could control he cut open an egg a day, so that he could observe the progress of development. Although there are obscurities in the text of his report there can be no serious difference of opinion about the matter of his discourse, for we can examine an egg for ourselves and need not fear that nature's arrangements in this sphere have changed much since Aristotle's day. The object of inquiry is here still before our eyes. The same is true of certain matters examined in the *Poetics*. *Catharsis* is either a figment of Aristotle's fancy or a variety of experience we too can examine. Varieties of experience are not so easily examined as an egg; we have nothing to put under a magnifying glass, and if we have to turn to psychologists, for such phenomena might be said to lie in their province, we shall perhaps get very diverse reports. *Catharsis,* however, is not a past event over and done with on which we can pronounce only after a careful examination of historical documents. Aristotle may have used the word in various senses; in the *Poetics* we can see to what its application is restricted. The /62/ question we have now to ask ourselves is this: Can we find a method more direct than those we have so far considered of studying the experience that Aristotle is describing when he says:

> *A tragedy is an imitation of an action... with incidents arousing pity and fear, wherewith to accomplish its* catharsis *of such emotions?*

*Catharsis,* if a reality, must, like the egg, be very much today what it was in Aristotle's time. There remains only the difficulty of focusing our attention on it.... /63/

To guard against doubtful testimony and to exclude, I trust, all disputable matter, I am adopting some rules for admissibility of evidence. The first is that the poet or critic must not be trying to explain Aristotle's words to us. This would rule out, did Milton come within our period, the explanation of *catharsis* prefixed to *Samson Agonistes.* I remind you of his views, however, that you may compare them with the observations of a later age:

> *Tragedy, as it was anciently composed, hath been ever held the gravest and most profitable of all other poems; therefore said by Aristotle to be of power, by raising pity and fear, or terror, to purge the mind of those and such like passions — that is, to temper and reduce them to just* /65/ *measure and a kind of delight, stirred up by reading or seeing those passions well imitated.*

That is, I think, the best the Renaissance can do for us on *catharsis* from the critical angle. Yet it seems to me far from clear, and learned rather than lucid. Milton does not seem to me, though I recognize that many feel differently, to see the matter with that inward sense that so illumines and clarifies his poetry.

My second rule, which is really a corollary to the first, is that the writer should be unaware he is talking of a phenomenon that has been called *catharsis,* yet that we should be able to recognize at once that he is referring to the variety of experience indicated by Aristotle.

This part of our inquiry is one in which those of you who are interested might help. I propose to examine with you now two passages that conform to the rules I have laid down for evidence, one briefly, the other at some length; later I shall cite other passages. Many of you, however, may think of even better instances of the unconscious elucidation of *catharsis,* and I shall be grateful for any references or suggestions you may care to offer me.

My first illustration is a very well known passage from Keats's letters:

> *The excellence of every art is its intensity, capable of* /66/ *making all disagreeables evaporate, from their being in close relationship with Beauty and Truth. Examine* King Lear, *and you will find this exemplified throughout.*

The Greek word *catharsis* could be used of purification by fire. Keats has for the moment seen the experience in this light. The 'disagreeables' that evaporate may be equated with Aristotle's fear and pity. . . .

Keats is for the moment speaking as a reader; we may regard the reader as sharing an experience that the author communicates to him. My next illustration shows the experience from the author's side and emphasizes what the author wishes to communicate. The author here is Keats's most influential teacher, Wordsworth, who comments at some length on the experience we wish to examine, and in his comment makes explicit what is regularly implicit in so much of his best prose and poetry.

In *Lyrical Ballads* of 1798 is the poem entitled *The Idiot Boy*. This, like *Simon Lee* in the same volume, has given occasion for a good deal of merriment at Wordsworth's expense. Soon after the First World War two young men published an anthology of what they regarded as among the /67/ world's worst poems. They included, I was told, *Simon Lee*. No one, however, who reads *Simon Lee* and its companions with the attention interest arouses can fail to see in them invaluable studies for later works that even the most critical recognize as excellent. The theme of *The Idiot Boy* is the relation of parent and child; Wordsworth is studying one of those great and simple affections of our nature that were to form the argument of his contribution to the *Ballads*. His purpose is most easily studied if we consider for a moment the doctrine from which he had just emancipated himself. His mentor for a brief period, William Godwin, had been for banishing the passions and affections in favour of political justice, and political justice forbad us to love our parents or our children merely because they were our parents or children. We should regard them (for love is too strong and unregulated a form of regard) on the same terms as all the world, and countenance them only in accordance with *their moral worth and their importance to the general weal.* It is doubtless true that parental affection is often of a mingled yarn. It may have strands of pride; sometimes, though not frequently in a civilized society, of hopes of gain. For I shall hardly be exaggerating if I say that most of the younger members of my audience can be written off by their parents even in our Welfare State as a /68/ total financial loss — yet their mothers are not likely to love them any the less. Wordsworth wishing to study the passion in its purity unsustained by any collateral supports makes the child of his poem an idiot that can quicken in the mother's heart no hopes of gain or worldly glory. To Godwin such a child could have no moral worth or importance to the general weal. The mother's love, therefore, is a free and natural expression of her own heart. Her love is in no way like political justice dependent on the apparent worth of the recipient. It is one of those unbought gifts of life that are specially dear at all times to the poets, however unreasonable they may seem to a mind of rationalistic bent. How dear to Wordsworth is clear from his reply to a critic of his poem.

Wordsworth's friend John Wilson (Christopher North) had written protesting against certain disagreeable features in the poem. The Idiot was in himself a displeasing sort of person, and nothing, argued Christopher North, is a fit subject for poetry that does not please. A similar objection had been raised against other of the *Ballads,* especially *Simon Lee,* whose swollen ankles had offended the feelings of some refined readers, as they sometimes do still; the ankles of a goddess are generally felt to be suitable for poetic comment, but those of a done old man, it was generally agreed, were not. Wordsworth's /69/ reply to these animadversions provides us with what I venture to regard as a classic account of the variety of experience Aristotle called *catharsis*.

The full force of Wordsworth's reply, however, is best felt if we have in mind not merely Christopher North's protest in 1800 but some observations on *The Idiot Boy* by Coleridge many years later. Coleridge thought that Wordsworth had not taken sufficient care to preclude from the reader's fancy the disgusting images of ordinary morbid idiocy; and he further objected

> *that the idiocy of the boy is so evenly balanced by the folly of the mother, as to present to the general reader rather a laughable burlesque on the blindness of anile dotage, than an analytic display of maternal affection in its ordinary workings.*

Wordsworth begins his reply to Christopher North by asking who is to be the judge of what is pleasing. Men sometimes fail to find pleasure because of their ignorance or prejudice; and therefore the business of the poet as Wordsworth conceives it is not merely to reflect the feelings of human nature; the poet ought, Wordsworth feels, to travel before men occasionally as well as at their sides:

> *he ought, to a certain degree, to rectify men's feelings, to give them new compositions of feeling, to render their feelings more sane, pure, and permanent, in short, more /70/ consonant to nature, that is, to eternal nature, and the great moving spirit of things.*

Wordsworth then goes on to consider the loathing and disgust which many people have at the sight of an idiot as a feeling which, though having some foundation in human nature, is not necessarily attached to it in any virtuous degree. Indeed such feelings seem to Wordsworth to show a certain want of comprehensiveness of thinking and feeling. Looking inward to his own thoughts he says:

> *I have often applied to idiots, in my own mind, that sublime expression of scripture that their life is hidden with God —*

and then turning to the poem and its characters he tells us how he sees the conduct of the mother

> *as the great triumph of the human heart. It is there we see the strength, disinterestedness, and grandeur of love; nor have I ever been able to contemplate an object that calls out so many excellent and virtuous sentiments without finding it hallowed thereby, and having something in me which bears down before it, like a deluge, every feeble sensation of disgust and aversion.*

If Keats described *catharsis* to us from the reader's side, this passage from Wordsworth lets us view it as the poet sees it. Keats uses the image of fire; Wordsworth that of the deluge; but the experience they describe is the same, and it is the experience to /71/ which Aristotle appealed in his refutation of Plato's charge that the poets and dramatists are the great corrupters of men. Wordsworth's analysis is not prompted directly as is that of Keats by some tragic action of the scope of *King Lear*; but he is contemplating the elements of our nature that are found compounded in tragedy, and his examination of the properties of these elements is the simplest and surest approach to our understanding of Shakespeare's profoundly studied syntheses. . . . /72/

That both Keats and Wordsworth are describing the variety of experience Aristotle had in mind is clear, I think, not merely because we have the 'disagreeables', to use Keats's word, disposed of by fire or deluge, but because the experience as described by the poets refutes Plato's charge against Homer and his descendants, that they encourage the weaker side of our nature. Any acceptable account of *catharsis* must satisfy this condition, for on the experience Aristotle built his reply to Plato. The effect Aristotle attributes implicitly to the experience is made fully explicit in the account by Keats and especially in Wordsworth's. Keats emphasizes Beauty and Truth as the elements producing the intensity that disposes of the disagreeables; Wordsworth talks of rendering our feelings more sane, pure, and permanent; our eye is directed to the strength, disinterestedness, and grandeur, of one of the primary affections. Plato could hardly have taken exception to a type of experience that left men so fortified, whatever his feelings might have been about the artistry of the *Ballads*; for what the great Romantics are insisting on is that poetic experience points to a wise and manly path in life, the way required of us by Plato. Naturally we wish to be as manful as the man of stone that Housman came on in the Grecian gallery; but we have to work in a different material /73/ from marble. To feel and yet to endure is an art beyond the virtue of stone; living at its best demands the art of reconciling apparent opposites that Pericles praised as the glory of the Athenian way of life. *Catharsis* is as it were a window on such an ideal, for through it what has appeared the weakness of man is seen to be strength. That is why Aristotle found in this variety of experience the complete justification of art. . . . /74/

We are now in a position to ask if this variety of experience we know as *catharsis* is induced only by tragedies in which the protagonist exhibits what is called a tragic flaw. There seems nothing in the nature of the experience itself to require such an assumption. Calamity and suffering are elements in tragedy; but does a man's bringing these on himself by folly or wickedness make his situation more tragic than that of the man who perishes for some loyalty or duty or sense of honour? Wordsworth's analysis of the experience might be taken as proving that the essential feature on which the mind finally rests is some positive virtue that kindles the intensity of conviction that is the essence of the experience. Such a virtue may be found as Wordsworth himself explains even in wicked men:

> For, strength to persevere and to support
> And energy to conquer and repel — /76/
> These elements of virtue, that declare
> The native grandeur of the human soul —
> Are ofttimes not unprofitably shown
> In the perverseness of a selfish course.

The bad man, if we may use so simple an expression, attains the dignity of a tragic hero only by the possession of 'those elements of virtue' in him that we must acknowledge and admire.

Perhaps then it is no disloyalty to Bradley to untwist one of the strands entangled in his views on tragedy. Bradley, in describing the tendency of the protagonist to identify his whole being with some interest, or object, as a gift of greatness, is pointing to the true nature of tragedy. Without this concentration the elements of virtue in the hero or villain could not be raised to that intensity in which the excellence of the work consists. That it is the elements of virtue that provide the intensity is recognized by Bradley when he talks of the tragic hero as in some sense superior to the world. As it is this sense of superiority or triumph that seems to obliterate all other considerations, we may fairly

argue that Bradley, in spite of his attempt to treat *hamartia* as the central fact
in tragedy, does realize that it takes its character and significance not from faults
but from virtues. . . . /77/

We are entitled to reconsider Aristotle's notion of the tragic flaw, if we
find it incompatible with his central idea of the nature of tragedy. The indispensable features of the form we have been able to study for ourselves. What
Aristotle called *catharsis* is still as available for examination as in the fourth
century before Christ. The examination we have so far been able to make does
not suggest that a tragic flaw is a pre-condition of the phenomenon. It is true,
as was admitted earlier, that this phenomenon is more difficult to examine than
an egg, and that we /83/ are bound to look for confirmation or contradiction
of our findings with some care. If, however, it could be shown that Aristotle
not only failed in the *Poetics* to establish his contention about the tragic flaw
but elsewhere decisively rejected the notion, he might then be put with Bradley
as one whose evidence about the tragic flaw may be regarded as doubtful.

Aristotle in the *Poetics* in support of his notion of *hamartia* commits himself to the statement that a plot in which a good man passes from happiness
to misery is not fear-inspiring but simply odious. This is an essential link in
his argument, and if it does not hold the general contention falls in pieces.
Even if we put aside the fate of the saints and the martyrs as inspiring only to
Christians, surely Plato had made the death of Socrates as nearly a form of
martyrdom as we can ask; further, to free Aristotle from all criticism on this
count, we should have to insist on what is very doubtful, namely that the Greek
dramatists never show us the good man suffering an unhappy fate. For, taking
Aristotle at his word, we must conclude that the hero of a proper tragedy
cannot be without some fault. Nor need there be, as some have argued, any
doubt that the fault must be not merely an error of judgement but a moral
fault. If the hero cannot be entirely good without his downfall giving us
offence, surely this implies that the /84/ fault must be of a moral kind.
The manner in which Aristotle links the doctrine of *hamartia* with the phenomenon of *catharsis* confirms this:

> The first situation [*that is one in which a good man passes from
> happiness to misery*] is not fear-inspiring or piteous, but simply odious to us.

Such goodness would exclude, so Aristotle argues, fear and pity, and these are
essential to *catharsis*.

If it were now objected that the distinctions Aristotle makes in his argument about the 'good' man and his place in tragedy are too fine to be summarized in this coarse and perhaps tendentious style, and that these distinctions
cannot be treated except at length and in the most thorough and scholarly
manner, we can only reply that there is fortunately other evidence concerning
Aristotle's own personal feelings about such a situation that makes the detailed
argument about his views in this section of the *Poetics* of what is called academic
interest. Aristotle was to experience in the fortunes of a friend an affair that can
only be described as odious, and we have a record of Aristotle's reactions to
the event.

On the death of Plato, Aristotle left the Academy and went to Asia Minor,
settling in the territory of Hermeias who had his centre of government at
Atarneus. Hermeias had already given hospitality to men associated with the
Academy; it is clear he /85/ gave a special welcome to Aristotle, for Hermeias,
although a ruler who had gained and maintained his authority not by philosophic
meditation but by force of arms, cherished the ideal of subordinating force to
a wisdom and conduct that could be called humane. He was unfortunately
between two mighty opposites: on one side the Persians, on the other the

rapidly maturing Macedon. In spite of his experience Hermeias took a risk that allowed the Persians to lay treacherous hands on him, and his death by torture was the sequel; for Hermeias would not disclose his knowledge of Macedon's intentions. Aristotle was particularly affected by the tragic end of his friend, for he must have known him well and indeed soon after married his niece. Aristotle like other members of the Academy had honoured Hermeias for his liberal and humane ideals, and now in his adversity Hermeias had conducted himself in what Aristotle felt was a truly heroic fashion. It is this mingling of affection and admiration that finds expression in the lines Aristotle wrote in memory of the dead ruler, the lines on *Virtue* that begin,

> *Virtue toilsome to mortal race,*
> *Fairest prize in life.*

'Virtue' is here used to translate the Greek *areté,* for our scholarly instructors, although they sometimes say that the Greek is never to be so translated, /86/ often find that no other word than *virtue* will serve. Here *virtue,* however inadequate an equivalent, is near enough for our present purpose, although I shall sometimes use the form *areté* in its place. The prize then that Hermeias has won is that immortal *areté,* the prize for which, the poem tells us, the heroes of old, Ajax and Achilles, reckoned death a cheap price. For that prize they did not hesitate to go to the halls of death. Because of this love of Virtue they are forever famous in song; this fame Hermeias now shares with them.

Aristotle makes no reference in the poem to any form of *hamartia* that might render the death of Hermeias less odious; although the comparison between the conduct of his friend and that of Ajax and Achilles could, it might be thought, have provided a philosopher with an excuse for the mention of faults.... It is clear /87/ that what Aristotle told his students in his lectures was now quite inadequate to express his passionate admiration for the heroic ideal as he found it in life, and he felt for his friend what he now realized the poets had felt for the virtue they embodied in Ajax and Achilles.

No thought of flaw or fault could have strengthened Aristotle's sense of his friend's heroism or have made less odious for the philosopher the murder of this enlightened ruler. The only redeeming feature in the terrible story was the courage and loyalty of Hermeias. We may fairly ask the question why the sense of redemption or reconciliation induced by the tragic drama demands a factor not required in life itself. To attempt some distinction between life and art in this particular that will explain such a discrepancy is to ignore Aristotle's own insistence on their congruence, for how otherwise should he appeal on his friend's behalf from life to literature. As Aristotle appealed to the poets to confirm his own convictions and experience, so we in turn may appeal to Aristotle's own experience when we consider his interpretation of the poets. What consumes or sweeps away the disagreeables is not some nice calculation arrived at by weighing the hero's fate against the faults and mistakes that are inseparable from mortality but the sense of something in mortals /88/ that has risen superior to their condition. In this Aristotle, as his tribute to Hermeias proves, is at one with Keats and Wordsworth.... /89/

I can now imagine your saying to me — Even if it could be shown from a single poem and from the seventh book of the *Ethics* that Aristotle really regarded the Tragedies of the fifth century as a glorification of the virtues of men and women rather than as examples of human frailty leading to disaster — even if this were admitted for argument's sake, what of the dramatists themselves? They have regularly been expounded to us in terms of the doctrine of *hamartia.* Do you reject this as inadequate and untrue to the spirit in which their authors looked on the life of man? Can you deny that the moral prudence taught in chorus and iambic stresses the faults and flaws of humanity? Do you refuse to believe that Antigone was undutifully stubborn, or Ajax unjustifiably proud, or Oedipus wilfully rash and violent? In short, am I prepared to argue that it was their virtues and not their vices that brought them to disaster — that in the words of Aristotle it was for love of virtue that the tragic heroes went to the halls of death?

Fortunately it requires no great courage to say yes to these questions; for, ... /90/ there are scholars who have come to regard the dramatists of the fifth century as the exponents of a heroic ideal and not as judges who summon to their tribunal the great spirits of antiquity only to convict them of some fault that justifies the gods in having visited on them their tragic fate....

... The fifth century saw at Athens a change in the moral outlook of mankind — or rather a development. It now became possible for men to believe that outward misery and distress were not necessarily proof of inward guilt. Such an enlightenment was not confined to Athens. It is, of course, the culmination of Hebrew prophecy and finds its embodiment there in the figure of the suffering servant. /100/ The Hebrew genius unlike the Greek did not find expression in dramatic form; but the work in their literature that approaches most nearly to the drama is the *Book of Job,* and, like the *Oedipus at Colonus,* the *Book of Job* presents to us a figure who asserts, in spite of all the testimony outward conditions seem to bear against him, that he is free from guilt, that his calamities are not the consequence of his actions.

Job might be speaking for Oedipus as he says:

> *He hath stripped me of my glory and taken the crown from my head.*
> *He hath put my brethren far from me and mine acquaintance are verily estranged from me.*

Like Oedipus Job is in rags and an outcast, but like Oedipus he never wavers and his faith is enshrined in the famous line:

> *For I know that my redeemer liveth.*

These words have since received an amplification in the mind of mankind that, however relevant, is not for the moment at issue. What is immediately relevant is that the words of Job, taken in their dramatic context, express the very heart of the faith of Oedipus. *His* plea, like that of Job, is against the material assessment that the world can hardly refrain from adopting. And Sophocles, like the author of the *Book of Job,* adapts his story to express his belief /101/ that the root of the matter, to borrow the words of Job, is found in Oedipus. To Job God speaks from heaven, and to Eliphaz the Temanite and his friends he says:

> *My wrath is kindled against thee, and against thy two friends: for ye have not spoken of me the thing that is right as my servant Job hath.*

In the *Oedipus at Colonus* the Greek dramatist uses his own but analogous symbols to obtain the same effect. The peals of thunder from heaven announce the completion of the hero's pilgrimage; he sends for Theseus and, although blind, leads the way into the sacred grove and there, having taken farewell of his daughters, he goes accompanied only by Theseus to his deification.

Sophocles is as objective an artist as Shakespeare; but as men draw towards their end they care less, as Newman observes of his own *Apologia,* for disclosures. In his last works Sophocles, like Shakespeare in his, seems to turn back on himself to offer in a more explicit form the vision that it has been his purpose to embody in his works; and to do so he has to have recourse to a symbolism that can be misunderstood apart from its context. It is so also in the *Book of Job*; you can say that God has treated Job like a puppet, and that to slaughter his children as a test of his faith is a crime for which there can be no atonement. /102/ To give him more sons and daughters can be no compensation whatever. Yet no one would think of taking the *Book of Job* as an indictment of God or regard its author, on the other hand, as some conservative apologist for a tyrannical Immortal. The *Book of Job* is a vindication of Job from the material judgement of the world — it is an affirmation of a faith in righteousness whatever the event. The affirmation that provides the inspiration of the *Oedipus at Colonus* is of the same kind. The man whom the gods have seemed to reject is vindicated. Sophocles no more than the author of the *Book of Job* stands forth as an accuser of the gods, or as an apologist for cruelty and tyranny. It is enough for him to have vindicated the heroic spirit and in spite of the superstition and the blind selfishness of the world to have made manifest on which side his heart is to be found. This was the inspiration of the *Oedipus* no less than that of the *Oedipus at Colonus,* but it is only at the end that the poet in the charity of his last years condescends to make explicit to us what we should have known was implicit from the first.

I have cited the *Oedipus at Colonus* as the testimony provided by Sophocles himself that any doctrine of *hamartia* makes nonsense of his purpose. To say that the sufferings of Oedipus or Job are, if not deserved, /103/ yet explicable, and not wholly inappropriate, is a mere perversion of the evidence, unless you add that suffering that leads to deification or draws commendation from heaven would be appropriate to us all.

Having cited the *Oedipus at Colonus* to dispose of the idea that Sophocles built his drama round some tragic flaw that thereby he might put on the shoulders of men the guilt of the gods, I turn to the play immediately preceding his last, to the *Philoctetes,* to illustrate the cathartic power of his vision, and to emphasize through this illustration that the experience we call *catharsis* is quite independent of all the considerations suggested by *hamartia.*

Philoctetes on the way to the siege of Troy lands with the other Greeks to sacrifice at an island shrine and is bitten in the foot by a snake that guards the holy place. So horrible is the nature of the wound, and so terrible the victim's sufferings, that the Greek leaders, unable to endure his cries of agony and the stench of the suppurating flesh, and regarding the afflicted man as a polluted being whose presence would render all sacrifice vain, contrive to abandon him on the island of Lemnos. There he languishes in solitude and pain saved only by the possession of his wonderful bow which never misses and whose arrows carry instant death. This bow Hercules had /104/ given him as a reward for lighting the pyre which was to deliver the hero from the torments of the shirt of Nessus. When the play begins ten years have passed since Philoctetes was doomed to solitude, and at Troy Achilles has fallen, and Ajax has killed himself when the arms of Achilles were adjudged to Odysseus; the Greeks, however, have now discovered in their despair that they cannot capture Troy till they bring to their camp the son of Achilles and with him Philoctetes and his magic bow.

The play opens with Odysseus and Neoptolemus landing on Lemnos, for Odysseus has promised to bring to Troy the men whose presence is needed for victory, and he has first collected Neoptolemus. Now Odysseus explains to Neoptolemus how they must conduct themselves if they are to make sure of Philoctetes. Odysseus dare not show himself to Philoctetes, for, as he explains, the lonely man would vent his anger on one whom he regarded as a chief betrayer; nor is it any good inviting Philoctetes to go to Troy so deep is his hatred of Agamemnon and Menelaus. Neoptolemus must pretend he is on his way home from Troy, having quarrelled with the leaders who gave his father's arms to Odysseus; he must offer to take Philoctetes home with him. Once aboard ship, however, they can tell another tale. Neoptolemus protests against such /105/ trickery; he is for using force or abandoning the task; he is, however, finally won over.

Neoptolemus quickly gains the confidence of the lonely man who inquires anxiously for his comrades at Troy only to learn that those he respected are dead and that it is the villains who survive; as they are about to leave for the ship the wound becomes overpoweringly painful, and Philoctetes falls into an exhausted slumber, having confided his bow to Neoptolemus. Neoptolemus, as soon as Philoctetes recovers, feels bound to confess the deception he is practising on him, and is so moved by the reproaches this calls forth that he would restore the bow, did not Odysseus suddenly appear from hiding and carry it off. Philoctetes is now confronted with the alternatives of following the bow to the ship or remaining behind quite helpless and doomed to certain death. He does not, however, hesitate: death is preferable to submission to such inhuman tricksters. The Chorus try to persuade him that he is the author of his own woe. He can choose to save his life if he cares. Such a choice Philoctetes regards as impossible. Just as he contemplates suicide Neoptolemus arrives with the bow and in spite of all Odysseus can do restores it to its owner. Odysseus has to take himself off hastily. Neoptolemus now puts it to Philoctetes that having regained his bow he can come of his own free /106/ will to Troy and that there he will be cured of his wound as the seer foretells and, in addition, gain immortal glory as the conqueror of Troy. But just as the prospect of death could not move Philoctetes, so now the promise of healing and of glory leaves his resolution unshaken. He will not go to Troy, and he now calls upon Neoptolemus to make good his promise to take him home. They are about to go when Hercules appears before them — to forbid them to return to Greece. He himself, the god reminds them, has won immortal glory by his many and great labours. 'For thee', he now says to Philoctetes,

> *For thee the destiny is ordained that through these thy sufferings thou shouldst glorify thy life.*

But you may say: is this not just the stubborn heart of man being corrected by the gods? Is the *Philoctetes* not just the best proof of what I am so ready to deny?

Let us suppose for a moment that we have all just returned from the siege of Troy and that I feel impelled to tell you what a good sort Philoctetes was to come along and finish off the weary business for us, especially after the rather shabby way we had treated him. But, you might well reply, who wouldn't have gone to Troy to be cured of so terrible an affliction and in addition to gain such glory from his exploits? Only a madman would have declined to /107/ go to Troy in such circumstances. To such an answer I could offer no reply, unless I could assure you that I had learnt from Neoptolemus and Ulysses themselves that even health and glory were not sufficient to tempt Philoctetes to help us — that it was Hercules himself who sent him, and that he could not deny Hercules only because he was bound to Hercules by ancient ties of purest loyalty and love. In short that Philoctetes joined us not for any material consideration, however worth while or much desired in itself, but only in obedience to the call of a loyalty that let him feel he was at last a free agent in a worthy service.

Hercules is the symbol of that freedom of the spirit that comes to those dedicated to a service to which their hearts can give no denial. Instead of being the tool of men, the slave of the Atreidae, Philoctetes is the companion and heir of Hercules. It is the service in which is perfect freedom. To say, as Mr. Ivor Brown suggests, that there is no free will in Greek tragedy is surely to ignore this paradox. At every stage Philoctetes chooses; at every stage his will is the deciding factor — he chooses as the artist himself chooses, and his will is finally identified with the service he accepts, as the will of the artist is identified with his art. We may call men like Bach or Beethoven or Rembrandt slaves of their Art if you like, /108/ or regard the man who trains to ride the Grand National on his own horse as a slave to sport, but only if we are so degenerate that we can do no more than envy and malign those who venture on those pinnacles and steeps of hardship on which we have turned our back. It is we who are the slaves and they who are the free men. And so it is in the tragedies of Sophocles — the protagonist you may call a slave to this or that, but his slavery proves on examination to be one of those passions or services that glorify men.

In the *Philoctetes* there is no support for those who insist that Sophocles is here concerned to discover for us the tragic flaw in some otherwise worthy character. It provides, however, an admirable proof of the force in Aristotle's answer to Plato's attack on the poets, and illustrates very clearly the variety of experience called *catharsis*. /109/

---

JOHN **GASSNER**: *Catharsis and the Modern Theater*

It is difficult to think of a more academic concept than that of catharsis. It is encrusted with antiquity and bears the rust of much speculation justly suspect to the practical worker. The concept is, nevertheless, one of those insights that philosophers sometimes achieve in spite of themselves. Aristotle touched bottom when he declared the effect of tragedy to be purgation of the soul by pity and fear.

The Aristotelian formula, supremely empirical, has a dual importance: the spectator is given a definition of his experience, and the playwright is provided with a goal for which certain means are requisite, the goal set for him being no other than the effect he must achieve if he is to hold an audience with high and serious matter of a painful nature. Unfortunately, however, Aristotle's analysis was altogether too fragmentary, and his *Poetics* has come down to us as little more than a collection of notes. We do not even know precisely what catharsis meant for him and how he thought "pity and fear" produced the purgation.

The subject has exercised commentators since the Renaissance when they seized upon the short passage: "Tragedy through pity and fear effects a purgation of such emotions." Each age has added its own interpretation, naturally reflecting its own interests and its own kind of drama. According to the Sixteenth Century pundits, including the famous Castelvetro, tragedy hardened the spectator to suffering by subjecting him to pity- and fear-inducing scenes of misery and violence. Corneille, who gave much thought to his craft, held that tragedy forced the spectator to fear for himself when he observed a character's passions causing disaster, and that the resolve to rule one's own passions effected the purgation. Others, including John Milton, took the /549/ homeo-

*From "Catharsis and the Modern Theater," in Barrett H. Clark, ed.,* European Theories of the Drama, *rev. ed. (New York: Crown Publishers, 1947).*

pathic view that pity and terror on the stage counteracted the disturbing elements of pity and terror in the spectator. For the liberals or humanitarians of the Enlightenment, including the author of *Nathan the Wise,* tragedy purified the observer by enabling him to exercise his sympathies. For Hegel tragedy reconciled conflicting views, thereby effecting catharsis. And so it went until Jacob Bernays, Wilhelm Stekel, and other psychologists arrived at the view that accords most easily with both the findings of psychopathology and common sense — namely, that catharsis is simply the expulsion of disturbing drives and conflicts.

Without adhering to any specific school of psychopathology, it is safe to say that if Aristotelian catharsis is a valid definition of tragic effect (and I believe it is), it means one thing above all: In the tragic experience we temporarily expel troublesome inner complications. We expel "pity" and "fear," to use Aristotle's terms, and the terms are broad enough to cover the most pathological or near-pathological elements — namely, anxieties, fears, morbid grief or self-pity, sadistic or masochistic desires, and the sense of guilt that these engender and are engendered by. In a successful tragedy we see these drives enacted on the stage directly or through their results by characters with whom we can identify ourselves. They are our proxies, so to speak.

We must observe, however, that the expulsion would certainly prove ephemeral and perhaps even incomplete or ineffective if the expelled matter were merely brought to the surface (to our "pre-conscious," if you will) instead of being fully recognized by our consciousness. Evoked "pity and fear" on the tragic stage may effect expulsion, but at least one other force is needed if real recognition is to be effectuated.

That something more is needed is evidenced by the whole history of the theater. The distinction between tragedy and melodrama is grounded in the opinion that excitement is not enough, that it does not produce the most satisfactory effects. Where the excitement emanates plausibly and serves an end beyond itself there is, we say, tragedy. Where the excitement exists solely for itself and is accomplished without the operation of reason or credibility we have melodrama. If purgation in tragedy were confined solely to the effects of pity and fear there could be little dramatic distinction between *Hamlet* and *The Bat.*

Has it not always been recognized that the superiority of the great tragedies, if we exclude purely stylistic differences, has resided in their powerful blending of passion with enlightenment? This is what we mean when we attribute their superiority to the significance of their content, the depth and scope of their conflict, or the relevance of their action to the major aspects and problems of humanity. In tragedy there is always a precipitate of final enlightenment — some inherent, cumulatively realized, understanding. We have seen an experience enacted on the stage, and have externalized its inner counterpart in ourselves by the process of vibrating to the acted passions; or possibly by some other means, since unconscious processes are open to infinite debate. Then, ensuring the externalization of the inner drives, we have given them form and meaning — that is, understood their causes and effects, which brings us to the furthest point from the unconscious, or from nebulous emotion, ever reached by the individual. Enlightenment is, therefore, the third component of the process of purgation.

It exists in perfect harmony with the components of "pity and fear," and it is even supported by them, just as enlightenment supports them. "Pity and fear," (using these terms to cover the emotional experience) are the *fixatives* of tragic enlightenment, for without their agency the meaning of a play would be superficial and fleeting; enlightenment unrooted in the emotions or unsupported and unevoked by them would be something imposed from without, unprecipitated from the struggle of the drama, and devoid of persuasive growth or cumulative effect. Moreover, pity and terror have mnemonic values which the drama cannot dispense with, because of its rapid course of action. Who would remember the significances of *Hamlet* without its anguish?

Finally, but keeping the above qualifi- /550/ cations strictly in mind, we can maintain that enlightenment is not only the third element in catharsis, but the decisive one. The ultimate relief comes when the dramatist brings the tragic struggle to a state of rest. This cannot occur so long as we are left in a state of tension. No matter how well the action or the main character's destiny is resolved and concluded, the anarchic forces, "the pity and fear," evoked by the tragedy cannot establish a suitable inner equilibrium. Only enlightenment, a clear comprehension of what was involved in the struggle, an understanding of cause and effect, a judgment on what we have witnessed, and an induced state of mind that places it above the riot of passion — can effect this necessary equilibrium. And it is a necessary one if there is to be purgation, and if for the moment we are to be healed of the wounds self-inflicted in the unconscious, inflicted on us from without by external circumstance before they settle our inmost self, then inflicted once more by the tragic story enacted before our eyes on the stage. Only enlightenment can therefore round out the esthetic experience in tragedy, can actually ensure complete esthetic gratification. True tragic exaltation, which we require of a tragedy, also lies in this. For the exaltation comes only if we have prevailed over the anarchy of our inner life and the ever present and ever pressing life around us; and how can we master this anarchy without understanding it, without putting order into this house of disorder?

Had Aristotle pursued his investigation of classic drama further, he would have surely arrived at this view himself. The author of the *Nichomachean Ethics* and the *Politics* could not have failed to discover the conclusive element of enlightenment in the purgation afforded by the tragedies of Aeschylus, Sophocles, and Euripides. To adopt Nietzschean (*The Birth of Tragedy*) terminology, Greek tragedy imposed the Apollonian world of light and reason upon the dynamic Dionysian world of passion. The Apollonian element in the warp and woof of the plays, including the great choral passages, ordered and so mastered the Dionysiac excitement or disequilibrium. I believe the same thing can be demonstrated in Elizabethan tragedy, in the work of Corneille and Racine, and in modern tragedy.

To conclude this argument, I should, I suppose, try to disabuse anyone who would look askance at this insistence on enlightenment because it suggests a moral in the outmoded Victorian sense. The "moral" is imposed from without by a convention; that was the prime limitation of William Winter's criticism. Enlightenment is not actually imposed, but wells up from the stream of the play itself, from the enacted events, actions, and reactions. The moral, in other words, is a predigested judgment, whereas enlightenment is empirical. The moral is a summation or tag; enlightenment is a process. The moral of a play can be put into a sententious sentence. The element of enlightenment can also be summarized, but the summary is only a portion of the whole. It is a state of grace, so to speak, a civilized attitude achieved in the course of experiencing the play: an Apollonian attitude, Santayana's "life of reason," a clarity of mind and spirit, a resilience and cheerfulness even. The moral is a law. The enlightenment is a state of mind, and includes specific conclusions only as a necessary concomitant of every state of mind that is not vacuous. It is even a kind of poetry of the mind, no matter how earnest, somber or sultry. /551/

JOSEPH WOOD **KRUTCH**: *The Modern Temper*

Tragedy, said Aristotle, is the "imitation of noble actions," and though it is some twenty-five hundred years since the dictum was uttered there is only one respect in which we are inclined to modify it. To us "imitation" seems a rather naïve word to apply to that process by which observation is turned into art, and we seek one which would define or at least imply the nature of that inter-position of the personality of the artist between the object and the beholder which constitutes his function and by means of which he transmits a modified version, rather than a mere imitation, of the thing which he has contemplated.

In the search for this word the estheticians of romanticism invented the term "expression" to describe the artistic purpose to which apparent imitation was subservient. Psychologists, on the other hand, feeling that the artistic process was primarily one by which reality is modified in such a way as to render it more acceptable to the desires of the artist, employed various terms in the effort to describe that distortion which the wish may produce in vision. And /120/ though many of the newer critics reject both romanticism and psychology, even they insist upon the fundamental fact that in art we are concerned, not with mere imitation, but with the imposition of some form upon the material which it would not have if it were merely copied as a camera copies.

Tragedy is not, then, as Aristotle said, the *imitation* of noble actions, for, indeed, no one knows what a *noble* action is or whether or not such a thing as nobility exists in nature apart from the mind of man. Certainly the action of Achilles in dragging the dead body of Hector around the walls of Troy and under the eyes of Andromache, who had begged to be allowed to give it decent burial, is not to us a noble action, though it was such to Homer, who made it the subject of a noble passage in the noble poem. Certainly, too, the same action might conceivably be made the subject of a tragedy and the subject of a farce, depending upon the way in which it was treated; so that to say that tragedy is the *imitation* of a *noble* action is to be guilty of assuming, first, that art and photography are the same, and, second, that there may be something inherently noble in an act as distinguished from the motives which prompted it or from the point of view from which it is regarded. /121/

And yet, nevertheless, the idea of nobility is inseparable from the idea of tragedy, which cannot exist without it. If tragedy is not the imitation or even the modified representation of noble actions, it is certainly a representation of actions *considered* as noble, and herein lies its essential nature, since no man can conceive it unless he is capable of believing in the greatness and im-portance of man. Its action is usually, if not always, calamitous, because it is only in calamity that the human spirit has the opportunity to reveal itself triumphant over the outward universe which fails to conquer it; but this calamity in tragedy is only a means to an end and the essential thing which distinguishes real tragedy from those distressing modern works sometimes called by its name is the fact that it is in the former alone that the artist has found himself capable of considering and of making us consider that his people and his actions have that amplitude and importance which make them noble. Tragedy arises then when, as in Periclean Greece or Elizabethan England, a people fully aware of the calamities of life is nevertheless serenely confident of the greatness of man,

From The Modern Temper *(New York: Harcourt, Brace & Co., 1929).*

whose mighty passions and supreme fortitude are revealed when one of these calamities overtakes him.

To those who mistakenly think of it as something /122/ gloomy or depressing, who are incapable of recognizing the elation which its celebration of human greatness inspires, and who, therefore, confuse it with things merely miserable or pathetic, it must be a paradox that the happiest, most vigorous, and most confident ages which the world has ever known — the Periclean and the Elizabethan — should be exactly those which created and which most relished the mightiest tragedies; but the paradox is, of course, resolved by the fact that tragedy is essentially an expression, not of despair, but of the triumph over despair and of confidence in the value of human life. If Shakespeare himself ever had that "dark period" which his critics and biographers have imagined for him, it was at least no darkness like that bleak and arid despair which sometimes settles over modern spirits. In the midst of it he created both the elemental grandeur of Othello and the pensive majesty of Hamlet and, holding them up to his contemporaries, he said in the words of his own Miranda, "Oh, rare new world that hath *such* creatures in it."

All works of art which deserve their name have a happy end. This is indeed the thing which constitutes them art and through which they perform their function. Whatever the character of the events, fortunate or unfortunate, which they recount, they so /123/ mold or arrange or interpret them that we accept gladly the conclusion which they reach and would not have it otherwise. They may conduct us into the realm of pure fancy where wish and fact are identical and the world is remade exactly after the fashion of the heart's desire or they may yield some greater or less allegiance to fact; but they must always reconcile us in one way or another to the representation which they make and the distinctions between the genres are simply the distinctions between the means by which this reconciliation is effected.

Comedy laughs the minor mishaps of its characters away; drama solves all the difficulties which it allows to arise; and melodrama, separating good from evil by simple lines, distributes its rewards and punishments in accordance with the principles of a naïve justice which satisfies the simple souls of its audience, which are neither philosophical enough to question its primitive ethics nor critical enough to object to the way in which its neat events violate the laws of probability. Tragedy, the greatest and the most difficult of the arts, can adopt none of these methods; and yet it must reach its own happy end in its own way. Though its conclusion must be, by its premise, outwardly calamitous, though it must speak to those who know that the good man is cut off and that the /124/ fairest things are the first to perish, yet it must leave them, as *Othello* does, content that this is so. We must be and we are glad that Juliet dies and glad that Lear is turned out into the storm.

Milton set out, he said, to justify the ways of God to man, and his phrase, if it be interpreted broadly enough, may be taken as describing the function of all art, which must, in some way or other, make the life which it seems to represent satisfactory to those who see its reflection in the magic mirror, and it must gratify or at least reconcile the desires of the beholder, not necessarily, as the naïver exponents of Freudian psychology maintain, by gratifying individual and often eccentric wishes, but at least by satisfying the universally human desire to find in the world some justice, some meaning, or, at the very least, some recognizable order. Hence it is that every real tragedy, however tremendous it may be, is an affirmation of faith in life, a declaration that even if God is not in his Heaven, then at least Man is in his world.

We accept gladly the outward defeats which it describes for the sake of the inward victories which it reveals. Juliet died, but not before she had shown how great and resplendent a thing love could be; Othello plunged the dagger into his own breast, but /125/ not before he had revealed that greatness of soul which makes his death seem unimportant. Had he died in the instant when he struck the blow, had he perished still believing that the world was as completely black as he saw it before the innocence of Desdemona was revealed to him, then, for him at least, the world would have been merely damnable, but Shakespeare kept him alive long enough to allow him to learn his error and hence to die, not in despair, but in the full acceptance of the tragic reconciliation to life. Perhaps it would be pleasanter if men could believe what the child is taught — that the good are happy and that things turn out as they should — but it is far more important to be able to believe, as Shakespeare did, that however much things in the outward world may go awry, man has, nevertheless, splendors of his own and that, in a word, Love and Honor and Glory are not words but realities.

Thus for the great ages tragedy is not an expression of despair but the means by which they saved themselves from it. It is a profession of faith, and a sort of religion; a way of looking at life by virtue of which it is robbed of its pain. The sturdy soul of the tragic author seizes upon suffering and uses it only as a means by which joy may be wrung out of existence, but it is not to be forgotten that he is en- /126/ abled to do so only because of his belief in the greatness of human nature and because, though he has lost the child's faith in life, he has not lost his far more important faith in human nature. A tragic writer does not have to believe in God, but he must believe in man.

And if, then, the Tragic Spirit is in reality the product of a religious faith in which, sometimes at least, faith in the greatness of God is replaced by faith in the greatness of man, it serves, of course, to perform the function of religion, to make life tolerable for those who participate in its beneficent illusion. It purges the souls of those who might otherwise despair and it makes endurable the realization that the events of the outward world do not correspond with the desires of the heart, and thus, in its own particular way, it does what all religions do, for it gives a rationality, a meaning, and a justification to the universe. But if it has the strength it has also the weakness of all faiths, since it may — nay, it must — be ultimately lost as reality, encroaching further and further into the realm of imagination, leaves less and less room in which that imagination can build its refuge. /127/

It is, indeed, only at a certain stage in the development of the realistic intelligence of a people that the tragic faith can exist. A naïver people may have, as the ancient men of the north had, a body of legends which are essentially tragic, or it may have only (and need only) its happy and childlike mythology which arrives inevitably at its happy end, where the only ones who suffer "deserve" to do so and in which, therefore, life is represented as directly and easily acceptable. A too sophisticated society on the other hand — one which, like ours, has outgrown not merely the simple optimism of the child but also that vigorous, one might almost say adolescent, faith in the nobility of man which marks a Sophocles or a Shakespeare, has neither fairy tales to assure it that all is always right in the end nor tragedies to make it believe that it rises superior in soul to the outward calamities which befall it.

Distrusting its thought, despising its passions, realizing its impotent unimportance in the universe, it can tell itself no stories except those which make it still more acutely aware of its trivial miseries. When its heroes (sad misnomer for the pitiful creatures who people contemporary fiction) are struck /128/ down it is not, like Oedipus, by the gods that they are struck but only, like Oswald Alving, by syphilis, for they know that the gods, even if they existed, would not trouble with them, and they cannot attribute to themselves in art an importance in which they do not believe. Their so-called tragedies do not and cannot end with one of those splendid calamities which in Shakespeare seem to reverberate through the universe, because they cannot believe that the universe trembles when their love is, like Romeo's, cut off or when the place where they (small as they are) have gathered up their trivial treasure is, like Othello's sanctuary, defiled. Instead, mean misery piles on mean misery, petty misfortune follows petty misfortune, and despair becomes intolerable because it is no longer even significant or important.

Ibsen once made one of his characters say that he did not read much because he found reading "irrelevant," and the adjective was brilliantly chosen because it held implications even beyond those of which Ibsen was consciously aware. What is it that made the classics irrelevant to him and to us? Is it not just exactly those to him impossible premises which make tragedy what it is, those assumptions that the soul of man is great, that the universe (together with whatever gods may be) concerns itself /129/ with him and that he is, in a word, noble? Ibsen turned to village politics for exactly the same reason that his contemporaries and his successors have, each in his own way, sought out some aspect of the common man and his common life — because, that is to say, here was at least something small enough for him to be able to believe.

Bearing this fact in mind, let us compare a modern "tragedy" with one of the great works of a happy age, not in order to judge of their relative technical merits but in order to determine to what extent the former deserves its name by achieving a tragic solution capable of purging the soul or of reconciling the emotions to the life which it pictures. And in order to make the comparison as fruitful as possible let us choose *Hamlet* on the one hand and on the other a play like *Ghosts* which was not only written by perhaps the most powerful as well as the most typical of modern writers but which is, in addition, the one of his works which seems most nearly to escape that triviality which cannot be entirely escaped by any one who feels, as all contemporary minds do, that man is relatively trivial.

In *Hamlet* a prince ("in understanding, how like a god!") has thrust upon him from the unseen world a duty to redress a wrong which concerns not merely /130/ him, his mother, and his uncle, but the moral order of the universe. Erasing all trivial fond records from his mind, abandoning at once both his studies and his romance because it has been his good fortune to be called upon to take part in an action of cosmic importance, he plunges (at first) not into action but into thought, weighing the claims which are made upon him and contemplating the grandiose complexities of the universe. And when the time comes at last for him to die he dies, not as a failure, but as a success. Not only has the universe regained the balance which had been upset by what *seemed* the monstrous crime of the guilty pair ("there is nothing either good nor ill but thinking makes it so"), but in the process by which that readjustment is made a mighty mind has been given the opportunity, first to contemplate the magnificent scheme of which it is a part, and then to demonstrate the greatness of its spirit by playing a rôle in the grand style which it called for. We do not need to despair in *such* a world if it has *such* creatures in it.

Turn now to *Ghosts* — look upon this picture and upon that. A young man has inherited syphilis from his father. Struck by a to him mysterious malady he returns to his northern village, learns the hopeless truth about himself, and persuades his mother to /131/ poison him. The incidents prove, perhaps, that pastors should not endeavor to keep a husband and wife together unless they know what they are doing. But what a world is this in which a great writer can deduce nothing more than that from his greatest work and how are we to be purged or reconciled when we see it acted? Not only is the failure utter, but it is trivial and meaningless as well.

Yet the journey from Elsinore to Skien is precisely the journey which the human spirit has made, exchanging in the process princes for invalids and gods for disease. We say, as Ibsen would say, that the problems of Oswald Alving are more "relevant" to our life than the problems of Hamlet, that the play in which he appears is more "real" than the other more glamorous one, but it is exactly because we find it so that we are condemned. We can believe in Oswald but we cannot believe in Hamlet, and a light has gone out in the universe. Shakespeare justifies the ways of God to man, but in Ibsen there is no such happy end and with him tragedy, so called, has become merely an expression of our despair at finding that such justification is no longer possible.

Modern critics have sometimes been puzzled to account for the fact that the concern of ancient tragedy is almost exclusively with kings and courts. /132/ They have been tempted to accuse even Aristotle of a certain naïveté in assuming (as he seems to assume) that the "nobility" of which he speaks as necessary to a tragedy implies a nobility of rank as well as of soul, and they have sometimes regretted that Shakespeare did not devote himself more than he did to the serious consideration of those common woes of the common man which subsequent writers have exploited with increasing pertinacity. Yet the tendency to lay the scene of a tragedy at the court of a king is not the result of any arbitrary convention but of the fact that the tragic writers believed easily in greatness just as we believe easily in meanness. To Shakespeare, robes and crowns and jewels are the garments most appropriate to man because they are the fitting outward manifestation of his inward majesty, but to us they seem absurd because the man who bears them has, in our estimation, so pitifully shrunk. We do not write about kings because we do not believe that any man is worthy to be one and we do not write about courts because hovels seem to us to be dwellings more appropriate to the creatures who inhabit them. Any modern attempt to dress characters in robes ends only by making us aware of a comic incongruity and any modern attempt to furnish them with a language /133/ resplendent like Shakespeare's ends only in bombast.

True tragedy capable of performing its function and of purging the soul by reconciling man to his woes can exist only by virtue of a certain pathetic fallacy far more inclusive than that to which the name is commonly given. The romantics, feeble descendants of the tragic writers to whom they are linked by their effort to see life and nature in grandiose terms, loved to imagine that the sea or the sky had a way of according itself with their moods, of storming when they stormed and smiling when they smiled. But the tragic spirit sustains itself by an assumption much more far-reaching and no more justified. Man as it sees him lives in a world which he may not dominate but which is always aware of him. Occupying the exact center of a universe which would have no meaning except for him and being so little below the angels that, if he believes in God, he has no hesitation in imagining Him formed as he is formed and crowned with a crown like that which he or one of his fellows wears, he assumes that each of his acts reverberates through the universe. His passions are important to him because he believes them important throughout all time and all space; the very fact that he can sin (no modern can) means that this universe is watching his acts; and though /134/ he may perish, a God leans out from infinity to strike him down. And it is exactly because an Ibsen cannot think of man in any such terms as these that his persons have so shrunk and that his "tragedy" has lost that power which real tragedy always has of making that infinitely ambitious creature called man content to accept his misery if only he can be made to feel great enough and important enough. An Oswald is not a Hamlet chiefly because he has lost that tie with the natural and supernatural world which the latter had. No ghost will leave the other world to warn or encourage him, there is no virtue and no vice which he can possibly have which can be really important, and when he dies neither his death nor the manner of it will be, outside the circle of two or three people as unnecessary as himself, any more important than that of a rat behind the arras.

Perhaps we may dub the illusion upon which the tragic spirit is nourished the Tragic, as opposed to the Pathetic, Fallacy, but fallacy though it is, upon its existence depends not merely the writing of tragedy but the existence of that religious feeling of which tragedy is an expression and by means of which a people aware of the dissonances of life manages nevertheless to hear them as harmony. Without it neither man nor his passions can seem great enough /135/ or important enough to justify the sufferings which they entail, and literature, expressing the mood of a people, begins to despair where once it had exulted. Like the belief in love and like most of the other mighty illusions by means of which human life has been given a value, the Tragic Fallacy depends ultimately upon the assumption which man so readily makes that something outside his own being, some "spirit not himself" — be it God, Nature, or that still vaguer thing called a Moral Order — joins him in the emphasis which he places upon this or that and confirms him in his feeling that his passions and his opinions are important. When his instinctive faith in that correspondence between the outer and the inner world fades, his grasp upon the faith that sustained him fades also, and Love or Tragedy or what not ceases to be the reality which it was because he is never strong enough in his own insignificant self to stand alone in a universe which snubs him with its indifference.

In both the modern and the ancient worlds tragedy was dead long before writers were aware of the fact. Seneca wrote his frigid melodramas under the impression that he was following in the footsteps of Sophocles, and Dryden probably thought that his *All for Love* was an improvement upon Shakespeare, /136/ but in time we awoke to the fact that no amount of rhetorical bombast could conceal the fact that grandeur was not to be counterfeited when the belief in its possibility was dead, and turning from the hero to the common man, we inaugurated the era of realism. For us no choice remains except that between mere rhetoric and the frank consideration of our fellow men, who may be the highest of the anthropoids but who are certainly too far below the angels to imagine either that these angels can concern themselves with them or that they can catch any glimpse of even the soles of angelic feet. We can no longer tell tales of the fall of noble men because we do not believe that noble men exist. The best that we can achieve is pathos and the most that we can do is to feel sorry for ourselves. Man has put off his royal robes and it is only in sceptered pomp that tragedy can come sweeping by. /137/

---

ARTHUR **MILLER**: *Tragedy and the Common Man*

In this age few tragedies are written. It has often been held that the lack is due to a paucity of heroes among us, or else that modern man has had the blood drawn out of his organs of belief by the skepticism of science, and the heroic attack on life cannot feed on an attitude of reserve and circumspection. For one reason or another, we are often held to be below tragedy — or tragedy above us. The inevitable conclusion is, of course, that the tragic mode is archaic, fit only for the very highly placed, the kings or the kingly, and where this admission is not made in so many words it is most often implied.

*"Tragedy and the Common Man,"* The New York Times, *February 27, 1949, Section 2.*

I believe that the common man is as apt a subject for tragedy in its highest sense as kings were. On the face of it this ought to be obvious in the light of modern psychiatry, which bases its analysis upon classific formulations, such as the Oedipus and Orestes complexes, for instance, which were enacted by royal beings, but which apply to everyone in similar emotional situations.

More simply, when the question of tragedy in art is not at issue, we never hesitate to attribute to the well-placed and the exalted the very same mental processes as the lowly. And finally, if the exaltation of tragic action were truly a property of the high-bred character alone, it is inconceivable that the mass of mankind should cherish tragedy above all other forms, let alone be capable of understanding it.

As a general rule, to which there may be exceptions unknown to me, I think the tragic feeling is evoked in us when we are in the /p. 1, col. 5/ presence of a character who is ready to lay down his life, if need be, to secure one thing — his sense of personal dignity. From Orestes to Hamlet, Medea to Macbeth, the underlying struggle is that of the individual attempting to gain his "rightful" position in his society.

Sometimes he is one who has been displaced from it, sometimes one who seeks to attain it for the first time, but the fateful wound from which the inevitable events spiral is the wound of indignity, and its dominant force is indignation. Tragedy, then, is the consequence of a man's total compulsion to evaluate himself justly.

In the sense of having been initiated by the hero himself, the tale always reveals what has been called his "tragic flaw," a failing that is not peculiar to grand or elevated characters. Nor is it necessarily a weakness. The flaw, or crack in the character, is really nothing — and need be nothing — but his inherent unwillingness to remain passive in the face of what he conceives to be a challenge to his dignity, his image of his rightful status. Only the passive, only those who accept their lot without active retaliation, are "flawless." Most of us are in that category.

But there are among us today, as there always have been, those who act against the scheme of things that degrades them, and in the process of action everything we have accepted out of fear or insensitivity or ignorance is shaken before us and examined, and from this total onslaught by an individual against the seemingly stable cosmos surrounding us — from this total examination of the "unchangeable" environment — comes the terror and the fear that is classically associated with tragedy.

More important, from this total questioning of what has been previously unquestioned, we learn. And /p. 1, col. 6/ such a process is not beyond the common man. In revolutions around the world, these past thirty years, he has demonstrated again and again this inner dynamic of all tragedy.

Insistence upon the rank of the tragic hero, or the so-called nobility of his character, is really but a clinging to the outward forms of tragedy. If rank or nobility of character was indispensable, then it would follow that the problems of those with rank were the particular problems of tragedy. But surely the right of one monarch to capture the domain from another no longer raises our passions, nor are our concepts of justice what they were to the mind of an Elizabethan king.

The quality in such plays that does shake us, however, derives from the underlying fear of being displaced, the disaster inherent in being torn away from our chosen image of what and who we are in this world. Among us today this fear is as strong, and perhaps stronger, than it ever was. In fact, it is the common man who knows this fear best.

Now, if it is true that tragedy is the consequence of a man's total compulsion to evaluate himself justly, his destruction in the attempt posits a wrong or an evil in his environment. And this is precisely the morality of tragedy and its lesson. The discovery of the moral law, which is what the enlightenment of tragedy consists of, is not the discovery of some abstract or metaphysical quantity.

The tragic right is a condition of life, a condition in which the human personality is able to flower and realize itself. The wrong is the condition which suppresses man, perverts the flowing out of his love and creative instinct. Tragedy /p. 1, col. 7/ enlightens — and it must, in that it points the heroic finger at the enemy of man's freedom. The thrust for freedom is the quality in tragedy which exalts. The revolutionary questioning of the stable environment is what terrifies. In no way is the common man debarred from such thoughts or such actions.

Seen in this light, our lack of tragedy may be partially accounted for by the turn which modern literature has taken toward the purely psychiatric view of life, or the purely sociological. If all our miseries, our indignities, are born and bred within our minds, then all action, let alone the heroic action, is obviously impossible.

And if society alone is responsible for the cramping of our lives, then the protagonist must needs be so pure and faultless as to force us to deny his validity as a character. From neither of these views can tragedy derive, simply because neither represents a balanced concept of life. Above all else, tragedy /p. 3, col. 3/ requires the finest appreciation by the writer of cause and effect.

No tragedy can therefore come about when its author fears to question absolutely everything, when he regards any institution, habit or custom as being either everlasting, immutable or inevitable. In the tragic view the need of man to wholly realize himself is the only fixed star, and whatever it is that hedges his nature and lowers it is ripe for attack and examination. Which is not to say that tragedy must preach revolution.

The Greeks could probe the very heavenly origin of their ways and return to confirm the rightness of laws. And Job could face God in anger, demanding his right, and end in submission. But for a moment everything is in suspension, nothing is accepted, and in this stretching and tearing apart of the cosmos, in the very action of so doing, the character gains "size," the tragic stature which is spuriously attached to the royal or the high born in our minds. The /p. 3, col. 4/ commonest of men may take on that stature to the extent of his willingness to throw all he has into the contest, the battle to secure his rightful place in his world.

There is a misconception of tragedy with which I have been struck in review after review, and in many conversations with writers and readers alike. It is the idea that tragedy is of necessity allied to pessimism. Even the dictionary says nothing more about the word than that it means a story with a sad or unhappy ending. This impression is so firmly fixed that I almost hesitate to claim that in truth tragedy implies more optimism in its author than does comedy, and that its final result ought to be the reinforcement of the on-looker's brightest opinions of the human animal.

For, if it is true to say that in essence the tragic hero is intent upon claiming his whole due as a personality, and if this struggle must be total and without reservation, then it automatically demonstrates the indestructible will /p. 3, col. 5/ of man to achieve his humanity.

The possibility of victory must be there in tragedy. Where pathos rules, where pathos is finally derived, a character has fought a battle he could not possibly have won. The pathetic is achieved when the protagonist is, by virtue of his witlessness, his insensitivity, or the very air he gives off, incapable of grappling with a much superior force.

Pathos truly is the mode for the pessimist. But tragedy requires a nicer balance between what is possible and what is impossible. And it is curious, although edifying, that the plays we revere, century after century, are the tragedies. In them, and in them alone, lies the belief — optimistic, if you will — in the perfectibility of man.

It is time, I think, that we who are without kings, took up this bright thread of our history and followed it to the only place it can possibly lead in our time — the heart and spirit of the average man. */p. 3, col. 6/*

# PART TWO

※

# TRAGEDY

❉

# SOPHOCLES

## *King Oedipus*

---

Characters:    OEDIPUS, king of Thebes

JOCASTA, wife of Oedipus

CREON, brother of Jocasta

TEIRESIAS, a blind prophet

A PRIEST

A MESSENGER

A SHEPHERD

AN ATTENDANT

CHORUS of Theban elders

King's attendants, queen's attendants,
citizens of Thebes

*Scene: Before the royal palace at Thebes.*

*In front of the king's palace, upon the steps and around the altars which
stand in the forecourt, are grouped numerous citizens of Thebes, sitting in
attitudes of supplication.*

*Enter* OEDIPUS *from the central door, attended.*

OEDIPUS. Children, new blood of Cadmus' ancient line —
What is the meaning of this supplication,
These branches and garlands, the incense filling the city,
These prayers for the healing of pain, these lamentations?
I have not thought it fit to rely on my messengers,
But am here to learn for myself — I, Oedipus,
Whose name is known afar.
[*To the* PRIEST] You, reverend sir,

---

King Oedipus, *tr. E. F. Watling*, The Theban Plays *(New York: Penguin Books, 1947). The
play was written* circa *430* B.C.

In right of age should speak for all of them.
What is the matter? Some fear? Something you desire? 10
I would willingly do anything to help you;
Indeed I should be heartless, were I to stop my ears
To a general petition such as this.
   PRIEST. My lord and king: we are gathered here, as you see,
Young and old, from the tenderest chicks to the age-bent seniors;
Priests — I of Zeus — and the pick of our young manhood.
More sit in the market-place, carrying boughs like these,
And around the twin altars of Pallas and the sacred embers
Of divination, beside the river of Ismenus.
   You too have seen our city's affliction, caught 20
In a tide of death from which there is no escaping —
Death in the fruitful flowering of her soil;
Death in the pastures; death in the womb of woman;
And pestilence, a fiery demon gripping the city,
Stripping the house of Cadmus, to fatten hell
With profusion of lamentation.
   If we come to you now, sir, as your suppliants,
I and these children, it is not as holding you
The equal of gods, but as the first of men,
Whether in the ordinary business of mortal life, 30
Or in the encounters of man with more than man.
It was you, we remember, a newcomer to Cadmus' town,
That broke our bondage to the vile Enchantress.
With no foreknowledge or hint that we could give,
But, as we truly believe, with the help of God,
You gave us back our life.
   Now, Oedipus great and glorious, we seek
Your help again. Find some deliverance for us
By any way that god or man can show.
We know that experience of trials past gives strength 40
To present counsel. Therefore, O greatest of men,
Restore our city to life. Have a care for your fame.
Your diligence saved us once; let it not be said
That under your rule we were raised up only to fall.
Save, save our city, and keep her safe for ever.
   Under the same bright star that gave us then
Good fortune, guide us into good to-day.
If you are to be our King, as now you are,
Be king of living men, not emptiness.
Surely there is no strength in wall or ship, 50
Where men are lacking and no life breathes within them.
   OEDIPUS. I grieve for you, my children. Believe me, I know
All that you desire of me, all that you suffer;
And while you suffer, none suffers more than I.
You have your several griefs, each for himself;
But my heart bears the weight of my own, and yours
And all my people's sorrows. I am not asleep.
I weep; and walk through endless ways of thought.
   But I have not been idle; one thing I have already done —
The only thing that promised hope. My kinsman 60
Creon, the son of Menoeceus, has been sent
To the Pythian house of Apollo, to learn what act
Or word of mine could help you. This is the day

I reckoned he should return. It troubles me
That he is not already here. But when he comes,
Whatever the god requires, upon my honour
It shall be done.
    PRIEST. Well said. [*He descries someone approaching from a distance.*
And look! They are making signs
That Creon is on his way. Yes. He is here!             70
    OEDIPUS. [*Looking also*] And with smiling face! O Apollo!
If his news is good!
    PRIEST. It must be good; his head is crowned with bay
Full-berried; that is a sign.
    OEDIPUS.             We shall soon know . . .
He can hear us now . . . Royal brother! What news?
What message for us from the mouth of God?

    *Enter* CREON.

    CREON. Good news. That is to say that good may come
Even out of painful matters, if all goes well.
    OEDIPUS. And the answer? You hold me between fear and hope.
The answer?             80
    CREON. I will tell you — if you wish me to speak in the presence of all.
If not, let us go in.
    OEDIPUS.        Speak before all.
Their plight concerns me now, more than my life.
    CREON. This, then, is the answer, and this the plain command
Of Phoebus our lord. There is an unclean thing,
Born and nursed on our soil, polluting our soil,
Which must be driven away, not kept to destroy us.
    OEDIPUS. What unclean thing? And what purification is required?
    CREON. The banishment of a man, or the payment of blood for blood.
For the shedding of blood is the cause of our city's peril.      90
    OEDIPUS. What blood does he mean? Did he say who it was that died?
    CREON. We had a king, sir, before you came to lead us.
His name was Laius.
    OEDIPUS.          I know. I never saw him.
    CREON. He was killed. And clearly the meaning of the god's command
Is that we bring the unknown killer to justice.
    OEDIPUS. And where might *he* be? Where shall we hope to uncover
The faded traces of that far-distant crime?
    CREON. Here — the god said. Seek, and ye shall find.
Unsought goes undetected.
    OEDIPUS.          Was it at home,
Or in the field, or abroad on foreign soil,      100
That Laius met his death, this violent death?
    CREON. He left the country, as he said, on a pilgrimage;
And from that day forth we never saw him again.
    OEDIPUS. Was there no word, no fellow-traveller
Who saw what happened, whose evidence could have been used?
    CREON. All died; save one, who fled from the scene in terror,
And had nothing to tell for certain — except one thing.
    OEDIPUS. What was it? One thing might point the way to others,
If once we could lay our hands on the smallest clue.
    CREON. His story was that robbers — not one but many —    110
Fell in with the King's party and put them to death.
    OEDIPUS. Robbers would hardly commit such a daring outrage —

Unless they were paid to do it by someone here.
CREON. That too was suggested. But in the troubles that followed
No avenger came forward to punish the murderers.
OEDIPUS. What troubles? Surely none great enough to hinder
A full inquiry into a royal death?
CREON. The Sphinx with her riddles forced us to turn our attention
From insoluble mysteries to more immediate matters.
OEDIPUS. I will start afresh; and bring everything into the light.                120
All praise to Phoebus — and thanks, for your part, to you —
For thus pointing out our duty to the dead.
You will find me as willing an ally as you could wish
In the cause of God and our country. My own cause too —
Not merely from a fellow-creature will I clear this taint,
But from myself. The killer of Laius,
Whoever he was, might think to turn his hand
Against *me*; thus, serving Laius, I serve myself.
    Now, up from your seats, my children! Away with these boughs!
Bring all the people of Cadmus here, and tell them                              130
There is nothing I will not do. Certain it is
That by the help of God we stand — or fall.

    OEDIPUS *goes into the palace. A messenger goes to summon the people.*
    *The* PRIEST *dismisses the suppliants.*

PRIEST. Up, children. Now the King has promised us
All that we came to ask. Let us pray that Phoebus,
From whom the answer came, himself may come
To save and deliver us out of our heavy afflictions.
                                        [*The suppliants disperse.*

*Enter the* CHORUS *of Theban elders.*

CHORUS. In Thebes, City of Light, from the Pythian House of Gold
The gracious voice of heaven is heard.
With fear my heart is riven, fear of what shall be told.
O Healer of Delos, hear!                                                        140
Fear is upon us. What wilt thou do?
Things new, or old as the circling year?
Speak to us, Daughter of Golden Hope! Come, deathless word!

    Deathless Athena! First, Daughter of Zeus, on thee
We call; then on thy sister Queen
Artemis, over our city enthroned in her majesty;
And Phoebus, Lord of the Bow;
Show us again your threefold power
This hour, as in ages long ago.
From the fire and pain of pestilence save us and make us clean.                 150

    Sorrows beyond all telling —
Sickness rife in our ranks, outstripping
Invention of remedy — blight
On barren earth,
And barren agonies of birth —
Life after life from the wild-fire winging
Swiftly into the night.

    Beyond all telling, the city
Reeks with the death in her streets, death-bringing.
None weeps, and her children die,                                               160

None by to pity.
Mothers at every altar kneel.
Golden Athena, come near to our crying!
Apollo, hear us and heal!

   Not with the rattle of bronze, but loud around us
The battle is raging, swift the death-fiend flying.
Fling to the farthest corners of the sea,
Or to some bleak North bay,
The onset of his armoury!
Night's agony grows into tortured day.            170
Zeus, let thy thunders crush, thy lightning slay!

   Slay with thy golden bow, Lycean! Slay him,
Artemis, over the Lycian hills resplendent!
Bacchus, our name-god, golden in the dance
Of Maenad revelry,
Euoe! thy fiery torch advance
To slay the Death-god, the grim enemy,
God whom all other gods abhor to see.

    *Enter* OEDIPUS *from the palace.*

OEDIPUS. You have prayed; and your prayers shall be answered with
    help and release
If you will obey me, and are willing to put in hand       180
The remedy your distress requires. I speak
As a stranger, except by hearsay, to what has passed
And the story that has been told — without this clue
I should make but little headway in my search.
Therefore, as a citizen newly received among you,
It is to you, Thebans, I make this proclamation:
If any one of you knows whose hand it was
That killed Laius, the son of Labdacus,
Let him declare it fully, now, to me.     *[He pauses: there is silence.*
Or if any man's conscience is guilty, let him give himself up.   190
He will suffer the less. His fate will be nothing worse
Than banishment. No other harm will touch him.
                      *[The hearers are still silent.*
Or, if some alien is known to have been the assassin,
Declare it. The informer shall have his reward of me,
As well as the thanks he will earn from all of you.     *[Silence still.*
But — if you will not speak, and any man
Is found to be screening himself or another, in fear,
I here pronounce my sentence upon his head:
No matter who he may be, he is forbidden
Shelter or intercourse with any man         200
In all this country over which I rule;
From fellowship of prayer or sacrifice
Or lustral rite is excommunicated;
Expelled from every house, unclean, accursed,
In accordance with the word of the Pythian oracle.
Thus I shall have done my duty to the god,
And to the dead. And it is my solemn prayer
That the unknown murderer, and his accomplices,
If such there be, may wear the brand of shame
For their shameful act, unfriended, to their life's end.   210

Nor do I exempt myself from the imprecation:
If, with my knowledge, house or hearth of mine
Receive the guilty man, upon my head
Lie all the curses I have laid on others.
It is for you to see this faithfully carried out,
As in duty bound to me, and to the god,
And to our suffering plague-tormented country.
Indeed I am surprised that no purification was made,
Even without the express command of heaven.
The death of a man so worthy, and your King,                          220
Should surely have been probed to the utmost. Be that as it may,
Now that I hold the place that he once held —
His bed, his wife — whose children, had fate so willed,
Would have grown to be another bond of blood between us —
And upon him, alas, has this disaster fallen;
I mean to fight for him now, as I would fight
For my own father, and leave no way untried
To bring to light the killer of Laius,
The son of Labdacus, the son of Polydorus, the son of Cadmus, the son
    of Agenor.
    The gods curse all that disobey this charge!                     230
For them the earth be barren of harvest, for them
Women be childless; and may this present calamity,
And worse than this, pursue them to their death!
For the rest — you sons of Cadmus who are on my side —
May Justice and all the gods be with you for ever.
    CHORUS. Under your curse, O King, I make bold to answer:
I am not the man, nor can I point him out.
The question came from Phoebus, and he, if anyone,
Could surely tell us who the offender is.
    OEDIPUS. No doubt, but to compel a god to speak                  240
Against his will, is not in mortal power.
    CHORUS. I have another thing to say.
    OEDIPUS.                Say on.
Second, or third, thoughts — we will hear them all.
    CHORUS. To the lord Phoebus the lord Teiresias
Stands nearest, I would say, in divination.
He is the one who could help us most in our search.
    OEDIPUS. I have not overlooked it. I have sent for him —
It was Creon's advice — twice I have sent for him,
And am much surprised he is not already here.
    CHORUS. There were rumours, of course; but mostly old wives' tales.   250
    OEDIPUS. Rumours? What rumours? I must hear them all.
    CHORUS. He was said to have been killed by travellers on the road.
    OEDIPUS. So I have heard. But where are the witnesses?
    CHORUS. He'd be a bold man, sir, that would pay no heed
To such a curse as yours, when he had heard it.
    OEDIPUS. Will he fear words, that did not shrink from the deed?
    CHORUS. There is one can find him out. They are bringing the prophet
In whom, of all men, lives the incarnate truth.

    *Enter* TEIRESIAS, *blind, led by an attendant.*

    OEDIPUS. Teiresias, we know there is nothing beyond your ken;
Lore sacred and profane, all heavenly and earthly knowledge         260
Are in your grasp. In your heart, if not with the eye,

You see our city's condition: we look to you
As our only help and protector. We have sent —
They may have told you — to Phoebus, and he has answered.
The only way of deliverance from our plague
Is for us to find out the killers of Laius
And kill or banish them.
Now, sir, spare not your skill
In bird-lore or whatever other arts
Of prophecy you profess. It is for yourself,                              270
It is for Thebes, it is for me. Come, save us all,
Save all that is polluted by this death.
We look to you. To help his fellow-men
With all his power is man's most noble work.
    TEIRESIAS. Wise words; but O, when wisdom brings no profit,
To be wise is to suffer. And why did I forget this,
Who knew it well? I never should have come.
    OEDIPUS. It seems you bring us little encouragement.
    TEIRESIAS. Let me go home. It will be easier thus
For you to bear your burden, and me mine.                                280
    OEDIPUS. Take care, sir. You show yourself no friend to Thebes,
Whose son you are, if you refuse to answer.
    TEIRESIAS. It is because I see your words, sir, tending
To no good end; therefore I guard my own.
    OEDIPUS. By the gods! If you know, do not refuse to speak!
We all beseech you; we are all your suppliants.
    TEIRESIAS. You are all deluded. I refuse to utter
The heavy secrets of my soul — and yours.
    OEDIPUS. What? Something you know, and will not tell? You mean
To fail us and to see your city perish?                                  290
    TEIRESIAS. I mean to spare you, and myself. Ask me
No more. It is useless. I will tell you nothing.
    OEDIPUS. Nothing? Insolent scoundrel, you would rouse
A stone to fury! Will you never speak?
You are determined to be obstinate to the end?
    TEIRESIAS. Do not blame me; put your own house in order.
    OEDIPUS. Hear him! Such words — such insults to the State
Would move a saint to anger.
    TEIRESIAS.                    What will be
Will be, though I should never speak again.
    OEDIPUS. What is to be, it is your trade to tell.                     300
    TEIRESIAS. I tell no more. Rage with what wrath you will.
    OEDIPUS. I shall; and speak my mind unflinchingly.
I tell you I do believe *you* had a hand
In plotting, and all but doing, this very act.
If you had eyes to see with, I would have said
Your hand, and yours alone, had done it all.
    TEIRESIAS. You would so? Then hear this: upon your head
Is the ban your lips have uttered — from this day forth
Never to speak to me or any here.
*You* are the cursed polluter of this land.                              310
    OEDIPUS. You dare to say it! Have you no shame at all?
And do you expect to escape the consequence?
    TEIRESIAS. I have escaped. The truth is my defence.
    OEDIPUS. Whose work is this? This is no soothsaying.
    TEIRESIAS. You taught me. You made me say it against my will.

OEDIPUS. Say it again. Let there be no mistake.

TEIRESIAS. Was it not plain? Or will you tempt me further?

OEDIPUS. I would have it beyond all doubt. Say it again.

TEIRESIAS. I say that the killer you are seeking is yourself.

OEDIPUS. The second time. You shall be sorry for this.                        320

TEIRESIAS. Will you have more, to feed your anger?

OEDIPUS. Yes!

More, and more madness. Tell us all you know.

TEIRESIAS. I know, as you do not, that you are living

In sinful union with the one you love,

Living in ignorance of your own undoing.

OEDIPUS. Do you think you can say such things with impunity?

TEIRESIAS. I do — if truth has any power to save.

OEDIPUS. It has — but not for you; no, not for you,

Shameless and brainless, sightless, senseless sot!                          330

TEIRESIAS. You are to be pitied, uttering such taunts

As all men's mouths must some day cast at *you.*

OEDIPUS. Living in perpetual night, you cannot harm

Me, nor any man else that sees the light.

TEIRESIAS. No; it is not for me to bring you down.

That is in Apollo's hands, and he will do it.

OEDIPUS. [*Scenting a possible connection with Creon's embassy*]

Creon! Was this trick his, then, if not yours?

TEIRESIAS. Not Creon either. Your enemy is yourself.

OEDIPUS. [*Pursuing his own thought*]

Ah, riches and royalty, and wit matched against wit

In the race of life, must they always be mated with envy?                    340

Must Creon, so long my friend, my most trusted friend,

Stalk me by stealth, and study to dispossess me

Of the power this city has given me — freely given —

Not of my asking — setting this schemer on me,

This pedlar of fraudulent magical tricks, with eyes

Wide open for profit, but blind in prophecy?

[*To* TEIRESIAS] What was your vaunted seercraft ever worth?

And where were you, when the Dog-faced Witch was here?

Had you any word of deliverance then for our people?

*There* was a riddle too deep for common wits;                               350

A seer should have answered it; but answer came there none

From you; bird-lore and god-craft all were silent.

Until *I* came — I, ignorant Oedipus, came —

And stopped the riddler's mouth, guessing the truth

By mother-wit, not bird-lore. This is the man

Whom you would dispossess, hoping to stand

Nearest to Creon's throne. You shall repent,

You and your fellow-plotter, of your zeal

For scapegoat-hunting. Were you not as old

As you appear to be, sharp punishment                                       360

Would soon convince you of your wickedness.

CHORUS. Sir, to our thinking, both of you have spoken

In the heat of anger. Surely this is not well,

When all our thought should be, how to discharge

The god's command.

TEIRESIAS. King though you are, one right —

To answer — makes us equal; and I claim it.

It is not you, but Loxias, whom I serve;

Nor am I bound to Creon's patronage.
You are pleased to mock my blindness. Have you eyes,                    370
And do not see your own damnation? Eyes,
And cannot see what company you keep?
Whose son are you? I tell you, you have sinned —
And do not know it — against your own on earth
And in the grave. A swift and two-edged sword,
Your mother's and your father's curse, shall sweep you
Out of this land. Those now clear-seeing eyes
Shall then be darkened, then no place be deaf,
No corner of Cithaeron echoless,
To your loud crying, when you learn the truth                          380
Of that sweet marriage-song that hailed you home
To the fair-seeming haven of your hopes —
With more, more misery than you can guess,
To show you what you are, and who they are
That call you father. Rail as you will at Creon,
And at my speaking — you shall be trodden down
With fouler scorn than ever fell on man.
    OEDIPUS. Shall I bear more of this? Out of my sight!
Go! Quickly, go! Back where you came from! Go!
    TEIRESIAS. I will. It was your wish brought me here, not mine.      390
    OEDIPUS. Had I known what madness I was to listen to,
I would have spared myself the trouble.
    TEIRESIAS. Mad I may seem
To you. Your parents would not think me so.
    OEDIPUS. What's that? My parents? Who then ... gave me birth?
    TEIRESIAS. This day brings you your birth; and brings you death.
    OEDIPUS. Man, must you still wrap up your words in riddles?
    TEIRESIAS. Were you not famed for skill at solving riddles?
    OEDIPUS. You taunt me with the gift that is my greatness?
    TEIRESIAS. Your great misfortune, and your ruin.
    OEDIPUS.                        No matter!                 400
I have saved this land from ruin. I am content.
    TEIRESIAS. Well, I will go. Your hand, boy. Take me home.
    OEDIPUS. We well can spare you. Let him take you home.
    TEIRESIAS. When I have said my all. Thus, to your face,
Fearful of nothing you can do to me:
The man for whom you have ordered hue and cry,
The killer of Laius — that man is *here*;
Passing for an alien, a sojourner here among us;
But, as presently shall appear, a Theban born,
To his cost. He that came seeing, blind shall he go;                   410
Rich now, then a beggar; stick-in-hand, groping his way
To a land of exile; brother, as it shall be shown,
And father at once, to the children he cherishes; son,
And husband, to the woman who bore him; father-killer,
And father-supplanter.
Go in, and think on this.
When you can prove me wrong, then call me blind.      [*Exeunt.*
    CHORUS. From the Delphian rock the heavenly voice denounces
The shedder of blood, the doer of deeds unnamed.
Who is the man?                                                        420
Let him fly with the speed of horses racing the wind.
The son of Zeus, armed with his fires, his lightnings,

Leaps to destroy,
And the Fates sure-footed close around him.

Out from the snowy dawn on high Parnassus
The order flashed, to hunt a man from his hiding.
And where is he?
In forest or cave, a wild ox roaming the mountains,
Footing a friendless way; but the deathless voices
Live in his ear;                                                   430
From the Heart of Earth they cry against him.

Terrible things indeed has the prophet spoken.
We cannot believe, we cannot deny; all's dark.
We fear, but we cannot see, what is before us.
Was there a quarrel between the house of Labdacus
And the son of Polybus? None that we ever knew,
For which to impugn the name of Oedipus,
Or seek to avenge the house of Labdacus
For the undiscovered death.

All secrets of earth are known to Zeus and Apollo;        440
But of mortal prophets, that one knows more than another
No man can surely say; wisdom is given
To all in their several degrees. I impute no blame
Till blame is proved. He faced the winged Enchantress,
And stood to the test, winning golden opinions.
Never, therefore, will I consent
To think him other than good.

    *Enter* CREON.

    CREON. Citizens! They tell me that King Oedipus
Has laid a slanderous accusation on me.
I will not bear it! If he thinks that I                            450
Have done him any harm, by word or act,
In this calamitous hour, I will not live —
Life is too long a time — to hear such scandal!
Nay, more than scandal, a grievous imputation,
If you, my friends, my country, call me traitor.
    CHORUS. The words, I think, were spoken in the stress
Of anger, ill-considered.
    CREON.               And did he say
The prophet lied under my instigation?
    CHORUS. He did; with what intention I cannot tell.
    CREON. Said with unflinching eye was it? Deliberate —     460
This accusation that he made against me?
    CHORUS. I do not scrutinize my master's actions.
But here he comes.

    *Enter* OEDIPUS.

    OEDIPUS. Well, sir? What brings you here?
Have you the face to stand before my door,
Proved plotter against my life, thief of my crown?
Do you take me for a coward, or a fool?
Did you suppose I wanted eyes to see
The plot preparing, wits to counter it?
And what a foolish plot! You, without backing            470
Of friends or purse, to go in quest of kingship!

Kingdoms are won by men and moneybags.
    CREON. Hear my reply. And when you know, then judge.
    OEDIPUS. I doubt your eloquence will teach me much.
You are my bitterest enemy; that I know.
    CREON. First, let me tell you —
    OEDIPUS.                   Tell me anything
Except that you are honest.
    CREON.            Can you believe
This obstinacy does you any good?
    OEDIPUS. Can *you* believe that you may carry on
Intrigues against your house and go scot-free?         480
    CREON. I should be a fool to believe it. Tell me, though,
What wrong you think I have done you.
    OEDIPUS.               Was it you
That made me bring that canting prophet here?
    CREON. It was; and I would do the same again.
    OEDIPUS. Tell me . . . how long ago did Laius . . .
    CREON. Did Laius — what? I do not understand.
    OEDIPUS. How long is it since Laius . . . disappeared?
    CREON. A long time now; longer than I can say.
    OEDIPUS. Was this old prophet at his business then?
    CREON. Yes, held in equal honour then as now.         490
    OEDIPUS. In those days, did he ever mention me?
    CREON. Not in my hearing.
    OEDIPUS.              Was there no inquest made
Into his death?
    CREON.      Indeed there was. In vain.
    OEDIPUS. And the man of wisdom — why was he silent then?
    CREON. I do not presume to say more than I know.
    OEDIPUS. One thing you know, and would be wise to confess.
    CREON. What I know I will freely confess. What do I know?
    OEDIPUS. This: that without your prompting, the fortune-teller
Would never have dared to name *me* killer of Laius.
    CREON. If he did so, you know best. But give me leave,     500
As you have questioned me, to question you.
    OEDIPUS. Ask on. You cannot prove me guilty of blood.
    CREON. Are you my sister's husband?
    OEDIPUS.                Sir, I am.
    CREON. And she your equal partner in rule and possession?
    OEDIPUS. All that she can desire is hers by right.
    CREON. Have I a third and equal share of honour?
    OEDIPUS. You have; so much the more your proven falseness.
    CREON. But I deny it. Reason with yourself,
As I; and ask, would any man exchange
A quiet life, with royal rank assured,         510
For an uneasy throne? To be a king
In name, was never part of my ambition;
Enough for me to live a kingly life.
What more could any moderate man desire?
I have your ear for all my fair requests;
But, in your place, I should have much to do
That irked me. How could kingship please me more
Than royalty and rule without regret?
I am not yet so besotted as to seek
More honours than are good for me. I stand     520

In all men's favour, I am all men's friend.
Why, those who seek your audience, ask for me,
Knowing that way the surest to success!
And would I change this life for the other? No;
None but a fool would be so faithless. Treason?
That's not my policy, nor, if I know it,
The policy of any friend of mine.
    To test me; first, go to the Pythian shrine;
Ask if the message I brought back was true.
Second; prove me guilty of any compact                    530
With the soothsayer; then take me and condemn
To death. My voice will join with yours in the sentence.
    But charged behind my back on blind suspicion
I will not be. To slur a good man's name
With baseless slander is one crime — another
Is rashly to mistake bad men for good.
Cast out an honest friend, and you cast out
Your life, your dearest treasure. Time will teach
The truth of this; for time alone can prove
The honest man; one day proclaims the sinner.              540
    CHORUS. Good words; and fitting for a prudent man
To hear and heed. Quick thoughts are seldom safest.
    OEDIPUS. When a quick plotter's on the move, my friend,
It's safest to be quick in counter-plotting.
Am I to sit and wait for him, and lose
My opportunity while he takes his?
    CREON. What do you want then? Will you banish me?
    OEDIPUS. By no means. I would have you dead, not banished.
    CREON. If you can show in what way I have wronged you —
    OEDIPUS. Still clinging to your obstinate arguments?       550
    CREON. Because I know you are wrong.
    OEDIPUS.                          I know I am right.
    CREON. In your *own* eyes, not in mine.
    OEDIPUS.                          *You* are a knave.
    CREON. And what if you are mistaken?
    OEDIPUS.                          Kings must rule.
    CREON. Not when they rule unjustly.
    OEDIPUS.                          Hear him, Thebes!
My city!
    CREON. Yours? Is she not also mine?
    CHORUS. Sirs, sirs, enough. Here comes the queen, Jocasta.
She should be able to compose this quarrel.

*Enter* JOCASTA *from the palace.*

    JOCASTA. What is the meaning of this loud argument,
You quarrelsome men? I wonder you are not ashamed,
In this time of distress, to air your private troubles.     560
Come in, my husband; and Creon, you go home.
You are making much of some unimportant grievance.
    CREON. Not so, my sister. Your husband Oedipus
Condemns me out of hand with a terrible sentence,
A choice of death or banishment.
    OEDIPUS.                          It is true.
I have found him craftily plotting against my person.
    CREON. May the curse of heaven rest on me for ever,

If I am guilty of any such design!
    JOCASTA. For the love of God, believe it, Oedipus!
For his oath's sake, O believe it, and for mine           570
And theirs who are here to witness!
    CHORUS. Consent, O King, consent.
Be merciful, and learn to yield.
    OEDIPUS. And why should I repent?
    CHORUS. His oath should be his shield,
Who never played you false before.
    OEDIPUS. You know for what you pray?
    CHORUS. We know.
    OEDIPUS.        Say more.
    CHORUS.                He swore
His friendship; is it right to cast away
A friend, condemned unheard,             580
Upon an idle word?
    OEDIPUS. In asking this you ask my death or banishment.
    CHORUS. Forbid the thought! O by the Lord of Life,
The Sun, forbid! Lost may I be
To God and man, if it was ever mine.
But while our people pine,
My heart is racked anew
If you,
My princes, add your strife
To our old misery.                       590
    OEDIPUS. Then let him go; even though it mean my death
Or exile in disgrace. Your voice, not his,
Has won my mercy; him I hate for ever.
    CREON. In mercy obdurate, as harsh in anger —
Such natures earn self-torture.
    OEDIPUS. Will you begone?
    CREON. I will; unjustly judged by you alone.        [*Exit.*
    CHORUS. Persuade, madam, persuade
The King to go awhile apart.
    JOCASTA. How was this trouble made?             600
    CHORUS. Wild surmise; and the smart
Of baseless calumny grew hot.
    JOCASTA. Each holding each to blame?
    CHORUS.                Just so.
    JOCASTA.                   For what?
    CHORUS.                       Ask not
Again; enough our stricken country's shame.
To let this other rest
Where it remains, were best.
    OEDIPUS. A fine peacemakers' part your worships would have played!
    CHORUS. Hear yet again, O King; believe us true!
Could ours be such simplicity
As rashly from his sheltering arms to stray,        610
Whose wisdom in the day
Of wrath upheld our land,
Whose hand
Again shall lead us through
Storm to tranquillity?
    JOCASTA. Will you not tell me too? Tell me, I implore you,
Why you have conceived this terrible hatred against him.

OEDIPUS. I will. You are more to me than these good men.
The fault is Creon's, and his this plot against me.

    JOCASTA. How was it his? What is the accusation?       620

    OEDIPUS. He says the murder of Laius was my doing.

    JOCASTA. From his own knowledge, or other men's report?

    OEDIPUS. Ah, there's his cleverness; he shields himself
By using a rascally soothsayer as his tool.

    JOCASTA. Then absolve yourself at once. For I can tell you,
No man possesses the secret of divination.
And I have proof. An oracle was given to Laius —
From Phoebus, no; but from his ministers —
That he should die by the hands of his own child,
His child and mine. What came of it? Laius,       630
It is common knowledge, was killed by outland robbers
At a place where three roads meet. As for the child,
It was not yet three days old, when he cast it out
(By other hands, not his) with rivetted ankles
To perish on the empty mountain-side.
There, then, Apollo did not so contrive it.
The offspring did not kill the father; the father,
For all his fears, was killed — not by his son.
Yet such were the prophets' warnings. Why should you,
Then, heed them for a moment? What he intends,      640
The god will show us in his own good time.

    OEDIPUS. My wife, what you have said has troubled me.
My mind goes back ... and something in me moves ...

    JOCASTA. Why? What is the matter? How you turn and start!

    OEDIPUS. Did you not say that Laius was killed
At a place where three roads meet?

    JOCASTA.                That was the story;
And is the story still.

    OEDIPUS.       Where? In what country?

    JOCASTA. The land called Phocis — where the road divides,
Leading to Delphi and to Daulia.

    OEDIPUS. How long ago did it happen?

    JOCASTA.                It became known       650
A little time before your reign began.

    OEDIPUS. O God, what wilt thou do to me!

    JOCASTA.               Why, Oedipus,
What weighs upon your mind?

    OEDIPUS.       O do not ask!
But tell me, what was Laius like? How old?

    JOCASTA. Tall — silver-frosted hair — about your figure.

    OEDIPUS. Ah, wretch! Am I unwittingly self-cursed?

    JOCASTA. What, O my King, what is it? You frighten me.

    OEDIPUS. Had then the prophet eyes? O is it possible?
To prove it certain, tell me one thing more.

    JOCASTA. You frighten me. I will tell you all I know.      660

    OEDIPUS. How was the King attended? By a few,
Or in full state with numerous bodyguard?

    JOCASTA. Five men in all, a herald leading them;
One carriage only, in which King Laius rode.

    OEDIPUS. Clearer, alas, too clear! Who told you this?

    JOCASTA. A servant, the only survivor that returned.

    OEDIPUS. Is he still in the household?

JOCASTA. No. When he came back,
And found you king in his late master's place,
He earnestly begged me to let him go away            670
Into the country to become a shepherd,
Far from the city's eyes. I let him go.
Poor fellow, he might have asked a greater favour;
He was a good slave.
       OEDIPUS. Could we have him here
Without delay?
       JOCASTA.       We could. Why do you ask?
       OEDIPUS. O wife, I fear . . . I fear that I have said
Too much, and therefore I must see this man.
       JOCASTA. Well, you shall see him. Meanwhile, may I not hear
What weighs so heavily on your heart?
       OEDIPUS.                     You shall.            680
If things are as I see them, you are the first
To whom I would tell my story. Listen then.

     My father was a Corinthian, Polybus;
My mother a Dorian, Meropé. At home
I rose to be a person of some pre-eminence;
Until a strange thing happened – a curious thing –
Though perhaps I took it to heart more than it deserved.
One day at table, a fellow who had been drinking deeply
Made bold to say I was not my father's son.
That hurt me; but for the time I suffered in silence       690
As well as I could. Next day I approached my parents
And asked them to tell me the truth. They were bitterly angry
That anyone should dare to put such a story about;
And I was relieved. Yet somehow the smart remained;
And a thing like that soon passes from hand to hand.
     So, without my parents' knowledge, I went to Pytho;
But came back disappointed of any answer
To the question I asked, having heard instead a tale
Of horror and misery: how I must marry my mother,
And become the parent of a misbegotten brood,         700
An offence to all mankind – and kill my father.
At this I fled away, putting the stars
Between me and Corinth, never to see home again,
That no such horror should ever come to pass.
     My journey brought me into the neighbourhood where
Your late king met his end. Listen, my wife:
This is the truth.
When I came to the place where three roads join, I met
A herald followed by a horse-drawn carriage, and a man
Seated therein, just as you have described.         710
The leader roughly ordered me out of the way;
And his venerable master joined in with a surly command.
It was the driver that thrust me aside, and him I struck,
For I was angry. The old man saw it, leaning from the carriage,
Waited until I passed, then, seizing for weapon
The driver's two-pronged goad, struck me on the head.
He paid with interest for his temerity;
Quick as lightning, the staff in this right hand
Did its work; he tumbled headlong out of the carriage,

And every man of them there I killed.
              But now,                                    720
If the blood of Laius ran in this stranger's veins,
Is there any more wretched mortal than I, more hated
By God and man? It is I whom no stranger, no citizen,
Must take to his house; I to whom none may speak;
On me is the curse that none but I have laid.
His wife! — these hands that killed him have touched *her*!
Is this my sin? Am I not utterly foul?
Banished from here, and in my banishment
Debarred from home and from my fatherland,
Which I must shun for ever, lest I live                    730
To make my mother my wife, and kill my father . . .
My father . . . Polybus, to whom I owe my life.
Can it be any but some monstrous god
Of evil that has sent this doom upon me?
   O never, never, holy powers above,
May that day come! May I be sooner dead
And blotted from the face of earth, than live
To bear the scars of such vile circumstance.
        CHORUS. Sir, these are terrible words. But yet be hopeful,
Until you learn the whole truth from our witness.         740
        OEDIPUS. That is my only hope; to await the shepherd.
        JOCASTA. And why? What help do you expect from him?
        OEDIPUS. This: if we find his story fits with yours,
I am absolved.
        JOCASTA.      In what particular point?
What did I say?
        OEDIPUS.      You said he spoke of *robbers* —
That *robbers* killed him. If he still says *robbers*,
It was not I; one is not more than one.
But if he speaks of one lone wayfarer,
There is no escape; the finger points to me.
        JOCASTA. Oh but I assure you that was what he said;    750
He cannot go back on it now — the whole town heard it.
Not only I. And even if he changes his story
In some small point, he cannot in any event
Pretend that Laius died as was foretold.
For Loxias said a child of mine should kill him.
It was not to be; poor child, it was he that died.
A fig for divination! After this
I would not cross the road for any of it.
        OEDIPUS. You are right. Still, let us have the shepherd here.
Send one to fetch him.
        JOCASTA.          I will at once. Come in.          760
I will do nothing other than you wish.          [*Exeunt.*
        CHORUS. I only ask to live, with pure faith keeping
In word and deed that Law which leaps the sky,
Made of no mortal mould, undimmed, unsleeping
Whose living godhead does not age or die.

   Pride breeds the Tyrant; swollen with ill-found booty,
From castled height Pride tumbles to the pit,
All footing lost. Zeal, stripped for civic duty,
No law forbids; may God still prosper it.

Who walks his own high-handed way, disdaining 770
True righteousness and holy ornament;
Who falsely wins, all sacred things profaning;
Shall he escape his doomed pride's punishment?

Shall he by any armour be defended
From God's sharp wrath, who casts out right for wrong?
If wickedness for virtue be commended,
Farewell, sweet harmonies of sacred song;

Farewell, Abaean and Olympian altar;
Farewell, O Heart of Earth, inviolate shrine,
If at this time your omens fail or falter, 780
And man no longer own your voice divine.

Zeus! If thou livest, all-ruling, all-pervading,
Awake; old oracles are out of mind;
Apollo's name denied, his glory fading;
There is no godliness in all mankind.

*Enter* JOCASTA *from the palace, carrying a garlanded branch and incense.*

JOCASTA. My lords, I am minded to visit the holy temples,
Bringing in my hands these tokens of supplication
And gifts of incense. The King is over-wrought
With fancies, and can no longer sanely judge
The present by the past, listening to every word 790
That feeds his apprehension. I can do nothing
To comfort him.
To thee, Bright Shining Apollo,
Who art nearest to my door, is my first prayer.
Save us from the curse of this uncleanness, save!
We are afraid, seeing our master-pilot distraught.
                    [*She makes her oblations to the altars.*

*Enter a* MESSENGER *from Corinth.*

MESSENGER. By your leave, strangers; I am seeking the house of Oedipus.
Can you guide me to it — or to him, if you know where he is?
CHORUS. This is the house, sir; and he is within. This lady
Is his wife and the mother of his children. 800
MESSENGER. Blessing attend her,
And all her house, true consort of such a man.
JOCASTA. Blessing on you, sir, and thanks for your kindly greeting.
You bring a request or message, sir?
MESSENGER.                    Good news
For your husband, honourable lady, and for his house.
JOCASTA. What news? And from whom?
MESSENGER. From Corinth. You cannot but be glad
At the message — though you may also be distressed.
JOCASTA. What is it that can have such power to please and grieve?
MESSENGER. Our people — such was the talk — will make him king 810
Of all the Isthmus.
JOCASTA.          Is Polybus king no longer?
MESSENGER. King Polybus, madam, is dead and in his grave.
JOCASTA. What? Dead? The father of Oedipus?
MESSENGER. Ay, on my life.
JOCASTA. [*To an attendant*] Girl! To your master quickly!
Tell him this news.                    [*The attendant goes.*

Where are you now, divine prognostications!
The man whom Oedipus has avoided all these years,
Lest he should kill him — dead! By a natural death,
And by no act of his!

   *Enter* OEDIPUS.

  OEDIPUS.        My dear Jocasta,
Why have you called me out of doors again?            820
  JOCASTA. Hear this man's news; and when you have heard it, say
What has become of the famous oracles.
  OEDIPUS. Who is this man? What news has he for me?
  JOCASTA. He comes from Corinth. Your father, Polybus,
Is dead — dead!
  OEDIPUS.    What, sir? Tell me yourself.
  MESSENGER. I do assure you, sir — if you must have this first —
He is gone the way of all mortality.
  OEDIPUS. By foul play, or the accident of sickness?
  MESSENGER. Such little accident as puts the old to sleep.
  OEDIPUS. You mean he died of illness, poor old man.     830
  MESSENGER. That, and the tale of years he had fulfilled.
  OEDIPUS. Well, well . . . So, wife, what of the Pythian fire,
The oracles, the prophesying birds,
That scream above us? I was to kill my father;
Now he lies in his grave, and here am I
Who never touched a weapon . . . unless it could be said
Grief at my absence killed him . . . and so *I* killed him.
But no, the letter of the oracle
Is unfulfilled and lies, like Polybus, dead.
  JOCASTA. Have I not said so all this while?
  OEDIPUS.                You have.     840
My fear misled me.
  JOCASTA.      Think no more of it.
  OEDIPUS. There is the other still to fear . . . my mother . . .
  JOCASTA. Fear? What has a man to do with fear?
Chance rules our lives, and the future is all unknown.
Best live as best we may, from day to day.
Nor need this mother-marrying frighten you;
Many a man has dreamt as much. Such things
Must be forgotten, if life is to be endured.
  OEDIPUS. If she were dead, you might have spoken so
With justice; but she lives; and while she lives,     850
Say what you will, I cannot cease to fear.
  JOCASTA. At least your father's death is a relief.
  OEDIPUS. Agreed; but while *she* lives, I am not safe.
  MESSENGER. But pray, sir, who is the woman whom you still fear?
  OEDIPUS. Why, sir, Queen Meropé, wife of Polybus.
  MESSENGER. And she? How does her life endanger yours?
  OEDIPUS. We have an oracle, sir, of deadly tenor.
  MESSENGER. Is it one that may rightly be uttered to a stranger?
  OEDIPUS. It is. Loxias said I was foredoomed
To make my mother my wife, and kill my father,     860
With my own hands shedding his blood. This is the reason
Of my long estrangement from Corinth. And I have fared well,
Though nothing can fill the place of absent parents.
  MESSENGER. Was that the fear that has banished you all this while?

OEDIPUS. Yes. I was determined not to kill my father.

MESSENGER. Then let me rid you of this other fear.
I came to do you good —

OEDIPUS.                My gratitude
Shall not be stinted.

MESSENGER.            And, if the truth were told,
To do myself good on your coming home.

OEDIPUS. Home, never! Never beneath my parents' roof —                870

MESSENGER. My dear young man, you are deceived.

OEDIPUS.                          How so?
Good sir, for God's sake, tell me.

MESSENGER. This fear that bars you from your home —

OEDIPUS.                                    Ay, that.
The word of Phoebus may yet be true for me.

MESSENGER. That story of pollution through your parents?

OEDIPUS. Ay, that, sir; that, my ever-present torment.

MESSENGER. All idle, sir; your fears are groundless, vain.

OEDIPUS. How can that be, seeing I am their son?

MESSENGER. No. Polybus is no kin of yours.

OEDIPUS.                          No kin?
Polybus not my father?

MESSENGER.            No more than I.                880

OEDIPUS. Come, sir; no more than you? Explain yourself.

MESSENGER. I am not your father, neither is Polybus.

OEDIPUS. How comes it then that I was called his son?

MESSENGER. I will tell you. You were given to him—by me.

OEDIPUS. Given? And yet he loved me as his son?

MESSENGER.                          He had no other.

OEDIPUS. Was I . . . found? Or boúght?

MESSENGER. Found, in a wooded hollow of Cithaeron.

OEDIPUS. What brought you there?

MESSENGER.                Sheep-tending on the mountain.

OEDIPUS. Were you a hireling shepherd then?

MESSENGER.                          I was;
And, by that happy chance, your rescuer.                890

OEDIPUS. Why, was I in pain or danger when you took me?

MESSENGER. The infirmity in your ankles tells the tale.

OEDIPUS. Oh, that old trouble; need we mention it?

MESSENGER. Your ankles were rivetted, and I set you free.

OEDIPUS. It is true; I have carried the stigma from my cradle.

MESSENGER. To it you owe your present name.

OEDIPUS.                          O Gods!
Was this my father's or my mother's doing?

MESSENGER. I cannot say. Ask him who gave you to me.

OEDIPUS. Gave me? Did you not find me, then, yourself?

MESSENGER. Another shepherd entrusted you to my care.                900

OEDIPUS. And who was he? Can you tell us who he was?

MESSENGER. I think he was said to be one of Laius' men.

OEDIPUS. Laius? Our former king?

MESSENGER.                Why, yes; King Laius.
The man was one of his servants.

OEDIPUS.                Is he alive?
And could I see him?

MESSENGER.      Your people here should know.

OEDIPUS. Good men, does any of you know the fellow —
This shepherd of whom he speaks? Has anyone seen him
In the pastures or in the city? Speak if you know.
Now is the chance to get to the bottom of the mystery.

    CHORUS. I think he will prove to be that same countryman    910
Whom you have already asked to see. The Queen
Is the one most able to tell you if this is so.

    OEDIPUS. My wife, *you* know the man whom we have sent for.
Is that the man he means?

    JOCASTA. [*White with terror*] What does it matter
What man he means? It makes no difference now ...
Forget what he has told you ... It makes no difference.

    OEDIPUS. Nonsense: I must pursue this trail to the end,
Till I have unravelled the mystery of my birth.

    JOCASTA. No! In God's name — if you want to live, this quest    920
Must not go on. Have I not suffered enough?

    OEDIPUS. There is nothing to fear. Though I be proved slave-born
To the third generation, *your* honour is not impugned.

    JOCASTA. Yet do not do it. I implore you, do not do it.

    OEDIPUS. I must. I cannot leave the truth unknown.

    JOCASTA. I know I am right. I am warning you for your good.

    OEDIPUS. My 'good' has been my bugbear long enough.

    JOCASTA. Doomed man! O never live to learn the truth!

    OEDIPUS. Go, someone; fetch the shepherd. Leave the lady
To enjoy her pride of birth.    930

    JOCASTA. O lost and damned!
This is my last and only word to you
For ever!    [*Exit.*

    CHORUS. Why has the Queen, sir, left us in such deep passion?
I fear some vile catastrophe will out
From what she dare not tell.

    OEDIPUS.    Let all come out,
However vile! However base it be,
I must unlock the secret of my birth.
The woman, with more than woman's pride, is shamed
By my low origin. I am the child of Fortune,    940
The giver of good, and I shall not be shamed.
*She* is my mother; my sisters are the Seasons;
My rising and my falling march with theirs.
Born thus, I ask to be no other man
Than that I am, and *will know who I am.*

    CHORUS. If my prophetic eye fails not, tomorrow's moon
Makes known to all the earth
The secret of our master's birth.
Cithaeron's name shall fill
Our song; his father, mother, nurse was she,    950
And for this boon
To our great King, praised shall Cithaeron be.
Phoebus our Lord, be this according to thy will.

    Was this the offspring born of some primeval sprite
By the love-glance beguiled
Of mountain-haunting Pan? Or child
Of Loxias, very son
To our bright God who walks the high grass-lands?

Did he delight
Cyllene's lord? Did Dionysus' hands                                          960
Receive him from a nymph he loved on Helicon?
  OEDIPUS. Elders, I think I see our shepherd approaching.
I guess it is he, though I never set eyes on him.
He and our Corinthian friend are of like age.
And those are my men that bring him. It must be he.
But you could tell more surely, if you know him.
  CHORUS. Yes, it is he. I know him. Laius' shepherd —
As good a man as any in his service.

*Enter an elderly* SHEPHERD, *escorted by attendants.*

  OEDIPUS. Now, good Corinthian, your evidence first —
Is this the man you spoke of?
  MESSENGER.                This is the man.                          970
  OEDIPUS. Come now, old shepherd — please to look at me,
And answer my questions. Were you in Laius' service?
  SHEPHERD. Indeed I was, sir; born and bred, not bought.
  OEDIPUS. What trade or occupation did you follow?
  SHEPHERD. The most part of my life a shepherd, sir.
  OEDIPUS. What part of the country did you mostly work?
  SHEPHERD. 'Twould be . . . Cithaeron — or somewhere thereabouts.
  OEDIPUS. Do you remember having seen this man before?
  SHEPHERD. What man is that, sir? Where would I have seen him?
  OEDIPUS. This man. Did you ever meet him anywhere?              980
  SHEPHERD. I cannot say I did, sir — not to remember.
  MESSENGER. I am not surprised. I'll jog his memory.
He won't forget the days when he and I
Were neighbours on Cithaeron — he with two flocks
And I with one; three seasons we were there
From spring to autumn; and I would drive my flock
Back Corinth way for winter, and he to Thebes
To Laius' folds. Was that the way it was?
  SHEPHERD. Ay, that's how it was. 'Tis many years ago.
  MESSENGER. Well then, maybe you remember a baby boy              990
You gave me, and asked me to rear it as my own?
  SHEPHERD. [*With frightened eyes*] What do you mean?
What are you asking me to say?
  MESSENGER. Why, my old friend, *here* stands your baby boy!
  SHEPHERD. Damn you, man, hold your tongue!
  OEDIPUS. Come, come, old fellow;
He speaks more honestly than you, I think.
  SHEPHERD. Why, how have I offended, honourable master?
  OEDIPUS. Not answering straightly his question about that child.
  SHEPHERD. He doesn't know what he is saying. He is making a mistake. 1000
  OEDIPUS. If you won't speak willingly, we must make you speak.
  SHEPHERD. Don't hurt an old man, sir, for the love of God!
  OEDIPUS. Pinion his arms, there!
  SHEPHERD.              O sir, why, what is this?
What more do you ask to know?
  OEDIPUS.            This child he speaks of —
Was it you that gave it to him?
  SHEPHERD.          Yes, it was.
I wish I might have died that very day.
  OEDIPUS. As you shall now, unless you tell the truth.

SHEPHERD. 'Twill be my death to tell it.

OEDIPUS. Evasion still!

SHEPHERD. Have I not said I gave it him? What more?

OEDIPUS. Where did it come from? Your home or another's? 1010

SHEPHERD. Not mine. Another man's.

OEDIPUS. What man? What house?

SHEPHERD. By all the gods, master, ask me no more!

OEDIPUS. Answer! If I must speak again, you die!

SHEPHERD. It was . . . a child of Laius' house.

OEDIPUS. A slave?
Or of his own begetting?

SHEPHERD. Must I tell?

OEDIPUS. You must. And I must hear.

SHEPHERD. It was his child,
They said. Your lady could tell the truth of it.

OEDIPUS. *She* gave it you?

SHEPHERD. Yes, master.

OEDIPUS. To what purpose?

SHEPHERD. To be destroyed.

OEDIPUS. The child she bore!

SHEPHERD. Yes, master. 1020
They said 'twas on account of some wicked spell.

OEDIPUS. What spell?

SHEPHERD. Saying the child should kill his father.

OEDIPUS. In God's name, what made you give it to this man?

SHEPHERD. I hadn't the heart to destroy it, master. I thought
'He will take it away to another country, his home'.
He took it and saved its life — to come to this!
If you are the man, O then your life is lost!

OEDIPUS. Alas! All out! All known, no more concealment!
O Light! May I never look on you again,
Revealed as I am, sinful in my begetting, 1030
Sinful in marriage, sinful in shedding of blood!

[*Exit. The* MESSENGER *and* SHEPHERD *depart.*

CHORUS. All the generations of mortal man add up to nothing!
Show me the man whose happiness was anything more than illusion
Followed by disillusion.
Here is the instance, here is Oedipus, here is the reason
Why I will call no mortal creature happy.

With what supreme sureness of aim he winged his quarry;
Grasped every prize, by Zeus! once he had drowned the She-devil,
The Claw-foot Lady.
He was our bastion against disaster, our honoured King; 1040
All Thebes was proud of the majesty of his name.

And now, where is a more heart-rending story of affliction?
Where a more awful swerve into the arms of torment?
O Oedipus, that proud head!
When the same bosom enfolded the son and the father,
Could not the engendering clay have shouted aloud its indignation?

Time sees all; and now he has found you, when you least expected it;
Has found you and judged that marriage-mockery, bridegroom-son!
This is your elegy:
I wish I had never seen you, offspring of Laius, 1050
Yesterday my morning of light, now my night of endless darkness!

*Enter an* ATTENDANT *from the palace.*

ATTENDANT. O you most honourable lords of the city of Thebes,
Weep for the things you shall hear, the things you must see,
If you are true sons and loyal to the house of Labdacus.
Not all the waters of Ister, the waters of Phasis,
Can wash this dwelling clean of the foulness within,
Clean of the deliberate acts that soon shall be known,
Of all horrible acts most horrible, wilfully chosen.
  CHORUS. Already we have wept enough for the things we have known,
The things we have seen. What more will your story add?       1060
  ATTENDANT. First, and in brief — Her Majesty is dead.
  CHORUS. Alas, poor soul: what brought her to this end?
  ATTENDANT. Her own hand did it. You that have not seen,
And shall not see, this worst, shall suffer the less.
But I that saw, will remember, and will tell what I remember
Of her last agony.
  You saw her cross the threshold
In desperate passion. Straight to her bridal-bed
She hurried, fastening her fingers in her hair.
There in her chamber, the doors flung sharply to,       1070
She cried aloud to Laius long since dead,
Remembering the son she bore long since, the son
By whom the sire was slain, the son to whom
The mother bore yet other children, fruit
Of luckless misbegetting. There she bewailed
The twice confounded issue of her wifehood —
Husband begotten of husband, child of child.
So much we heard. Her death was hidden from us.
Before we could see out her tragedy,
The King broke in with piercing cries, and all       1080
Had eyes only for him. This way and that
He strode among us. 'A sword, a sword!' he cried;
'Where is that wife, no wife of mine — that soil
Where I was sown, and whence I reaped my harvest!'
While thus he raved, some demon guided him —
For none of us dared speak — to where she was.
As if in answer to some leader's call
With wild hallooing cries he hurled himself
Upon the locked doors, bending by main force
The bolts out of their sockets — and stumbled in.       1090
  We saw a knotted pendulum, a noose,
A strangled woman swinging before our eyes.
  The King saw too, and with heart-rending groans
Untied the rope, and laid her on the ground.
But worse was yet to see. Her dress was pinned
With golden brooches, which the King snatched out
And thrust, from full arm's length, into his eyes —
Eyes that should see no longer his shame, his guilt,
No longer see those they should never have seen,
Nor see, unseeing, those he had longed to see,       1100
Henceforth seeing nothing but night . . . To this wild tune
He pierced his eyeballs time and time again,
Till bloody tears ran down his beard — not drops
But in full spate a whole cascade descending

In drenching cataracts of scarlet rain.
   Thus two have sinned; and on two heads, not one —
On man and wife — falls mingled punishment.
Their old long happiness of former times
Was happiness earned with justice; but to-day
Calamity, death, ruin, tears, and shame,                1110
All ills that there are names for — all are here.
     CHORUS. And he — how is he now? Does he still suffer?
     ATTENDANT. He shouts for someone to unbar the doors,
And show all Thebes the father's murderer,
The mother's — shame forbids the unholy word.
Incontinently he will fly the country
To rid his house of the curse of his own lips;
But scarcely has the strength, poor sufferer,
And none to guide him. He cannot bear the pain.
As you shall see. The doors are opening.              1120
Yes, you shall see a sorry spectacle
That loathing cannot choose but pity . . .

   *Enter* OEDIPUS *blind.*

     CHORUS. Ah!
Horror beyond all bearing!
Foulest disfigurement
That ever I saw! O cruel,
Insensate agony!
What demon of destiny
With swift assault outstriding
Has ridden you down?                    1130
O tortured head!
I dare not see, I am hiding
My eyes, I cannot bear
What most I long to see;
And what I long to hear,
That most I dread.
     OEDIPUS. O agony!
Where am I? Is this my voice
That is borne on the air?
What fate has come to me?              1140
     CHORUS. Unspeakable to mortal ear,
Too terrible for eyes to see.
     OEDIPUS. O dark intolerable inescapable night
That has no day!
Cloud that no air can take away!
O and again
That piercing pain,
Torture in the flesh and in the soul's dark memory.
     CHORUS. It must be so; such suffering must needs be borne
Twice; once in the body and once in the soul.         1150
     OEDIPUS. Is that my true and ever-faithful friend
Still at my side?
Your hand shall be the blind man's guide.
Are you still near?
That voice I hear
Is yours, although your face I cannot see.

CHORUS. Those eyes — how could you do what you have done?
What evil power has driven you to this end?
OEDIPUS. Apollo, friends, Apollo
Has laid this agony upon me;                                          1160
Not by his hand; I did it.
What should I do with eyes
Where all is ugliness?
CHORUS. It cannot be denied.
OEDIPUS. Where is there any beauty
For me to see? Where loveliness
Of sight or sound? Away!
Lead me quickly away
Out of this land. I am lost,
Hated of gods, no man so damned.                                      1170
CHORUS. Twice-tormented; in the spirit, as in the flesh.
Would you had never lived to read this riddle.
OEDIPUS. Cursed be the benefactor
That loosed my feet and gave me life
For death; a poor exchange.
Death would have been a boon
To me and all of mine.
CHORUS. We could have wished it so.
OEDIPUS. Now, shedder of father's blood,
Husband of mother, is my name;                                        1180
Godless and child of shame,
Begetter of brother-sons;
What infamy remains
That is not spoken of Oedipus?
CHORUS. Yet to my thinking this act was ill-advised;
It would have been better to die than live in blindness.
OEDIPUS. I will not believe that this was not the best
That could have been done. Teach me no other lesson.
How could I meet my father beyond the grave
With seeing eyes; or my unhappy mother,                               1190
Against whom I have committed such heinous sin
As no mere death could pay for? Could I still love
To look at my children, begotten as they were begotten?
Could I want eyes to see that pretty sight?
To see the towers of Thebes, her holy images,
Which I, her noblest, most unhappy son
Have forbidden myself to see — having commanded
All men to cast away the offence, the unclean,
Whom the gods have declared accursed, the son of Laius,
And, having proved myself that branded man,                           1200
Could I want sight to face this people's stare?
No! Hearing neither! Had I any way
To dam that channel too, I would not rest
Till I had prisoned up this body of shame
In total blankness. For the mind to dwell
Beyond the reach of pain, were peace indeed.
Cithaeron! Foster-mother! Did you shelter me
For this? Could you not let me die that instant,
Instead of saving me to tell the world
How I was got? Corinth, and Polybus,                                  1210
My seeming home and parent, did you think

What foul corruption festered under the bloom
Of your adopted son's young loveliness? —
Now found all evil and of evil born.

   That silent crossroad in the forest clearing —
That copse beside the place where three roads met,
Whose soil I watered with my father's blood,
*My* blood — will they remember what they saw,
And what I came that way to Thebes to do?
Incestuous sin! Breeding where I was bred!        1220
Father, brother, and son; bride, wife, and mother;
Confounded in one monstrous matrimony!
All human filthiness in one crime compounded!
Unspeakable acts — I speak no more of them.
Hide me at once, for God's love, hide me away,
Away! Kill me! Drown me in the depths of the sea!
Take me!               [*The* CHORUS *shrink from his groping hands.*
For pity, touch me, and take me away!
Touch me, and have no fear. On no man else
But on me alone is the scourge of my punishment.      1230
   CHORUS. Creon comes here. On him will now depend,
In act and counsel, the answer to your desires.
He stands our sole protector in your stead.
   OEDIPUS. What can I say to him? What plea of mine
Can now have any justice in his eyes,
Whom I, as now is seen, have wronged so utterly?

   *Enter* CREON.

   CREON. Oedipus, I am not here to scoff at your fall,
Nor yet to reproach you for your past misdeeds.
   My friends, remember your respect for the Lord of Life,
The Sun above us — if not for the children of men.      1240
The unclean must not remain in the eye of day;
Nor earth nor air nor water may receive it.
Take him within; piety at least demands
That none but kinsmen should hear and see such suffering.
   OEDIPUS. I only ask one thing, my gentle friend,
Whose gentleness to such a one as I am
Was more than could be hoped for. One thing only —
For God's love — for your good, not mine —
   CREON.                    What thing,
So humbly begged?
   OEDIPUS.        Cast me away this instant
Out of this land, out of the sight of man.          1250
   CREON. Be sure it would have been done without delay,
But that I await instruction from the god.
   OEDIPUS. Is not his instruction already plain? The parricide,
The unclean one, was to die; and here he stands.
   CREON. It was so. Yet in the present turn of events
We need more certain guidance.
   OEDIPUS.            For my lost life?
Will you ask the god's direction for one so damned?
   CREON. Have you not found good cause to trust him?
   OEDIPUS.                           Yes.
Then I have only this to ask, of your goodness:
The funeral rites of her that lies within,          1260

Provide as you think fit. She is your sister,
And you will do rightly by her. As for me,
No longer let my living presence curse
This fatherland of mine, but let me go
And live upon the mountains — and die there.
Cithaeron! Name for ever linked with mine —
On Mount Cithaeron, which my parents chose
To be my deathbed, I will go and die
Obedient to their desires. And yet I know,
Not age, nor sickness, nor any common accident                    1270
Can end my life; I was not snatched from death
That once, unless to be preserved
For some more awful destiny. Be it so.
And the children . . . Don't trouble yourself about the boys,
Creon; they will be able to fend for themselves
Wherever they go. But the girls, poor little mites,
Have never known a meal without their father;
Everything was shared between us. Take care of them, Creon . . .
Creon . . . If I could touch them once, and weep . . .
Once more . . .                                                   1280
If you would permit it,
Gracious and generous . . .
Just touch them once, and I could think I had them
Once more before my eyes . . .
      [*The children,* ISMENE *and* ANTIGONE, *have already been led in, and stand*
                                          *before* OEDIPUS.

What! Do I hear my darlings sobbing?
Has Creon had pity, and sent them to me?
My darlings,
Are they here?
      CREON. They are here. I had them brought to you. I knew
How much you loved them — how you love them still.               1290
      OEDIPUS. Heaven bless you, Creon, for this, and make your way
Smoother than mine has been.
Where are you, children?
Come, feel your brother's hands. It was their work
That darkened these clear eyes — your father's eyes
As once you knew them, though he never saw
Nor knew what he did when he became your father.
They cannot see you; but they weep with you.
I think of your sorrowful life in the days to come,
When you must face the world: the holy days,                     1300
High days and days of state, joyless for you,
Returning sadly home while others play.
And when you look for marriage, will there be men,
Will there be one man brave enough to outface
The scandal that will cling to all my children
And children's children? Is there a name of ill
That is not ours? A father that killed his father;
Despoiled his birth-bed; begetting where he was begot;
Thus they will brand you. Where will you then find husbands?
There will be none, my children, for you; your days               1310
Can only end in fruitless maidenhood.
      Menoeceus' son, you are their kinsman still;
You are their only father; we are no more,

Who gave them life. These lost waifs must not wander
Homeless and husbandless; they must not see
Such days as I shall see. Take care of them,
So young, so poor, so lost to all but you.
You will do it? . . . Your hand to pledge your promise.
[CREON *gives his hand*] Friend!
   Children, there is much that you will understand         1320
When you are older; you cannot bear it now.
But in your prayers ask this: that you may live
Not more nor less than well, and so live better
Than did your father.
    CREON.          This is enough. Will you go in?
    OEDIPUS. I must; against my will.
    CREON. There is a measure in all things.
    OEDIPUS. I have your promise, then?
    CREON.              What promise?
    OEDIPUS. To send me away.
    CREON.          God will decide, not I.
    OEDIPUS. No god will speak for me.
    CREON.         Then you will have your wish.
    OEDIPUS. And your consent?
    CREON.       I do not speak beyond my knowledge.    1330
    OEDIPUS. [*Satisfied, but reluctantly*] Take me.
    CREON. Go then. [OEDIPUS *moves towards the palace, his arms still round
    the children.*] But leave the children.
    OEDIPUS. No! Never take them from me!
    CREON. Command no more. Obey. Your rule is ended.
                                [OEDIPUS *is led away.*
    CHORUS. Sons and daughters of Thebes, behold: this was Oedipus,
Greatest of men; he held the key to the deepest mysteries;
Was envied by all his fellow-men for his great prosperity;
Behold, what a full tide of misfortune swept over his head.
Then learn that mortal man must always look to his ending,
And none can be called happy until that day when he carries    1340
His happiness down to the grave in peace.              [*Exeunt.*

---

### FOR DISCUSSION AND WRITING

    *The tragic fall is, of course, in the common reading of Aristotle, based
upon the hero's possession of a tragic flaw; and whether as doctrine or habit,
the attempt to find a tragic flaw in Greek plays seems to me a persistent
stumbling-block. If you really look at the* Oedipus, *for instance, it is immediately clear that Oedipus' tragic flaw is hard to discover: one wants to
know — if you begin with the Aristotelian habit — just what in the hero's
nature or his acts makes him suffer as hideously as he does, and the
obvious answers — his anger, his treatment of Creon and Teiresias, his attempt to avoid his fate — are all unsatisfactory, or if satisfactory, indict the
gods that could afflict a man so grievously for such offense. One recent critic
of the play, an Aristotelian by conviction as well as habit, recognized this
dilemma immediately and proceeded to solve it by the suggestion that*

*Sophocles in this play has generalized* hamartia *into something like original sin: Oedipus has no particular flaws but suffers in the very flaw of his humanity. I suspect that very few classicists, whatever their religious color, will be happy with this /50/ theory, and I hope that even Aristotelians might object. But I use it to illustrate the kind of trouble that the expectation of a tragic flaw can create even in the treatment of a play which Aristotle regarded as the paradigm of his theories.*

*I cannot myself pretend to understand that mysterious play, but I wonder if we are perhaps not the better off for proceeding from the play rather than from Aristotle. Freed from our own a prioris, the experience of the play may at least propose itself in different terms. Thus it has always seemed to me that the single most pertinent fact of the* Oedipus *was not the hero's flaw, but his refusal to accept a ready-made fate: he wants his own fate, not the gods', and though his personal fate may be cut short by his doom, Oedipus at the close of the play insists upon distinguishing his own responsibility by blinding himself. It is the magnificence of his own declaration of responsibility that makes him so heroic: his fate is his and no one else's. His anger is anger, neither more nor less; it is not the source of his doom, but the irritant that he exhibits on the road to doom; and if he has a hamartia, it is not sin or flaw but the ungovernable tragic ignorance of all men: we do not know who we are nor who fathered us but go, blinded by life and hope, toward a wisdom bitter as the gates of hell. The cost of action is suffering, and heroism is the anguished acceptance of our own identities and natures, forged in action and pain in a world we never made. Whatever the final merits of this suggestion, it at least, I think, preserves the dignity of human passion in the play without violating in the name of a crude automatic justice the mysterious destiny that rules the play.*

*From William Arrowsmith, "The Criticism of Greek Tragedy,"*
Tulane Drama Review, *March 1959, pp. 50-51.*

1) Arrowsmith doubts the value of approaching *King Oedipus* in terms of the tragic flaw. He argues that the "most pertinent fact" is Oedipus' "refusal to accept a ready-made fate: he wants his own fate, not the gods'." Does Arrowsmith's argument tend to enhance the universality of the tragedy? Is there any way in which we can retain a more or less conventional view of the tragic flaw and yet make use of Arrowsmith's insights?

2) Aristotle treats *King Oedipus* as the key model of Greek tragedy. Briefly summarize the various qualities and elements he praises, paying special attention to what he says of "recognition" and "reversal."

3) To what extent is our appreciation of Oedipus as a tragic hero heightened by recurrences of "dramatic irony," by means of which we know more of his background and destiny than he does?

4) Perhaps more than any other drama in world literature, *King Oedipus* illustrates the truth of the idea voiced by Sir Philip Sidney, among others, that tragedy "teacheth the uncertainty of the world." Does this idea contradict the concept that the experience presented in *Oedipus* (and in tragedy generally) also implies an ordered, intelligible universe?

5) What specific evidence from *Oedipus* supports Alexander's contention that the doctrine of the tragic flaw is inappropriate to an interpretation of Sophocles' tragic view and that the play, like the book of *Job*, "is an affirmation of a faith in righteousness" (p. 57 ff.)?

6) Alexander also argues (against Bradley) that tragedy "takes its character and significance not from faults [tragic flaws] but from virtue" (p. 54). Does it seem possible to argue (on the basis of Alexander's terms) that tragedy takes

on its significance from the triumph of the manifestation of heroism in the doomed protagonist — whether or not the heroism be rooted in reasonable virtue? Is this the case in *Oedipus*?

7) The pride of Oedipus grows out of his assumption that he has mastered, through knowledge, the curse of Thebes. We are thus necessarily faced with several questions: What is there wrong in Oedipus' desire for rational explanation? Where does he overstep the bounds of a proper will to know? Is the heart of the tragedy the fact that such a will to know leads to self-knowledge, including the acceptance of responsibility for too much pride? If so, is not the heart of the tragedy also the heart of the triumph, as Oedipus unflinchingly accepts these implications? (For later discussion: Is the wisdom gained by Oedipus through suffering analogous to the late wisdom attained by Lear?)

8) Is there any serious conflict between Oedipus as man-who-must-know and Oedipus as ritualized sacrifice, or Theban Scapegoat? (*See* Murray.)

9) Aristotle says: "But most important of all is the structure of the incidents. For Tragedy is an imitation, not of men, but of action and of life, and life consists in action, and its end is a mode of action, not a quality." Can Oedipus' quest for knowledge be spoken of as the *action* of this play? Is the end of the play justifiably called a "mode of action"? Explain.

❋

WILLIAM

# SHAKESPEARE

## King Lear

---

| | |
|---|---|
| *Characters:* | LEAR, king of Britain |
| | KING OF FRANCE |
| | DUKE OF BURGUNDY |
| | DUKE OF CORNWALL |
| | DUKE OF ALBANY |
| | EARL OF KENT |
| | EARL OF GLOUCESTER |
| | EDGAR, son to Gloucester |
| | EDMUND, bastard son to Gloucester |
| | CURAN, a courtier |
| | OLD MAN, tenant to Gloucester |
| | DOCTOR |
| | FOOL |
| | OSWALD, steward to Goneril |
| | A Captain employed by Edmund |
| | Gentleman attendant on Cordelia |
| | A Herald |
| | Servants to Cornwall |
| | GONERIL, ⎫ |
| | REGAN, ⎬ daughters to Lear |
| | CORDELIA, ⎭ |
| | Knights of Lear's train, captains, messengers, soldiers, and attendants |

*Scene:* Britain.

King Lear, *reprinted from ed. Hardin Craig,* An Introduction to Shakespeare *(Chicago: Scott, Foresman and Company, 1952). The play was written in 1605.*
   *The lineation of this text is that of the standard Globe edition. The present editors have retained the most helpful of Professor Craig's notes, but the student may occasionally need to consult a dictionary for obsolete or archaic definitions.*

# ACT I

SCENE I: KING LEAR'S *palace.*

*Enter* KENT, GLOUCESTER, *and* EDMUND.

KENT. I thought the king had more affected the Duke of Albany than Cornwall.

GLOU. It did always seem so to us: but now, in the division of the king-dom, it appears not which of the dukes he values most; for equalities are so weighed, that curiosity in neither can make choice of either's moiety.

KENT. Is not this your son, my lord?

GLOU. His breeding, sir, hath been at my charge: I have so often blushed to acknowledge him, that now I am brazed to it.  11

KENT. I cannot conceive you.

GLOU. Sir, this young fellow's mother could: whereupon she grew round-wombed, and had, indeed, sir, a son for her cradle ere she had a husband for her bed. Do you smell a fault?

KENT. I cannot wish the fault undone, the issue of it being so proper.  18

GLOU. But I have, sir, a son by order of law, some year elder than this, who yet is no dearer in my account: though this knave came something saucily into the world before he was sent for, yet was his mother fair; there was good sport at his making, and the whoreson must be acknowl-edged. Do you know this noble gentleman, Edmund?

EDM. No, my lord.

GLOU. My lord of Kent: remember him hereafter as my honourable friend.

EDM. My services to your lordship.  30

KENT. I must love you, and sue to know you better.

EDM. Sir, I shall study deserving.

GLOU. He hath been out nine years, and away he shall again. The king is coming.

*Sennet. Enter* KING LEAR, CORNWALL, ALBANY, GONERIL, REGAN,
  CORDELIA, *and Attendants.*

LEAR. Attend the lords of France and Burgundy, Gloucester.

GLOU. I shall, my liege.       [*Exeunt* GLOUCESTER *and* EDMUND.

LEAR. Meantime we shall express our darker purpose.
Give me the map there. Know that we have divided
In three our kingdom: and 'tis our fast intent
To shake all cares and business from our age;  40
Conferring them on younger strengths, while we
Unburthen'd crawl toward death. Our son of Cornwall,
And you, our no less loving son of Albany,
We have this hour a constant will to publish
Our daughters' several dowers, that future strife
May be prevented now. The princes, France and Burgundy,
Great rivals in our youngest daughter's love,
Long in our court have made their amorous sojourn,
And here are to be answer'd. Tell me, my daughters, —
Since now we will divest us, both of rule,  50
Interest of territory, cares of state, —
Which of you shall we say doth love us most?
That we our largest bounty may extend

*Act I. Scene i.* 11. **brazed,** *hardened.*

Where nature doth with merit challenge. Goneril,
Our eldest-born, speak first.

    GON. Sir, I love you more than words can wield the matter;
Dearer than eye-sight, space, and liberty;
Beyond what can be valued, rich or rare;
No less than life, with grace, health, beauty, honour;
As much as child e'er loved, or father found;            60
A love that makes breath poor, and speech unable;
Beyond all manner of so much I love you.

    COR. [*Aside*] What shall Cordelia do? Love, and be silent.

    LEAR. Of all these bounds, even from this line to this,
With shadowy forests and with champains rich'd,
With plenteous rivers and wide-skirted meads,
We make thee lady: to thine and Albany's issue
Be this perpetual. What says our second daughter,
Our dearest Regan, wife to Cornwall? Speak.

    REG. Sir, I am made            70
Of the self-same metal that my sister is,
And prize me at her worth. In my true heart
I find she names my very deed of love;
Only she comes too short: that I profess
Myself an enemy to all other joys,
Which the most precious square of sense possesses;
And find I am alone felicitate
In your dear highness' love.

    COR.          [*Aside*] Then poor Cordelia!
And yet not so; since, I am sure, my love's
More richer than my tongue.            80

    LEAR. To thee and thine hereditary ever
Remain this ample third of our fair kingdom;
No less in space, validity, and pleasure,
Than that conferr'd on Goneril. Now, our joy,
Although the last, not least; to whose young love
The vines of France and milk of Burgundy
Strive to be interess'd; what can you say to draw
A third more opulent than your sisters? Speak.

    COR. Nothing, my lord.

    LEAR. Nothing!           90

    COR. Nothing.

    LEAR. Nothing will come of nothing: speak again.

    COR. Unhappy that I am, I cannot heave
My heart into my mouth: I love your majesty
According to my bond; nor more nor less.

    LEAR. How, how, Cordelia! mend your speech a little,
Lest it may mar your fortunes.

    COR.          Good my lord,
You have begot me, bred me, loved me: I
Return those duties back as are right fit,
Obey you, love you, and most honour you.          100
Why have my sisters husbands, if they say
They love you all? Haply, when I shall wed,

---

54. **Where ... challenge,** *where both natural affection and merit claim it as due.*  76. **square of
sense,** *reference to the psychological diagram of the mental powers in the form of a square whose
sides are sense, appetite, motion, and judgment.*  87. **to be interess'd,** *to a right in.*

That lord whose hand must take my plight shall carry
Half my love with him, half my care and duty:
Sure, I shall never marry like my sisters,
To love my father all.
    LEAR. But goes thy heart with this?
    COR.                  Ay, good my lord.
    LEAR. So young, and so untender?
    COR. So young, my lord, and true.
    LEAR. Let it be so; thy truth, then, be thy dower.     110
For, by the sacred radiance of the sun,
The mysteries of Hecate, and the night;
By all the operation of the orbs
From whom we do exist, and cease to be;
Here I disclaim all my paternal care,
Propinquity and property of blood,
And as a stranger to my heart and me
Hold thee, from this, for ever. The barbarous Scythian,
Or he that makes his generation messes
To gorge his appetite, shall to my bosom     120
Be as well neighbour'd, pitied, and relieved,
As thou my sometime daughter.
    KENT.              Good my liege, —
    LEAR. Peace, Kent!
Come not between the dragon and his wrath.
I loved her most, and thought to set my rest
On her kind nursery. Hence, and avoid my sight!
So be my grave my peace, as here I give
Her father's heart from her! Call France; who stirs?
Call Burgundy. Cornwall and Albany,
With my two daughters' dowers digest this third:     130
Let pride, which she calls plainness, marry her.
I do invest you jointly with my power,
Pre-eminence, and all the large effects
That troop with majesty. Ourself, by monthly course,
With reservation of an hundred knights,
By you to be sustain'd, shall our abode
Make with you by due turns. Only we still retain
The name, and all the additions to a king;
The sway, revenue, execution of the rest,
Beloved sons, be yours: which to confirm,     140
This coronet part betwixt you.     [*Giving the crown.*
    KENT.            Royal Lear,
Whom I have ever honour'd as my king,
Loved as my father, as my master follow'd,
As my great patron thought on in my prayers, —
    LEAR. The bow is bent and drawn, make from the shaft.
    KENT. Let it fall rather, though the fork invade
The region of my heart: be Kent unmannerly,
When Lear is mad. What wilt thou do, old man?
Think'st thou that duty shall have dread to speak,
When power to flattery bows? To plainness honour's bound,     150
When majesty stoops to folly. Reverse thy doom;

125. **set my rest,** *repose myself.*   126. **nursery,** *nursing.*   145. **make from,** *get out of the way of.*
150-151. **To ... folly.** *Allegiance demands frankness when kingship stoops to folly.*

And in thy best consideration, check
This hideous rashness: answer my life my judgement,
Thy youngest daughter does not love thee least;
Nor are those empty-hearted whose low sound
Reverbs no hollowness.
  LEAR.                  Kent, on thy life, no more.
  KENT. My life I never held but as a pawn
To wage against thy enemies; nor fear to lose it,
Thy safety being the motive.
  LEAR.                          Out of my sight!
  KENT. See better, Lear; and let me still remain          160
The true blank of thine eye.
  LEAR. Now, by Apollo, —
  KENT.                    Now, by Apollo, king,
Thou swear'st thy gods in vain.
  LEAR.                          O, vassal! miscreant!
                          [*Laying his hand on his sword.*

  ALB.  ⎱ Dear sir, forbear.
  CORN. ⎰
  KENT. Do;
Kill thy physician, and the fee bestow
Upon thy foul disease. Revoke thy doom;
Or, whilst I can vent clamour from my throat,
I'll tell thee thou dost evil.
  LEAR.                  Hear me, recreant!
On thine allegiance, hear me!                              170
Since thou hast sought to make us break our vow,
Which we durst never yet, and with strain'd pride
To come between our sentence and our power,
Which nor our nature nor our place can bear,
Our potency made good, take thy reward.
Five days we do allot thee, for provision
To shield thee from diseases of the world;
And on the sixth to turn thy hated back
Upon our kingdom: if, on the tenth day following,
Thy banish'd trunk be found in our dominions,            180
The moment is thy death. Away! by Jupiter,
This shall not be revoked.
  KENT. Fare thee well, king: sith thus thou wilt appear,
Freedom lives hence, and banishment is here.
[*To* CORDELIA] The gods to their dear shelter take thee, maid,
That justly think'st, and hast most rightly said!
[*To* REGAN *and* GONERIL] And your large speeches may your deeds approve,
That good effects may spring from words of love.
Thus Kent, O princes, bids you all adieu;
He'll shape his old course in a country new.         [*Exit.* 190

  *Flourish. Re-enter* GLOUCESTER, *with* FRANCE, BURGUNDY, *and Attendants.*

  GLOU. Here 's France and Burgundy, my noble lord.
  LEAR. My lord of Burgundy,
We first address towards you, who with this king
Hath rivall'd for our daughter: what, in the least,

---

172. **strain'd,** *excessive.*   175. **Our potency made good,** *our authority being maintained.*

Will you require in present dower with her,
Or cease your quest of love?
    BUR.                    Most royal majesty,
I crave no more than what your highness offer'd,
Nor will you tender less.
    LEAR.              Right noble Burgundy,
When she was dear to us, we did hold her so;
But now her price is fall'n. Sir, there she stands:         200
If aught within that little seeming substance,
Or all of it, with our displeasure pieced,
And nothing more, may fitly like your grace,
She 's there, and she is yours.
    BUR.              I know no answer.
    LEAR. Will you, with those infirmities she owes,
Unfriended, new-adopted to our hate,
Dower'd with our curse, and stranger'd with our oath,
Take her, or leave her?
    BUR.             Pardon me, royal sir;
Election makes not up on such conditions.
    LEAR. Then leave her, sir; for, by the power that made me,    210
I tell you all her wealth. [*To France*] For you, great king,
I would not from your love make such a stray,
To match you where I hate; therefore beseech you
To avert your liking a more worthier way
Than on a wretch whom nature is ashamed
Almost to acknowledge hers.
    FRANCE.          This is most strange,
That she, that even but now was your best object,
The argument of your praise, balm of your age,
Most best, most dearest, should in this trice of time
Commit a thing so monstrous, to dismantle         220
So many folds of favour. Sure, her offence
Must be of such unnatural degree,
That monsters it, or your fore-vouch'd affection
Fall'n into taint: which to believe of her,
Must be a faith that reason without miracle
Could never plant in me.
    COR.          I yet beseech your majesty, —
If for I want that glib and oily art,
To speak and purpose not; since what I well intend,
I'll do 't before I speak, — that you make known
It is no vicious blot, murder, or foulness,         230
No unchaste action, or dishonour'd step,
That hath deprived me of your grace and favour;
But even for want of that for which I am richer,
A still-soliciting eye, and such a tongue
As I am glad I have not, though not to have it
Hath lost me in your liking.
    LEAR.          Better thou
Hadst not been born than not to have pleased me better.
    FRANCE. Is it but this, — a tardiness in nature
Which often leaves the history unspoke
That it intends to do? My lord of Burgundy,         240

209. **Election . . . up,** *choice comes to no decision.*

What say you to the lady? Love's not love
When it is mingled with regards that stand
Aloof from the entire point. Will you have her?
She is herself a dowry.
    BUR.                    Royal Lear,
Give but that portion which yourself proposed,
And here I take Cordelia by the hand,
Duchess of Burgundy.
    LEAR. Nothing: I have sworn; I am firm.
    BUR. I am sorry, then, you have so lost a father
That you must lose a husband.
    COR.                Peace be with Burgundy!      250
Since that respects of fortune are his love,
I shall not be his wife.
    FRANCE. Fairest Cordelia, that art most rich, being poor;
Most choice, forsaken; and most loved, despised!
Thee and thy virtues here I seize upon:
Be it lawful I take up what 's cast away.
Gods, gods! 'tis strange that from their cold'st neglect
My love should kindle to inflamed respect.
Thy dowerless daughter, king, thrown to my chance,
Is queen of us, of ours, and our fair France:      260
Not all the dukes of waterish Burgundy
Can buy this unprized precious maid of me.
Bid them farewell, Cordelia, though unkind:
Thou losest here, a better where to find.
    LEAR. Thou hast her, France: let her be thine, for we
Have no such daughter, nor shall ever see
That face of hers again. Therefore be gone
Without our grace, our love, our benison.
Come, noble Burgundy.
         [*Flourish. Exeunt all but* FRANCE, GONERIL, REGAN, *and* CORDELIA.
    FRANCE. Bid farewell to your sisters.      270
    COR. The jewels of our father, with wash'd eyes
Cordelia leaves you: I know you what you are;
And like a sister am most loath to call
Your faults as they are named. Use well our father:
To your professed bosoms I commit him:
But yet, alas, stood I within his grace,
I would prefer him to a better place.
So, farewell to you both.
    REG. Prescribe not us our duties.
    GON.                  Let your study
Be to content your lord, who hath received you      280
At fortune's alms. You have obedience scanted,
And well are worth the want that you have wanted.
    COR. Time shall unfold what plaited cunning hides:
Who cover faults, at last shame them derides.
Well may you prosper!
    FRANCE.            Come, my fair Cordelia.
         [*Exeunt* FRANCE *and* CORDELIA.
    GON. Sister, it is not a little I have to say of what most nearly appertains
to us both. I think our father will hence to-night.

---

282. **well ... wanted,** *well deserve the lack of affection which you yourself have shown.*

REG. That's most certain, and with you; next month with us.                    290

GON. You see how full of changes his age is; the observation we have made of it hath not been little: he always loved our sister most; and with what poor judgement he hath now cast her off appears too grossly.

REG. 'Tis the infirmity of his age: yet he hath ever but slenderly known himself.                                                                            297

GON. The best and soundest of his time hath been but rash; then must we look to receive from his age, not alone the imperfections of long-engraffed condition, but therewithal the unruly waywardness that infirm and choleric years bring with them.

REG. Such unconstant starts are we like to have from him as this of Kent's banishment.

GON. There is further compliment of leave-taking between France and him. Pray you, let's hit together: if our father carry authority with such dispositions as he bears, this last surrender of his will but offend us.      310

REG. We shall further think on 't.

GON. We must do something, and i' the heat.                      [*Exeunt.*

SCENE II: *The* EARL OF GLOUCESTER'S *castle.*

*Enter* EDMUND, *with a letter.*

EDM. Thou, nature, art my goddess; to thy law
My services are bound. Wherefore should I
Stand in the plague of custom, and permit
The curiosity of nations to deprive me,
For that I am some twelve or fourteen moonshines
Lag of a brother? Why bastard? wherefore base?                            10
When my dimensions are as well compact,
My mind as generous, and my shape as true,
As honest madam's issue? Why brand they us
With base? with baseness? bastardy? base, base?
Who, in the lusty stealth of nature, take
More composition and fierce quality
Than doth, within a dull, stale, tired bed,
Go to the creating a whole tribe of fops,
Got 'tween asleep and wake? Well, then,
Legitimate Edgar, I must have your land:
Our father's love is to the bastard Edmund
As to the legitimate: fine word, — legitimate!
Well, my legitimate, if this letter speed,
And my invention thrive, Edmund the base                                 20
Shall top the legitimate. I grow; I prosper:
Now, gods, stand up for bastards!

*Enter* GLOUCESTER.

GLOU. Kent banish'd thus! and France in choler parted!
And the king gone to-night! subscribed his power!

---

301. **long-engraffed condition,** *long-implanted habit. Goneril's case against Lear, which seems in this explanatory scene to be Shakespeare's, is (1) that "he hath ever but slenderly known himself" (self-knowledge was a Renaissance ideal), (2) that he has the infirmity of old age, and (3) that he is habituated to self-indulgence.*

*Scene ii.* 1. **nature,** *natural force; also, course of life undisciplined by culture.* 3. **plague,** *vexatious injustice.* 11. **lusty . . . nature.** *Edmund and all bastards, being born outside the pale of law and owing their origin to untrammeled nature, were thought to be of necessity in rebellion against the ordinances of society. Therefore Edmund appeals to nature to assist him in his warfare.*

Confined to exhibition! All this done
Upon the gad! Edmund, how now! what news?

EDM. So please your lordship, none.     [*Putting up the letter.*

GLOU. Why so earnestly seek you to put up that letter?

EDM. I know no news, my lord.

GLOU. What paper were you reading?     30

EDM. Nothing, my lord.

GLOU. No? What needed, then, that terrible dispatch of it into your pocket? the quality of nothing hath not such need to hide itself. Let's see: come, if it be nothing, I shall not need spectacles.

EDM. I beseech you, sir, pardon me: it is a letter from my brother, that I have not all o'er-read; and for so much as I have perused, I find it not fit for your o'er-looking.     40

GLOU. Give me the letter, sir.

EDM. I shall offend, either to detain or give it. The contents, as in part I understand them, are to blame.

GLOU. Let's see, let's see.

EDM. I hope, for my brother's justification, he wrote this but as an essay or taste of my virtue.

GLOU. [*Reads*] 'This policy and reverence of age makes the world bitter to the best of our times; keeps our fortunes from us till our oldness cannot relish them. I begin to find an idle and fond bondage in the oppression of aged tyranny; who sways, not as it hath power, but as it is suffered. Come to me, that of this I may speak more. If our father would sleep till I waked him, you should enjoy half his revenue for ever, and live the beloved of your brother,

        EDGAR.'

Hum—conspiracy! — 'Sleep till I waked him, — you should enjoy half his revenue,' — My son Edgar! Had he a hand to write this? a heart and brain to breed it in? — When came this to you? who brought it?     62

EDM. It was not brought me, my lord; there's the cunning of it; I found it thrown in at the casement of my closet.

GLOU. You know the character to be your brother's?

EDM. If the matter were good, my lord, I durst swear it were his; but, in respect of that, I would fain think it were not.     70

GLOU. It is his.

EDM. It is his hand, my lord; but I hope his heart is not in the contents.

GLOU. Hath he never heretofore sounded you in this business?

EDM. Never, my lord: but I have heard him oft maintain it to be fit, that, sons at perfect age, and fathers declining, the father should be as ward to the son, and the son manage his revenue.     79

GLOU. O villain, villain! His very opinion in the letter! Abhorred villain! Unnatural, detested, brutish villain! worse than brutish! Go, sirrah, seek him; I'll apprehend him: abominable villain! Where is he?

EDM. I do not well know, my lord. If it shall please you to suspend your indignation against my brother till you can derive from him better testimony of his intent, you shall run a certain course; where, if you violently proceed against him, mistaking his purpose, it would make a great gap in your own honour, and shake in pieces the heart of his obedience. I dare pawn down my life for him, that he hath wrote this to feel my affection to your honour, and to no further pretence of danger.     95

GLOU. Think you so?

EDM. If your honour judge it meet, I will place you where you shall hear us confer of this, and by an auricular assurance have your satisfaction; and that without any further delay than this very evening.     101

GLOU. He cannot be such a monster —

EDM. Nor is not, sure.

GLOU. To his father, that so tenderly and entirely loves him. Heaven and earth! Edmund, seek him out; wind me into him, I pray you: frame the business after your own wisdom. I would unstate myself, to be in a due resolution.

EDM. I will seek him, sir, presently; convey the business as I shall find means, and acquaint you withal. 111

GLOU. These late eclipses in the sun and moon portend no good to us: though the wisdom of nature can reason it thus and thus, yet nature finds itself scourged by the sequent effects: love cools, friendship falls off, brothers divide: in cities, mutinies; in countries, discord; in palaces, treason; and the bond cracked 'twixt son and father. This villain of mine comes under the prediction; there 's son against father: the king falls from bias of nature; there 's father against child. We have seen the best of our time: machinations, hollowness, treachery, and all ruinous disorders, follow us disquietly to our graves. Find out this villain, Edmund; it shall lose thee nothing; do it carefully. And the noble and true-hearted Kent banished! his offence, honesty! 'Tis strange. [*Exit.*

EDM. This is the excellent foppery of the world, that, when we are sick in fortune, — often the surfeit of our own behaviour, — we make guilty of our disasters the sun, the moon, and the stars: as if we were villains by necessity; fools by heavenly compulsion; knaves, thieves, and treachers, by spherical predominance; drunkards, liars, and adulterers, by an enforced obedience of planetary influence; and all that we are evil in, by a divine thrusting on: an admirable evasion of whoremaster man, to lay his goatish disposition to the charge of a star! My father compounded with my mother under the dragon's tail; and my nativity was under Ursa major; so that it follows, I am rough and lecherous. Tut, I should have been that I am, had the maidenliest star in the firmament twinkled on my bastardizing. Edgar —

*Enter* EDGAR.

and pat he comes like the catastrophe of the old comedy: my cue is villanous melancholy, with a sigh like Tom o' Bedlam. O, these eclipses do portend these divisions! fa, sol, la, mi.

EDG. How now, brother Edmund! what serious contemplation are you in? 151

EDM. I am thinking, brother, of a prediction I read this other day, what should follow these eclipses.

EDG. Do you busy yourself about that?

EDM. I promise you, the effects he writes of succeed unhappily; as of unnaturalness between the child and the parent; death, dearth, dissolutions of ancient amities; divisions in state, menaces and maledictions against king and nobles; needless diffidences, banishment of friends, dissipation of cohorts, nuptial breaches, and I know not what. 163

EDG. How long have you been a sectary astronomical?

EDM. Come, come; when saw you my father last?

EDG. Why, the night gone by.

EDM. Spake you with him?

EDG. Ay, two hours together. 170

EDM. Parted you in good terms? Found you no displeasure in him by word or countenance?

---

106. **wind me into him,** *insinuate yourself into his confidence;* **me** *is an ethical dative.* 108. **unstate myself,** *give up my position and dignity.* 114. **wisdom of nature,** *natural science.* 120. **bias of nature,** *natural affections and promptings.* 148. **Tom o' Bedlam,** *called also "Bedlam beggars" and "Abraham men"; they were lunatic patients of Bethlehem Hospital turned out to beg for their bread.* 164. **sectary astronomical,** *student of astrology.*

EDG. None at all.

EDM. Bethink yourself wherein you may have offended him: and at my entreaty forbear his presence till some little time hath qualified the heat of his displeasure; which at this instant so rageth in him, that with the mischief of your person it would scarcely allay.

EDG. Some villain hath done me wrong. 180

EDM. That 's my fear. I pray you, have a continent forbearance till the speed of his rage goes slower; and, as I say, retire with me to my lodging, from whence I will fitly bring you to hear my lord speak: pray ye, go; there's my key: if you do stir abroad, go armed.

EDG. Armed, brother!

EDM. Brother, I advise you to the best; go armed: I am no honest man if there be any good meaning towards you: I have told you what I have seen and heard; but faintly, nothing like the image and horror of it: pray you, away.

EDG. Shall I hear from you anon?

EDM. I do serve you in this business.    [*Exit* EDGAR.

A credulous father! and a brother noble,
Whose nature is so far from doing harms,
That he suspects none; on whose foolish honesty
My practices ride easy! I see the business.
Let me, if not by birth, have lands by wit:
All with me 's meet that I can fashion fit.    [*Exit.* 200

SCENE III: *The* DUKE OF ALBANY'S *palace.*

*Enter* GONERIL, *and* OSWALD, *her steward.*

GON. Did my father strike my gentleman for chiding of his fool?
OSW. Yes, madam.
GON. By day and night he wrongs me; every hour
He flashes into one gross crime or other,
That sets us all at odds: I'll not endure it:
His knights grow riotous, and himself upbraids us
On every trifle. When he returns from hunting,
I will not speak with him; say I am sick:
If you come slack of former services,
You shall do well; the fault of it I'll answer. 10
OSW. He's coming, madam; I hear him.    [*Horns within.*
GON. Put on what weary negligence you please,
You and your fellows; I 'ld have it come to question:
If he dislike it, let him to our sister,
Whose mind and mine, I know, in that are one,
Not to be over-ruled. Idle old man,
That still would manage those authorities
That he hath given away! Now, by my life,
Old fools are babes again; and must be used
With checks as flatteries, — when they are seen abused. 20
Remember what I tell you.
OSW.               Well, madam.
GON. And let his knights have colder looks among you;
What grows of it, no matter; advise your fellows so:
I would breed from hence occasions, and I shall
That I may speak: I'll write straight to my sister,
To hold my very course. Prepare for dinner.    [*Exeunt.*

King Lear  *115*

SCENE IV: *A hall in the same.*

*Enter* KENT, *disguised.*

KENT. If but as well I other accents borrow,
That can my speech defuse, my good intent
May carry through itself to that full issue
For which I razed my likeness. Now, banish'd Kent,
If thou canst serve where thou dost stand condemn'd,
So may it come, thy master, whom thou lovest,
Shall find thee full of labours.

*Horns within. Enter* LEAR, *Knights, and Attendants.*

LEAR. Let me not stay a jot for dinner; go get it ready.
[*Exit an Attendant*] How now! what art thou?                    10
KENT. A man, sir.
LEAR. What dost thou profess? what wouldst thou with us?
KENT. I do profess to be no less than I seem; to serve him truly that will
put me in trust; to love him that is honest; to converse with him that is
wise, and says little; to fear judgement; to fight when I cannot choose;
and to eat no fish.
LEAR. What art thou?
KENT. A very honest-hearted fellow, and as poor as the king.          21
LEAR. If thou be as poor for a subject as he is for a king, thou art poor
enough. What wouldst thou?
KENT. Service.
LEAR. Who wouldst thou serve?
KENT. You.
LEAR. Dost thou know me, fellow?
KENT. No, sir; but you have that in your countenance which I would fain
call master.                                                          30
LEAR. What 's that?
KENT. Authority.
LEAR. What services canst thou do?
KENT. I can keep honest counsel, ride, run, mar a curious tale in telling
it, and deliver a plain message bluntly: that which ordinary men are fit for,
I am qualified in; and the best of me is diligence.
LEAR. How old art thou?                                               39
KENT. Not so young, sir, to love a woman for singing, nor so old to dote
on her for any thing: I have years on my back forty eight.
LEAR. Follow me; thou shalt serve me: if I like thee no worse after
dinner, I will not part from thee yet. Dinner, ho, dinner! Where 's my knave?
my fool? Go you, and call my fool hither.            [*Exit an Attendant.*

*Enter* OSWALD.

You, you, sirrah, where 's my daughter?
  osw. So please you, –                                        [*Exit.*
LEAR. What says the fellow there? Call the clotpoll back.
[*Exit a Knight*] Where 's my fool, ho? I think the world 's asleep.   52

*Re-enter Knight.*

How now! where 's that mongrel?
  KNIGHT. He says, my lord, your daughter is not well.

*Scene iv.* 18. **eat no fish.** *Roman Catholics, who observed the custom of eating fish on Fridays,
were thought of as enemies of the government.*

LEAR. Why came not the slave back to me when I called him?

KNIGHT. Sir, he answered me in the roundest manner, he would not.

LEAR. He would not!                                                    60

KNIGHT. My lord, I know not what the matter is; but, to my judgement, your highness is not entertained with that ceremonious affection as you were wont; there's a great abatement of kindness appears as well in the general dependants as in the duke himself also and your daughter.

LEAR. Ha! sayest thou so?

KNIGHT. I beseech you, pardon me, my lord, if I be mistaken; for my duty cannot be silent when I think your highness wronged.        71

LEAR. Thou but rememberest me of mine own conception: I have perceived a most faint neglect of late; which I have rather blamed as mine own jealous curiosity than as a very pretence and purpose of unkindness: I will look further into 't. But where's my fool? I have not seen him this two days.

KNIGHT. Since my young lady's going into France, sir, the fool hath much pined away.                                                      80

LEAR. No more of that; I have noted it well. Go you, and tell my daughter I would speak with her. [*Exit an Attendant*] Go you, call hither my fool.                                        [*Exit an Attendant.*

*Re-enter* OSWALD.

O, you sir, you, come you hither, sir: who am I, sir?

OSW. My lady's father.

LEAR. 'My lady's father'! my lord's knave: you whoreson dog! you slave! you cur!

OSW. I am none of these, my lord; I beseech your pardon.

LEAR. Do you bandy looks with me, you rascal?        [*Striking him.*

OSW. I'll not be struck, my lord.

KENT. Nor tripped neither, you base foot-ball player.

                                                   [*Tripping up his heels.*

LEAR. I thank thee, fellow; thou servest me, and I'll love thee.

KENT. Come, sir, arise, away! I'll teach you differences: away, away! If you will measure your lubber's length again, tarry: but away! go to; have you wisdom? so.                        [*Pushes* OSWALD *out.*  102

LEAR. Now, my friendly knave, I thank thee: there's earnest of thy service.                                        [*Giving* KENT *money.*

*Enter* FOOL.

FOOL. Let me hire him too: here's my coxcomb.

                                                   [*Offering* KENT *his cap.*

LEAR. How now, my pretty knave! how dost thou?

FOOL. Sirrah, you were best take my coxcomb.

KENT. Why, fool?                                                      110

FOOL. Why, for taking one's part that's out of favour: nay, an thou canst not smile as the wind sits, thou 'lt catch cold shortly: there, take my coxcomb: why, this fellow has banished two on 's daughters, and did the third a blessing against his will; if thou follow him, thou must needs wear my coxcomb. How now, nuncle! Would I had two coxcombs and two daughters!

---

75. **jealous curiosity,** *overscrupulous regard for his own dignity.*   95. **foot-ball player.** *Football was a rough, dangerous, public sport without organization or officials, and under statutory ban; it was played in the streets by the worst elements of the population.*   99. **differences,** *i.e., between kings and servants.*   112. **as . . . sits,** *as fashion and fortune dictate.*   113. **catch cold,** *i.e., be turned out.* 117. **nuncle,** *contraction of "mine uncle," customary address of the licensed fool to his superior.*

LEAR. Why, my boy? 119

FOOL. If I gave them all my living, I 'ld keep my coxcombs myself. There's mine; beg another of thy daughters.

LEAR. Take heed, sirrah; the whip.

FOOL. Truth 's a dog must to kennel; he must be whipped out, when Lady the brach may stand by the fire and stink.

LEAR. A pestilent gall to me!

FOOL. Sirrah, I'll teach thee a speech.

LEAR. Do.

FOOL. Mark it, nuncle: 130
    Have more than thou showest,
    Speak less than thou knowest,
    Lend less than thou owest,
    Ride more than thou goest,
    Learn more than thou trowest,
    Set less than thou throwest;
    Leave thy drink and thy whore,
    And keep in-a-door,
    And thou shalt have more
    Than two tens to a score. 140

KENT. This is nothing, fool.

FOOL. Then 'tis like the breath of an unfee'd lawyer; you gave me nothing for 't. Can you make no use of nothing, nuncle?

LEAR. Why, no, boy; nothing can be made out of nothing.

FOOL. [*To* KENT] Prithee, tell him, so much the rent of his land comes to: he will not believe a fool.

LEAR. A bitter fool! 150

FOOL. Dost thou know the difference, my boy, between a bitter fool and a sweet fool?

LEAR. No, lad; teach me.

FOOL. That lord that counsell'd thee
  To give away thy land,
    Come place him here by me,
  Do thou for him stand:
    The sweet and bitter fool
  Will presently appear;
    The one in motley here, 160
  The other found out there.

LEAR. Dost thou call me fool, boy?

FOOL. All thy other titles thou hast given away; that thou wast born with.

KENT. This is not altogether fool, my lord.

FOOL. No, faith, lords and great men will not let me; if I had a monopoly out, they would have part on 't: and ladies too, they will not let me have all fool to myself; they'll be snatching. Give me an egg, nuncle, and I'll give thee two crowns. 171

LEAR. What two crowns shall they be?

FOOL. Why, after I have cut the egg i' the middle, and eat up the meat, the two crowns of the egg. When thou clovest thy crown i' the middle, and gavest away both parts, thou borest thy ass on thy back o'er the dirt: thou hadst little wit in thy bald crown, when thou gavest thy golden one away. If I speak like myself in this, let him be whipped that first finds it so. 180

---

134. **goest**, *i.e., on foot.* 135. **Learn...trowest**, *don't believe all you hear (or learn).* 136. **Set ...throwest**, *stake less at dice than you have a chance to throw, i.e., don't bet all you can.*

[*Singing*] Fools had ne'er less wit in a year;
    For wise men are grown foppish,
    They know not how their wits to wear,
      Their manners are so apish.

LEAR. When were you wont to be so full of songs, sirrah?

FOOL. I have used it, nuncle, ever since thou madest thy daughters thy mother: for when thou gavest them the rod, and put'st down thine own breeches, 190

[*Singing*] Then they for sudden joy did weep,
    And I for sorrow sung,
    That such a king should play bo-peep,
      And go the fools among.

Prithee, nuncle, keep a schoolmaster that can teach thy fool to lie: I would fain learn to lie.

LEAR. An you lie, sirrah, we'll have you whipped. 198

FOOL. I marvel what kin thou and thy daughters are: they'll have me whipped for speaking true, thou 'lt have me whipped for lying; and sometimes I am whipped for holding my peace. I had rather be any kind o' thing than a fool: and yet I would not be thee, nuncle; thou hast pared thy wit o' both sides, and left nothing i' the middle: here comes one o' the parings.

    *Enter* GONERIL.

LEAR. How now, daughter! what makes that frontlet on?
Methinks you are too much of late i' the frown. 209

FOOL. Thou wast a pretty fellow when thou hadst no need to care for her frowning; now thou art an O without a figure: I am better than thou art now; I am a fool, thou art nothing. [*To* GON.] Yes, forsooth, I will hold my tongue; so your face bids me, though you say nothing. Mum, mum,
    He that keeps nor crust nor crum,
      Weary of all, shall want some.
[*Pointing to* LEAR] That 's a shealed peascod.

GON. Not only, sir, this your all-licensed fool, 220
But other of your insolent retinue
Do hourly carp and quarrel; breaking forth
In rank and not-to-be-endured riots. Sir,
I had thought, by making this well known unto you,
To have found a safe redress; but now grow fearful,
By what yourself too late have spoke and done,
That you protect this course, and put it on
By your allowance; which if you should, the fault
Would not 'scape censure, nor the redresses sleep,
Which, in the tender of a wholesome weal, 230
Might in their working do you that offence,
Which else were shame, that then necessity
Will call discreet proceeding.

FOOL. For, you know, nuncle,
    The hedge-sparrow fed the cuckoo so long,
    That it had it head bit off by it young.
So, out went the candle, and we were left darkling.

---

208. **frontlet,** *forehead; here, frowning visage.* 212. **O without a figure,** *cipher of no value unless joined to a figure.* 229. **nor the redresses sleep,** *punishment for the riotous conduct of Lear's attendants will be inflicted.* 230. **tender . . . weal,** *preservation of the peace of the state.* 232-233. **necessity . . . proceeding,** *i.e., everyone will justify her because of the necessity of the action.*

LEAR. Are you our daughter?

GON. Come, sir,
I would you would make use of that good wisdom,                    240
Whereof I know you are fraught; and put away
These dispositions, that of late transform you
From what you rightly are.

    FOOL. May not an ass know when the cart draws the horse?
Whoop, Jug! I love thee.

    LEAR. Doth any here know me? This is not Lear:
Doth Lear walk thus? speak thus? Where are his eyes?
Either his notion weakens, his discernings
Are lethargied — Ha! waking? 'tis not so.
Who is it that can tell me who I am?                                250

    FOOL. Lear's shadow.

    LEAR. I would learn that; for, by the marks of sovereignty, knowledge,
and reason, I should be false persuaded I had daughters.

    FOOL. Which they will make an obedient father.

    LEAR. Your name, fair gentlewoman?

    GON. This admiration, sir, is much o' the savour
Of other your new pranks. I do beseech you
To understand my purposes aright:                                  260
As you are old and reverend, you should be wise.
Here do you keep a hundred knights and squires;
Men so disorder'd, so debosh'd and bold,
That this our court, infected with their manners,
Shows like a riotous inn: epicurism and lust
Make it more like a tavern or a brothel
Than a graced palace. The shame itself doth speak
For instant remedy: be then desired
By her, that else will take the thing she begs,
A little to disquantity your train;                                270
And the remainder, that shall still depend,
To be such men as may besort your age,
And know themselves and you.

    LEAR.                   Darkness and devils!
Saddle my horses; call my train together.
Degenerate bastard! I'll not trouble thee:
Yet have I left a daughter.

    GON. You strike my people; and your disorder'd rabble
Make servants of their betters.

*Enter* ALBANY.

    LEAR. Woe, that too late repents, — [*To* ALB.] O, sir, are you come?
Is it your will? Speak, sir. Prepare my horses.                    280
Ingratitude, thou marble-hearted fiend,
More hideous when thou show'st thee in a child
Than the sea-monster!

    ALB.              Pray, sir, be patient.

    LEAR. [*To* GON.] Detested kite! thou liest:
My train are men of choice and rarest parts,
That all particulars of duty know,
And in the most exact regard support

---

283. **sea-monster,** *possible allusion to the hippopotamus, reputed in Egyptian mythology to be a monster of ingratitude.*

The worships of their name. O most small fault,
How ugly didst thou in Cordelia show!
That, like an engine, wrench'd my frame of nature          290
From the fix'd place; drew from my heart all love,
And added to the gall. O Lear, Lear, Lear!
Beat at this gate, that let thy folly in,              [*Striking his head.*
And thy dear judgement out! Go, go, my people.
    ALB. My lord, I am guiltless, as I am ignorant
Of what hath moved you.
    LEAR.               It may be so, my lord.
Hear, nature, hear; dear goddess, hear!
Suspend thy purpose, if thou didst intend
To make this creature fruitful!
Into her womb convey sterility!                   300
Dry up in her the organs of increase;
And from her derogate body never spring
A babe to honour her! If she must teem,
Create her child of spleen; that it may live,
And be a thwart disnatured torment to her!
Let it stamp wrinkles in her brow of youth;
With cadent tears fret channels in her cheeks;
Turn all her mother's pains and benefits
To laughter and contempt; that she may feel
How sharper than a serpent's tooth it is              310
To have a thankless child! Away, away!              [*Exit.*
    ALB. Now, gods that we adore, whereof comes this?
    GON. Never afflict yourself to know the cause;
But let his disposition have that scope
That dotage gives it.

    *Re-enter* LEAR.

    LEAR. What, fifty of my followers at a clap!
Within a fortnight!
    ALB.           What 's the matter, sir?
    LEAR. I'll tell thee: [*To* GON.] Life and death! I am ashamed
That thou hast power to shake my manhood thus;
That these hot tears, which break from me perforce,          320
Should make thee worth them. Blasts and fogs upon thee!
The untented woundings of a father's curse
Pierce every sense about thee! Old fond eyes,
Beweep this cause again, I'll pluck ye out,
And cast you, with the waters that you lose,
To temper clay. Yea, is it come to this?
Let it be so: yet have I left a daughter,
Who, I am sure, is kind and comfortable:
When she shall hear this of thee, with her nails
She'll flay thy wolvish visage. Thou shalt find          330
That I'll resume the shape which thou dost think
I have cast off for ever: thou shalt, I warrant thee.
                    [*Exeunt* LEAR, KENT, *and Attendants.*
    GON. Do you mark that, my lord?
    ALB. I cannot be so partial, Goneril,
To the great love I bear you, —

---

297. **nature . . . goddess.** *This is the first of Lear's terrible curses.*

GON. Pray you, content. What, Oswald, ho!
[*To the* FOOL] You, sir, more knave than fool, after your master.
  FOOL. Nuncle Lear, nuncle Lear, tarry and take the fool with thee.
  A fox, when one has caught her,         340
  And such a daughter,
  Should sure to the slaughter,
  If my cap would buy a halter:
  So the fool follows after.          [*Exit.*
  GON. This man hath had good counsel: — a hundred knights!
'Tis politic and safe to let him keep
At point a hundred knights: yes, that, on every dream,
Each buzz, each fancy, each complaint, dislike,
He may enguard his dotage with their powers,
And hold our lives in mercy. Oswald, I say!     350
  ALB. Well, you may fear too far.
  GON.        Safer than trust too far:
Let me still take away the harms I fear,
Not fear still to be taken: I know his heart.
What he hath utter'd I have writ my sister:
If she sustain him and his hundred knights,
When I have show'd the unfitness, —

 *Re-enter* OSWALD.

        How now, Oswald!
What, have you writ that letter to my sister?
  OSW. Yes, madam.
  GON. Take you some company, and away to horse:
Inform her full of my particular fear;       360
And thereto add such reasons of your own
As may compact it more. Get you gone;
And hasten your return. [*Exit* OSWALD] No, no, my lord,
This milky gentleness and course of yours
Though I condemn not, yet, under pardon,
You are much more attask'd for want of wisdom
Than praised for harmful mildness.
  ALB. How far your eyes may pierce I cannot tell:
Striving to better, oft we mar what 's well.
  GON. Nay, then —            370
  ALB. Well, well; the event.        [*Exeunt.*

 SCENE V: *Court before the same.*

 *Enter* LEAR, KENT, *and* FOOL.

  LEAR. Go you before to Gloucester with these letters. Acquaint my
daughter no further with any thing you know than comes from her
demand out of the letter. If your diligence be not speedy, I shall be there
afore you.
  KENT. I will not sleep, my lord, till I have delivered your letter. [*Exit.*
  FOOL. If a man's brains were in 's heels, were 't not in danger of kibes?
  LEAR. Ay, boy.             10
  FOOL. Then, I prithee, be merry; thy wit shall ne'er go slip-shod.
  LEAR. Ha, ha, ha!

---

 *Scene v.* 12. **slip-shod,** *in slippers. There are no brains, thinks the Fool, in Lear's heels when they
are on their way to visit Regan.*

FOOL. Shalt see thy other daughter will use thee kindly; for though she 's as like this as a crab 's like an apple, yet I can tell what I can tell.

LEAR. Why, what canst thou tell, my boy?

FOOL. She will taste as like this as a crab does to a crab. Thou canst tell why one's nose stands i' the middle on 's face?                                    20

LEAR. No.

FOOL. Why, to keep one's eyes of either side 's nose; that what a man cannot smell out, he may spy into.

LEAR. I did her wrong —

FOOL. Canst tell how an oyster makes his shell?

LEAR. No.

FOOL. Nor I neither; but I can tell why a snail has a house.

LEAR. Why?

FOOL. Why, to put his head in; not to give it away to his daughters, and leave his horns without a case.

LEAR. I will forget my nature. So kind a father! Be my horses ready?

FOOL. Thy asses are gone about 'em. The reason why the seven stars are no more than seven is a pretty reason.

LEAR. Because they are not eight?                                               40

FOOL. Yes, indeed: thou wouldst make a good fool.

LEAR. To take 't again perforce! Monster ingratitude!

FOOL. If thou wert my fool, nuncle, I 'ld have thee beaten for being old before thy time.

LEAR. How 's that?

FOOL. Thou shouldst not have been old till thou hadst been wise.

LEAR. O, let me not be mad, not mad, sweet heaven!                             50
Keep me in temper: I would not be mad!

*Enter Gentleman.*

How now! are the horses ready?

GENT. Ready, my lord.

LEAR. Come, boy.

FOOL. She that 's a maid now, and laughs at my departure,
Shall not be a maid long, unless things be cut shorter.          *[Exeunt.*

## ACT II

SCENE I: *The* EARL OF GLOUCESTER'S *castle.*

*Enter* EDMUND, *and* CURAN *meets him.*

EDM. Save thee, Curan.

CUR. And you, sir. I have been with your father, and given him notice that the Duke of Cornwall and Regan his duchess will be here with him this night.

EDM. How comes that?

CUR. Nay, I know not. You have heard of the news abroad; I mean the whispered ones, for they are yet but ear-bussing arguments?

EDM. Not I: pray you, what are they?                                          10

CUR. Have you heard of no likely wars toward, 'twixt the Dukes of Cornwall and Albany?

EDM. Not a word.

15. **kindly,** *double sense: according to filial nature and according to her own nature.*   50. **let . . .**
**mad.** *Lear thus marks his first symptom of coming madness. It will be noted that he thinks of madness as the loss of the even balance of spirits, i.e., temper, and as the forgetting of his nature.*

CUR. You may do, then, in time. Fare you well, sir.                    [*Exit.*
 EDM. The duke be here to-night? The better! best!
This weaves itself perforce into my business.
My father hath set guard to take my brother;
And I have one thing, of a queasy question,
Which I must act: briefness and fortune, work!                         20
Brother, a word; descend: brother, I say!

  *Enter* EDGAR.

My father watches: O sir, fly this place;
Intelligence is given where you are hid;
You have now the good advantage of the night:
Have you not spoken 'gainst the Duke of Cornwall?
He 's coming hither; now, i' the night, i' the haste,
And Regan with him: have you nothing said
Upon his party 'gainst the Duke of Albany?
Advise yourself.
 EDG.             I am sure on 't, not a word.
 EDM. I hear my father coming: pardon me;                              30
In cunning I must draw my sword upon you:
Draw; seem to defend yourself; now quit you well.
Yield: come before my father. Light, ho, here!
Fly, brother. Torches, torches! So, farewell.          [*Exit* EDGAR.
Some blood drawn on me would beget opinion            [*Wounds his arm.*
Of my more fierce endeavour: I have seen drunkards
Do more than this in sport. Father, father!
Stop, stop! No help?

  *Enter* GLOUCESTER, *and Servants with torches.*

 GLOU. Now, Edmund, where 's the villain?
 EDM. Here stood he in the dark, his sharp sword out,                  40
Mumbling of wicked charms, conjuring the moon
To stand auspicious mistress, —
 GLOU.                     But where is he?
 EDM. Look, sir, I bleed.
 GLOU.                     Where is the villain, Edmund?
 EDM. Fled this way, sir. When by no means he could —
 GLOU. Pursue him, ho! Go after. [*Exeunt some Servants*] By no means
   what?
 EDM. Persuade me to the murder of your lordship;
But that I told him, the revenging gods
'Gainst parricides did all their thunders bend;
Spoke, with how manifold and strong a bond
The child was bound to the father; sir, in fine,                      50
Seeing how loathly opposite I stood
To his unnatural purpose, in fell motion,
With his prepared sword, he charges home
My unprovided body, lanced mine arm:
But when he saw my best alarum'd spirits,
Bold in the quarrel's right, roused to the encounter,
Or whether gasted by the noise I made,
Full suddenly he fled.

*Act II. Scene i.* 19. **queasy question,** *hazardous, or ticklish, nature.* 57. **gasted,** *frightened.*

GLOU.            Let him fly far:
Not in this land shall he remain uncaught;
And found — dispatch. The noble duke my master,          60
My worthy arch and patron, comes to-night:
By his authority I will proclaim it,
That he which finds him shall deserve our thanks,
Bringing the murderous caitiff to the stake;
He that conceals him, death.
     EDM. When I dissuaded him from his intent,
And found him pight to do it, with curst speech
I threaten'd to discover him: he replied,
'Thou unpossessing bastard! dost thou think,
If I would stand against thee, could the reposal          70
Of any trust, virtue, or worth in thee
Make thy words faith'd? No: what I should deny, —
As this I would; ay, though thou didst produce
My very character, — I 'ld turn it all
To thy suggestion, plot, and damned practice:
And thou must make a dullard of the world,
If they not thought the profits of my death
Were very pregnant and potential spurs
To make thee seek it.'
     GLOU.         Strong and fasten'd villain!
Would he deny his letter? I never got him.      [*Tucket within.*   80
Hark, the duke's trumpets! I know not why he comes.
All ports I'll bar; the villain shall not 'scape;
The duke must grant me that: besides, his picture
I will send far and near, that all the kingdom
May have due note of him; and of my land,
Loyal and natural boy, I'll work the means
To make thee capable.

*Enter* CORNWALL, REGAN, *and Attendants.*

     CORN. How now, my noble friend! since I came hither,
Which I can call but now, I have heard strange news.
     REG. If it be true, all vengeance comes too short          90
Which can pursue the offender. How dost, my lord?
     GLOU. O, madam, my old heart is crack'd, is crack'd!
     REG. What, did my father's godson seek your life?
He whom my father named? your Edgar?
     GLOU. O, lady, lady, shame would have it hid!
     REG. Was he not companion with the riotous knights
That tend upon my father?
     GLOU. I know not, madam: 'tis too bad, too bad.
     EDM. Yes, madam, he was of that consort.
     REG. No marvel, then, though he were ill affected:      100
'Tis they have put him on the old man's death,
To have the waste and spoil of his revenues.
I have this present evening from my sister
Been well inform'd of them; and with such cautions,
That if they come to sojourn at my house,
I'll not be there.
     CORN.        Nor I, assure thee, Regan.

---

60. **dispatch,** *I will dispatch him.*   67. **pight,** *determined.*   69. **unpossessing,** *unable to inherit,*
*beggarly.*   76. **make ... world,** *think the world an idiot.*

Edmund, I hear that you have shown your father
A child-like office.

EDM.                    'Twas my duty, sir.

GLOU. He did bewray his practice; and received
This hurt you see, striving to apprehend him.                    110

CORN. Is he pursued?

GLOU.                    Ay, my good lord.

CORN. If he be taken, he shall never more
Be fear'd of doing harm: make your own purpose,
How in my strength you please. For you, Edmund,
Whose virtue and obedience doth this instant
So much commend itself, you shall be ours:
Natures of such deep trust we shall much need;
You we first seize on.

EDM.                    I shall serve you, sir,
Truly, however else.

GLOU.                    For him I thank your grace.

CORN. You know not why we came to visit you, —                    120

REG. Thus out of season, threading dark-eyed night:
Occasions, noble Gloucester, of some poise,
Wherein we must have use of your advice:
Our father he hath writ, so hath our sister,
Of differences, which I least thought it fit
To answer from our home; the several messengers
From hence attend dispatch. Our good old friend,
Lay comforts to your bosom; and bestow
Your needful counsel to our business,
Which craves the instant use.

GLOU.                    I serve you, madam:                    130
Your graces are right welcome.                    [*Exeunt.*

SCENE II: *Before* GLOUCESTER'S *castle.*

*Enter* KENT *and* OSWALD, *severally.*

OSW. Good dawning to thee, friend: art of this house?

KENT. Ay.

OSW. Where may we set our horses?

KENT. I' the mire.

OSW. Prithee, if thou lovest me, tell me.

KENT. I love thee not.

OSW. Why, then, I care not for thee.

KENT. If I had thee in Lipsbury pinfold, I would make thee care for me.    10

OSW. Why dost thou use me thus? I know thee not.

KENT. Fellow, I know thee.

OSW. What dost thou know me for?

KENT. A knave; a rascal; an eater of broken meats; a base, proud,
shallow, beggarly, three-suited, hundred-pound, filthy, worsted-stocking
knave; a lily-livered, action-taking knave, a whoreson, glass-gazing, super-

---

114. **in my strength,** *by my power and authority.*    121. **threading,** *passing through (as thread through the eye of a needle).*
    *Scene ii.* 16. **broken meats,** *left-over food.*    17. **three-suited,** *probable allusion to three suits a year allowed to servants.*    **hundred-pound,** *possible allusion to the minimum property qualification for the status of gentleman.*    **worsted-stocking,** *too poor and menial to wear silk stockings.*    18. **action-taking,** *settling quarrels by resort to law instead of arms; cowardly.*    19. **glass-gazing,** *fond of looking in the mirror.*

serviceable, finical rogue; one-trunk-inheriting slave; one that wouldst be a bawd, in way of good service, and art nothing but the composition of a knave, beggar, coward, pandar, and the son and heir of a mongrel bitch: one whom I will beat into clamorous whining, if thou deniest the least syllable of thy addition.

OSW. Why, what a monstrous fellow art thou, thus to rail on one that is neither known of thee nor knows thee!                                                   29

KENT. What a brazen-faced varlet art thou, to deny thou knowest me! Is it two days ago since I tripped up thy heels, and beat thee before the king? Draw, you rogue: for, though it be night, yet the moon shines; I'll make a sop o' the moonshine of you: draw, you whoreson cullionly barber-monger, draw.                                                   [*Drawing his sword.*

OSW. Away! I have nothing to do with thee.                          · 37

KENT. Draw, you rascal: you come with letters against the king; and take vanity the puppet's part against the royalty of her father; draw, you rogue, or I'll so carbonado your shanks: draw, you rascal; come your ways.

OSW. Help, ho! murder! help!

KENT. Strike, you slave; stand, rogue, stand; you neat slave, strike.

[*Beating him.*

OSW. Help, ho! murder! murder!                                       46

*Enter* EDMUND, *with his rapier drawn,* CORNWALL, REGAN, GLOUCESTER, *and Servants.*

EDM. How now! What 's the matter?

KENT. With you, goodman boy, an you please: come, I'll flesh ye: come on, young master.

GLOU. Weapons! arms! What 's the matter here?                       51

CORN. Keep peace, upon your lives;
He dies that strikes again. What is the matter?

REG. The messengers from our sister and the king.

CORN. What is your difference? speak.

OSW. I am scarce in breath, my lord.

KENT. No marvel, you have so bestirred your valour. You cowardly rascal, nature disclaims in thee: a tailor made thee.                             60

CORN. Thou art a strange fellow: a tailor make a man?

KENT. Ay, a tailor, sir: a stone-cutter or a painter could not have made him so ill, though he had been but two hours at the trade.

CORN. Speak yet, how grew your quarrel?

OSW. This ancient ruffian, sir, whose life I have spared at suit of his gray beard, —                                                             68

KENT. Thou whoreson zed! thou unnecessary letter! My lord, if you will give me leave, I will tread this unbolted villain into mortar, and daub the walls of a jakes with him. Spare my gray beard, you wagtail?

CORN. Peace, sirrah!
You beastly knave, know you no reverence?

KENT. Yes, sir; but anger hath a privilege.

CORN. Why art thou angry?

KENT. That such a slave as this should wear a sword,
Who wears no honesty. Such smiling rogues as these,
Like rats, oft bite the holy cords a-twain                             80

---

20. **one-trunk-inheriting,** *possessing effects sufficient for one trunk only.*  45. **neat,** *foppish.*  47. **matter.** *Kent takes the secondary meaning, "cause for quarrel."*  69. **zed,** *the letter Z, a Greek character; in the spelling of English words, known but unnecessary, and often not included in dictionaries.*  80. **holy cords,** *natural bonds of affection.*

Which are too intrinse t' unloose; smooth every passion
That in the natures of their lords rebel;
Bring oil to fire, snow to their colder moods;
Renege, affirm, and turn their halcyon beaks
With every gale and vary of their masters,
Knowing nought, like dogs, but following.
A plague upon your epileptic visage!
Smile you my speeches, as I were a fool?
Goose, if I had you upon Sarum plain,
I 'ld drive ye cackling home to Camelot.                              90
    CORN. What, art thou mad, old fellow?
    GLOU. How fell you out? say that.
    KENT. No contraries hold more antipathy
Than I and such a knave.
    CORN. Why dost thou call him knave? What 's his offence?
    KENT. His countenance likes me not.
    CORN. No more, perchance, does mine, nor his, nor hers.
    KENT. Sir, 'tis my occupation to be plain:
I have seen better faces in my time
Than stands on any shoulder that I see                                100
Before me at this instant.
    CORN.              This is some fellow,
Who, having been praised for bluntness, doth affect
A saucy roughness, and constrains the garb
Quite from his nature: he cannot flatter, he,
An honest mind and plain, he must speak truth!
An they will take it, so; if not, he 's plain.
These kind of knaves I know, which in this plainness
Harbour more craft and more corrupter ends
Than twenty silly ducking observants
That stretch their duties nicely.                                     110
    KENT. Sir, in good sooth, in sincere verity,
Under the allowance of your great aspect,
Whose influence, like the wreath of radiant fire
On flickering Phœbus' front, —
    CORN.              What mean'st by this?
    KENT. To go out of my dialect, which you discommend so much. I
know, sir, I am no flatterer: he that beguiled you in a plain accent was a
plain knave; which for my part I will not be, though I should win your
displeasure to entreat me to 't.                                      120
    CORN. What was the offence you gave him?
    OSW. I never gave him any:
It pleased the king his master very late
To strike at me, upon his misconstruction;
When he, conjunct, and flattering his displeasure,
Tripp'd me behind; being down, insulted, rail'd,
And put upon him such a deal of man,
That worthied him, got praises of the king
For him attempting who was self-subdued;

---

81. **intrinse**, *entangled; very tightly drawn.*   84. **halcyon beaks.** *The halcyon or kingfisher, if hung up, would turn his beak against the wind.*   87. **epileptic**, *indication of Oswald's visage, pale with fright and distorted with a grin.*   103-104. **constrains . . . nature**, *assumes by an effort a bearing or manner of speech which is wholly unnatural.*   109. **ducking observants**, *bowing, obsequious courtiers.*   127. **put . . . man**, *acted like such a hero.*   128. **worthied**, *won reputation.*   129. **attempting**, *assailing.*

And, in the fleshment of this dread exploit,                              130
Drew on me here again.
    KENT.                    None of these rogues and cowards
But Ajax is their fool.
    CORN.                    Fetch forth the stocks!
You stubborn ancient knave, you reverend braggart,
We'll teach you —
    KENT.            Sir, I am too old to learn:
Call not your stocks for me: I serve the king;
On whose employment I was sent to you:
You shall do small respect, show too bold malice
Against the grace and person of my master,
Stocking his messenger.
    CORN. Fetch forth the stocks! As I have life and honour,   140
There shall he sit till noon.
    REG. Till noon! till night, my lord; and all night too.
    KENT. Why, madam, if I were your father's dog,
You should not use me so.
    REG.                    Sir, being his knave, I will.
    CORN. This is a fellow of the self-same colour
Our sister speaks of. Come, bring away the stocks!   [*Stocks brought out.*
    GLOU. Let me beseech your grace not to do so:
His fault is much, and the good king his master
Will check him for 't: your purposed low correction
Is such as basest and contemned'st wretches              150
For pilferings and most common trespasses
Are punish'd with: the king must take it ill,
That he 's so slightly valued in his messenger,
Should have him thus restrain'd.
    CORN.                    I'll answer that.
    REG. My sister may receive it much more worse,
To have her gentleman abused, assaulted,
For following her affairs. Put in his legs.   [KENT *is put in the stocks.*
Come, my good lord, away.        [*Exeunt all but* GLOUCESTER *and* KENT.
    GLOU. I am sorry for thee, friend; 'tis the duke's pleasure,
Whose disposition, all the world well knows,              160
Will not be rubb'd nor stopp'd: I'll entreat for thee.
    KENT. Pray, do not, sir: I have watched and travell'd hard;
Some time I shall sleep out, the rest I'll whistle.
A good man's fortune may grow out at heels:
Give you good morrow!
    GLOU. The duke 's to blame in this: 'twill be ill taken.   [*Exit.*
    KENT. Good king, that must approve the common saw,
Thou out of heaven's benediction comest
To the warm sun!
Approach, thou beacon to this under globe,              170
That by thy comfortable beams I may
Peruse this letter! Nothing almost sees miracles
But misery: I know 'tis from Cordelia,
Who hath most fortunately been inform'd
Of my obscured course; and shall find time

---

130. **fleshment,** *excitement resulting from a first success.*   132. **Ajax is their fool.** *Ajax, tradi-tional braggart, is outdone by them in boasting.*   167-169. **saw,** *proverb: "To run out of God's blessing into the warm sun," meaning "to go from better to worse."*

From this enormous state, seeking to give
Losses their remedies. All weary and o'er-watch'd,
Take vantage, heavy eyes, not to behold
This shameful lodging.
Fortune, good night: smile once more; turn thy wheel!        [*Sleeps.* 180

SCENE III: *A wood.*

*Enter* EDGAR.

EDG. I heard myself proclaim'd;
And by the happy hollow of a tree
Escaped the hunt. No port is free; no place,
That guard, and most unusual vigilance,
Does not attend my taking. Whiles I may 'scape,
I will preserve myself: and am bethought
To take the basest and most poorest shape
That ever penury, in contempt of man,
Brought near to beast: my face I'll grime with filth;
Blanket my loins; elf all my hair in knots;                                    10
And with presented nakedness out-face
The winds and persecutions of the sky.
The country gives me proof and precedent
Of Bedlam beggars, who, with roaring voices,
Strike in their numb'd and mortified bare arms
Pins, wooden pricks, nails, sprigs of rosemary;
And with this horrible object, from low farms,
Poor pelting villages, sheep-cotes, and mills,
Sometime with lunatic bans, sometime with prayers,
Enforce their charity. Poor Turlygod! poor Tom!                            20
That 's something yet: Edgar I nothing am.                        [*Exit.*

SCENE IV: *Before* GLOUCESTER's *castle.* KENT *in the stocks.*

*Enter* LEAR, FOOL, *and Gentleman.*

LEAR. 'Tis strange that they should so depart from home,
And not send back my messenger.
GENT.                                     As I learn'd,
The night before there was no purpose in them
Of this remove.
KENT.              Hail to thee, noble master!
LEAR. Ha!
Makest thou this shame thy pastime?
KENT.                                     No, my lord.
FOOL. Ha, ha! he wears cruel garters. Horses are tied by the heads, dogs
and bears by the neck, monkeys by the loins, and men by the legs: when
a man 's over-lusty at legs, then he wears wooden nether-stocks.              11
LEAR. What 's he that hath so much thy place mistook
To set thee here?
KENT.                     It is both he and she;
Your son and daughter.

Scene iii. 17. **object,** *appearance.* 21. **nothing,** *probably, not at all, in no respect.*
Scene iv. 7. **cruel.** Q: crewell, *a double meaning: (1) "unkind," (2) "crewel," a thin yarn of*
*which garters were made.*

LEAR. No.

KENT. Yes.

LEAR. No, I say.

KENT. I say, yea.

LEAR. No, no, they would not.

KENT. Yes, they have.                                                    20

LEAR. By Jupiter, I swear, no.

KENT. By Juno, I swear, ay.

    LEAR.              They durst not do 't;
They could not, would not do 't; 'tis worse than murder,
To do upon respect such violent outrage:
Resolve me, with all modest haste, which way
Thou mightst deserve, or they impose, this usage,
Coming from us.

    KENT.          My lord, when at their home
I did commend your highness' letters to them,
Ere I was risen from the place that show'd
My duty kneeling, came there a reeking post,                             30
Stew'd in his haste, half breathless, panting forth
From Goneril his mistress salutations;
Deliver'd letters, spite of intermission,
Which presently they read: on whose contents,
They summon'd up their meiny, straight took horse;
Commanded me to follow, and attend
The leisure of their answer; gave me cold looks:
And meeting here the other messenger,
Whose welcome, I perceived, had poison'd mine, —
Being the very fellow that of late                                       40
Display'd so saucily against your highness, —
Having more man than wit about me, drew:
He raised the house with loud and coward cries.
Your son and daughter found this trespass worth
The shame which here it suffers.

    FOOL. Winter 's not gone yet, if the wild-geese fly that way.

          Fathers that wear rags
             Do make their children blind;
          But fathers that bear bags                                        50
             Shall see their children kind.
          Fortune, that arrant whore,
          Ne'er turns the key to the poor.

But, for all this, thou shalt have as many dolours for thy daughters as
thou canst tell in a year.

    LEAR. O, how this mother swells up toward my heart!
Hysterica passio, down, thou climbing sorrow,
Thy element 's below! Where is this daughter?

    KENT. With the earl, sir, here within.

    LEAR.              Follow me not;
Stay here.                                [*Exit.*   60

    GENT. Made you no more offence but what you speak of?

    KENT. None.
How chance the king comes with so small a train?

---

24. **upon respect,** *deliberately.*   35. **meiny,** *household.*   42. **drew,** *i.e., my sword.*   56, 57. **mother,**
**Hysterica passio,** *a disease, apparently called by both these names, accompanied by a sense of*
*strangulation. Lear mistakes the epigastric discomfort of extreme grief for the disease.*

FOOL. An thou hadst been set i' the stocks for that question, thou hadst
well deserved it.

KENT. Why, fool?

FOOL. We'll set thee to school to an ant, to teach thee there 's no
labouring i' the winter. All that follow their noses are led by their eyes
but blind men; and there 's not a nose among twenty but can smell him
that 's stinking. Let go thy hold when a great wheel runs down a hill,
lest it break thy neck with following it; but the great one that goes up
the hill, let him draw thee after. When a wise man gives thee better
counsel, give me mine again: I would have none but knaves follow it,
since a fool gives it.

> That sir which serves and seeks for gain,
>> And follows but for form,                   80
> Will pack when it begins to rain,
>> And leave thee in the storm.
> But I will tarry; the fool will stay,
>> And let the wise man fly:
> The knave turns fool that runs away;
>> The fool no knave, perdy.

KENT. Where learned you this, fool?

FOOL. Not i' the stocks, fool.

*Re-enter* LEAR, *with* GLOUCESTER.

LEAR. Deny to speak with me? They are sick? they are weary?
They have travell'd all the night? Mere fetches;         90
The images of revolt and flying off.
Fetch me a better answer.

GLOU.               My dear lord,
You know the fiery quality of the duke;
How unremoveable and fix'd he is
In his own course.

LEAR.            Vengeance! plague! death! confusion!
Fiery? what quality? Why, Gloucester, Gloucester,
I 'ld speak with the Duke of Cornwall and his wife.

GLOU. Well, my good lord, I have inform'd them so.

LEAR. Inform'd them! Dost thou understand me, man?     100

GLOU. Ay, my good lord.

LEAR. The king would speak with Cornwall; the dear father
Would with his daughter speak, commands her service:
Are they inform'd of this? My breath and blood!
Fiery? the fiery duke? Tell the hot duke that —
No, but not yet: may be he is not well:
Infirmity doth still neglect all office
Whereto our health is bound; we are not ourselves
When nature, being oppress'd, commands the mind
To suffer with the body: I'll forbear;           110
And am fall'n out with my more headier will,
To take the indisposed and sickly fit
For the sound man. Death on my state! wherefore    [*Looking on* KENT.
Should he sit here? This act persuades me
That this remotion of the duke and her
Is practice only. Give me my servant forth.
Go tell the duke and 's wife I 'ld speak with them,

---

111-112. **am . . . take,** *am wrong because of my more impetuous will in taking.*

Now, presently: bid them come forth and hear me,
Or at their chamber-door I'll beat the drum
Till it cry sleep to death.                                                                     120
    GLOU. I would have all well betwixt you.                    [*Exit.*
    LEAR. O me, my heart, my rising heart! but, down!
    FOOL. Cry to it, nuncle, as the cockney did to the eels when she put
'em i' the paste alive; she knapped 'em o' the coxcombs with a stick,
and cried 'Down, wantons, down!' 'Twas her brother that, in pure kindness
to his horse, buttered his hay.

    *Enter* CORNWALL, REGAN, GLOUCESTER, *and Servants.*

    LEAR. Good morrow to you both.
    CORN.                                Hail to your grace!
                               [KENT *is set at liberty.*
    REG. I am glad to see your highness.                                     130
    LEAR. Regan, I think you are; I know what reason
I have to think so: if thou shouldst not be glad,
I would divorce me from thy mother's tomb,
Sepulchring an adultress. [*To* KENT] O, are you free?
Some other time for that. Beloved Regan,
Thy sister 's naught: O Regan, she hath tied
Sharp-tooth'd unkindness, like a vulture, here:        [*Points to his heart.*
I can scarce speak to thee; thou 'lt not believe
With how depraved a quality — O Regan!
    REG. I pray you, sir, take patience: I have hope            140
You less know how to value her desert
Than she to scant her duty.
    LEAR.                                Say, how is that?
    REG. I cannot think my sister in the least
Would fail her obligation: if, sir, perchance
She have restrain'd the riots of your followers,
'Tis on such ground, and to such wholesome end,
As clears her from all blame.
    LEAR. My curses on her!
    REG.                                O, sir, you are old;
Nature in you stands on the very verge
Of her confine: you should be ruled and led                                 150
By some discretion, that discerns your state
Better than you yourself. Therefore, I pray you,
That to our sister you do make return;
Say you have wrong'd her, sir.
    LEAR.                                Ask her forgiveness?
Do you but mark how this becomes the house:
'Dear daughter, I confess that I am old;                              [*Kneeling.*
Age is unnecessary: on my knees I beg
That you'll vouchsafe me raiment, bed, and food.'
    REG. Good sir, no more; these are unsightly tricks:
Return you to my sister.
    LEAR.    [*Rising*] Never, Regan:                               160
She hath abated me of half my train;
Look'd black upon me; struck me with her tongue,

---

123. **cockney,** *a word of disputed origin and meaning. It is said to have meant a pampered, affected
woman, a spoiled child, a milksop; the passage here suggests the meaning "cook."* 139. **quality,**
*manner.* 151. **discretion,** *discreet person.* 155. **how . . . house,** *how this would be suitable to our
position.*

Most serpent-like, upon the very heart:
All the stored vengeances of heaven fall
On her ingrateful top! Strike her young bones,
You taking airs, with lameness!
    CORN.          Fie, sir, fie!
    LEAR. You nimble lightnings, dart your blinding flames
Into her scornful eyes! Infect her beauty,
You fen-suck'd fogs, drawn by the powerful sun,
To fall and blast her pride!                         170
    REG. O the blest gods! so will you wish on me,
When the rash mood is on.
    LEAR. No, Regan, thou shalt never have my curse:
Thy tender-hefted nature shall not give
Thee o'er to harshness: her eyes are fierce; but thine
Do comfort and not burn. 'Tis not in thee
To grudge my pleasures, to cut off my train,
To bandy hasty words, to scant my sizes,
And in conclusion to oppose the bolt
Against my coming in: thou better know'st            180
The offices of nature, bond of childhood,
Effects of courtesy, dues of gratitude;
Thy half o' the kingdom hast thou not forgot,
Wherein I thee endow'd.
    REG.          Good sir, to the purpose.
    LEAR. Who put my man i' the stocks?        [*Tucket within.*
    CORN.              What trumpet 's that?
    REG. I know 't, my sister's: this approves her letter,
That she would soon be here.

*Enter* OSWALD.

                     Is your lady come?
    LEAR. This is a slave, whose easy-borrow'd pride
Dwells in the fickle grace of her he follows.
Out, varlet, from my sight!
    CORN.          What means your grace?       190
    LEAR. Who stock'd my servant? Regan, I have good hope
Thou didst not know on 't. Who comes here? O heavens,

*Enter* GONERIL.

If you do love old men, if your sweet sway
Allow obedience, if yourselves are old,
Make it your cause; send down, and take my part!
[*To* GON.] Art not ashamed to look upon this beard?
O Regan, wilt thou take her by the hand?
    GON. Why not by the hand, sir? How have I offended?
All 's not offence that indiscretion finds
And dotage terms so.
    LEAR.          O sides, you are too tough;     200
Will you yet hold? How came my man i' the stocks?
    CORN. I set him there, sir: but his own disorders
Deserved much less advancement.

165. **young bones,** *i.e., unborn child.* 169. **fen-suck'd.** *It was supposed that the sun sucked up poisons from fens or marshes.* 178. **sizes,** *allowances.* 180-183. **thou ... forgot.** *Lear enumerates what are ethically the pillars of society.* 195. **make ... cause,** *make my cause yours.* 200. **sides ... tough.** *This is not figurative but indicates belief in an actual swelling of the heart so that it might break through the sides.*

LEAR.                          You! did you?
REG. I pray you, father, being weak, seem so.
If, till the expiration of your month,
You will return and sojourn with my sister,
Dismissing half your train, come then to me:
I am now from home, and out of that provision
Which shall be needful for your entertainment.
    LEAR. Return to her, and fifty men dismiss'd?          210
No, rather I abjure all roofs, and choose
To wage against the enmity o' the air;
To be a comrade with the wolf and owl, —
Necessity's sharp pinch! Return with her?
Why, the hot-blooded France, that dowerless took
Our youngest born, I could as well be brought
To knee his throne, and, squire-like, pension beg
To keep base life afoot. Return with her?
Persuade me rather to be slave and sumpter
To this detested groom.                          [*Pointing at* OSWALD.
    GON.                          At your choice, sir.          220
    LEAR. I prithee, daughter, do not make me mad:
I will not trouble thee, my child; farewell:
We'll no more meet, no more see one another:
But yet thou art my flesh, my blood, my daughter;
Or rather a disease that's in my flesh,
Which I must needs call mine: thou art a boil,
A plague-sore, an embossed carbuncle,
In my corrupted blood. But I'll not chide thee;
Let shame come when it will, I do not call it:
I do not bid the thunder-bearer shoot,          230
Nor tell tales of thee to high-judging Jove:
Mend when thou canst; be better at thy leisure:
I can be patient; I can stay with Regan,
I and my hundred knights.
    REG.                          Not altogether so:
I look'd not for you yet, nor am provided
For your fit welcome. Give ear, sir, to my sister;
For those that mingle reason with your passion
Must be content to think you old, and so —
But she knows what she does.
    LEAR.                          Is this well spoken?
    REG. I dare avouch it, sir: what, fifty followers?          240
Is it not well? What should you need of more?
Yea, or so many, sith that both charge and danger
Speak 'gainst so great a number? How, in one house,
Should many people, under two commands,
Hold amity? 'Tis hard; almost impossible.
    GON. Why might not you, my lord, receive attendance
From those that she calls servants or from mine?
    REG. Why not, my lord? If then they chanced to slack you,
We could control them. If you will come to me, —
For now I spy a danger, — I entreat you          250
To bring but five and twenty: to no more
Will I give place or notice.
    LEAR. I gave you all —
    REG.                          And in good time you gave it.

LEAR. Made you my guardians, my depositaries;
But kept a reservation to be follow'd
With such a number. What, must I come to you
With five and twenty, Regan? said you so?
  REG. And speak 't again, my lord; no more with me.
  LEAR. Those wicked creatures yet do look well-favour'd,
When others are more wicked; not being the worst          260
Stands in some rank of praise. [*To* GON.] I'll go with thee:
Thy fifty yet doth double five-and-twenty,
And thou art twice her love.
  GON.                             Hear me, my lord:
What need you five and twenty, ten, or five,
To follow in a house where twice so many
Have a command to tend you?
  REG.                             What need one?
  LEAR. O, reason not the need: our basest beggars
Are in the poorest thing superfluous:
Allow not nature more than nature needs,
Man's life 's as cheap as beast's: thou art a lady;          270
If only to go warm were gorgeous,
Why, nature needs not what thou gorgeous wear'st,
Which scarcely keeps thee warm. But, for true need, —
You heavens, give me that patience, patience I need!
You see me here, you gods, a poor old man,
As full of grief as age; wretched in both!
If it be you that stir these daughters' hearts
Against their father, fool me not so much
To bear it tamely; touch me with noble anger,
And let not women's weapons, water-drops,                     280
Stain my man's cheeks! No, you unnatural hags,
I will have such revenges on you both,
That all the world shall — I will do such things, —
What they are, yet I know not; but they shall be
The terrors of the earth. You think I'll weep;
No, I'll not weep:
I have full cause of weeping; but this heart
Shall break into a hundred thousand flaws,
Or ere I'll weep. O fool, I shall go mad!
        [*Exeunt* LEAR, GLOUCESTER, KENT, *and* FOOL. *Storm and tempest.*
  CORN. Let us withdraw; 'twill be a storm.                    290
  REG. This house is little: the old man and his people
Cannot be well bestow'd.
  GON. 'Tis his own blame; hath put himself from rest,
And must needs taste his folly.
  REG. For his particular, I'll receive him gladly,
But not one follower.

254. **my guardians.** *Lear understands his contract to be that the daughters were guardians, or stewardesses, of his realm under him.* 259-260. **Those . . . wicked.** *Bad as Goneril is, there is a more exquisite quality of cruelty in Regan.* 266. **What need one.** *Lear's answer (ll. 267 ff.) is in some respects an expression of the underlying theme of the story: Why* reason, *i.e., discuss, the need, since it is not a question of need? It is a spiritual, not a temporal, matter which is involved.* 274. **patience.** *Patience seems to have been a term for the counterbalance which reason might set up against the passions.* 279. **noble anger.** *One cannot understand either the character of Lear or the significance of his story without a sound conception of righteous indignation as a noble virtue; with it is connected the ethical propriety of revenge.*

GON.                     So am I purposed.
Where is my lord of Gloucester?
CORN. Follow'd the old man forth: he is return'd.

*Re-enter* GLOUCESTER.

GLOU. The king is in high rage.
CORN.                          Whither is he going?
GLOU. He calls to horse; but will I know not whither.              300
CORN. 'Tis best to give him way; he leads himself.
GON. My lord, entreat him by no means to stay.
GLOU. Alack, the night comes on, and the bleak winds
Do sorely ruffle; for many miles about
There 's scarce a bush.
REG.                     O, sir, to wilful men,
The injuries that they themselves procure
Must be their schoolmasters. Shut up your doors:
He is attended with a desperate train;
And what they may incense him to, being apt
To have his ear abused, wisdom bids fear.                           310
CORN. Shut up your doors, my lord; 'tis a wild night:
My Regan counsels well: come out o' the storm.          [*Exeunt.*

# ACT III

SCENE I: *A heath.*

*Storm still. Enter* KENT *and a Gentleman, meeting.*

KENT. Who 's there, besides foul weather?
GENT. One minded like the weather, most unquietly.
KENT. I know you. Where 's the king?
GENT. Contending with the fretful element;
Bids the wind blow the earth into the sea,
Or swell the curled waters 'bove the main,
That things might change or cease; tears his white hair,
Which the impetuous blasts, with eyeless rage,
Catch in their fury, and make nothing of;
Strives in his little world of man to out-scorn                     10
The to-and-fro-conflicting wind and rain.
This night, wherein the cub-drawn bear would couch,
The lion and the belly-pinched wolf
Keep their fur dry, unbonneted he runs,
And bids what will take all.
KENT.                        But who is with him?
GENT. None but the fool; who labours to out-jest
His heart-struck injuries.
KENT.                       Sir, I do know you;
And dare, upon the warrant of my note,
Commend a dear thing to you. There is division,
Although as yet the face of it be cover'd                           20
With mutual cunning, 'twixt Albany and Cornwall;
Who have — as who have not, that their great stars
Throned and set high? — servants, who seem no less,

---

*Act III. Scene i.* 10. **little world of man,** *the microcosm; allusion to the theory that man is an epitome of the macrocosm, or universe, and moves in accordance with its laws and influences.*

Which are to France the spies and speculations
Intelligent of our state; what hath been seen,
Either in snuffs and packings of the dukes,
Or the hard rein which both of them have borne
Against the old kind king; or something deeper,
Whereof perchance these are but furnishings;
But, true it is, from France there comes a power                30
Into this scatter'd kingdom; who already,
Wise in our negligence, have secret feet
In some of our best ports, and are at point
To show their open banner. Now to you:
If on my credit you dare build so far
To make your speed to Dover, you shall find
Some that will thank you, making just report
Of how unnatural and bemadding sorrow
The king hath cause to plain.
I am a gentleman of blood and breeding;                        40
And, from some knowledge and assurance, offer
This office to you.
    GENT. I will talk further with you.
    KENT.                    No, do not.
For confirmation that I am much more
Than my out-wall, open this purse, and take
What it contains. If you shall see Cordelia, —
As fear not but you shall, — show her this ring;
And she will tell you who your fellow is
That yet you do not know. Fie on this storm!
I will go seek the king.                                        50
    GENT. Give me your hand: have you no more to say?
    KENT. Few words, but, to effect, more than all yet;
That, when we have found the king, — in which your pain
That way, I'll this, — he that first lights on him
Holla the other.                              [*Exeunt severally.*

SCENE II: *Another part of the heath. Storm still.*

*Enter* LEAR *and* FOOL.

    LEAR. Blow, winds, and crack your cheeks! rage! blow!
You cataracts and hurricanoes, spout
Till you have drench'd our steeples, drown'd the cocks!
You sulphurous and thought-executing fires,
Vaunt-couriers to oak-cleaving thunderbolts,
Singe my white head! And thou, all-shaking thunder,
Smite flat the thick rotundity o' the world!
Crack nature's moulds, all germens spill at once,
That make ingrateful man!                                        9
    FOOL. O nuncle, court holy-water in a dry house is better than this rain-
water out o' door. Good nuncle, in, and ask thy daughters' blessing: here 's
a night pities neither wise man nor fool.
    LEAR. Rumble thy bellyful! Spit, fire! spout, rain!
Nor rain, wind, thunder, fire, are my daughters:
I tax not you, you elements, with unkindness;

26. **snuffs,** *quarrels.* **packings,** *plots.*   45. **out-wall,** *exterior.*
  *Scene ii.* 10. **court holy-water,** *flattery.*

I never gave you kingdom, call'd you children,
You owe me no subscription: then let fall
Your horrible pleasure; here I stand, your slave,
A poor, infirm, weak, and despised old man:           20
But yet I call you servile ministers,
That have with two pernicious daughters join'd
Your high engender'd battles 'gainst a head
So old and white as this. O! O! 'tis foul!
    FOOL. He that has a house to put 's head in has a good head-piece.
      The cod-piece that will house
        Before the head has any,
      The head and he shall louse;
        So beggars marry many.           30
      The man that makes his toe
        What he his heart should make
      Shall of a corn cry woe,
        And turn his sleep to wake.
For there was never yet fair woman but she made mouths in a glass.
    LEAR. No, I will be the pattern of all patience;
I will say nothing.

    *Enter* KENT.

    KENT. Who 's there?
    FOOL. Marry, here 's grace and a cod-piece; that 's a wise man and
a fool.           41
    KENT. Alas, sir, are you here? things that love night
Love not such nights as these; the wrathful skies
Gallow the very wanderers of the dark,
And make them keep their caves: since I was man,
Such sheets of fire, such bursts of horrid thunder,
Such groans of roaring wind and rain, I never
Remember to have heard: man's nature cannot carry
The affliction nor the fear.
    LEAR.               Let the great gods,
That keep this dreadful pother o'er our heads,        50
Find out their enemies now. Tremble, thou wretch,
That hast within thee undivulged crimes,
Unwhipp'd of justice: hide thee, thou bloody hand;
Thou perjured, and thou simular man of virtue
That art incestuous: caitiff, to pieces shake,
That under covert and convenient seeming
Hast practised on man's life: close pent-up guilts,
Rive your concealing continents, and cry
These dreadful summoners grace. I am a man
More sinn'd against than sinning.
    KENT.              Alack, bare-headed!      60
Gracious my lord, hard by here is a hovel;

---

27-34. **The cod-piece ... wake.** *A man who prefers a mean member in place of a vital one shall suffer enduring pain where others would suffer merely a twinge. Lear had preferred Regan and Goneril to Cordelia.* 49. **Let the great gods,** *etc. An expression of Lear's faith in the power of the gods, or, as we should say, God; it is the symbol of the retention of his sanity. When he loses his reason he loses also his faith in divinity.* 58. **Rive ... continents,** *break open whatever conceals and protects you.* 58-59. **cry ... grace,** *pray for mercy at the hands of the officers of divine justice. A* summoner *was the police officer of an ecclesiastical court.* 60. **More sinn'd against than sinning.** *This famous phrase is a perfect indication that Lear is still sane.*

Some friendship will it lend you 'gainst the tempest:
Repose you there; while I to this hard house —
More harder than the stones whereof 'tis raised;
Which even but now, demanding after you,
Denied me to come in — return, and force
Their scanted courtesy.
    LEAR.        My wits begin to turn.
Come on, my boy: how dost, my boy, art cold?
I am cold myself. Where is this straw, my fellow?
The art of our necessities is strange,                  70
That can make vile things precious. Come, your hovel.
Poor fool and knave, I have one part in my heart
That 's sorry yet for thee.
    FOOL.  [*Singing*] He that has and a little tiny wit, —
        With hey, ho, the wind and the rain, —
      Must make content with his fortunes fit,
        For the rain it raineth every day.
    LEAR. True, my good boy. Come, bring us to this hovel.
                              [*Exeunt* LEAR *and* KENT.
    FOOL. This is a brave night to cool a courtezan.
I'll speak a prophecy ere I go:                     80
      When priests are more in word than matter;
      When brewers mar their malt with water;
      When nobles are their tailors' tutors;
      No heretics burn'd, but wenches' suitors;
      When every case in law is right;
      No squire in debt, nor no poor knight;
      When slanders do not live in tongues;
      Nor cutpurses come not to throngs;
      When usurers tell their gold i' the field;
      And bawds and whores do churches build;        90
      Then shall the realm of Albion
      Come to great confusion:
      Then comes the time, who lives to see 't,
      That going shall be used with feet.
This prophecy Merlin shall make; for I live before his time.    [*Exit.*

SCENE III: GLOUCESTER'S *castle.*

*Enter* GLOUCESTER *and* EDMUND.

    GLOU. Alack, alack, Edmund, I like not this unnatural dealing. When I desired their leave that I might pity him, they took from me the use of mine own house; charged me, on pain of their perpetual displeasure, neither to speak of him, entreat for him, nor any way sustain him.
    EDM. Most savage and unnatural!                                7
    GLOU. Go to; say you nothing. There 's a division betwixt the dukes; and a worse matter than that: I have received a letter this night; 'tis dangerous to be spoken; I have locked the letter in my closet: these injuries the king now bears will be revenged home; there 's part of a power already footed: we must incline to the king. I will seek him, and

---

67. **My wits begin to turn,** *a premonition followed by an expression of more than Lear's normal sanity, since it is his first reflection of sympathy for others.* 70-71. **The art ... precious,** *our necessities create in us a skill that makes us (like alchemists) able to transform vile into precious things.*

privily relieve him: go you and maintain talk with the duke, that my charity be not of him perceived: if he ask for me, I am ill, and gone to bed. Though I die for it, as no less is threatened me, the king my old master must be relieved. There is some strange thing toward, Edmund; pray you, be careful.      [*Exit.*

EDM. This courtesy, forbid thee, shall the duke      22
Instantly know; and of that letter too:
This seems a fair deserving, and must draw me
That which my father loses; no less than all:
The younger rises when the old doth fall.      [*Exit.*

SCENE IV: *The heath. Before a hovel.*

*Enter* LEAR, KENT, *and* FOOL.

KENT. Here is the place, my lord; good my lord, enter:
The tyranny of the open night 's too rough
For nature to endure.      [*Storm still.*
     LEAR.      Let me alone.
     KENT. Good my lord, enter here.
     LEAR.      Wilt break my heart?
     KENT. I had rather break mine own. Good my lord, enter.
     LEAR. Thou think'st 'tis much that this contentious storm
Invades us to the skin: so 'tis to thee;
But where the greater malady is fix'd,
The lesser is scarce felt. Thou 'ldst shun a bear;
But if thy flight lay toward the raging sea,      10
Thou 'ldst meet the bear i' the mouth. When the mind 's free,
The body 's delicate: the tempest in my mind
Doth from my senses take all feeling else
Save what beats there. Filial ingratitude!
Is it not as this mouth should tear this hand
For lifting food to 't? But I will punish home:
No, I will weep no more. In such a night
To shut me out! Pour on; I will endure.
In such a night as this! O Regan, Goneril!
Your old kind father, whose frank heart gave all, —      20
O, that way madness lies; let me shun that;
No more of that.
     KENT.      Good my lord, enter here.
     LEAR. Prithee, go in thyself; seek thine own ease:
This tempest will not give me leave to ponder
On things would hurt me more. But I'll go in.
[*To the* FOOL] In, boy; go first. You houseless poverty, —
Nay, get thee in. I'll pray, and then I'll sleep.      [FOOL *goes in.*
Poor naked wretches, wheresoe'er you are,
That bide the pelting of this pitiless storm,
How shall your houseless heads and unfed sides,      30
Your loop'd and window'd raggedness, defend you
From seasons such as these? O, I have ta'en
Too little care of this! Take physic, pomp;

---

     *Scene iv. 28-36.* **Poor naked wretches,** *etc. Lear's error has been a violation of that law of nature which is called justice. His sufferings have brought him round to a complete recognition and expression of general distributive justice. This quality, we may suppose, was in his nature, but his obstinacy and self-conceit had stifled it.*

Expose thyself to feel what wretches feel,
That thou mayst shake the superflux to them,
And show the heavens more just.
    EDG. [*Within*] Fathom and half, fathom and half! Poor Tom!
                [*The* FOOL *runs out from the hovel.*
    FOOL. Come not in here, nuncle, here 's a spirit. Help me, help me!    40
    KENT. Give me thy hand. Who 's there?
    FOOL. A spirit, a spirit: he says his name 's poor Tom.
    KENT. What art thou that dost grumble there i' the straw?
Come forth.

*Enter* EDGAR *disguised as a madman.*

    EDG. Away! the foul fiend follows me!
Through the sharp hawthorn blows the cold wind.
Hum! go to thy cold bed, and warm thee.
    LEAR. Hast thou given all to thy two daughters?
And art thou come to this?    50
    EDG. Who gives any thing to poor Tom? whom the foul fiend hath led
through fire and through flame, through ford and whirlpool, o'er bog and
quagmire; that hath laid knives under his pillow, and halters in his
pew; set ratsbane by his porridge; made him proud of heart, to ride on
a bay trotting-horse over four-inched bridges, to course his own shadow
for a traitor. Bless thy five wits! Tom 's a-cold, — O, do de, do de, do de.
Bless thee from whirlwinds, star-blasting, and taking! Do poor Tom some
charity, whom the foul fiend vexes: there could I have him now, — and
there, — and there again, and there.    [*Storm still.*  64
    LEAR. What, have his daughters brought him to this pass?
Couldst thou save nothing? Didst thou give them all?
    FOOL. Nay, he reserved a blanket, else we had been all shamed.
    LEAR. Now, all the plagues that in the pendulous air
Hang fated o'er men's faults light on thy daughters!    70
    KENT. He hath no daughters, sir.
    LEAR. Death, traitor! nothing could have subdued nature
To such a lowness but his unkind daughters.
Is it the fashion, that discarded fathers
Should have thus little mercy on their flesh?
Judicious punishment! 'twas this flesh begot
Those pelican daughters.
    EDG. Pillicock sat on Pillicock-hill:
Halloo, halloo, loo, loo!
    FOOL. This cold night will turn us all to fools and madmen.    81
    EDG. Take heed o' the foul fiend: obey thy parents; keep thy word justly;
swear not; commit not with man's sworn spouse; set not thy sweet heart
on proud array. Tom 's a-cold.
    LEAR. What hast thou been?    86
    EDG. A serving-man, proud in heart and mind; that curled my hair;
wore gloves in my cap; served the lust of my mistress' heart, and did the
act of darkness with her; swore as many oaths as I spake words, and broke
them in the sweet face of heaven: one that slept in the contriving of lust,
and waked to do it: wine loved I deeply, dice dearly; and in woman out-
paramoured the Turk: false of heart, light of ear, bloody of hand; hog in

---

49-50. **Hast ... this.** *Lear can interpret only in terms of his own great sorrow; the passage illustrates obsession but is still sound psychologically.*   59. **five wits,** *the five mental faculties: common wit, imagination, fantasy, judgment, memory.*   77. **pelican,** *greedy; a reference to the belief that young pelicans feed on the flesh of their mother's breasts.*   95. **light of ear,** *foolishly credulous.*

sloth, fox in stealth, wolf in greediness, dog in madness, lion in prey. Let
not the creaking of shoes nor the rustling of silks betray thy poor heart to
woman: keep thy foot out of brothels, thy hand out of plackets, thy pen
from lenders' books, and defy the foul fiend.                                101

    Still through the hawthorn blows the cold wind:
    Says suum, mun, ha, no, nonny.
    Dolphin my boy, my boy, sessa! let him trot by.           [*Storm still.*

LEAR. Why, thou wert better in thy grave than to answer with thy un-
covered body this extremity of the skies. Is man no more than this? Consider him well. Thou owest the worm no silk, the beast no hide, the sheep
no wool, the cat no perfume. Ha! here 's three on 's are sophisticated!
Thou art the thing itself: unaccommodated man is no more but such a
poor, bare, forked animal as thou art. Off, off, you lendings! come, un-
button here.                                               [*Tearing off his clothes.*

FOOL. Prithee, nuncle, be contented; 'tis a naughty night to swim in.
Now a little fire in a wild field were like an old lecher's heart; a small
spark, all the rest on 's body cold. Look, here comes a walking fire.      119

*Enter* GLOUCESTER, *with a torch.*

EDG. This is the foul fiend Flibbertigibbet: he begins at curfew, and
walks till the first cock; he gives the web and the pin, squints the eye,
and makes the hare-lip; mildews the white wheat, and hurts the poor
creature of earth.
    S. Withold footed thrice the old;
    He met the night-mare, and her nine-fold;
      Bid her alight,
      And her troth plight,
    And, aroint thee, witch, aroint thee!
KENT. How fares your grace?                                          130
LEAR. What 's he?
KENT. Who 's there? What is 't you seek?
GLOU. What are you there? Your names?
EDG. Poor Tom; that eats the swimming frog, the toad, the tadpole, the
wall-newt and the water; that in the fury of his heart, when the foul fiend
rages, eats cow-dung for sallets; swallows the old rat and the ditch-dog;
drinks the green mantle of the standing pool; who is whipped from tithing
to tithing, and stock-punished, and imprisoned; who hath had three suits
to his back, six shirts to his body, horse to ride, and weapon to wear;     143
    But mice and rats, and such small deer,
    Have been Tom's food for seven long year.
Beware my follower. Peace, Smulkin; peace, thou fiend!
GLOU. What, hath your grace no better company?
EDG. The prince of darkness is a gentleman:
Modo he 's call'd, and Mahu.
GLOU. Our flesh and blood is grown so vile, my lord,                 150
That it doth hate what gets it.
EDG. Poor Tom 's a-cold.
GLOU. Go in with me: my duty cannot suffer
To obey in all your daughters' hard commands:

114. **Off, off, you lendings.** *It may be said that Lear plunges logically into insanity. This is the climax of his story. He is convinced that chaos is come again, that it is not God's world; reason is dethroned and faith abandoned.*   125. **S. Withold,** *understood as a corruption of St. Vitalis, who is said to have been invoked against nightmare.* **footed thrice the old,** *thrice traversed the wold (tract of hilly upland).*   126. **nine-fold,** *nine familiars; suggestive also, certainly, of nine foals.*

Though their injunction be to bar my doors,
And let this tyrannous night take hold upon you,
Yet have I ventured to come seek you out,
And bring you where both fire and food is ready.
  LEAR. First let me talk with this philosopher.
What is the cause of thunder?                         160
  KENT. Good my lord, take his offer; go into the house.
  LEAR. I'll talk a word with this same learned Theban.
What is your study?
  EDG. How to prevent the fiend, and to kill vermin.
  LEAR. Let me ask you one word in private.
  KENT. Importune him once more to go, my lord;
His wits begin to unsettle.
  GLOU.           Canst thou blame him?         [*Storm still.*
His daughters seek his death; ah, that good Kent!
He said it would be thus, poor banish'd man!
Thou say'st the king grows mad; I'll tell thee, friend,   170
I am almost mad myself: I had a son,
Now outlaw'd from my blood; he sought my life,
But lately, very late: I loved him, friend:
No father his son dearer: truth to tell thee,
The grief hath crazed my wits. What a night 's this!
I do beseech your grace, —
  LEAR.               O, cry you mercy, sir.
Noble philosopher, your company.
  EDG. Tom 's a-cold.
  GLOU. In, fellow, there, into the hovel: keep thee warm.
  LEAR. Come, let 's in all.
  KENT.          This way, my lord.
  LEAR.                With him;           180
I will keep still with my philosopher.
  KENT. Good my lord, soothe him; let him take the fellow.
  GLOU. Take him you on.
  KENT. Sirrah, come on; go along with us.
  LEAR. Come, good Athenian.
  GLOU. No words, no words: hush.
  EDG. Child Rowland to the dark tower came,
      His word was still, — Fie, foh, and fum,
        I smell the blood of a British man.         [*Exeunt.*

SCENE V: GLOUCESTER'S *castle.*

*Enter* CORNWALL *and* EDMUND.

  CORN. I will have my revenge ere I depart his house.
  EDM. How, my lord, I may be censured, that nature thus gives way to
loyalty, something fears me to think of.
  CORN. I now perceive, it was not altogether your brother's evil disposition made him seek his death; but a provoking merit, set a-work by a re-
proveable badness in himself.                              9
  EDM. How malicious is my fortune, that I must repent to be just! This is
the letter he spoke of, which approves him an intelligent party to the
advantages of France. O heavens! that this treason were not, or not I
the detector!

  *Scene v. 8.* **provoking merit,** *etc., i.e., a forward-looking merit (in Edgar) incited by the badness
of Gloucester.*

CORN. Go with me to the duchess.

EDM. If the matter of this paper be certain, you have mighty business in hand.

CORN. True or false, it hath made thee earl of Gloucester. Seek out where thy father is, that he may be ready for our apprehension.     20

EDM. [*Aside*] If I find him comforting the king, it will stuff his suspicion more fully. — I will persevere in my course of loyalty, though the conflict be sore between that and my blood.

CORN. I will lay trust upon thee; and thou shalt find a dearer father in my love.     [*Exeunt.*

SCENE VI: *A chamber in a farmhouse adjoining the castle.*

*Enter* GLOUCESTER, LEAR, KENT, FOOL, *and* EDGAR.

GLOU. Here is better than the open air; take it thankfully. I will piece out the comfort with what addition I can: I will not be long from you.

KENT. All the power of his wits have given way to his impatience: the gods reward your kindness!     [*Exit* GLOUCESTER.     6

EDG. Fraterretto calls me; and tells me Nero is an angler in the lake of darkness. Pray, innocent, and beware the foul fiend.

FOOL. Prithee, nuncle, tell me whether a madman be a gentleman or a yeoman?     11

LEAR. A king, a king!

FOOL. No, he 's a yeoman that has a gentleman to his son; for he 's a mad yeoman that sees his son a gentleman before him.

LEAR. To have a thousand with red burning spits
Come hissing in upon 'em, —

EDG. The foul fiend bites my back.

FOOL. He 's mad that trusts in the tameness of a wolf, a horse's health, a boy's love, or a whore's oath.     21

LEAR. It shall be done; I will arraign them straight.
[*To* EDGAR] Come, sit thou here, most learned justicer;
[*To the* FOOL] Thou, sapient sir, sit here. Now, you she foxes!

EDG. Look, where he stands and glares!
Wantest thou eyes at trial, madam?
        Come o'er the bourn, Bessy, to me, —

FOOL.         Her boat hath a leak,
            And she must not speak
            Why she dares not come over to thee.     30

EDG. The foul fiend haunts poor Tom in the voice of a nightingale. Hopdance cries in Tom's belly for two white herring. Croak not, black angel; I have no food for thee.

KENT. How do you, sir? Stand you not so amazed:
Will you lie down and rest upon the cushions?

LEAR. I'll see their trial first. Bring in the evidence.
[*To* EDGAR] Thou robed man of justice, take thy place;
[*To the* FOOL] And thou, his yoke-fellow of equity,
Bench by his side: [*To* KENT] you are o' the commission,     40
Sit you too.

EDG. Let us deal justly.
        Sleepest or wakest thou, jolly shepherd?
            Thy sheep be in the corn;

---

*Scene vi.* 17. **a thousand,** *i.e., attackers.* 33. **Croak,** *make a rumbling sound in the stomach to denote hunger.* 37. **evidence,** *witnesses.*

And for one blast of thy minikin mouth,
        Thy sheep shall take no harm.
Pur! the cat is gray.

LEAR. Arraign her first; 'tis Goneril. I here take my oath before this
honourable assembly, she kicked the poor king her father.                     50

FOOL. Come hither, mistress. Is your name Goneril?

LEAR. She cannot deny it.

FOOL. Cry you mercy, I took you for a joint-stool.

LEAR. And here 's another, whose warp'd looks proclaim
What store her heart is made on. Stop her there!
Arms, arms, sword, fire! Corruption in the place!
False justicer, why hast thou let her 'scape?

EDG. Bless thy five wits!                                                     60

KENT. O pity! Sir, where is the patience now,
That you so oft have boasted to retain?

EDG. [*Aside*] My tears begin to take his part so much,
They'll mar my counterfeiting.

LEAR. The little dogs and all,
Tray, Blanch, and Sweet-heart, see, they bark at me.

EDG. Tom will throw his head at them.
Avaunt, you curs!
        Be thy mouth or black or white,
        Tooth that poisons if it bite;                                        70
        Mastiff, greyhound, mongrel grim,
        Hound or spaniel, brach or lym,
        Or bobtail tike or trundle-tail,
        Tom will make them weep and wail:
        For, with throwing thus my head,
        Dogs leap the hatch, and all are fled.
Do de, de, de. Sessa! Come, march to wakes and fairs and market-towns.
Poor Tom, thy horn is dry.                                                    79

LEAR. Then let them anatomize Regan; see what breeds about her heart.
Is there any cause in nature that makes these hard hearts? [*To* EDGAR]
You, sir, I entertain for one of my hundred; only I do not like the fashion
of your garments: you will say they are Persian attire; but let them be
changed.

KENT. Now, good my lord, lie here and rest awhile.

LEAR. Make no noise, make no noise; draw the curtains: so, so, so. We'll
go to supper i' the morning. So, so, so.                                      91

FOOL. And I'll go to bed at noon.

*Re-enter* GLOUCESTER.

GLOU. Come hither, friend: where is the king my master?

KENT. Here sir; but trouble him not, his wits are gone.

GLOU. Good friend, I prithee, take him in thy arms;
I have o'erheard a plot of death upon him:
There is a litter ready; lay him in 't,
And drive towards Dover, friend, where thou shalt meet
Both welcome and protection. Take up thy master:
If thou shouldst dally half an hour, his life,                                100
With thine, and all that offer to defend him,
Stand in assured loss: take up, take up;
And follow me, that will to some provision
Give thee quick conduct.

KENT.                         Oppressed nature sleeps:

This rest might yet have balm'd thy broken sinews,
Which, if convenience will not allow,
Stand in hard cure. [*To the* FOOL] Come, help to bear thy master;
Thou must not stay behind.

    GLOU.                      Come, come, away.    [*Exeunt all but* EDGAR.

    EDG. When we our betters see bearing our woes,
We scarcely think our miseries our foes.                                110
Who alone suffers suffers most i' the mind,
Leaving free things and happy shows behind:
But then the mind much sufferance doth o'erskip,
When grief hath mates, and bearing fellowship.
How light and portable my pain seems now,
When that which makes me bend makes the king bow,
He childed as I father'd! Tom, away!
Mark the high noises; and thyself bewray.
When false opinion, whose wrong thought defiles thee,
In thy just proof, repeals and reconciles thee.                  120
What will hap more to-night, safe 'scape the king!
Lurk, lurk.                                          [*Exit.*

SCENE VII: GLOUCESTER'S *castle.*

*Enter* CORNWALL, REGAN, GONERIL, EDMUND, *and Servants.*

    CORN. Post speedily to my lord your husband; show him this letter: the army of France is landed. Seek out the villain Gloucester.

                          [*Exeunt some of the Servants.*

    REG. Hang him instantly.

    GON. Pluck out his eyes.

    CORN. Leave him to my displeasure. Edmund, keep you our sister company: the revenges we are bound to take upon your traitorous father are not fit for your beholding. Advise the duke, where you are going, to a most festinate preparation: we are bound to the like. Our posts shall be swift and intelligent betwixt us. Farewell, dear sister: farewell, my lord of Gloucester.

    *Enter* OSWALD.

How now! where 's the king?                                    14
    OSW. My lord of Gloucester hath convey'd him hence:
Some five or six and thirty of his knights,
Hot questrists after him, met him at gate;
Who, with some other of the lords dependants,
Are gone with him towards Dover; where they boast
To have well-armed friends.

    CORN.                  Get horses for your mistress.           20

    GON. Farewell, sweet lord, and sister.

    CORN. Edmund, farewell.    [*Exeunt* GONERIL, EDMUND, *and* OSWALD.
                              Go seek the traitor Gloucester,
Pinion him like a thief, bring him before us.    [*Exeunt other Servants.*
Though well we may not pass upon his life
Without the form of justice, yet our power
Shall do a courtesy to our wrath, which men
May blame, but not control. Who 's there? the traitor?

---

114. **bearing,** *tribulation.*   117. **He ... father'd,** *he has found the same cruelty in his children which I found in my father.*

*Enter* GLOUCESTER, *brought in by two or three.*

REG. Ingrateful fox! 'tis he.

CORN. Bind fast his corky arms.

GLOU. What mean your graces? Good my friends, consider       30
You are my guests: do me no foul play, friends.

CORN. Bind him, I say.                    [*Servants bind him.*

REG.                     Hard, hard. O filthy traitor!

GLOU. Unmerciful lady as you are, I'm none.

CORN. To this chair bind him. Villain, thou shalt find —

                    [REGAN *plucks his beard.*

GLOU. By the kind gods, 'tis most ignobly done
To pluck me by the beard.

REG. So white, and such a traitor!

GLOU.                    Naughty lady,
These hairs, which thou dost ravish from my chin,
Will quicken, and accuse thee: I am your host:
With robbers' hands my hospitable favours                    40
You should not ruffle thus. What will you do?

CORN. Come, sir, what letters had you late from France?

REG. Be simple answerer, for we know the truth.

CORN. And what confederacy have you with the traitors
Late footed in the kingdom?

REG. To whose hands have you sent the lunatic king?
Speak.

GLOU.                    I have a letter guessingly set down,
Which came from one that 's of a neutral heart,
And not from one opposed.

CORN.                    Cunning.

REG.                    And false.

CORN. Where hast thou sent the king?                    50

GLOU. To Dover.

REG. Wherefore to Dover? Wast thou not charged at peril —

CORN. Wherefore to Dover? Let him first answer that.

GLOU. I am tied to the stake, and I must stand the course.

REG. Wherefore to Dover, sir?

GLOU. Because I would not see thy cruel nails
Pluck out his poor old eyes; nor thy fierce sister
In his anointed flesh stick boarish fangs.
The sea, with such a storm as his bare head
In hell-black night endured, would have buoy'd up,                    60
And quench'd the stelled fires:
Yet, poor old heart, he holp the heavens to rain.
If wolves had at thy gate howl'd that stern time,
Thou shouldst have said 'Good porter, turn the key,'
All cruels else subscribed: but I shall see
The winged vengeance overtake such children.

CORN. See 't shalt thou never. Fellows, hold the chair.
Upon these eyes of thine I'll set my foot.

GLOU. He that will think to live till he be old,
Give me some help! O cruel! O you gods!                    70

REG. One side will mock another; the other too.

---

*Scene vii.* 29. **corky,** *withered with age.*   65. **All ... subscribed,** *all their usual cruelties condoned or forgiven.*   66. **winged vengeance.** *Note Gloucester's faith in the rectitude of the gods; note also that in his speech he twice suggests ironically his own fate.*

CORN. If you see vengeance, —
FIRST SERV.                  Hold your hand, my lord:
I have served you ever since I was a child;
But better service have I never done you
Than now to bid you hold.
     REG.                How now, you dog!
FIRST SERV. If you did wear a beard upon your chin,
I'd shake it on this quarrel. What do you mean?
     CORN. My villain!                [*They draw and fight.*
FIRST SERV. Nay, then, come on, and take the chance of anger.
REG. Give me thy sword. A peasant stand up thus!      80
               [*Takes a sword, and runs at him behind.*
     FIRST SERV. O, I am slain! My lord, you have one eye left
To see some mischief on him. O!             [*Dies.*
     CORN. Lest it see more, prevent it. Out, vile jelly!
Where is thy lustre now?
     GLOU. All dark and comfortless. Where 's my son Edmund?
Edmund, enkindle all the sparks of nature,
To quit this horrid act.
     REG.             Out, treacherous villain!
Thou call'st on him that hates thee: it was he
That made the overture of thy treasons to us;
Who is too good to pity thee.      90
     GLOU. O my follies! then Edgar was abused.
Kind gods, forgive me that, and prosper him!
     REG. Go thrust him out at gates, and let him smell
His way to Dover. [*Exit one with* GLOUCESTER] How is 't, my lord? how
     look you?
     CORN. I have received a hurt: follow me, lady.
Turn out that eyeless villain; throw this slave
Upon the dunghill. Regan, I bleed apace:
Untimely comes this hurt: give me your arm.
            [*Exit* CORNWALL, *led by* REGAN.
     SEC. SERV. I'll never care what wickedness I do,
If this man come to good.
     THIRD SERV.            If she live long,      100
And in the end meet the old course of death,
Women will all turn monsters.
     SEC. SERV. Let 's follow the old earl, and get the Bedlam
To lead him where he would: his roguish madness
Allows itself to any thing.
     THIRD SERV. Go thou: I'll fetch some flax and whites of eggs
To apply to his bleeding face. Now, heaven help him! [*Exeunt severally.*

## ACT IV

SCENE I: *The heath.*

*Enter* EDGAR.

EDG. Yet better thus, and known to be contemn'd,
Than still contemn'd and flatter'd. To be worst,
The lowest and most dejected thing of fortune,

---

79. **take ... anger,** *run the risk of fighting when angry.*    89. **overture,** *disclosure.*    103. **Bedlam,**
*Bedlamite, lunatic, i.e., Edgar.*

Stands still in esperance, lives not in fear:
The lamentable change is from the best;
The worst returns to laughter. Welcome, then,
Thou unsubstantial air that I embrace!
The wretch that thou hast blown unto the worst
Owes nothing to thy blasts. But who comes here?

*Enter* GLOUCESTER, *led by an* OLD MAN.

My father, poorly led? World, world, O world!                    10
But that thy strange mutations make us hate thee,
Life would not yield to age.
   OLD MAN. O, my good lord, I have been your tenant, and your father's
tenant, these fourscore years.
   GLOU. Away, get thee away; good friend, be gone:
Thy comforts can do me no good at all;
Thee they may hurt.
   OLD MAN. Alack, sir, you cannot see your way.
   GLOU. I have no way, and therefore want no eyes;                20
I stumbled when I saw: full oft 'tis seen,
Our means secure us, and our mere defects
Prove our commodities. O dear son Edgar,
The food of thy abused father's wrath!
Might I but live to see thee in my touch,
I 'ld say I had eyes again!
   OLD MAN.       How now! Who 's there?
   EDG. [*Aside*] O gods! Who is 't can say 'I am at the worst'?
I am worse than e'er I was.
   OLD MAN.      'Tis poor mad Tom.
   EDG. [*Aside*] And worse I may be yet: the worst is not
So long as we can say 'This is the worst.'                       30
   OLD MAN. Fellow, where goest?
   GLOU.      Is it a beggar-man?
   OLD MAN. Madman and beggar too.
   GLOU. He has some reason, else he could not beg.
I' the last night's storm I such a fellow saw;
Which made me think a man a worm: my son
Came then into my mind; and yet my mind
Was then scarce friends with him: I have heard more since.
As flies to wanton boys, are we to the gods,
They kill us for their sport.
   EDG.     [*Aside*] How should this be?
Bad is the trade that must play fool to sorrow,                  40
Angering itself and others. — Bless thee, master!
   GLOU. Is that the naked fellow?
   OLD MAN.      Ay, my lord.
   GLOU. Then, prithee, get thee gone: if, for my sake,
Thou wilt o'ertake us, hence a mile or twain,
I' the way toward Dover, do it for ancient love;
And bring some covering for this naked soul,
Who I'll entreat to lead me.
   OLD MAN.     Alack, sir, he is mad.

---

*Act IV. Scene i.* 22. **Our means secure us,** *our resources make us overconfident.* 23. **commodities,**
*benefits.* 38-39. **As . . . sport.** *This is a clear statement of Gloucester's loss of faith, which he*
*signalizes (ll. 76 ff.) by forming a plan to commit suicide.*

GLOU. 'Tis the times' plague, when madmen lead the blind.
Do as I bid thee, or rather do thy pleasure;
Above the rest, be gone.                                                    50

OLD MAN. I'll bring him the best 'parel that I have,
Come on 't what will.                                                [*Exit.*

GLOU. Sirrah, naked fellow, —

EDG. Poor Tom 's a-cold. [*Aside*] I cannot daub it further.

GLOU. Come hither, fellow.

EDG. [*Aside*] And yet I must. — Bless thy sweet eyes, they bleed.      56

GLOU. Know'st thou the way to Dover?

EDG. Both stile and gate, horse-way and foot-path. Poor Tom hath been
scared out of his good wits: bless thee, good man's son, from the foul
fiend! five fiends have been in poor Tom at once; of lust, as Obidicut;
Hobbididance, prince of dumbness; Mahu, of stealing; Modo, of murder;
Flibbertigibbet, of mopping and mowing, who since possesses chamber-
maids and waiting-women. So, bless thee, master!

GLOU. Here, take this purse, thou whom the heavens' plagues
Have humbled to all strokes: that I am wretched
Makes thee the happier: heavens, deal so still!
Let the superfluous and lust-dieted man,                                    70
That slaves your ordinance, that will not see
Because he doth not feel, feel your power quickly;
So distribution should undo excess,
And each man have enough. Dost thou know Dover?

EDG. Ay, master.

GLOU. There is a cliff, whose high and bending head
Looks fearfully in the confined deep:
Bring me but to the very brim of it,
And I'll repair the misery thou dost bear
With something rich about me: from that place                              80
I shall no leading need.

EDG.                    Give me thy arm:
Poor Tom shall lead thee.                                          [*Exeunt.*


SCENE II: *Before the* DUKE OF ALBANY'S *palace.*

*Enter* GONERIL *and* EDMUND.

GON. Welcome, my lord: I marvel our mild husband
Not met us on the way.

*Enter* OSWALD.

                     Now, where 's your master?
OSW. Madam, within; but never man so changed.
I told him of the army that was landed;
He smiled at it: I told him you were coming;
His answer was 'The worse:' of Gloucester's treachery,
And of the loyal service of his son,
When I inform'd him, then he call'd me sot,
And told me I had turn'd the wrong side out:
What most he should dislike seems pleasant to him;                          10
What like, offensive.

54. **daub it further,** *keep up the disguise.*   71. **slaves your ordinance,** *i.e., makes the laws of heaven his slaves.*   73. **distribution,** *the principle of distributive justice in ethics.*
    *Scene ii.* 9. **turn'd the wrong side out,** *put a wrong interpretation on the matter.*

GON.    [*To* EDM.] Then shall you go no further.
It is the cowish terror of his spirit,
That dares not undertake: he'll not feel wrongs
Which tie him to an answer. Our wishes on the way
May prove effects. Back, Edmund, to my brother;
Hasten his musters and conduct his powers:
I must change arms at home, and give the distaff
Into my husband's hands. This trusty servant
Shall pass between us: ere long you are like to hear,
If you dare venture in your own behalf,                        20
A mistress's command. Wear this; spare speech;    [*Giving a favour.*
Decline your head: this kiss, if it durst speak,
Would stretch thy spirits up into the air:
Conceive, and fare thee well.
    EDM. Yours in the ranks of death.
    GON.                    My most dear Gloucester! [*Exit* EDMUND.
O, the difference of man and man!
To thee a woman's services are due:
My fool usurps my body.
    OSW.                Madam, here comes my lord.            [*Exit.*

    *Enter* ALBANY.

    GON. I have been worth the whistle.
    ALB.                        O Goneril!
You are not worth the dust which the rude wind            30
Blows in your face. I fear your disposition:
That nature, which contemns it origin,
Cannot be border'd certain in itself;
She that herself will sliver and disbranch
From her material sap, perforce must wither
And come to deadly use.
    GON. No more; the text is foolish.
    ALB. Wisdom and goodness to the vile seem vile:
Filths savour but themselves. What have you done?
Tigers, not daughters, what have you perform'd?            40
A father, and a gracious aged man,
Whose reverence even the head-lugg'd bear would lick,
Most barbarous, most degenerate! have you madded.
Could my good brother suffer you to do it?
A man, a prince, by him so benefited!
If that the heavens do not their visible spirits
Send quickly down to tame these vile offences,
It will come,
Humanity must perforce prey on itself,
Like monsters of the deep.
    GON.                Milk-liver'd man!                    50
That bear'st a cheek for blows, a head for wrongs:
Who hast not in thy brows an eye discerning
Thine honour from thy suffering; that not know'st
Fools do those villains pity who are punish'd

---

13-14. **he'll ... answer**, *i.e., in his cowardice he will ignore injuries he ought to resent.* 14-15.
**Our ... effects**, *my wishes expressed to you on the way may come to pass.* 17. **arms, distaff**, *i.e.,
she must turn warrior and give into Albany's hands the arms, or insignia, of housewifery.* 29.
**whistle**. *She alludes to the proverb: "It is a poor dog that is not worth the whistling."* 33. **border'd
certain**, *kept securely within bounds.*

Ere they have done their mischief. Where 's thy drum?
France spreads his banners in our noiseless land,
With plumed helm thy state begins to threat;
Whiles thou, a moral fool, sit'st still, and criest
'Alack, why does he so?'
    ALB.           See thyself, devil!
Proper deformity seems not in the fiend                60
So horrid as in woman.
    GON.          O vain fool!
    ALB. Thou changed and self-cover'd thing, for shame,
Be-monster not thy feature. Were 't my fitness
To let these hands obey my blood,
They are apt enough to dislocate and tear
Thy flesh and bones: howe'er thou art a fiend,
A woman's shape doth shield thee.
    GON. Marry, your manhood now –

*Enter a Messenger.*

    ALB. What news?
    MESS. O, my good lord, the Duke of Cornwall 's dead;    70
Slain by his servant, going to put out
The other eye of Gloucester.
    ALB.              Gloucester's eyes!
    MESS. A servant that he bred, thrill'd with remorse,
Opposed against the act, bending his sword
To his great master; who, thereat enraged,
Flew on him, and amongst them fell'd him dead;
But not without that harmful stroke, which since
Hath pluck'd him after.
    ALB.          This shows you are above,
You justicers, that these our nether crimes
So speedily can venge! But, O poor Gloucester!    80
Lost he his other eye?
    MESS.        Both, both, my lord.
This letter, madam, craves a speedy answer;
'Tis from your sister.
    GON.        [*Aside*] One way I like this well;
But being widow, and my Gloucester with her,
May all the building in my fancy pluck
Upon my hateful life: another way,
The news is not so tart. – I'll read, and answer.    [*Exit.*
    ALB. Where was his son when they did take his eyes?
    MESS. Come with my lady hither.
    ALB.            He is not here.    90
    MESS. No, my good lord; I met him back again.
    ALB. Knows he the wickedness?
    MESS. Ay, my good lord; 'twas he inform'd against him;
And quit the house on purpose, that their punishment
Might have the freer course.
    ALB.          Gloucester, I live
To thank thee for the love thou show'dst the king,

---

60. **Proper,** *i.e., the deformity appropriate to the fiend.*   62. **self-cover'd,** *having the true self concealed.*   63. **Be-monster . . . feature,** *do not, being fiend, take on the outward form of woman.*   78-79. **This . . . justicers,** *premonition of ultimate justice.*   79. **nether,** *committed here below.*

And to revenge thine eyes. Come hither, friend:
Tell me what more thou know'st.                    [*Exeunt.*

SCENE III: *The French camp near Dover.*

*Enter* KENT *and a Gentleman.*

KENT. Why the King of France is so suddenly gone back know you
the reason?

GENT. Something he left imperfect in the state, which since his coming
forth is thought of; which imports to the kingdom so much fear and
danger, that his personal return was most required and necessary.

KENT. Who hath he left behind him general?

GENT. The Marshal of France, Monsieur La Far.                    10

KENT. Did your letters pierce the queen to any demonstration of grief?

GENT. Ay, sir; she took them, read them in my presence;
And now and then an ample tear trill'd down
Her delicate cheek: it seem'd she was a queen
Over her passion; who, most rebel-like,
Sought to be king o'er her.

KENT.                    O, then it moved her.

GENT. Not to a rage: patience and sorrow strove
Who should express her goodliest. You have seen
Sunshine and rain at once: her smiles and tears                    20
Were like a better way: those happy smilets,
That play'd on her ripe lip, seem'd not to know
What guests were in her eyes; which parted thence,
As pearls from diamonds dropp'd. In brief,
Sorrow would be a rarity most beloved,
If all could so become it.

KENT.                    Made she no verbal question?

GENT. 'Faith, once or twice she heaved the name of 'father'
Pantingly forth, as if it press'd her heart;
Cried 'Sisters! sisters! Shame of ladies! sisters!
Kent! father! sisters! What, i' the storm? i' the night?                    30
Let pity not be believed!' There she shook
The holy water from her heavenly eyes,
And clamour moisten'd: then away she started
To deal with grief alone.

KENT.                    It is the stars,
The stars above us, govern our conditions;
Else one self mate and mate could not beget
Such different issues. You spoke not with her since?

GENT. No.

KENT. Was this before the king return'd?

GENT.                    No, since.

KENT. Well, sir, the poor distressed Lear 's i' the town;                    40
Who sometime, in his better tune, remembers
What we are come about, and by no means
Will yield to see his daughter.

GENT.                    Why, good sir?

---

*Scene iii.* 33. **clamour moisten'd,** *wailing relieved by tears.*    34. **It is the stars.** *One of the many
expressions in the play of the inscrutability of Providence.*    41. **better tune,** *saner moments.*

KENT. A sovereign shame so elbows him: his own unkindness,
That stripp'd her from his benediction, turn'd her
To foreign casualties, gave her dear rights
To his dog-hearted daughters, these things sting
His mind so venomously, that burning shame
Detains him from Cordelia.
    GENT.               Alack, poor gentleman!
    KENT. Of Albany's and Cornwall's powers you heard not?    50
    GENT. 'Tis so, they are afoot.
    KENT. Well, sir, I'll bring you to our master Lear,
And leave you to attend him: some dear cause
Will in concealment wrap me up awhile;
When I am known aright, you shall not grieve
Lending me this acquaintance. I pray you, go
Along with me.                                *[Exeunt.*

SCENE IV: *The same. A tent.*

*Enter, with drum and colours,* CORDELIA, DOCTOR, *and Soldiers.*

    COR. Alack, 'tis he: why, he was met even now
As mad as the vex'd sea; singing aloud;
Crown'd with rank fumiter and furrow-weeds,
With bur-docks, hemlock, nettles, cuckoo-flowers,
Darnel, and all the idle weeds that grow
In our sustaining corn. A century send forth;
Search every acre in the high-grown field,
And bring him to our eye. [*Exit an Officer*] What can man's wisdom
In the restoring his bereaved sense?
He that helps him take all my outward worth.    10
    DOCT. There is means, madam:
Our foster-nurse of nature is repose,
The which he lacks; that to provoke in him,
Are many simples operative, whose power
Will close the eye of anguish.
    COR.                All blest secrets,
All you unpublish'd virtues of the earth,
Spring with my tears! be aidant and remediate
In the good man's distress! Seek, seek for him;
Lest his ungovern'd rage dissolve the life
That wants the means to lead it.

    *Enter a Messenger.*

    MESS.                News, madam;    20
The British powers are marching hitherward.
    COR. 'Tis known before; our preparation stands
In expectation of them. O dear father,
It is thy business that I go about;
Therefore great France
My mourning and important tears hath pitied.
No blown ambition doth our arms incite,

---

*Scene iv. 3-5. The plants mentioned in this passage are probably selected because of their bitter and poisonous quality.*  **8. can,** *knows.* **wisdom,** *science.*  **27. blown,** *puffed up with pride.*

But love, dear love, and our aged father's right:
Soon may I hear and see him!                          [*Exeunt.*


SCENE V: GLOUCESTER'S *castle.*

*Enter* REGAN *and* OSWALD.

REG. But are my brother's powers set forth?
OSW.                                   Ay, madam.
REG. Himself in person there?
OSW.                        Madam, with much ado:
Your sister is the better soldier.
   REG. Lord Edmund spake not with your lord at home?
OSW. No, madam.
   REG. What might import my sister's letter to him?
OSW. I know not, lady.
   REG. 'Faith, he is posted hence on serious matter.
It was great ignorance, Gloucester's eyes being out,
To let him live: where he arrives he moves                    10
All hearts against us: Edmund, I think, is gone,
In pity of his misery, to dispatch
His nighted life; moreover, to descry
The strength o' the enemy.
   OSW. I must needs after him, madam, with my letter.
   REG. Our troops set forth to-morrow: stay with us;
The ways are dangerous.
   OSW.             I may not, madam:
My lady charged my duty in this business.
   REG. Why should she write to Edmund? Might not you
Transport her purposes by word? Belike,                       20
Something — I know not what: I'll love thee much,
Let me unseal the letter.
   OSW.             Madam, I had rather —
   REG. I know your lady does not love her husband;
I am sure of that: and at her late being here
She gave strange œillades and most speaking looks
To noble Edmund. I know you are of her bosom.
   OSW. I, madam?
   REG. I speak in understanding; you are, I know 't:
Therefore I do advise you, take this note:
My lord is dead; Edmund and I have talk'd;                    30
And more convenient is he for my hand
Than for your lady's: you may gather more.
If you do find him, pray you, give him this;
And when your mistress hears thus much from you,
I pray, desire her call her wisdom to her.
So, fare you well.
If you do chance to hear of that blind traitor,
Preferment falls on him that cuts him off.
   OSW. Would I could meet him, madam! I should show
What party I do follow.
   REG.             Fare thee well.                    [*Exeunt.* 40

---

   *Scene v.* 11-14. **Edmund...enemy.** *Note the irony which reveals Edmund's real reason as it states his pretended one.* 29. **take this note,** *take note of this.* 30. **have talk'd,** *are affianced to one another.*

SCENE VI: *Fields near Dover.*

*Enter* GLOUCESTER, *and* EDGAR *dressed like a peasant.*

GLOU. When shall we come to the top of that same hill?
EDG. You do climb up it now: look, how we labour.
GLOU. Methinks the ground is even.
EDG.                                    Horrible steep.
Hark, do you hear the sea?
GLOU.                       No, truly.
EDG. Why, then, your other senses grow imperfect
By your eyes' anguish.
GLOU.                 So may it be, indeed:
Methinks thy voice is alter'd; and thou speak'st
In better phrase and matter than thou didst.
EDG. You 're much deceived: in nothing am I changed
But in my garments.
GLOU.               Methinks you 're better spoken.            10
EDG. Come on, sir; here 's the place: stand still. How fearful
And dizzy 'tis, to cast one's eyes so low!
The crows and choughs that wing the midway air
Show scarce so gross as beetles: half way down
Hangs one that gathers samphire, dreadful trade!
Methinks he seems no bigger than his head:
The fishermen, that walk upon the beach,
Appear like mice; and yond tall anchoring bark,
Diminish'd to her cock; her cock, a buoy
Almost too small for sight: the murmuring surge,            20
That on the unnumber'd idle pebbles chafes,
Cannot be heard so high. I'll look no more;
Lest my brain turn, and the deficient sight
Topple down headlong.
GLOU.                 Set me where you stand.
EDG. Give me your hand: you are now within a foot
Of the extreme verge: for all beneath the moon
Would I not leap upright.
GLOU.                   Let go my hand.
Here, friend, 's another purse; in it a jewel
Well worth a poor man's taking: fairies and gods
Prosper it with thee! Go thou farther off;            30
Bid me farewell, and let me hear thee going.
EDG. Now fare you well, good sir.
GLOU.                         With all my heart.
EDG. Why I do trifle thus with his despair
Is done to cure it.
GLOU.         [*Kneeling*] O you mighty gods!
This world I do renounce, and, in your sights,
Shake patiently my great affliction off:
If I could bear it longer, and not fall
To quarrel with your great opposeless wills,
My snuff and loathed part of nature should
Burn itself out. If Edgar live, O, bless him!            40
Now, fellow, fare thee well.                     [*He falls forward.*

Scene vi. 19. **cock,** *cock-boat.* 33-80. **Why . . . thoughts.** *The teaching of this passage is against suicide; in that, as in other matters, the play is Christian in spite of its pagan setting.* 38. **opposeless,** *irresistible.*

EDG.                    Gone, sir: farewell.
And yet I know not how conceit may rob
The treasury of life, when life itself
Yields to the theft: had he been where he thought,
By this, had thought been past. Alive or dead?
Ho, you sir! friend! Hear you, sir! speak!
Thus might he pass indeed: yet he revives.
What are you, sir?
   GLOU.           Away, and let me die.
   EDG. Hadst thou been aught but gossamer, feathers, air,
So many fathom down precipitating,                              50
Thou 'dst shiver'd like an egg: but thou dost breathe;
Hast heavy substance; bleed'st not; speak'st; art sound.
Ten masts at each make not the altitude
Which thou hast perpendicularly fell:
Thy life 's a miracle. Speak yet again.
   GLOU. But have I fall'n, or no?
   EDG. From the dread summit of this chalky bourn.
Look up a-height; the shrill-gorged lark so far
Cannot be seen or heard: do but look up.
   GLOU. Alack, I have no eyes.                              60
Is wretchedness deprived that benefit,
To end itself by death? 'Twas yet some comfort,
When misery could beguile the tyrant's rage,
And frustrate his proud will.
   EDG.                    Give me your arm:
Up: so. How is 't? Feel you your legs? You stand.
   GLOU. Too well, too well.
   EDG.                    This is above all strangeness.
Upon the crown o' the cliff, what thing was that
Which parted from you?
   GLOU.               A poor unfortunate beggar.
   EDG. As I stood here below, methought his eyes
Were two full moons; he had a thousand noses,                   70
Horns whelk'd and waved like the enridged sea:
It was some fiend; therefore, thou happy father,
Think that the clearest gods, who make them honours
Of men's impossibilities, have preserved thee.
   GLOU. I do remember now: henceforth I'll bear
Affliction till it do cry out itself
'Enough, enough,' and die. That thing you speak of,
I took it for a man; often 'twould say
'The fiend, the fiend:' he led me to that place.
   EDG. Bear free and patient thoughts. But who comes here?     80

*Enter* LEAR, *fantastically dressed with wild flowers.*

The safer sense will ne'er accommodate
His master thus.
   LEAR. No, they cannot touch me for coining;
I am the king himself.
   EDG. O thou side-piercing sight!                            85
   LEAR. Nature 's above art in that respect. There 's your press-money.

---

47. **pass,** *die.*  53. **at each,** *end to end.*  73. **clearest,** *most righteous.*  74. **men's impossibilities,**
*things impossible to men.*  81. **safer,** *saner.*  **accommodate,** *furnish, equip.*

That fellow handles his bow like a crow-keeper: draw me a clothier's
yard. Look, look, a mouse! Peace, peace; this piece of toasted cheese will
do 't. There 's my gauntlet; I'll prove it on a giant. Bring up the brown
bills. O, well flown, bird! i' the clout, i' the clout: hewgh! Give the word.

    EDG. Sweet marjoram.

    LEAR. Pass.

    GLOU. I know that voice.                                     96

    LEAR. Ha! Goneril, with a white beard! They flattered me like a dog;
and told me I had white hairs in my beard ere the black ones were there.
To say 'ay' and 'no' to every thing that I said! — 'Ay' and 'no' too was no
good divinity. When the rain came to wet me once, and the wind to make
me chatter; when the thunder would not peace at my bidding; there I
found 'em, there I smelt 'em out. Go to, they are not men o' their words:
they told me I was every thing; 'tis a lie, I am not ague-proof.    107

    GLOU. The trick of that voice I do well remember:
Is 't not the king?

    LEAR.          Ay, every inch a king:
When I do stare, see how the subject quakes.                   110
I pardon that man's life. What was thy cause?
Adultery?
Thou shalt not die: die for adultery! No:
The wren goes to 't, and the small gilded fly
Does lecher in my sight.
Let copulation thrive; for Gloucester's bastard son
Was kinder to his father than my daughters
Got 'tween the lawful sheets.
To 't, luxury, pell-mell! for I lack soldiers.
Behold yond simpering dame,                                  120
Whose face between her forks presages snow;
That minces virtue, and does shake the head
To hear of pleasure's name;
The fitchew, nor the soiled horse, goes to 't
With a more riotous appetite.
Down from the waist they are Centaurs,
Though women all above:
But to the girdle do the gods inherit,
Beneath is all the fiends';
There 's hell, there 's darkness, there 's the sulphurous pit,    130
Burning, scalding, stench, consumption; fie, fie, fie! pah, pah! Give me
an ounce of civet, good apothecary, to sweeten my imagination: there 's
money for thee.

    GLOU. O, let me kiss that hand!

    LEAR. Let me wipe it first; it smells of mortality.

    GLOU. O ruin'd piece of nature! This great world
Shall so wear out to nought. Dost thou know me?

    LEAR. I remember thine eyes well enough. Dost thou squiny at me?
No, do thy worst, blind Cupid; I'll not love. Read thou this challenge;
mark but the penning of it.                                       142

    GLOU. Were all the letters suns, I could not see one.

---

**98-107. They flattered . . . ague-proof.** *This strangely sane passage echoes one of the themes of the
play, namely, the wickedness of flattery.*    **109. Ay, every inch a king.** *Gloucester's words bring
Lear back to the recollection of his kingly state, and he begins to speak in blank verse, irregular
to correspond to his wandering sanity. The whole passage is full of the deepest social pessimism.
It is the reflection in Lear's crazed mind of the chaos, domestic and political, wrought in the
state by wickedness in high places.*    **137. piece,** *masterpiece.*

EDG. I would not take this from report; it is,
And my heart breaks at it.

LEAR. Read.

GLOU. What, with the case of eyes?                                              147

LEAR. O, ho, are you there with me? No eyes in your head, nor no
money in your purse? Your eyes are in a heavy case, your purse in a light:
yet you see how this world goes.

GLOU. I see it feelingly.                                                       152

LEAR. What, art mad? A man may see how this world goes with no
eyes. Look with thine ears: see how yond justice rails upon yond simple
thief. Hark, in thine ear: change places; and, handy-dandy, which is the
justice, which is the thief? Thou hast seen a farmer's dog bark at a beggar?

GLOU. Ay, sir.                                                                  160

LEAR. And the creature run from the cur? There thou mightst behold the
great image of authority: a dog 's obeyed in office.
Thou rascal beadle, hold thy bloody hand!
Why dost thou lash that whore? Strip thine own back;
Thou hotly lust'st to use her in that kind
For which thou whipp'st her. The usurer hangs the cozener.
Through tatter'd clothes small vices do appear;
Robes and furr'd gowns hide all. Plate sin with gold,
And the strong lance of justice hurtless breaks;                               170
Arm it in rags, a pigmy's straw does pierce it.
None does offend, none, I say, none; I'll able 'em:
Take that of me, my friend, who have the power
To seal the accuser's lips. Get thee glass eyes;
And, like a scurvy politician, seem
To see the things thou dost not. Now, now, now, now:
Pull off my boots: harder, harder: so.

EDG. O, matter and impertinency mix'd!
Reason in madness!

LEAR. If thou wilt weep my fortunes, take my eyes.                              180
I know thee well enough; thy name is Gloucester:
Thou must be patient; we came crying hither:
Thou know'st, the first time that we smell the air,
We wawl and cry. I will preach to thee: mark.

GLOU. Alack, alack the day!

LEAR. When we are born, we cry that we are come
To this great stage of fools: this' a good block;
It were a delicate stratagem, to shoe
A troop of horse with felt: I'll put 't in proof;
And when I have stol'n upon these sons-in-law,                                  190
Then, kill, kill, kill, kill, kill, kill!

*Enter a Gentleman, with Attendants.*

GENT. O, here he is: lay hand upon him. Sir,
Your most dear daughter —

LEAR. No rescue? What, a prisoner? I am even
The natural fool of fortune. Use me well;

---

147. **case,** *mere sockets.*    161-171. **And the . . . pierce it.** *Into these ravings should be read the
conception of a state resting upon authority solely, and this state fallen into ruin because the
holders of this divinely constituted authority are themselves corrupt.*    167. **usurer,** *magistrate who
is secretly a usurer.*    **cozener,** *cheater.*    169. **furr'd gowns,** *as worn by officials.*    175. **politician,**
*trickster.*

You shall have ransom. Let me have surgeons;
I am cut to the brains.
    GENT.            You shall have any thing.
    LEAR. No seconds? all myself?
Why, this would make a man a man of salt,
To use his eyes for garden water-pots,                      200
Ay, and laying autumn's dust.
    GENT.                 Good sir, —
    LEAR. I will die bravely, like a bridegroom. What!
I will be jovial: come, come; I am a king,
My masters, know you that.
    GENT. You are a royal one, and we obey you.
    LEAR. Then there 's life in 't. Nay, if you get it, you shall get it with
running. Sa, sa, sa, sa.             [*Exit running; Attendants follow.*
    GENT. A sight most pitiful in the meanest wretch,
Past speaking of in a king! Thou hast one daughter,
Who redeems nature from the general curse               210
Which twain have brought her to.
    EDG. Hail, gentle sir.
    GENT.                Sir, speed you: what 's your will?
    EDG. Do you hear aught, sir, of a battle toward?
    GENT. Most sure and vulgar: every one hears that,
Which can distinguish sound.
    EDG.             But, by your favour,
How near 's the other army?
    GENT. Near and on speedy foot; the main descry
Stands on the hourly thought.
    EDG.              I thank you, sir: that 's all.
    GENT. Though that the queen on special cause is here,
Her army is moved on.
    EDG.           I thank you, sir.          [*Exit Gent.* 220
    GLOU. You ever-gentle gods, take my breath from me;
Let not my worser spirit tempt me again
To die before you please!
    EDG.             Well pray you, father.
    GLOU. Now, good sir, what are you?
    EDG. A most poor man, made tame to fortune's blows;
Who, by the art of known and feeling sorrows,
Am pregnant to good pity. Give me your hand,
I'll lead you to some biding.
    GLOU.           Hearty thanks:
The bounty and the benison of heaven
To boot, and boot!

    *Enter* OSWALD.

    OSW.          A proclaim'd prize! Most happy!         230
That eyeless head of thine was first framed flesh
To raise my fortunes. Thou old unhappy traitor,
Briefly thyself remember: the sword is out
That must destroy thee.
    GLOU.         Now let thy friendly hand
Put strength enough to 't.             [EDGAR *interposes.*

---

214. **vulgar,** *in everyone's mouth, generally known.*

osw.                  Wherefore, bold peasant,
Darest thou support a publish'd traitor? Hence;
Lest that the infection of his fortune take
Like hold on thee. Let go his arm.

   EDG. Chill not let go, zir, without vurther 'casion.      240

   osw. Let go, slave, or thou diest!

   EDG. Good gentleman, go your gait, and let poor volk pass. An chud ha' bin zwaggered out of my life, 'twould not ha' bin zo long as 'tis by a vortnight. Nay, come not near th' old man; keep out, che vor ye, or ise try whether your costard or my ballow be the harder: chill be plain with you.

   osw. Out, dunghill!

   EDG. Chill pick your teeth, zir: come; no matter vor your foins.   251
                      [*They fight, and* EDGAR *knocks him down.*

   osw. Slave, thou hast slain me: villain, take my purse:
If ever thou wilt thrive, bury my body;
And give the letters which thou find'st about me
To Edmund earl of Gloucester; seek him out
Upon the British party: O, untimely death!          [*Dies.*

   EDG. I know thee well: a serviceable villain;
As duteous to the vices of thy mistress
As badness would desire.

   GLOU.               What, is he dead?

   EDG. Sit you down, father; rest you.              260
Let 's see these pockets: the letters that he speaks of
May be my friends. He 's dead; I am only sorry
He had no other death's-man. Let us see:
Leave, gentle wax; and, manners, blame us not:
To know our enemies' minds, we 'ld rip their hearts;
Their papers, is more lawful.              266

   [*Reads*] 'Let our reciprocal vows be remembered. You have many opportunities to cut him off: if your will want not, time and place will be fruitfully offered. There is nothing done, if he return the conqueror: then am I the prisoner, and his bed my gaol; from the loathed warmth whereof deliver me, and supply the place for your labour.
    'Your — wife, so I would say —
       'Affectionate servant,           'GONERIL.'
O undistinguish'd space of woman's will!
A plot upon her virtuous husband's life;
And the exchange my brother! Here, in the sands,     280
Thee I'll rake up, the post unsanctified
Of murderous lechers: and in the mature time
With this ungracious paper strike the sight
Of the death-practised duke: for him 'tis well
That of thy death and business I can tell.

   GLOU. The king is mad: how stiff is my vile sense,
That I stand up, and have ingenious feeling
Of my huge sorrows! Better I were distract:
So should my thoughts be sever'd from my griefs,
And woes by wrong imaginations lose          290
The knowledge of themselves.

240-251. *Edgar adopts a dialect, apparently of the south country.* 278. **undistinguish'd ... will,** *incalculable range of woman's appetite.* 281. **rake up,** *cover up.* 284. **death-practised,** *whose death is plotted.*

EDG.                          Give me your hand:            [*Drum afar off.*
Far off, methinks, I hear the beaten drum:
Come, father, I'll bestow you with a friend.                    [*Exeunt.*


SCENE VII: *A tent in the French camp.* LEAR *on a bed asleep, soft music
playing; Gentleman, and others attending.*

*Enter* CORDELIA, KENT, *and* DOCTOR.

COR. O thou good Kent, how shall I live and work,
To match thy goodness? My life will be too short,
And every measure fail me.
KENT. To be acknowledged, madam, is o'er-paid.
All my reports go with the modest truth;
Nor more nor clipp'd, but so.
COR.                          Be better suited:
These weeds are memories of those worser hours:
I prithee, put them off.
KENT.                          Pardon me, dear madam;
Yet to be known shortens my made intent:
My boon I make it, that you know me not                          10
Till time and I think meet.
COR. Then be 't so, my good lord. [*To the* DOCTOR] How does the king?
DOCT. Madam, sleeps still.
COR.                          O you kind gods,
Cure this great breach in his abused nature!
The untuned and jarring senses, O, wind up
Of this child-changed father!
DOCT.                          So please your majesty
That we may wake the king: he hath slept long.
COR. Be govern'd by your knowledge, and proceed
I' the sway of your own will. Is he array'd?                     20
GENT. Ay, madam; in the heaviness of his sleep
We put fresh garments on him.
DOCT. Be by, good madam, when we do awake him;
I doubt not of his temperance.
COR.                          Very well.
DOCT. Please you, draw near. Louder the music there!
COR. O my dear father! Restoration hang
Thy medicine on my lips; and let this kiss
Repair those violent harms that my two sisters
Have in thy reverence made!
KENT.                          Kind and dear princess!
COR. Had you not been their father, these white flakes          30
Had challenged pity of them. Was this a face
To be opposed against the warring winds?
To stand against the deep dread-bolted thunder?
In the most terrible and nimble stroke
Of quick, cross lightning? to watch — poor perdu! —
With this thin helm? Mine enemy's dog,
Though he had bit me, should have stood that night
Against my fire; and wast thou fain, poor father,

---

*Scene vii.* 17. **child-changed,** *changed (in mind) by children's cruelty.*   24. **temperance,** *sanity.*

To hovel thee with swine, and rogues forlorn,
In short and musty straw? Alack, alack!                    40
'Tis wonder that thy life and wits at once
Had not concluded all. He wakes; speak to him.
    DOCT. Madam, do you; 'tis fittest.
    COR. How does my royal lord? How fares your majesty?
    LEAR. You do me wrong to take me out o' the grave:
Thou art a soul in bliss; but I am bound
Upon a wheel of fire, that mine own tears
Do scald like molten lead.
    COR.            Sir, do you know me?
    LEAR. You are a spirit, I know: when did you die?
    COR. Still, still, far wide!                    50
    DOCT. He 's scarce awake: let him alone awhile.
    LEAR. Where have I been? Where am I? Fair daylight?
I am mightily abused. I should e'en die with pity,
To see another thus. I know not what to say.
I will not swear these are my hands: let 's see;
I feel this pin prick. Would I were assured
Of my condition!
    COR.        O, look upon me, sir,
And hold your hands in benediction o'er me:
No, sir, you must not kneel.
    LEAR.         Pray, do not mock me:
I am a very foolish fond old man,                    60
Fourscore and upward, not an hour more nor less;
And, to deal plainly,
I fear I am not in my perfect mind.
Methinks I should know you, and know this man;
Yet I am doubtful: for I am mainly ignorant
What place this is; and all the skill I have
Remembers not these garments; nor I know not
Where I did lodge last night. Do not laugh at me;
For, as I am a man, I think this lady
To be my child Cordelia.
    COR.        And so I am, I am.                    70
    LEAR. By your tears wet? yes, 'faith. I pray, weep not:
If you have poison for me, I will drink it.
I know you do not love me; for your sisters
Have, as I do remember, done me wrong:
You have some cause, they have not.
    COR.             No cause, no cause.
    LEAR. Am I in France?
    KENT.         In your own kingdom, sir.
    LEAR. Do not abuse me.
    DOCT. Be comforted, good madam: the great rage,
You see, is kill'd in him: and yet it is danger
To make him even o'er the time he has lost.                    80
Desire him to go in; trouble him no more
Till further settling.
    COR. Will 't please your highness walk?

---

42. **concluded all,** *came to an end all together.*  73-75. **I know ... not.** *This pathetic passage is not merely the strugglings of Lear's mind back to recognition; it is also a momentary restoration of the bargain-and-sale ethics which characterized the partition of his kingdom.*  82. **settling,** *composing of his mind.*

LEAR. You must bear with me:
Pray you now, forget and forgive: I am old and foolish.
[*Exeunt all but* KENT *and Gentleman.*
GENT. Holds it true, sir, that the Duke of Cornwall was so slain?
KENT. Most certain, sir.
GENT. Who is conductor of his people?
KENT. As 'tis said, the bastard son of Gloucester. 90
GENT. They say Edgar, his banished son, is with the Earl of Kent in
Germany.
KENT. Report is changeable. 'Tis time to look about; the powers of the
kingdom approach apace.
GENT. The arbitrement is like to be bloody. Fare you well, sir. [*Exit.*
KENT. My point and period will be throughly wrought,
Or well or ill, as this day's battle 's fought. [*Exit.* 99

# ACT V

SCENE I: *The British camp, near Dover.*

*Enter, with drum and colours,* EDMUND, REGAN, *Gentlemen, and Soldiers.*

EDM. Know of the duke if his last purpose hold,
Or whether since he is advised by aught
To change the course: he 's full of alteration
And self-reproving: bring his constant pleasure.
[*To a Gentleman, who goes out.*
REG. Our sister's man is certainly miscarried.
EDM. 'Tis to be doubted, madam.
REG. Now, sweet lord,
You know the goodness I intend upon you:
Tell me — but truly — but then speak the truth,
Do you not love my sister?
EDM. In honour'd love.
REG. But have you never found my brother's way 10
To the forfended place?
EDM. That thought abuses you.
REG. I am doubtful that you have been conjunct
And bosom'd with her, as far as we call hers.
EDM. No, by mine honour, madam.
REG. I never shall endure her: dear my lord,
Be not familiar with her.
EDM. Fear me not:
She and the duke her husband!

*Enter, with drum and colours,* ALBANY, GONERIL, *and Soldiers.*

GON. [*Aside*] I had rather lose the battle than that sister
Should loosen him and me.
ALB. Our very loving sister, well be-met. 20
Sir, this I hear; the king is come to his daughter,
With others whom the rigour of our state
Forced to cry out. Where I could not be honest,
I never yet was valiant: for this business,
It toucheth us, as France invades our land,
Not bolds the king, with others, whom, I fear,

95. **arbitrement,** *decision by arms.* 98. **period,** *end aimed at.*
*Act V. Scene i.* 3. **alteration,** *vacillation.* 4. **constant pleasure,** *settled decision.*

Most just and heavy causes make oppose.
    EDM. Sir, you speak nobly.
    REG.                            Why is this reason'd?
    GON. Combine together 'gainst the enemy;
For these domestic and particular broils                         30
Are not the question here.
    ALB.                          Let 's then determine
With the ancient of war on our proceedings.
    EDM. I shall attend you presently at your tent.
    REG. Sister, you'll go with us?
    GON. No.
    REG. 'Tis most convenient; pray you, go with us.
    GON. [*Aside*] O, ho, I know the riddle. — I will go.

    *As they are going out, enter* EDGAR, *disguised.*

    EDG. If e'er your grace had speech with man so poor,
Hear me one word.
    ALB.                    I'll overtake you. Speak.
                        [*Exeunt all but* ALBANY *and* EDGAR.
    EDG. Before you fight the battle, ope this letter.        40
If you have victory, let the trumpet sound
For him that brought it: wretched though I seem,
I can produce a champion that will prove
What is avouched there. If you miscarry,
Your business of the world hath so an end,
And machination ceases. Fortune love you!
    ALB. Stay till I have read the letter.
    EDG.                            I was forbid it.
When time shall serve, let but the herald cry,
And I'll appear again.
    ALB. Why, fare thee well: I will o'erlook thy paper.    [*Exit* EDGAR.   50

    *Re-enter* EDMUND.

    EDM. The enemy 's in view; draw up your powers.
Here is the guess of their true strength and forces
By diligent discovery; but your haste
Is now urged on you.
    ALB.                    We will greet the time.        [*Exit.*
    EDM. To both these sisters have I sworn my love;
Each jealous of the other, as the stung
Are of the adder. Which of them shall I take?
Both? one? or neither? Neither can be enjoy'd,
If both remain alive: to take the widow
Exasperates, makes mad her sister Goneril;                    60
And hardly shall I carry out my side,
Her husband being alive. Now then we'll use
His countenance for the battle; which being done,
Let her who would be rid of him devise
His speedy taking off. As for the mercy
Which he intends to Lear and to Cordelia,
The battle done, and they within our power,
Shall never see his pardon; for my state
Stands on me to defend, not to debate.                [*Exit.*   69

54. **greet the time,** *face the situation.*

SCENE II: *A field between the two camps.*

*Alarum within. Enter, with drum and colours,* LEAR, CORDELIA, *and Soldiers, over the stage; and exeunt.*

*Enter* EDGAR *and* GLOUCESTER.

EDG. Here, father, take the shadow of this tree
For your good host; pray that the right may thrive:
If ever I return to you again,
I'll bring you comfort.
    GLOU.         Grace go with you, sir!          [*Exit* EDGAR.

*Alarum and retreat within. Re-enter* EDGAR.

EDG. Away, old man; give me thy hand; away!
King Lear hath lost, he and his daughter ta'en:
Give me thy hand; come on.
    GLOU. No farther, sir; a man may rot even here.
    EDG. What, in ill thoughts again? Men must endure
Their going hence, even as their coming hither:          10
Ripeness is all: come on.
    GLOU.         And that 's true too.          [*Exeunt.*

SCENE III: *The British camp near Dover.*

*Enter, in conquest, with drum and colours,* EDMUND;
    LEAR *and* CORDELIA, *prisoners; Captain, Soldiers, &c.*

EDM. Some officers take them away: good guard,
Until their greater pleasures first be known
That are to censure them.
    COR.         We are not the first
Who, with best meaning, have incurr'd the worst.
For thee, oppressed king, am I cast down;
Myself could else out-frown false fortune's frown.
Shall we not see these daughters and these sisters?
    LEAR. No, no, no, no! Come, let 's away to prison:
We two alone will sing like birds i' the cage:
When thou dost ask me blessing, I'll kneel down,          10
And ask of thee forgiveness: so we'll live,
And pray, and sing, and tell old tales, and laugh
At gilded butterflies, and hear poor rogues
Talk of court news; and we'll talk with them too,
Who loses and who wins; who 's in, who 's out;
And take upon 's the mystery of things,
As if we were God's spies: and we'll wear out,
In a wall'd prison, packs and sects of great ones,
That ebb and flow by the moon.
    EDM.          Take them away.
    LEAR. Upon such sacrifices, my Cordelia,          20
The gods themselves throw incense. Have I caught thee?
He that parts us shall bring a brand from heaven,
And fire us hence like foxes. Wipe thine eyes;
The good-years shall devour them, flesh and fell,

---

*Scene ii.* 9-11. **Men ... all,** *a stern utterance of the doctrine of fortitude.* 11. **Ripeness,** *readiness.*
*Scene iii.* 23. **fire ... foxes,** *i.e., as foxes are driven out of their holes by fire and smoke.* 24.
**good-years,** *apparently a general word for evil; thought sometimes to be the name of a disease.*

Ere they shall make us weep: we'll see 'em starve first.
Come.                                  [*Exeunt* LEAR *and* CORDELIA, *guarded.*
   EDM. Come hither, captain; hark.
Take thou this note [*giving a paper*]; go follow them to prison:
One step I have advanced thee; if thou dost
As this instructs thee, thou dost make thy way
To noble fortunes: know thou this, that men                              30
Are as the time is: to be tender-minded
Does not become a sword: thy great employment
Will not bear question; either say thou 'lt do 't,
Or thrive by other means.
   CAPT.                    I'll do 't, my lord.
   EDM. About it; and write happy when thou hast done.
Mark, I say, instantly; and carry it so
As I have set it down.
   CAPT. I cannot draw a cart, nor eat dried oats;
If it be man's work, I'll do it.                              [*Exit.*

   *Flourish. Enter* ALBANY, GONERIL, REGAN, *another Captain, and Soldiers.*

   ALB. Sir, you have shown to-day your valiant strain,                 40
And fortune led you well: you have the captives
That were the opposites of this day's strife:
We do require them of you, so to use them
As we shall find their merits and our safety
May equally determine.
   EDM.                    Sir, I thought it fit
To send the old and miserable king
To some retention and appointed guard;
Whose age has charms in it, whose title more,
To pluck the common bosom on his side,
And turn our impress'd lances in our eyes                              50
Which do command them. With him I sent the queen;
My reason all the same; and they are ready
To-morrow, or at further space, to appear
Where you shall hold your session. At this time
We sweat and bleed: the friend hath lost his friend;
And the best quarrels, in the heat, are cursed
By those that feel their sharpness:
The question of Cordelia and her father
Requires a fitter place.
   ALB.                    Sir, by your patience,
I hold you but a subject of this war,                              60
Not as a brother.
   REG.          That 's as we list to grace him.
Methinks our pleasure might have been demanded,
Ere you had spoke so far. He led our powers;
Bore the commission of my place and person;
The which immediacy may well stand up,
And call itself your brother.
   GON.                    Not so hot:
In his own grace he doth exalt himself,

---

47. **retention,** *custody.*  49. **common bosom,** *the affection of the mob.*  50. **impress'd lances,** weapons of troops pressed into service.

More than in your addition.

REG.                    In my rights,
By me invested, he compeers the best.

GON. That were the most, if he should husband you.          70

REG. Jesters do oft prove prophets.

GON.                          Holla, holla!
That eye that told you so look'd but a-squint.

REG. Lady, I am not well; else I should answer
From a full-flowing stomach. General,
Take thou my soldiers, prisoners, patrimony;
Dispose of them, of me; the walls are thine:
Witness the world, that I create thee here
My lord and master.

GON.                Mean you to enjoy him?

ALB. The let-alone lies not in your good will.

EDM. Nor in thine, lord.

ALB.                        Half-blooded fellow, yes.          80

REG. [*To* EDMUND] Let the drum strike, and prove my title thine.

ALB. Stay yet; hear reason. Edmund, I arrest thee
On capital treason; and, in thine attaint,
This gilded serpent [*pointing to* GON.]. For your claim, fair sister,
I bar it in the interest of my wife;
'Tis she is sub-contracted to this lord,
And I, her husband, contradict your bans.
If you will marry, make your loves to me,
My lady is bespoke.

GON.              An interlude!

ALB. Thou art arm'd, Gloucester: let the trumpet sound:          90
If none appear to prove upon thy head
Thy heinous, manifest, and many treasons,
There is my pledge [*throwing down a glove*]; I'll prove it on thy heart,
Ere I taste bread, thou art in nothing less
Than I have here proclaim'd thee.

REG.                          Sick, O, sick!

GON. [*Aside*] If not, I'll ne'er trust medicine.

EDM. There 's my exchange [*throwing down a glove*]: what in the world
      he is
That names me traitor, villain-like he lies:
Call by thy trumpet: he that dares approach,
On him, on you, who not? I will maintain          100
My truth and honour firmly.

ALB. A herald, ho!

EDM.              A herald, ho, a herald!

ALB. Trust to thy single virtue; for thy soldiers,
All levied in my name, have in my name
Took their discharge.

REG.                My sickness grows upon me.

ALB. She is not well; convey her to my tent.          [*Exit* REGAN, *led.*

*Enter a Herald.*

Come hither, herald, — Let the trumpet sound, —
And read out this.          108

76. **the walls are thine,** *probably a phrase signifying complete surrender.*   79. **let-alone,** *power to forbid it.*   83. **attaint,** *impeachment.*   89. **interlude,** *play, i.e., you are melodramatic.*   97. **what . . . is,** *whatever may be his rank or position.*

CAPT. Sound, trumpet!                              [*A trumpet sounds.*

HER. [*Reads*] 'If any man of quality or degree within the lists of the army
will maintain upon Edmund, supposed Earl of Gloucester, that he is a
manifold traitor, let him appear by the third sound of the trumpet: he is
bold in his defence.'

EDM. Sound!                                        [*First trumpet.*
HER. Again!                                        [*Second trumpet.*
HER. Again!                                        [*Third trumpet.*
                                                   [*Trumpet answers within.*

*Enter* EDGAR, *at the third sound, armed, with a trumpet before him.*

ALB. Ask him his purposes, why he appears
Upon this call o' the trumpet.
    HER.                        What are you?
Your name, your quality? and why you answer                    120
This present summons?
    EDG.                     Know, my name is lost;
By treason's tooth bare-gnawn and canker-bit:
Yet am I noble as the adversary
I come to cope.
    ALB.           Which is that adversary?
EDG. What 's he that speaks for Edmund Earl of Gloucester?
EDM. Himself: what say'st thou to him?
    EDG.                        Draw thy sword,
That, if my speech offend a noble heart,
Thy arm may do thee justice: here is mine.
Behold, it is the privilege of mine honours,
My oath, and my profession: I protest,                         130
Maugre thy strength, youth, place, and eminence,
Despite thy victor sword and fire-new fortune,
Thy valour and thy heart, thou art a traitor;
False to thy gods, thy brother, and thy father;
Conspirant 'gainst this high-illustrious prince;
And, from the extremest upward of thy head
To the descent and dust below thy foot,
A most toad-spotted traitor. Say thou 'No,'
This sword, this arm, and my best spirits, are bent
To prove upon thy heart, whereto I speak,                      140
Thou liest.
    EDM.     In wisdom I should ask thy name;
But, since thy outside looks so fair and warlike,
And that thy tongue some say of breeding breathes,
What safe and nicely I might well delay
By rule of knighthood, I disdain and spurn:
Back do I toss these treasons to thy head;
With the hell-hated lie o'erwhelm thy heart;
Which, for they yet glance by and scarcely bruise,
This sword of mine shall give them instant way,
Where they shall rest for ever. Trumpets, speak!              150
                        [*Alarums. They fight.* EDMUND *falls.*
    ALB. Save him, save him!

---

141. **wisdom,** *prudence; i.e., Edmund might have demanded that his adversary be his equal in
rank.*   147. **hell-hated,** *hated as hell is hated.*

GON.                This is practice, Gloucester:
By the law of arms thou wast not bound to answer
An unknown opposite; thou art not vanquish'd,
But cozen'd and beguiled.
ALB.                Shut your mouth, dame,
Or with this paper shall I stop it. Hold, sir;
Thou worse than any name, read thine own evil:
No tearing, lady; I perceive you know it.   [*Gives the letter to* EDMUND.
GON. Say, if I do, the laws are mine, not thine:
Who can arraign me for 't?
ALB.                Most monstrous! oh!
Know'st thou this paper?
GON.                Ask me not what I know.        [*Exit.* 160
ALB. Go after her: she 's desperate; govern her.
EDM. What you have charged me with, that have I done;
And more, much more; the time will bring it out:
'Tis past, and so am I. But what art thou
That hast this fortune on me? If thou 'rt noble,
I do forgive thee.
EDG.            Let 's exchange charity.
I am no less in blood than thou art, Edmund;
If more, the more thou hast wrong'd me.
My name is Edgar, and thy father's son.
The gods are just, and of our pleasant vices                170
Make instruments to plague us:
The dark and vicious place where thee he got
Cost him his eyes.
EDM.                Thou hast spoken right, 'tis true;
The wheel is come full circle; I am here.
ALB. Methought thy very gait did prophesy
A royal nobleness: I must embrace thee:
Let sorrow split my heart, if ever I
Did hate thee or thy father!
EDG.                Worthy prince, I know 't.
ALB. Where have you hid yourself?
How have you known the miseries of your father?        180
EDG. By nursing them, my lord. List a brief tale;
And when 'tis told, O, that my heart would burst!
The bloody proclamation to escape,
That follow'd me so near, — O, our lives' sweetness!
That we the pain of death would hourly die
Rather than die at once! — taught me to shift
Into a madman's rags; to assume a semblance
That very dogs disdain'd: and in this habit
Met I my father with his bleeding rings,
Their precious stones new lost; became his guide,        190
Led him, begg'd for him, saved him from despair;
Never, — O fault! — reveal'd myself unto him,
Until some half-hour past, when I was arm'd:
Not sure, though hoping, of this good success,
I ask'd his blessing, and from first to last
Told him my pilgrimage: but his flaw'd heart,
Alack, too weak the conflict to support!

189. **rings,** *sockets.*   196. **flaw'd,** *damaged.*

'Twixt two extremes of passion, joy and grief,
Burst smilingly.
     EDM.        This speech of yours hath moved me,
And shall perchance do good: but speak you on;           200
You look as you had something more to say.
     ALB. If there be more, more woeful, hold it in;
For I am almost ready to dissolve,
Hearing of this.
     EDG.        This would have seem'd a period
To such as love not sorrow; but another,
To amplify too much, would make much more,
And top extremity.
Whilst I was big in clamour came there in a man,
Who, having seen me in my worst estate,
Shunn'd my abhorr'd society; but then, finding       210
Who 'twas that so endured, with his strong arms
He fasten'd on my neck, and bellow'd out
As he 'ld burst heaven; threw him on my father;
Told the most piteous tale of Lear and him
That ever ear received: which in recounting
His grief grew puissant, and the strings of life
Began to crack: twice then the trumpets sounded,
And there I left him tranced.
     ALB.             But who was this?
     EDG. Kent, sir, the banish'd Kent; who in disguise
Follow'd his enemy king, and did him service        220
Improper for a slave.

*Enter a Gentleman, with a bloody knife.*

     GENT. Help, help, O, help!
     EDG.               What kind of help?
     ALB.                     Speak, man.
     EDG. What means that bloody knife?
     GENT.               'Tis hot, it smokes;
It came even from the heart of — O, she 's dead!
     ALB. Who dead? speak, man.
     GENT. Your lady, sir, your lady: and her sister
By her is poisoned; she hath confess'd it.
     EDM. I was contracted to them both: all three
Now marry in an instant.
     EDG.            Here comes Kent.
     ALB. Produce their bodies, be they alive or dead:     230
This judgement of the heavens, that makes us tremble,
Touches us not with pity.              [*Exit Gentleman.*

*Enter* KENT.

               O, is this he?
The time will not allow the compliment
Which very manners urges.
     KENT.            I am come
To bid my king and master aye good night:
Is he not here?
     ALB.        Great thing of us forgot!
Speak, Edmund, where 's the king? and where 's Cordelia?

See'st thou this object, Kent?

> [*The bodies of* GONERIL *and* REGAN *are brought in.*

KENT. Alack, why thus?

EDM.                    Yet Edmund was beloved:
The one the other poison'd for my sake,                    240
And after slew herself.

ALB. Even so. Cover their faces.

EDM. I pant for life: some good I mean to do,
Despite of mine own nature. Quickly send,
Be brief in it, to the castle; for my writ
Is on the life of Lear and on Cordelia:
Nay, send in time.

ALB.            Run, run, O, run!

EDG. To who, my lord? Who hath the office? send
Thy token of reprieve.

EDM. Well thought on: take my sword,                    250
Give it the captain.

ALB.            Haste thee, for thy life.            [*Exit* EDGAR.

EDM. He hath commission from thy wife and me
To hang Cordelia in the prison, and
To lay the blame upon her own despair,
That she fordid herself.

ALB. The gods defend her! Bear him hence awhile.

> [EDMUND *is borne off.*

*Re-enter* LEAR, *with* CORDELIA *dead in his arms;* EDGAR, Captain, and
others following.

LEAR. Howl, howl, howl, howl! O, you are men of stones:
Had I your tongues and eyes, I 'ld use them so
That heaven's vault should crack. She 's gone for ever!
I know when one is dead, and when one lives;                    260
She 's dead as earth. Lend me a looking-glass;
If that her breath will mist or stain the stone,
Why, then she lives.

KENT.            Is this the promised end?

EDG. Or image of that horror?

ALB.                    Fall, and cease!

LEAR. This feather stirs; she lives! if it be so,
It is a chance which does redeem all sorrows
That ever I have felt.

KENT.    [*Kneeling*] O my good master!

LEAR. Prithee, away.

EDG.            'Tis noble Kent, your friend.

LEAR. A plague upon you, murderers, traitors all!
I might have saved her; now she 's gone for ever!                    270
Cordelia, Cordelia! stay a little. Ha!
What is 't thou say'st? Her voice was ever soft,
Gentle, and low, an excellent thing in woman.
I kill'd the slave that was a-hanging thee.

CAPT. 'Tis true, my lords, he did.

---

243-244. **some good ... nature.** *It is made clear to us in the first act that Edmund, born outside the pale of social organization, is adverse and hostile to the laws of gods and men; he repents and is therefore not an inhuman monster.* 262. **stone,** *crystal (of which the mirror is made).* 263. **end,** *Last Judgment.* 272-273. **Her ... low.** *Lear fancies he has heard Cordelia speak.*

LEAR.                     Did I not, fellow?
I have seen the day, with my good biting falchion
I would have made them skip: I am old now,
And these same crosses spoil me. Who are you?
Mine eyes are not o' the best: I'll tell you straight.
    KENT. If fortune brag of two she loved and hated,          280
One of them we behold.
    LEAR. This is a dull sight. Are you not Kent?
    KENT.                         The same,
Your servant Kent. Where is your servant Caius?
    LEAR. He 's a good fellow, I can tell you that;
He'll strike, and quickly too: he 's dead and rotten.
    KENT. No, my good lord; I am the very man, —
    LEAR. I'll see that straight.
    KENT. That, from your first of difference and decay,
Have follow'd your sad steps.
    LEAR.                You are welcome hither.
    KENT. Nor no man else: all 's cheerless, dark, and deadly.     290
Your eldest daughters have fordone themselves,
And desperately are dead.
    LEAR.            Ay, so I think.
    ALB. He knows not what he says: and vain it is
That we present us to him.
    EDG.           Very bootless.

*Enter a Captain.*

    CAPT. Edmund is dead, my lord.
    ALB.               That 's but a trifle here.
You lords and noble friends, know our intent.
What comfort to this great decay may come
Shall be applied: for us, we will resign,
During the life of this old majesty,
To him our absolute power: [*To* EDGAR *and* KENT] you, to your rights;    300
With boot, and such addition as your honours
Have more than merited. All friends shall taste
The wages of their virtue, and all foes
The cup of their deservings. O, see, see!
    LEAR. And my poor fool is hang'd! No, no, no life!
Why should a dog, a horse, a rat, have life,
And thou no breath at all? Thou 'lt come no more,
Never, never, never, never, never!
Pray you, undo this button: thank you, sir.
Do you see this? Look on her, look, her lips,                310
Look there, look there!                           [*Dies.*
    EDG.            He faints! My lord, my lord!
    KENT. Break, heart; I prithee, break!
    EDG.                  Look up, my lord.
    KENT. Vex not his ghost: O, let him pass! he hates him much
That would upon the rack of this tough world
Stretch him out longer.
    EDG.           He is gone, indeed.
    KENT. The wonder is, he hath endured so long:

---

288. **first of difference,** *beginning of your change of fortune for the worst.*    305. **my poor fool,**
*i.e.,* Cordelia; fool, *as here used, is a term of endearment.*

He but usurp'd his life.

ALB. Bear them from hence. Our present business
Is general woe. [*To* KENT *and* EDGAR] Friends of my soul, you twain
Rule in this realm, and the gored state sustain. 320

KENT. I have a journey, sir, shortly to go;
My master calls me, I must not say no.

ALB. The weight of this sad time we must obey;
Speak what we feel, not what we ought to say.
The oldest hath borne most: we that are young
Shall never see so much, nor live so long. [*Exeunt, with a dead march.*

---

## FOR DISCUSSION AND WRITING

*... Today, the direction 'enter Lear, fantastically dressed with weeds'
can easily seem mere fantasy without a background, or have merely some
kind of enrichment in generalized associations with fertility and its converse.
For Shakespeare, Lear's status in this scene must have been much more
exact and significant. The figure*

> *Crown'd with rank fumiter and furrow weeds,*
> *With hardocks, hemlock, nettles, cuckoo-flow'rs,*
> *Darnel and all the idle weeds that grow*
> *In our sustaining corn ...* (IV. iv. 3)

*whose first words are 'I am the King himself,' who jests and preaches (IV.
vi. 181), who is filled with a conviction that he is soon to be killed ('I will
die bravely, like a smug bridegroom', IV. vi. 202; 'If you have poison for me,
I will drink it', IV. vii. 72), who can say: 'Nay, an you get it, you shall get
it by running', and run away dressed in his flowers and pursued by the attendants; – this figure is easily recognizable. He is a Jack-a-Green, at once
hero and victim of a popular ceremony. For a moment, he is a hunted man
literally, as he is in spirit throughout the play. Nor is such a level of interest
in any way out of place for Lear. There is much of the quality of folk
thinking or acting, of the folk-tale, about his whole career. This shows in
the stylized opening scene, in the formality and symmetry of his break with
the three sisters, in his mock court in the outhouse and in this Jack-a-Green
spectacle, right through to his final entry, – which cannot but call up the
legendary 'Come not between the dragon and his wrath' of the opening
tableau, and in which Lear and Cordelia must appear not as king and
princess, but, beyond normal life, as emblems of the extremes of what is
possible in life.*

*Over the four plays which have been discussed so far* [Hamlet, Othello,
Macbeth, King Lear] *there seems by now to emerge, with increasing clarity,
a repeated and recognizable pattern. In* Lear *it is surely inescapable. Despite
the rich detail and realism of this play, the action and the staging are
stylized largely throughout. The protagonist (followed, less fully but in some
ways more plainly, by Gloucester) pursues a well-marked rôle. He is the man
who begins as centre of his whole world, but who is progressively set, both by
the other characters and by himself, apart from it and against it. 'Against'*

*means above, in solitary defiance, and below, in an ordeal of protracted suf-*
*fering which takes on the quality of a hunt. His response to this may indeed*
*be a growing awareness and comprehension of where he stands; but if this*
*makes the onward movement of the action profounder and more impressive,*
*it in no way retards or re-directs it; and its end is a death which, though*
*realistically the outcome of the human situation of the play, has at the same*
*time the quality of stylized and ritual execution. All is foreseen, nothing*
*can be delayed or hastened or mitigated. We are led, in fact, to envisage a*
*new metaphor for the status of the tragic rôle in these plays; to see running*
*through the work, besides its other interests, its detailed representation of*
*life, its flow of ideas, its sense of good and evil, something which might be*
*called the vertebrate structure of its intrinsic design; the developing line, un-*
*abridged, of a human sacrifice.*

From John Holloway, The Story of the Night<br>
(London: Routledge and Kegan Paul, 1961), pp. 96-98.

1) After rereading Gilbert Murray's essay, assess the relevance of Hollo-way's conception of Lear as a ritual figure. Is there other evidence in the play to support his view?

2) Would it be possible to bring Holloway's analysis into question by saying that tragedy often records the liberation of the human spirit, not its imprisonment, and that the career of *King Lear* fulfills this pattern?

3) Alexander states that both the Biblical Job and the Oedipus of *Oedipus at Colonus* make a plea "against the material assessment that the world can hardly refrain from adopting" (p. 56). In what sense does *King Lear* set forth a similar plea?

4) Both *King Oedipus* and *King Lear* are "about" clear and unclear vision. The heroes in both must gain clearer sight, come to an understanding of their human plight or involvement. The understanding achieved by Oedipus — of the implications of a fateful curse — is relatively simple, but Lear's self-willed blind-ness initiates reverberations that range from animality to lofty humanity, from political anarchy to kingly statecraft, from stubborn pride to humbling love, from Lear as Fool to Lear as "every inch a king," from the falsity of disguise to the truth of nakedness. Explain how the vast range of these ethic explora-tions increases the intensity of the tragedy.

5) Is Arrowsmith's statement concerning Oedipus, that it is "his own declaration of responsibility that makes him so heroic," equally applicable to Lear? Does Lear grow in heroic responsibility from the time that he fully realizes the cruelty of Goneril and Regan? Explain.

6) Alexander argues against Bradley that tragedy "takes its character and significance not from faults [tragic flaws] but from virtue." Can it be argued (on the basis of Alexander's terms) that tragedy takes on its significance from the triumph of the manifestation of heroism in the doomed protagonist — whether or not the heroism is rooted in reasonable virtue? Is this the case in *King Lear?*

7) The lines said of Gloucester,

Men must endure

Their going hence, even as their coming hither:
Ripeness is all.            (V. ii. 9-11)

suggest that in *King Lear,* as in *King Oedipus, ripeness* — that is, the fullness of suffering — leads to a kind of high wisdom. Does Lear's attainment of wisdom constitute a catharsis in the Aristotelian sense? Is the nature of the purgation elicited by Lear analogous to that effected by Gloucester?

8) Bradley argues (in *Shakespearean Tragedy,* pp. 251-253) that from a "strictly dramatic or tragic" point of view the deaths of Gloucester, Goneril, and Regan are enough and that he wished Lear and Cordelia to live. He argues that the ending is neither inevitable nor adequately motivated. Do you share his view?

✳

HENRIK

# IBSEN

## *Rosmersholm*

---

*Characters:*    JOHANNES ROSMER, of Rosmersholm, formerly
clergyman of the parish

REBECCA WEST, in charge of Rosmer's household

RECTOR* KROLL, Rosmer's brother-in-law

ULRIC BRENDEL

PETER MORTENSGÅRD†

MADAM HELSETH, housekeeper at Rosmersholm

*The action takes place at Rosmersholm, an old family seat
near a small coast town in the west of Norway.*

## ACT FIRST

*Sitting-room at Rosmersholm; spacious, old-fashioned, and comfortable.
In front, on the right, a stove decked with fresh birch-branches and
wild flowers. Farther back, on the same side, a door. In the back wall,
folding-doors opening into the hall. To the left, a window, and before
it a stand with flowers and plants. Beside the stove a table with a sofa
and easy chairs. On the walls, old and more recent portraits of clergymen, officers, and government officials in uniform. The window is open;
so are the door into the hall and the house door beyond. Outside can
be seen an avenue of fine old trees, leading up to the house. It is a
summer evening, after sunset.*

REBECCA WEST *is sitting in an easy-chair by the window, and crocheting
a large white woollen shawl, which is nearly finished. She now and
then looks out expectantly through the leaves of the plants.* MADAM
HELSETH *presently enters from the right.*

Rosmersholm, *tr. William Archer,* Collected Works of Henrik Ibsen *(New York: Charles
Scribner's Sons, 1906-1908). The play was written in 1886.*

*\*"Rector" in the Scotch and Continental sense of headmaster of a school, not in the English
sense of a beneficed clergyman.*

†*Pronounce* Mortensgore.

MADAM HELSETH. I suppose I had better begin to lay the table, Miss?

REBECCA WEST. Yes, please do. The Pastor must soon be in now.

MADAM HELSETH. Don't you feel the draught, Miss, where you're sitting?

REBECCA. Yes, there is a little draught. Perhaps you had better shut the window.                                      [MADAM HELSETH *shuts the door into the hall, and then comes to the window.*

MADAM HELSETH. [*About to shut the window, looks out*] Why, isn't that the Pastor over there?

REBECCA. [*Hastily*] Where? [*Rises*] Yes, it is he. [*Behind the curtain*] Stand aside — don't let him see us.

MADAM HELSETH. [*Keeping back from the window*] Only think, Miss —       10
he's beginning to take the path by the mill again.

REBECCA. He went that way the day before yesterday too. [*Peeps out between the curtains and the window-frame*] But let us see whether —

MADAM HELSETH. Will he venture across the foot-bridge?

REBECCA. That is what I want to see. [*After a pause*] No, he is turning. He is going by the upper road again. [*Leaves the window*] A long way round.

MADAM HELSETH. Dear Lord, yes. No wonder the Pastor thinks twice about setting foot on that bridge. A place where a thing like that has happened —                                                                  20

REBECCA. [*Folding up her work*] They cling to their dead here at Rosmersholm.

MADAM HELSETH. Now *I* would say, Miss, that it's the dead that clings to Rosmersholm.

REBECCA. [*Looks at her*] The dead?

MADAM HELSETH. Yes, it's almost as if they couldn't tear themselves away from the folk that are left.

REBECCA. What makes you fancy that?

MADAM HELSETH. Well, if it wasn't for that, there would be no White Horse, I suppose.                                                            30

REBECCA. Now what is all this about the White Horse, Madam Helseth?

MADAM HELSETH. Oh, I don't like to talk about it. And, besides, you don't believe in such things.

REBECCA. Do you believe in it, then?

MADAM HELSETH. [*Goes and shuts the window*] Oh, you'd only be for laughing at me, Miss. [*Looks out*] Why, isn't that Mr. Rosmer on the mill-path again — ?

REBECCA. [*Looks out*] That man there? [*Goes to the window*] No, that's the Rector!

MADAM HELSETH. Yes, so it is.                                            40

REBECCA. This is delightful. You may be sure he's coming here.

MADAM HELSETH. He goes straight over the foot-bridge, he does. And yet she was his sister, his own flesh and blood. Well, I'll go and lay the table then, Miss West.

[*She goes out to the right.* REBECCA *stands at the window for a short time; then smiles and nods to some one outside. It begins to grow dark.*

REBECCA. [*Goes to the door on the right*] Oh, Madam Helseth, you might let us have some little extra dish for supper. You know what the Rector likes best.

MADAM HELSETH. [*Outside*] Oh yes, Miss, I'll see to it.

REBECCA. [*Opens the door to the hall*] At last — ! How glad I am to see you, my dear Rector.                                                       50

RECTOR KROLL. [*In the hall, laying down his stick*] Thanks. Then I am not disturbing you?

REBECCA.  You? How can you ask?

KROLL.  [*Comes in*] Amiable as ever. [*Looks round*] Is Rosmer upstairs in his room?

REBECCA.  No, he is out walking. He has stayed out rather longer than usual; but he is sure to be in directly. [*Motioning him to sit on the sofa*] Won't you sit down till he comes?

KROLL.  [*Laying down his hat*] Many thanks. [*Sits down and looks about him*] Why, how you have brightened up the old room! Flowers everywhere!  60

REBECCA.  Mr. Rosmer is so fond of having fresh, growing flowers about him.

KROLL.  And you are too, are you not?

REBECCA.  Yes; they have a delightfully soothing effect on me. We had to do without them, though, till lately.

KROLL.  [*Nods sadly*] Yes, their scent was too much for poor Beata.

REBECCA.  Their colours, too. They quite bewildered her —

KROLL.  I remember, I remember. [*In a lighter tone*] Well, how are things going out here?

REBECCA.  Oh, everything is going its quiet, jog-trot way. One day is just  70 like another. — And with you? Your wife — ?

KROLL.  Ah, my dear Miss West, don't let us talk about my affairs. There is always something or other amiss in a family; especially in times like these.

REBECCA.  [*After a pause, sitting down in an easy-chair beside the sofa*] How is it you haven't once been near us during the whole of the holidays?

KROLL.  Oh, it doesn't do to make oneself a nuisance —

REBECCA.  If you knew how we have missed you —

KROLL.  And then I have been away —

REBECCA.  Yes, for the last week or two. We have heard of you at  80 political meetings.

KROLL.  [*Nods*] Yes, what do you say to that? Did you think I would turn political agitator in my old age, eh?

REBECCA.  [*Smiling*] Well, you have always been a bit of an agitator, Rector Kroll.

KROLL.  Why, yes, just for my private amusement. But henceforth it is to be no laughing matter, I can tell you. — Do you ever see those radical newspapers?

REBECCA.  Well yes, my dear Rector, I can't deny that —

KROLL.  My dear Miss West, I have nothing to say against it — nothing  90 in your case.

REBECCA.  No, surely not. One likes to know what's going on — to keep up with the time —

KROLL.  And of course I should not think of expecting you, as a woman, to side actively with either party in the civil contest — I might almost say the civil war — that is raging among us. — But you have seen then, I suppose, how these gentlemen of "the people" have been pleased to treat me? What infamous abuse they have had the audacity to heap on me?

REBECCA.  Yes; but it seems to me you gave as good as you got.

KROLL.  So I did, though I say it that shouldn't. For now I have tasted  100 blood; and they shall soon find to their cost that I am not the man to turn the other cheek — [*Breaks off*] But come come — don't let us get upon that subject this evening — it's too painful and irritating.

REBECCA.  Oh no, don't let us talk of it.

KROLL.  Tell me now — how do you get on at Rosmersholm, now that you are alone? Since our poor Beata —

REBECCA.  Thank you, I get on very well. Of course one feels a great blank in many ways — a great sorrow and longing. But otherwise —

KROLL. And do you think of remaining here? — permanently, I mean.

REBECCA. My dear Rector, I really haven't thought about it, one way  110
or the other. I have got so used to the place now, that I feel almost as if
I belonged to it.

KROLL. Why, of course you belong to it.

REBECCA. And so long as Mr. Rosmer finds that I am of any use or
comfort to him — why, so long, I suppose, I shall stay here.

KROLL. [*Looks at her with emotion*] Do you know, — it is really fine for
a woman to sacrifice her whole youth to others as you have done.

REBECCA. Oh, what else should I have had to live for?

KROLL. First, there was your untiring devotion to your paralytic and
exacting foster-father —  120

REBECCA. You mustn't suppose that Dr. West was such a charge when
we were up in Finmark. It was those terrible boat-voyages up there that
broke him down. But after we came here — well yes, the two years before
he found rest were certainly hard enough.

KROLL. And the years that followed — were they not even harder for
you?

REBECCA. Oh how can you say such a thing? When I was so fond of
Beata — and when she, poor dear, stood so sadly in need of care and
forbearance.

KROLL. How good it is of you to think of her with so much kindness!  130

REBECCA. [*Moves a little nearer*] My dear Rector, you say that with
such a ring of sincerity that I cannot think there is any ill-feeling lurking
in the background.

KROLL. Ill-feeling? Why, what do you mean?

REBECCA. Well, it would be only natural if you felt it painful to see a
stranger managing the household here at Rosmersholm.

KROLL. Why, how on earth — !

REBECCA. But you have no such feeling? [*Takes his hand*] Thanks, my
dear Rector; thank you again and again.

KROLL. How on earth did you get such an idea into your head?  140

REBECCA. I began to be a little afraid when your visits became so rare.

KROLL. Then you have been on a totally wrong scent, Miss West. Besides
— after all, there has been no essential change. Even while poor Beata was
alive — in her last unhappy days — it was you, and you alone, that managed
everything.

REBECCA. That was only a sort of regency in Beata's name.

KROLL. Be that as it may — . Do you know, Miss West — for my part,
I should have no objection whatever if you — . But I suppose I mustn't
say such a thing.

REBECCA. What must you not say?  150

KROLL. If matters were to shape so that you took the empty place —

REBECCA. I have the only place I want, Rector.

KROLL. In fact, yes; but not in —

REBECCA. [*Interrupting gravely*] For shame, Rector Kroll. How can you
joke about such things?

KROLL. Oh well, our good Johannes Rosmer very likely thinks he has
had more than enough of married life already. But nevertheless —

REBECCA. You are really too absurd, Rector.

KROLL. Nevertheless — . Tell me, Miss West — if you will forgive the
question — what is your age?  160

REBECCA. I'm sorry to say I am over nine-and-twenty, Rector; I am in
my thirtieth year.

KROLL. Indeed. And Rosmer — how old is he? Let me see: he is five years younger than I am, so that makes him well over forty-three. I think it would be most suitable.

REBECCA. [*Rises*] Of course, of course; most suitable. — Will you stay to supper this evening?

KROLL. Yes, many thanks; I thought of staying. There is a matter I want to discuss with our good friend. — And I suppose, Miss West, in case you should take fancies into your head again, I had better come out pretty 170 often for the future — as I used to in the old days.

REBECCA. Oh yes, do — do. [*Shakes both his hands*] Many thanks — how kind and good you are!

KROLL. [*Gruffly*] Am I? Well, that's not what they tell me at home.

JOHANNES ROSMER *enters by the door on the right.*

REBECCA. Mr. Rosmer, do you see who is here?

JOHANNES ROSMER. Madam Helseth told me. [RECTOR KROLL *has risen.*

ROSMER. [*Gently and softly, pressing his hands*] Welcome back to this house, my dear Kroll. [*Lays his hands on* KROLL'S *shoulders and looks into his eyes*] My dear old friend! I knew that sooner or later things would come all right between us. 180

KROLL. Why, my dear fellow — do you mean to say you too have been so foolish as to fancy there was anything wrong?

REBECCA. [*To* ROSMER] Yes, only think, — it was nothing but fancy after all!

ROSMER. Is that really the case, Kroll? Then why did you desert us so entirely?

KROLL. [*Gravely, in a low voice*] Because my presence would always have been reminding you of the years of your happiness, and of — the life that ended in the mill-race.

ROSMER. Well, it was a kind thought — you were always considerate. But 190 it was quite unnecessary to remain away on that account. — Come, sit here on the sofa. [*They sit down*] No, I assure you, the thought of Beata has no pain for me. We speak of her every day. We feel almost as if she were still one of the household.

KROLL. Do you really?

REBECCA. [*Lighting the lamp*] Yes, indeed we do.

ROSMER. It is quite natural. We were both so deeply attached to her. And both Rebec — both Miss West and I know that we did all that was possible for her in her affliction. We have nothing to reproach ourselves with. — So I feel nothing but a tranquil tenderness now at the thought of Beata. 200

KROLL. You dear, good people! Henceforward, I declare I shall come out and see you every day.

REBECCA. [*Seats herself in an arm chair*] Mind, we shall expect you to keep your word.

ROSMER. [*With some hesitation*] My dear Kroll — I wish very much that our intercourse had never been interrupted. Ever since we have known each other, you have seemed predestined to be my adviser — ever since I went to the University.

KROLL. Yes, and I have always been proud of the office. But is there anything particular just now — ? 210

ROSMER. There are many things that I would give a great deal to talk over with you, quite frankly — straight from the heart.

REBECCA. Ah yes, Mr. Rosmer — that must be such a comfort — between old friends —

KROLL. Oh I can tell you I have still more to talk to you about. I suppose you know I have turned a militant politician?

ROSMER. Yes, so you have. How did that come about?

KROLL. I was forced into it in spite of myself. It is impossible to stand idly looking on any longer. Now that the Radicals have unhappily come into power, it is high time something should be done, — so I have got our little group of friends in the town to close up their ranks. I tell you it is high time! 220

REBECCA. [*With a faint smile*] Don't you think it may even be a little late?

KROLL. Unquestionably it would have been better if we had checked the stream at an earlier point in its course. But who could foresee what was going to happen? Certainly not I. [*Rises and walks up and down*] But now I have had my eyes opened once for all; for now the spirit of revolt has crept into the school itself.

ROSMER. Into the school? Surely not into your school? 230

KROLL. I tell you it has — into my own school. What do you think? It has come to my knowledge that the sixth-form boys — a number of them at any rate — have been keeping up a secret society for over six months; and they take in Mortensgård's paper!

REBECCA. The "Beacon"?

KROLL. Yes; nice mental sustenance for future government officials, is it not? But the worst of it is that it's all the cleverest boys in the form that have banded together in this conspiracy against me. Only the dunces at the bottom of the class have kept out of it.

REBECCA. Do you take this so very much to heart, Rector? 240

KROLL. Do I take it to heart! To be so thwarted and opposed in the work of my whole life! [*Lower*] But I could almost say I don't care about the school — for there is worse behind. [*Looks round*] I suppose no one can hear us?

REBECCA. Oh no, of course not.

KROLL. Well, then, I must tell you that dissension and revolt have crept into my own house — into my own quiet home. They have destroyed the peace of my family life.

ROSMER. [*Rises*] What! Into your own house — ?

REBECCA. [*Goes over to the* RECTOR] My dear Rector, what has happened? 250

KROLL. Would you believe that my own children — In short, it is Laurits that is the ringleader of the school conspiracy; and Hilda has embroidered a red portfolio to keep the "Beacon" in.

ROSMER. I should certainly never have dreamt that, in your own house —

KROLL. No, who would have dreamt of such a thing? In my house, the very home of obedience and order — where one will, and one only, has always prevailed —

REBECCA. How does your wife take all this?

KROLL. Why, that is the most incredible part of it. My wife, who all her life long has shared my opinions and concurred in my views, both in great things and small — she is actually inclined to side with the children on many points. And she blames me for what has happened. She says I tyrannise over the children. As if it weren't necessary to — . Well, you see how my house is divided against itself. But of course I say as little about it as possible. Such things are best kept quiet. [*Wanders up the room*] Ah, well, well, well. [*Stands at the window with his hands behind his back, and looks out.* 260

REBECCA. [*Comes up close to* ROSMER, *and says rapidly and in a low voice, so that the* RECTOR *does not hear her*] Do it now! 270

ROSMER. [*Also in a low voice*] Not this evening.

REBECCA. [*As before*] Yes, just this evening.

[*Goes to the table and busies herself with the lamp.*

KROLL. [*Comes forward*] Well, my dear Rosmer, now you know how the spirit of the age has overshadowed both my domestic and my official life. And am I to refrain from combating this pernicious, subversive, anarchic spirit, with any weapons I can lay my hands on? Fight it I will, trust me for that, both with tongue and pen.

ROSMER. Have you any hope of stemming the tide in that way?

KROLL. At any rate I shall have done my duty as a citizen in defence of 280 the State. And I hold it the duty of every right-minded man with an atom of patriotism to do likewise. In fact — that was my principal reason for coming out here this evening.

ROSMER. Why, my dear Kroll, what do you mean — ? What can I — ?

KROLL. You can stand by your old friends. Do as we do. Lend a hand, with all your might.

REBECCA. But, Rector Kroll, you know Mr. Rosmer's distaste for public life.

KROLL. He must get over his distaste. — You don't keep abreast of things, Rosmer. You bury yourself alive here, with your historical col- 290 lections. Far be it from me to speak disrespectfully of family trees and so forth; but, unfortunately, this is no time for hobbies of that sort. You cannot imagine the state things are in, all over the country. There is hardly a single accepted idea that hasn't been turned topsy-turvy. It will be a gigantic task to get all the errors rooted out again.

ROSMER. I have no doubt of it. But I am the last man to undertake such a task.

REBECCA. And besides, I think Mr. Rosmer has come to take a wider view of life than he used to.

KROLL. [*With surprise*] Wider? 300

REBECCA. Yes; or freer, if you like — less one-sided.

KROLL. What is the meaning of this? Rosmer — surely you are not so weak as to be influenced by the accident that the leaders of the mob have won a temporary advantage?

ROSMER. My dear Kroll, you know how little I understand of politics. But I confess it seems to me that within the last few years people are beginning to show greater independence of thought.

KROLL. Indeed! And you take it for granted that that must be an improvement! But in any case you are quite mistaken, my friend. Just inquire a little into the opinions that are current among the Radicals, both out 310 here and in the town. They are neither more nor less than the wisdom that's retailed in the "Beacon."

REBECCA. Yes; Mortensgård has great influence over many people hereabouts.

KROLL. Yes, just think of it! A man of his foul antecedents — a creature that was turned out of his place as a schoolmaster on account of his immoral life! A fellow like that sets himself up as a leader of the people! And succeeds too! Actually succeeds! I hear he is going to enlarge his paper. I know on good authority that he is on the lookout for a capable assistant. 320

REBECCA. I wonder that you and your friends don't set up an opposition to him.

KROLL. That is the very thing we are going to do. We have to-day bought the "County News"; there was no difficulty about the money question. But — [*Turns to* ROSMER] Now I come to my real errand. The difficulty lies in the conduct of the paper — the editing — Tell me, Rosmer, — don't you feel it your duty to undertake it, for the sake of the good cause?

ROSMER. [*Almost in consternation*] I?

REBECCA. Oh, how can you think of such a thing?          330

KROLL. I can quite understand your horror of public meetings, and your reluctance to expose yourself to their tender mercies. But an editor's work is less conspicuous, or rather —

ROSMER. No, no, my dear friend, you must not ask me to do this.

KROLL. I should be quite willing to try my own hand at that style of work too; but I couldn't possibly manage it. I have such a multitude of irons in the fire already. But for you, with no profession to tie you down — Of course the rest of us would give you as much help as we could.

ROSMER. I cannot, Kroll. I am not fitted for it.

KROLL. Not fitted? You said the same thing when your father preferred  340 you to the living here —

ROSMER. And I was right. That was why I resigned it.

KROLL. Oh, if only you are as good an editor as you were a clergyman, we shall not complain.

ROSMER. My dear Kroll — I tell you once for all — I cannot do it.

KROLL. Well, at any rate, you will lend us your name.

ROSMER. My name?

KROLL. Yes, the mere name, Johannes Rosmer, will be a great thing for the paper. We others are looked upon as confirmed partisans — indeed I hear I am denounced as a desperate fanatic — so that if we work the paper  350 in our own names, we can't reckon upon its making much way among the misguided masses. You, on the contrary, have always kept out of the fight. Everybody knows and values your humanity and uprightness — your delicacy of mind — your unimpeachable honour. And then the prestige of your former position as a clergyman still clings to you; and, to crown all, you have your grand old family name!

ROSMER. Oh, my name —

KROLL. [*Points to the portraits*] Rosmers of Rosmersholm — clergymen and soldiers; government officials of high place and trust; gentlemen to the finger-tips, every man of them — a family that for nearly two centuries  360 has held its place as the first in the district. [*Lays his hand on* ROSMER'S *shoulder*] Rosmer — you owe it to yourself and to the traditions of your race to take your share in guarding all that has hitherto been held sacred in our society. [*Turns round*] What do you say, Miss West?

REBECCA. [*Laughing softly, as if to herself*] My dear Rector — I can't tell you how ludicrous all this seems to me.

KROLL. What do you say? Ludicrous?

REBECCA. Yes, ludicrous. For you must let me tell you frankly —

ROSMER. [*Quickly*] No, no — be quiet! Not just now!

KROLL. [*Looks from one to the other*] My dear friends, what on earth  370 — ? [*Interrupting himself*] H'm.

MADAME HELSETH *appears in the doorway on the right.*

MADAM HELSETH. There's a man out in the kitchen passage that says he wants to see the Pastor.

ROSMER. [*Relieved*] Ah, very well. Ask him to come in.

MADAM HELSETH. Into the sitting-room?

ROSMER. Yes, of course.

MADAM HELSETH. But he looks scarcely the sort of man to bring into the sitting-room.

REBECCA. Why, what does he look like, Madam Helseth?

MADAM HELSETH. Well, he's not much to look at, Miss, and that's a fact. 380

ROSMER. Did he not give his name?

MADAM HELSETH. Yes — I think he said his name was Hekman or something of the sort.

ROSMER. I know nobody of that name.

MADAM HELSETH. And then he said he was called Uldric, too.

ROSMER. [*In surprise*] Ulric Hetman! Was that it?

MADAM HELSETH. Yes, so it was — Hetman.

KROLL. I've surely heard that name before —

REBECCA. Wasn't that the name he used to write under — that strange being — 390

ROSMER. [*To* KROLL] It is Ulric Brendel's pseudonym.

KROLL. That black sheep Ulric Brendel's — of course it is.

REBECCA. Then he is still alive.

ROSMER. I heard he had joined a company of strolling players.

KROLL. When last *I* heard of him, he was in the House of Correction.

ROSMER. Ask him to come in, Madam Helseth.

MADAM HELSETH. Oh, very well.                    [*She goes out.*

KROLL. Are you really going to let a man like that into your house?

ROSMER. You know he was once my tutor.

KROLL. Yes, I know he went and crammed your head full of revolu- 400
tionary ideas, until your father showed him the door — with his horsewhip.

ROSMER. [*With a touch of bitterness*] Father was a martinet at home as well as in his regiment.

KROLL. Thank him in his grave for that, my dear Rosmer. — Well!

MADAM HELSETH *opens the door on the right for* ULRIC BRENDEL, *and then withdraws, shutting the door behind him. He is a handsome man, with grey hair and beard; somewhat gaunt, but active and well set up. He is dressed like a common tramp; threadbare frock-coat; worn-out shoes; no shirt visible. He wears an old pair of black gloves, and carries a soft, greasy felt hat under his arm, and a walking-stick in his hand.*

ULRIC BRENDEL. [*Hesitates at first, then goes quickly up to the* RECTOR, *and holds out his hand*] Good evening, Johannes!

KROLL. Excuse me —

BRENDEL. Did you expect to see me again? And within these hated walls, too?

KROLL. Excuse me — [*Pointing*] There — 410

BRENDEL. [*Turns*] Right. There he is. Johannes — my boy — my best-beloved — !

ROSMER. [*Takes his hand*] My old teacher.

BRENDEL. Notwithstanding certain painful memories, I could not pass by Rosmersholm without paying you a flying visit.

ROSMER. You are heartily welcome here now. Be sure of that.

BRENDEL. Ah, this charming lady — ? [*Bows*] Mrs. Rosmer, of course.

ROSMER. Miss West.

BRENDEL. A near relation, no doubt. And yonder unknown — ? A brother of the cloth, I see. 420

ROSMER. Rector Kroll.

BRENDEL. Kroll? Kroll? Wait a bit? — Weren't you a student of philology in your young days?

KROLL. Of course I was.

BRENDEL. Why *Donnerwetter*, then I knew you!

KROLL. Pardon me —

BRENDEL. Weren't you —

KROLL. Pardon me —

BRENDEL. — one of those myrmidons of morality that got me turned out of the Debating Club? 430

KROLL. Very likely. But I disclaim any closer acquaintanceship.

BRENDEL. Well, well! *Nach Belieben, Herr Doctor.* It's all one to me. Ulric Brendel remains the man he is for all that.

REBECCA. You are on your way into town, Mr. Brendel?

BRENDEL. You have hit it, gracious lady. At certain intervals, I am constrained to strike a blow for existence. It goes against the grain; but — *enfin* — imperious necessity —

ROSMER. Oh, but, my dear Mr. Brendel, you must allow me to help you. In one way or another, I am sure —

BRENDEL. Ha, such a proposal to me! Would you desecrate the bond 440 that unites us? Never, Johannes, never!

ROSMER. But what do you think of doing in town? Believe me, you won't find it easy to —

BRENDEL. Leave that to me, my boy. The die is cast. Simple as I stand here before you, I am engaged in a comprehensive campaign — more comprehensive than all my previous excursions put together. [*To* RECTOR KROLL] Dare I ask the Herr Professor — *unter uns* — have you a tolerably decent, reputable, and commodious Public Hall in your estimable city?

KROLL. The hall of the Workmen's Society is the largest.

BRENDEL. And has the Herr Professor any official influence in this 450 doubtless most beneficent Society?

KROLL. I have nothing to do with it.

REBECCA. [*To* BRENDEL] You should apply to Peter Mortensgård.

BRENDEL. Pardon, madame — what sort of an idiot is he?

ROSMER. What makes you take him for an idiot?

BRENDEL. Can't I tell at once by the name that it belongs to a plebeian?

KROLL. I did not expect that answer.

BRENDEL. But I will conquer my reluctance. There is no alternative. When a man stands — as I do — at a turning-point in his career — . It is settled. I will approach this individual — will open personal negotiations — 460

ROSMER. Are you really and seriously standing at a turning-point?

BRENDEL. Surely my own boy knows that, stand he where he may, Ulric Brendel always stands really and seriously. — Yes, Johannes, I am going to put on a new man — to throw off the modest reserve I have hitherto maintained —

ROSMER. How — ?

BRENDEL. I am about to take hold of life with a strong hand; to step forth; to assert myself. We live in a tempestuous, an equinoctial age. — I am about to lay my mite on the altar of Emancipation.

KROLL. You, too? 470

BRENDEL. [*To them all*] Is the local public at all familiar with my occasional writings?

KROLL. No, I must candidly confess that —

REBECCA. I have read several of them. My adopted father had them in his library.

BRENDEL. Fair lady, then you have wasted your time. For, let me tell you, they are so much rubbish.

REBECCA. Indeed!

BRENDEL. What you have read, yes. My really important works no man or woman knows. No one — except myself. 480

REBECCA. How does that happen?

BRENDEL. Because they are not written.

ROSMER. But, my dear Mr. Brendel —

BRENDEL. You know, my Johannes, that I am a bit of a Sybarite — a *Feinschmecker.* I have been so all my days. I like to take my pleasures in solitude; for then I enjoy them doubly — tenfold. So, you see, when golden dreams descended and enwrapped me — when new, dizzy, far-reaching thoughts were born in me, and wafted me aloft on their sustaining pinions — I bodied them forth in poems, visions, pictures — in the rough, as it were, you understand.                                    490

ROSMER. Yes, yes.

BRENDEL. Oh, what pleasures, what intoxications I have enjoyed in my time! The mysterious bliss of creation — in the rough, as I said — applause, gratitude, renown, the wreath of bays — all these I have garnered with full hands quivering with joy. I have sated myself, in my secret thoughts, with a rapture — oh! so intense, so inebriating — !

KROLL. H'm.

ROSMER. But you have written nothing down?

BRENDEL. Not a word. The soulless toil of the scrivener has always aroused a sickening aversion in me. And besides, why should I profane 500 my own ideals, when I could enjoy them in their purity by myself? But now they shall be offered up. I assure you I feel like a mother who delivers her tender daughters into their bridegrooms' arms. But I will offer them up, none the less. I will sacrifice them on the altar of Emancipation. A series of carefully elaborated lectures — over the whole country — !

REBECCA. [*With animation*] This is noble of you, Mr. Brendel! You are yielding up the dearest thing you possess.

ROSMER. The only thing.

REBECCA. [*Looking significantly at* ROSMER] How many are there who do as much — who dare do as much?                        510

ROSMER. [*Returning the look*] Who knows?

BRENDEL. My audience is touched. That does my heart good — and steels my will. So now I will proceed to action. Stay — one thing more. [*To the* RECTOR] Can you tell me, Herr Preceptor, — is there such a thing as a Temperance Society in the town? A Total Abstinence Society? I need scarcely ask.

KROLL. Yes, there is. I am the president, at your service.

BRENDEL. I saw it in your face! Well, it is by no means impossible that I may come to you and enroll myself as a member for a week.

KROLL. Excuse me — we don't receive members by the week.      520

BRENDEL. *A la bonne heure,* Herr Pedagogue. Ulric Brendel has never forced himself into that sort of Society. [*Turns*] But I must not prolong my stay in this house, so rich in memories. I must get on to the town and select a suitable lodging. I presume there is a decent hotel in the place.

REBECCA. Mayn't I offer you anything before you go?

BRENDEL. Of what sort, gracious lady?

REBECCA. A cup of tea, or —

BRENDEL. I thank my bountiful hostess — but I am always loath to trespass on private hospitality. [*Waves his hand*] Farewell, gentlefolks all! [*Goes towards the door, but turns again*] Oh, by the way — Johannes — 530 Pastor Rosmer — for the sake of our ancient friendship, will you do your former teacher a service?

ROSMER. Yes, with all my heart.

BRENDEL. Good. Then lend me — for a day or two — a starched shirt — with cuffs.

ROSMER. Nothing else?

BRENDEL. For you see I am travelling on foot — at present. My trunk is being sent after me.

ROSMER. Quite so. But is there nothing else?

BRENDEL. Well, do you know — perhaps you could spare me an oldish, 540 well-worn summer overcoat.

ROSMER. Yes, yes; certainly I can.

BRENDEL. And if a respectable pair of boots happened to go along with the coat ——

ROSMER. That we can manage, too. As soon as you let us know your address, we will send the things in.

BRENDEL. Not on any account. Pray do not let me give you any trouble! I will take the bagatelles with me.

ROSMER. As you please. Come upstairs with me then.

REBECCA. Let me go. Madam Helseth and I will see to it.                550

BRENDEL. I cannot think of suffering this distinguished lady to —

REBECCA. Oh, nonsense! Come along, Mr. Brendel.

[*She goes out to the right.*

ROSMER. [*Detaining him*] Tell me — is there nothing else I can do for you?

BRENDEL. Upon my word, I know of nothing more. Well, yes, damn it all — now that I think of it — ! Johannes, do you happen to have eight crowns in your pocket?

ROSMER. Let me see. [*Opens his purse*] Here are two ten-crown notes.

BRENDEL. Well, well, never mind! I can take them. I can always get them 560 changed in the town. Thanks in the meantime. Remember it was two tenners you lent me. Good-night my own dear boy. Good-night, respected Sir.

[*Goes out to the right.* ROSMER *takes leave of him, and shuts the door behind him.*

KROLL. Merciful Heaven — so that is the Ulric Brendel people once expected such great things of.

ROSMER. [*Quietly*] At least he has had the courage to live his life his own way. I don't think that is such a small matter either.

KROLL. What? A life like his! I almost believe he has it in him to turn your head afresh.                                                          570

ROSMER. Oh, no. My mind is quite clear now, upon all points.

KROLL. I wish I could believe it, my dear Rosmer. You are so terribly impressionable.

ROSMER. Let us sit down. I want to talk to you.

KROLL. Yes, let us.                              [*They seat themselves on the sofa.*

ROSMER. [*After a slight pause*] Don't you think we lead a pleasant and comfortable life here?

KROLL. Yes, your life is pleasant and comfortable now — and peaceful. You have found yourself a home, Rosmer. And I have lost mine.

ROSMER. My dear friend, don't say that. The wound will heal again in 580 time.

KROLL. Never; never. The barb will always rankle. Things can never be as they were.

ROSMER. Listen to me, Kroll. We have been fast friends for many and many a year. Does it seem to you conceivable that our friendship should ever go to wreck?

KROLL. I know of nothing in the world that could estrange us. What puts that into your head?

ROSMER. You attach such paramount importance to uniformity of opinions and views.                                                          590

KROLL. No doubt; but we two are in practical agreement — at any rate on the great essential questions.

ROSMER. [*In a low voice*] No; not now.

KROLL. [*Tries to spring up*] What is this?

ROSMER. [*Holding him*] No, you must sit still — I entreat you, Kroll.

KROLL. What can this mean? I don't understand you. Speak plainly.

ROSMER. A new summer has blossomed in my soul. I see with eyes grown young again. And so now I stand —

KROLL. Where — where, Rosmer?

ROSMER. Where your children stand. 600

KROLL. You? You! Impossible! Where do you say you stand?

ROSMER. On the same side as Laurits and Hilda.

KROLL. [*Bows his head*] An apostate! Johannes Rosmer an apostate!

ROSMER. I should have felt so happy — so intensely happy, in what you call my apostasy. But, nevertheless, I suffered deeply; for I knew it would be a bitter sorrow to you.

KROLL. Rosmer — Rosmer! I shall never get over this! [*Looks gloomily at him*] To think that you, too, can find it in your heart to help on the work of corruption and ruin in this unhappy land.

ROSMER. It is the work of emancipation I wish to help on. 610

KROLL. Oh, yes, I know. That is what both the tempters and their victims call it. But do you think there is any emancipation to be expected from the spirit that is now poisoning our social life?

ROSMER. I am not in love with the spirit that is in the ascendant, nor with either of the contending parties. I will try to bring together men from both sides — as many as I can — and to unite them as closely as possible. I will devote my life and all my energies to this one thing — the creation of a true democracy in this country.

KROLL. So you don't think we have democracy enough already! For my part it seems to me we are all in a fair way to be dragged down into the 620 mire, where hitherto only the mob have been able to thrive.

ROSMER. That is just why I want to awaken the democracy to its true task.

KROLL. What task?

ROSMER. That of making all the people of this country noble —

KROLL. All the people — ?

ROSMER. As many as possible, at any rate.

KROLL. By what means?

ROSMER. By freeing their minds and purifying their wills.

KROLL. You are a dreamer, Rosmer. Will you free them? Will you 630 purify them?

ROSMER. No, my dear friend — I will only try to arouse them to their task. They themselves must accomplish it.

KROLL. And you think they can?

ROSMER. Yes.

KROLL. By their own strength?

ROSMER. Yes, precisely by their own strength. There is no other.

KROLL. [*Rises*] Is this becoming language for a priest?

ROSMER. I am no longer a priest.

KROLL. Well but — the faith of your fathers — ? 640

ROSMER. It is mine no more.

KROLL. No more — !

ROSMER. [*Rises*] I have given it up. I had to give it up, Kroll.

KROLL. [*Controlling his agitation*] Oh, indeed — Yes, yes, yes. I suppose one thing goes with another. Was this, then, your reason for leaving the Church?

ROSMER. Yes. As soon as my mind was clear — as soon as I was quite certain that this was no passing attack of scepticism, but a conviction I neither could nor would shake off — then I at once left the Church.

KROLL. So this has been your state of mind all this time! And we — your 650 friends — have heard nothing of it. Rosmer — Rosmer — how could you hide the miserable truth from us!

ROSMER. Because it seemed to me a matter that concerned myself alone. And besides, I did not wish to give you and my other friends any needless pain. I thought I might live on here, as before, quietly, serenely, happily. I wanted to read, to bury myself in all the studies that until then had been sealed books to me. I wanted to make myself thoroughly at home in the great world of truth and freedom that has been revealed to me.

KROLL. Apostate! Every word proves it. But why, then, do you confess your secret apostasy after all? And why just at this time? 660

ROSMER. You yourself have driven me to it, Kroll.

KROLL. I? Have I driven you — ?

ROSMER. When I heard of your violence on the platform — when I read all the rancorous speeches you made — your bitter onslaughts on your opponents — the contemptuous invectives you heaped on them — oh, Kroll, to think that you — you — could come to this! — then my duty stood imperatively before me. Men are growing evil in this struggle. Peace and joy and mutual forbearance must once more enter into our souls. That is why I now intend to step forward and openly avow myself for what I am. I, too, will try my strength. Could not you — from your side — help me in 670 this, Kroll?

KROLL. Never so long as I live will I make peace with the subversive forces in society.

ROSMER. Then at least let us fight with honourable weapons — since fight we must.

KROLL. Whoever is not with me in the essential things of life, him I no longer know. I owe him no consideration.

ROSMER. Does that apply to me, too?

KROLL. It is you that have broken with me, Rosmer.

ROSMER. Is this a breach then? 680

KROLL. This! It is a breach with all who have hitherto been your friends. You must take the consequences.

REBECCA WEST *enters from the right, and opens the door wide.*

REBECCA. There now; he is on his way to his great sacrifice. And now we can go to supper. Will you come in, Rector?

KROLL. [*Takes up his hat*] Good-night, Miss West. I have nothing more to do here.

REBECCA. [*Eagerly*] What is this? [*Shuts the door and comes forward*] Have you spoken?

ROSMER. He knows everything.

KROLL. We will not let you go, Rosmer. We will force you to come back 690 to us.

ROSMER. I can never stand where I did.

KROLL. We shall see. You are not the man to endure standing alone.

ROSMER. I shall not be so completely alone after all. — There are two of us to bear the loneliness together.

KROLL. Ah — . [*A suspicion appears in his face*] That too! Beata's words — !

ROSMER. Beata's — ?

KROLL. [*Shaking off the thought*] No, no — that was vile. Forgive me.

ROSMER. What? What do you mean?                                              700

KROLL. Don't ask. Bah! Forgive me! Good-bye!

> [*Goes towards the entrance door.*

ROSMER. [*Follows him*] Kroll! Our friendship must not end like this. I will come and see you to-morrow.

KROLL. [*In the hall, turns*] You shall never cross my threshold again.

*He takes up his stick and goes out.* ROSMER *stands for a moment in the doorway, then shuts the door and walks up to the table.*

ROSMER. It does not matter, Rebecca. We will see it out, we two faithful friends — you * and I.

REBECCA. What do you think he meant when he said "That was vile"?

ROSMER. Don't trouble about that, dear. He himself didn't believe what was in his mind. To-morrow I will go and see him. Good-night!             710

REBECCA. Are you going upstairs so early to-night? After this?

ROSMER. To-night as usual. I feel so relieved, now it is over. You see — I am quite calm, Rebecca. Do you, too, take it calmly. Good-night!

REBECCA. Good-night, dear friend! Sleep well!

ROSMER *goes out by the hall door; his steps are heard ascending the stair-case.* REBECCA *goes and pulls a bell-rope near the stove. Shortly after,* MADAM HELSETH *enters from the right.*

REBECCA. You can take away the supper things, Madam Helseth. Mr. Rosmer doesn't want anything, and the Rector has gone home.

MADAM HELSETH. Has the Rector gone? What was the matter with him?

REBECCA. [*Takes up her crochet work*] He said he thought there was a heavy storm brewing —

MADAM HELSETH. What a strange notion! There's not a cloud in the sky 720 this evening.

REBECCA. Let us hope he mayn't meet the White Horse! I'm afraid we shall soon be hearing something from the bogies now.

MADAM HELSETH. Lord forgive you, Miss! Don't say such awful things.

REBECCA. Well, well, well —

MADAM HELSETH. [*Softly*] Do you really think some one is to go soon, Miss?

REBECCA. No; why should I think so? But there are so many sorts of white horses in this world, Madam Helseth. — Well, good-night. I shall go to my room now.                                                          730

MADAM HELSETH. Good-night, Miss.

> [REBECCA *goes out to the right, with her crochet-work.*

MADAM HELSETH. [*Turns the lamp down, shaking her head and muttering to herself*] Lord — Lord! That Miss West! The things she does say!

## ACT SECOND

JOHANNES ROSMER'S *study. Entrance door on the left. At the back, a door-way with a curtain drawn aside, leading into* ROSMER'S *bedroom. On the right a window, and in front of it a writing-table covered with books and papers. Book-shelves and cases round the room. The furniture is simple. On the left, an old-fashioned sofa, with a table in front of it.*

---

*From this point, and throughout when alone, Rosmer and Rebecca use the du of intimate friendship in speaking to each other.

JOHANNES ROSMER, *in an indoor jacket, is sitting in a high-backed chair at the writing-table. He is cutting and turning over the leaves of a pamphlet, and reading a little here and there.*
*There is a knock at the door on the left.*

ROSMER. [*Without moving*] Come in.

REBECCA WEST. [*Enters, dressed in a morning gown*] Good morning.

ROSMER. [*Turning the leaves of the pamphlet*] Good morning, dear. Do you want anything?

REBECCA. I only wanted to hear if you had slept well.

ROSMER. Oh, I have had a beautiful, peaceful night. [*Turns*] And you?

REBECCA. Oh, yes, thanks – towards morning —

ROSMER. I don't know when I have felt so light-hearted as I do now. I am so glad I managed to speak out at last.

REBECCA. Yes, it is a pity you remained silent so long, Rosmer.　　10

ROSMER. I don't understand myself how I could be such a coward.

REBECCA. It wasn't precisely cowardice —

ROSMER. Oh, yes, dear – when I think the thing out, I can see there was a touch of cowardice at the bottom of it.

REBECCA. All the braver, then, to make the plunge at last. [*Sits on a chair at the writing-table, close to him*] But now I want to tell you of something I have done – and you mustn't be vexed with me about it.

ROSMER. Vexed? How can you think — ?

REBECCA. Well, it was perhaps rather indiscreet of me but —

ROSMER. Let me hear what it was.　　20

REBECCA. Yesterday evening, when Ulric Brendel was leaving – I gave him a note to Peter Mortensgård.

ROSMER. [*A little doubtful*] Why, my dear Rebecca — Well, what did you say?

REBECCA. I said that he would be doing you a service if he would look after that unfortunate creature a little, and help him in any way he could.

ROSMER. Dear, you shouldn't have done that. You have only done Brendel harm. And Mortensgård is not a man I care to have anything to do with. You know of that old episode between us.

REBECCA. But don't you think it would be as well to make it up with　　30
him again?

ROSMER. I? With Mortensgård? In what way do you mean?

REBECCA. Well, you know you can't feel absolutely secure now – after this breach with your old friends.

ROSMER. [*Looks at her and shakes his head*] Can you really believe that Kroll or any of the others would try to take revenge on me? That they would be capable of — ?

REBECCA. In the first heat of anger, dear — . No one can be sure. I think – after the way the Rector took it —

ROSMER. Oh, you ought surely to know him better than that. Kroll is a　　40
gentleman, to the backbone. I am going into town this afternoon to talk to him. I will talk to them all. Oh, you shall see how easily it will all go —

MADAM HELSETH *appears at the door on the left.*

REBECCA. [*Rises*] What is it, Madam Helseth?

MADAM HELSETH. Rector Kroll is downstairs in the hall.

ROSMER. [*Rises hastily*] Kroll!

REBECCA. The Rector! Is it possible —

MADAM HELSETH. He wants to know if he may come upstairs, Mr. Rosmer.

ROSMER. [*To* REBECCA] What did I tell you? – Of course he may. [*Goes* 50
*to the door and calls down the stairs*] Come up, dear friend! I am delighted to see you.

ROSMER *stands holding the door open.* MADAM HELSETH *goes out.* REBECCA
*draws the curtain before the doorway at the back, and then begins
arranging things in the room.*

RECTOR KROLL *enters, with his hat in his hand.*

ROSMER. [*With quiet emotion*] I knew it couldn't be the last time —
KROLL. I see things to-day in quite a different light from yesterday.
ROSMER. Ah yes, Kroll; I was sure you would, now that you have had
time to reflect.
KROLL. You misunderstand me completely. [*Lays his hat on the table
beside the sofa*] It is of the utmost importance that I should speak to you,
alone.
ROSMER. Why may not Miss West — ? 60
REBECCA. No no, Mr. Rosmer. I will go.
KROLL. [*Looks at her from head to foot*] And I must ask Miss West to
excuse my coming at such an untimely hour – taking her unawares before she has had time to —
REBECCA. [*Surprised*] What do you mean? Do you see any harm in my
wearing a morning gown about the house?
KROLL. Heaven forbid! I know nothing of what may now be customary
at Rosmersholm.
ROSMER. Why, Kroll – you are not yourself to-day!
REBECCA. Allow me to wish you good morning, Rector Kroll. 70
                        [*She goes out to the left.*
KROLL. By your leave —                [*Sits on the sofa*
ROSMER. Yes, Kroll, sit down, and let us talk things out amicably.
          [*He seats himself in a chair directly opposite to the* RECTOR.
KROLL. I haven't closed an eye since yesterday. I have been lying
thinking and thinking all night.
ROSMER. And what do you say to things to-day?
KROLL. It will be a long story, Rosmer. Let me begin with a sort of
introduction. I can give you news of Ulric Brendel.
ROSMER. Has he called on you? 80
KROLL. No. He took up his quarters in a low public-house – in the
lowest company of course – and drank and stood treat as long as he had
any money. Then he began abusing the whole company as a set of disreputable blackguards – and so far he was quite right – whereupon they
thrashed him and pitched him out into the gutter.
ROSMER. So he is incorrigible after all.
KROLL. He had pawned the coat, too; but I am told that has been redeemed for him. Can you guess by whom?
ROSMER. Perhaps by you?
KROLL. No; by the distinguished Mr. Mortensgård. 90
ROSMER. Ah, indeed.
KROLL. I understand that Mr. Brendel's first visit was to the "idiot"
and "plebeian."
ROSMER. Well, it was lucky for him —
KROLL. To be sure it was. [*Leans over the table towards* ROSMER] And
that brings me to a matter it is my duty to warn you about, for our old –
for our former friendship's sake.
ROSMER. My dear Kroll, what can that be?
KROLL. It is this: there are things going on behind your back in this
house. 100

ROSMER. How can you think so? Is it Reb — is it Miss West you are aiming at?

KROLL. Precisely. I can quite understand it on her part. She has so long been accustomed to have everything her own way here. But nevertheless —

ROSMER. My dear Kroll, you are utterly mistaken. She and I — we have no concealments from each other on any subject whatever.

KROLL. Has she told you, then, that she has entered into correspondence with the editor of the "Beacon"?

ROSMER. Oh, you are thinking of the few lines she sent by Ulric 110 Brendel?

KROLL. Then you have found it out. And do you approve of her entering into relations with a scurrilous scribbler, who never lets a week pass without holding me up to ridicule, both as a schoolmaster and as a public man?

ROSMER. My dear Kroll, I don't suppose that side of the matter ever entered her head. And besides, of course she has full liberty of action, just as I have.

KROLL. Indeed? Ah, no doubt that follows from your new line of thought. For Miss West presumably shares your present standpoint? 120

ROSMER. Yes, she does. We two have worked our way forward in faithful comradeship.

KROLL. [*Looks at him and slowly shakes his head*] Oh, you blind, deluded being!

ROSMER. I? Why do you say that?

KROLL. Because I dare not — I will not think the worst. No no, let me say my say out. — You really do value my friendship, Rosmer? And my respect too? Do you not?

ROSMER. I surely need not answer that question.

KROLL. Well, but there are other questions that do require an answer — 130 a full explanation on your part. — Will you submit to a sort of investigation — ?

ROSMER. Investigation?

KROLL. Yes; will you let me question you about certain things it may pain you to be reminded of? You see — this apostasy of yours — well, this emancipation, as you call it — is bound up with many other things that for your own sake you must explain to me.

ROSMER. My dear Kroll, ask what questions you please. I have nothing to conceal.

KROLL. Then tell me — what do you think was the real, the ultimate 140 reason why Beata put an end to her life?

ROSMER. Can you have any doubt on the subject? Or, rather, can you ask for reasons for what an unhappy, irresponsible invalid may do?

KROLL. Are you certain that Beata was completely irresponsible for her actions? The doctors, at any rate, were by no means convinced of it.

ROSMER. If the doctors had ever seen her as I have so often seen her, for days and nights together, they would have had no doubts.

KROLL. I had no doubts either — then.

ROSMER. Oh, no, unhappily, there wasn't the smallest room for doubt. I have told you of her wild frenzies of passion — which she expected me 150 to return. Oh, how they appalled me! And then her causeless, consuming self-reproaches during the last few years.

KROLL. Yes, when she had learnt that she must remain childless all her life.

ROSMER. Yes, just think of that! Such terrible, haunting agony of mind about a thing utterly beyond her control — ! How could you call her responsible for her actions?

KROLL. H'm — . Can you remember whether you had any books in the house at that time treating of the rationale of marriage — according to the "advanced" ideas of the day?

ROSMER. I remember Miss West lending me a work of the kind. The Doctor left her his library, you know. But, my dear Kroll, you surely cannot suppose we were so reckless as to let my poor sick wife get hold of any such ideas? I can solemnly assure you that the fault was not ours. It was her own distempered brain that drove her into these wild aberrations.

KROLL. One thing at any rate I can tell you; and that is, that poor, overstrung, tortured Beata put an end to her life in order that you might live happily — live freely, and — after your own heart.

ROSMER. [*Starts half up from his chair*] What do you mean by that?

KROLL. Listen to me quietly, Rosmer; for now I can speak of it. In the last year of her life she came to me twice to pour forth all her anguish and despair.

ROSMER. On this same subject?

KROLL. No. The first time she came, it was to declare that you were on the road to perversion — that you were going to break with the faith of your fathers.

ROSMER. [*Eagerly*] What you say is impossible, Kroll. Absolutely impossible! You must be mistaken.

KROLL. And why?

ROSMER. Because while Beata was alive I was still wrestling with myself in doubt. And that fight I fought out alone and in utter silence. I don't think even Rebecca —

KROLL. Rebecca?

ROSMER. Oh, well — Miss West. I call her Rebecca for convenience' sake.

KROLL. So I have remarked.

ROSMER. So it is inconceivable to me how Beata could have got hold of the idea. And why did she not speak to me about it? She never did — she never said a single word.

KROLL. Poor creature — she begged and implored me to talk to you.

ROSMER. And why did you not?

KROLL. At that time I never for a moment doubted that she was out of her mind. Such an accusation against a man like you! — And then she came again — about a month later. This time she seemed outwardly calmer; but as she was going she said: "They may soon expect the White Horse at Rosmersholm now."

ROSMER. Yes, yes. The White Horse — she often spoke of it.

KROLL. And when I tried to divert her mind from such melancholy fancies, she only answered: "I have not long to live; for Johannes must marry Rebecca at once."

ROSMER. [*Almost speechless*] What do you say? I marry — ?

KROLL. That was on a Thursday afternoon — . On the Saturday evening she threw herself from the bridge into the mill-race.

ROSMER. And you never warned us — !

KROLL. You know very well how often she used to say that she felt her end was near.

ROSMER. Yes, I know. But nevertheless — you should have warned us!

KROLL. I did think of it; but not till too late.

ROSMER. But afterwards, why did you not — ? Why have you said nothing about all this?

KROLL. What good would it have done for me to come torturing and harassing you still further? I took all she said for mere wild, empty ravings — until yesterday evening.

ROSMER. Then you have now changed your opinion?

KROLL. Did not Beata see quite clearly when she declared you were about to desert the faith of your fathers?

ROSMER. [*Looks fixedly, straight before him*] I cannot understand it. It is the most incomprehensible thing in the world.

KROLL. Incomprehensible or not — there it is. And now I ask you, Rosmer, — how much truth is there in her other accusation? The last one, 220 I mean.

ROSMER. Accusation? Was that an accusation?

KROLL. Perhaps you did not notice the way she worded it. She had to go, she said — why?

ROSMER. In order that I might marry Rebecca —

KROLL. These were not precisely her words. Beata used a different expression. She said: "I have not long to live; for Johannes must marry Rebecca at once."

ROSMER. [*Looks at him for a moment; then rises*] Now I understand you, Kroll. 230

KROLL. And what then? What is your answer?

ROSMER. [*Still quiet and self-restrained*] To such an unheard-of — ? The only fitting answer would be to point to the door.

KROLL. [*Rises*] Well and good.

ROSMER. [*Stands in front of him*] Listen to me. For more than a year — ever since Beata left us — Rebecca West and I have lived alone here at Rosmersholm. During all that time you have known of Beata's accusation against us. But I have never for a moment noticed that you disapproved of Rebecca's living in my house.

KROLL. I did not know till yesterday evening that it was an unbelieving 240 man who was living with an — emancipated woman.

ROSMER. Ah — ! Then you do not believe that purity of mind is to be found among the unbelieving and the emancipated? You do not believe that morality may be an instinctive law of their nature!

KROLL. I have no great faith in the morality that is not founded on the teachings of the Church.

ROSMER. And you mean this to apply to Rebecca and me? To the relation between us two — ?

KROLL. Not even out of consideration for you two can I depart from my opinion that there is no unfathomable gulf between free thought and — 250 h'm —

ROSMER. And what?

KROLL. — and free love, — since you will have it.

ROSMER. [*In a low voice*] And you are not ashamed to say this to me! You, who have known me from my earliest youth!

KROLL. For that very reason. I know how easily you are influenced by the people you associate with. And this Rebecca of yours — well, Miss West then — we really know little or nothing about her. In short, Rosmer — I will not give you up. And you — you must try to save yourself in time.

ROSMER. Save myself? How — ? 260

MADAM HELSETH *peeps in at the door on the left.*

ROSMER. What do you want?

MADAM HELSETH. I wanted to ask Miss West to step downstairs.

ROSMER. Miss West is not up here.

MADAM HELSETH. Isn't she? [*Looks round the room*] Well, that's strange.
[*She goes.*

ROSMER. You were saying — ?

KROLL. Listen to me. I am not going to inquire too closely into the secret history of what went on here in Beata's lifetime — and may still be going on. I know that your marriage was a most unhappy one; and I suppose that must be taken as some sort of excuse — 270

ROSMER. Oh, how little you really know me — !

KROLL. Don't interrupt me. What I mean is this: if your present mode of life with Miss West is to continue, it is absolutely necessary that the change of views — the unhappy backsliding — brought about by her evil influence, should be hushed up. Let me speak! Let me speak! I say, if the worst comes to the worst, in Heaven's name think and believe whatever you like about everything under the sun. But you must keep your views to yourself. These things are purely personal matters, after all. There is no need to proclaim them from the housetops.

ROSMER. I feel it an absolute necessity to get out of a false and equivocal 280 position.

KROLL. But you have a duty towards the traditions of your race, Rosmer! Remember that! Rosmersholm has, so to speak, radiated morality and order from time immemorial — yes, and respectful conformity to all that is accepted and sanctioned by the best people. The whole district has taken its stamp from Rosmersholm. It would lead to deplorable, irremediable confusion if it were known that you had broken with what I may call the hereditary idea of the house of Rosmer.

ROSMER. My dear Kroll, I cannot see the matter in that light. I look upon it as my imperative duty to spread a little light and gladness here, 290 where the Rosmer family has from generation to generation been a centre of darkness and oppression.

KROLL. [*Looks at him severely*] Yes, that would be a worthy life-work for the last of your race! No, Rosmer; let such things alone; you are the last man for such a task. You were born to be a quiet student.

ROSMER. Perhaps so. But for once in a way I mean to bear my part in the battle of life.

KROLL. And do you know what that battle of life will mean for you? It will mean a life-and-death struggle with all your friends.

ROSMER. [*Quietly*] They cannot all be such fanatics as you. 300

KROLL. You are a credulous creature, Rosmer. An inexperienced creature, too. You have no conception of the overwhelming storm that will burst upon you.

MADAM HELSETH *looks in at the door on the left.*

MADAM HELSETH. Miss West wants to know —

ROSMER. What is it?

MADAM HELSETH. There's a man downstairs wanting to have a word with the Pastor.

ROSMER. Is it the man who was here yesterday evening?

MADAM HELSETH. No, it's that Mortensgård.

ROSMER. Mortensgård? 310

KROLL. Aha! So it has come to this, has it? — Already!

ROSMER. What does he want with me? Why didn't you send him away?

MADAM HELSETH. Miss West said I was to ask if he might come upstairs.

ROSMER. Tell him I'm engaged —

KROLL. [*To* MADAM HELSETH] Let him come up, Madam Helseth.
[MADAM HELSETH *goes.*

KROLL. [*Takes up his hat*] I retire from the field — for the moment. But the main battle has yet to be fought.

ROSMER. On my honour, Kroll — I have nothing whatever to do with Mortensgård.                                          320

KROLL. I do not believe you. On no subject and in no relation whatever will I henceforth believe you. It is war to the knife now. We will try whether we cannot disarm you.

ROSMER. Oh, Kroll — how low — how very low you have sunk!

KROLL. I? And you think you have the right to say that to me! Remember Beata!

ROSMER. Still harping upon that?

KROLL. No. You must solve the enigma of the mill-race according to your own conscience — if you have anything of the sort left.

PETER MORTENSGÅRD *enters softly and quietly from the left. He is a small, wiry man with thin reddish hair and beard.*

KROLL. [*With a look of hatred*] Ah, here we have the "Beacon" —  330 burning at Rosmersholm! [*Buttons his coat*] Well, now I can no longer hesitate what course to steer.

MORTENSGÅRD. [*Deferentially*] The "Beacon" may always be relied upon to light the Rector home.

KROLL. Yes; you have long shown your goodwill. To be sure there's a commandment about bearing false witness against your neighbour —

MORTENSGÅRD. Rector Kroll need not instruct me in the commandments.

KROLL. Not even in the seventh?

ROSMER. — Kroll — !                                                  340

MORTENSGÅRD. If I needed instruction, it would rather be the Pastor's business.

KROLL. [*With covert sarcasm*] The Pastor's? Oh, yes, unquestionably Pastor Rosmer is the man for that. — Good luck to your conference, gentlemen!                    [*Goes out and slams the door behind him.*

ROSMER. [*Keeps his eyes fixed on the closed door and says to himself*] Well, well — so be it then. [*Turns*] Will you be good enough to tell me, Mr. Mortensgård, what brings you out here to me?

MORTENSGÅRD. It was really Miss West I came to see. I wanted to thank her for the friendly note I received from her yesterday.         350

ROSMER. I know she wrote to you. Have you seen her then?

MORTENSGÅRD. Yes, for a short time. [*Smiles slightly*] I hear there has been a certain change of views out here at Rosmersholm.

ROSMER. My views are altered in many respects. I might almost say in all.

MORTENSGÅRD. So Miss West told me; and that's why she thought I had better come up and talk things over with the Pastor.

ROSMER. What things, Mr. Mortensgård?

MORTENSGÅRD. May I announce in the "Beacon" that there has been a change in your views — that you have joined the party of freedom and  360 progress?

ROSMER. Certainly you may. In fact, I beg you to make the announcement.

MORTENSGÅRD. Then it shall appear in to-morrow's paper. It will cause a great sensation when it's known that Pastor Rosmer of Rosmersholm is prepared to take up arms for the cause of light, in that sense, too.

ROSMER. I don't quite understand you.

MORTENSGÅRD. I mean that the moral position of our party is greatly strengthened whenever we gain an adherent of serious, Christian principles.

ROSMER. [*With some surprise*] Then you do not know —— ? Did not Miss 370
West tell you that, too?

MORTENSGÅRD. What, Pastor Rosmer? Miss West was in a great hurry.
She said I was to go upstairs and hear the rest from yourself.

ROSMER. Well, in that case I may tell you that I have emancipated myself
entirely, and on every side. I have broken with all the dogmas of the
Church. Henceforth they are nothing to me.

MORTENSGÅRD. [*Looks at him in amazement*] Well — if the skies were to
fall I couldn't be more —— ! Pastor Rosmer himself announces ——

ROSMER. Yes, I now stand where you have stood for many years. That,
too, you may announce in the "Beacon" to-morrow. 380

MORTENSGÅRD. That too? No, my dear Pastor — excuse me — I don't
think it would be wise to touch on that side of the matter.

ROSMER. Not touch on it?

MORTENSGÅRD. Not at present, I mean.

ROSMER. I don't understand ——

MORTENSGÅRD. Well, you see, Pastor Rosmer — you probably don't
know the ins and outs of things so well as I do. But, since you have come
over to the party of freedom — and, as I hear from Miss West, you intend
to take an active share in the movement — I presume you would like to be
of as much service as possible, both to the cause in general and to this 390
particular agitation.

ROSMER. Yes, that is my earnest wish.

MORTENSGÅRD. Good. But now I must tell you, Pastor Rosmer, that if
you openly declare your defection from the Church, you tie your own
hands at the very outset.

ROSMER. Do you think so?

MORTENSGÅRD. Yes; believe me, you won't be able to do much for the
cause, in this part of the country at any rate. And besides — we have plenty
of free-thinkers already, Pastor Rosmer — I might almost say too many.
What the party requires, is a Christian element — something that every one 400
must respect. That is what we are sadly in need of. And, therefore, I
advise you to keep your own counsel about what doesn't concern the
public. That's my view of the matter, at least.

ROSMER. I understand. Then if I openly confess my apostasy, you dare
not have anything to do with me?

MORTENSGÅRD. [*Shaking his head*] I scarcely like to risk it, Pastor
Rosmer. I have made it a rule for some time past not to support any one
or anything that is actively opposed to the Church.

ROSMER. Then you have yourself returned to the Church?

MORTENSGÅRD. That concerns no one but myself. 410

ROSMER. Ah, so that is it. Now I understand you.

MORTENSGÅRD. Pastor Rosmer — you ought to remember that I — I in
particular — have not full liberty of action.

ROSMER. What hampers you?

MORTENSGÅRD. The fact that I am a marked man.

ROSMER. Ah — indeed.

MORTENSGÅRD. A marked man, Pastor Rosmer. You, above all men,
should remember that; for I have chiefly you to thank for the scandal
that branded me.

ROSMER. If I had then stood where I stand now, I should have dealt 420
more gently with your offence.

MORTENSGÅRD. That I don't doubt. But it is too late now. You have
branded me once for all — branded me for life. I suppose you can scarcely

understand what that means. But now you may perhaps come to feel the smart of it yourself, Pastor Rosmer.

ROSMER. I?

MORTENSGÅRD. Yes. You surely don't suppose that Rector Kroll and his set will ever forgive a desertion like yours? I hear the "County News" is going to be very savage in future. You, too, may find yourself a marked man before long.                                                                430

ROSMER. In personal matters, Mr. Mortensgård, I feel myself secure from attack. My life is beyond reproach.

MORTENSGÅRD. [*With a sly smile*] That's a large word, Mr. Rosmer.

ROSMER. Perhaps; but I have a right to use it.

MORTENSGÅRD. Even if you were to scrutinise your conduct as closely as you once scrutinised mine?

ROSMER. Your tone is very curious. What are you hinting at? Anything definite?

MORTENSGÅRD. Yes, something definite. Only one thing. But that might be bad enough, if malicious opponents got wind of it.                         440

ROSMER. Will you have the kindness to let me hear what it is?

MORTENSGÅRD. Cannot you guess for yourself, Pastor?

ROSMER. No, certainly not. I have not the slightest idea.

MORTENSGÅRD. Well, well, I suppose I must come out with it then. — I have in my possession a strange letter, dated from Rosmersholm.

ROSMER. Miss West's letter, do you mean? Is it so strange?

MORTENSGÅRD. No, there's nothing strange about that. But I once received another letter from this house.

ROSMER. Also from Miss West?

MORTENSGÅRD. No, Mr. Rosmer.                                             450

ROSMER. Well then, from whom? From whom?

MORTENSGÅRD. From the late Mrs. Rosmer.

ROSMER. From my wife! You received a letter from my wife!

MORTENSGÅRD. I did.

ROSMER. When?

MORTENSGÅRD. Towards the close of Mrs. Rosmer's life. Perhaps about a year and a half ago. That is the letter I call strange.

ROSMER. I suppose you know that my wife's mind was affected at that time.

MORTENSGÅRD. Yes; I know many people thought so. But I don't think  460 there was anything in the letter to show it. When I call it strange, I mean in another sense.

ROSMER. And what in the world did my poor wife take it into her head to write to you about?

MORTENSGÅRD. I have the letter at home. She begins to the effect that she is living in great anxiety and fear; there are so many malicious people about here, she says; and they think of nothing but causing you trouble and injury.

ROSMER. Me?

MORTENSGÅRD. Yes, so she says. And then comes the strangest part of  470 all. Shall I go on, Pastor Rosmer?

ROSMER. Assuredly! Tell me everything, without reserve.

MORTENSGÅRD. The deceased lady begs and implores me to be magnanimous. She knows, she says, that it was her husband that had me dismissed from my post as teacher; and she conjured me by all that's sacred not to avenge myself.

ROSMER. How did she suppose you could avenge yourself?

MORTENSGÅRD. The letter says that if I should hear rumours of sinful

doings at Rosmersholm, I am not to believe them; they are only spread
abroad by wicked people who wish to make you unhappy.                    480

ROSMER. Is all that in the letter?

MORTENSGÅRD. You may read it for yourself, sir, when you please.

ROSMER. But I don't understand — ! What did she imagine the rumours
to be about?

MORTENSGÅRD. Firstly, that the Pastor had deserted the faith of his
fathers. Your wife denied that absolutely — then. And next — h'm —

ROSMER. Next?

MORTENSGÅRD. Well, next she writes — rather confusedly — that she
knows nothing of any sinful intrigue at Rosmersholm; that she has never
been wronged in any way. And if any such rumours should get about,  490
she implores me to say nothing of the matter in the "Beacon."

ROSMER. Is no name mentioned?

MORTENSGÅRD. None.

ROSMER. Who brought you the letter?

MORTENSGÅRD. I have promised not to say. It was handed to me one
evening, at dusk.

ROSMER. If you had made inquiries at the time, you would have learnt
that my poor, unhappy wife was not fully accountable for her actions.

MORTENSGÅRD. I did make inquiries, Pastor Rosmer. But I must say
that was not the impression I received.                                 500

ROSMER. Was it not? — But what is your precise reason for telling me
now about this incomprehensible old letter?

MORTENSGÅRD. To impress on you the necessity for extreme prudence,
Pastor Rosmer.

ROSMER. In my life, do you mean?

MORTENSGÅRD. Yes. You must remember that from to-day you have
ceased to be a neutral.

ROSMER. Then you have quite made up your mind that I must have
something to conceal?

MORTENSGÅRD. I don't know why an emancipated man should refrain  510
from living his life out as fully as possible. But, as I said before, be exceedingly cautious in future. If anything should get abroad that conflicts
with current prejudices, you may be sure the whole liberal movement
will have to suffer for it. — Good-bye, Pastor Rosmer.

ROSMER. Good-bye.

MORTENSGÅRD. I shall go straight to the office and have the great news
put into the "Beacon."

ROSMER. Yes; omit nothing.

MORTENSGÅRD. I shall omit nothing that the public need know.

*He bows and goes out.* ROSMER *remains standing in the doorway while he
goes down the stairs. The outer door is heard to close.*

ROSMER. [*In the doorway, calls softly*] Rebecca! Re — H'm. [*Aloud*]  520
Madam Helseth, — is Miss West not there?

MADAM HELSETH. [*From the hall*] No, Pastor Rosmer, she's not here.

*The curtain at the back is drawn aside.* REBECCA *appears in the doorway.*

REBECCA. Rosmer!

ROSMER. [*Turns*] What! Were you in my room? My dear, what were you
doing there?

REBECCA. [*Goes up to him*] I was listening.

ROSMER. Oh, Rebecca, how could you?

REBECCA. I could not help it. He said it so hatefully — that about my
morning gown —

ROSMER. Then you were there when Kroll — ?    530

REBECCA. Yes. I wanted to know what was lurking in his mind.

ROSMER. I would have told you.

REBECCA. You would scarcely have told me all. And certainly not in his own words.

ROSMER. Did you hear everything, then?

REBECCA. Nearly everything, I think. I had to go downstairs for a moment when Mortensgård came.

ROSMER. And then you came back again — ?

REBECCA. Don't be vexed with me, dear friend!

ROSMER. Do whatever you think right. You are mistress of your own ac-    540 tions. — But what do you say to all this, Rebecca — ? Oh, I seem never to have needed you so much before!

REBECCA. Both you and I have been prepared for what must happen some time.

ROSMER. No, no — not for this.

REBECCA. Not for this?

ROSMER. I knew well enough that sooner or later our beautiful, pure friendship might be misinterpreted and soiled. Not by Kroll — I could never have believed such a thing of him — but by all those other people with the coarse souls and the ignoble eyes. Oh yes — I had reason enough for    550 keeping our alliance so jealously concealed. It was a dangerous secret.

REBECCA. Oh, why should we care what all those people think! We know in our own hearts that we are blameless.

ROSMER. Blameless? I? Yes. I thought so — till to-day. But now — now, Rebecca — ?

REBECCA. Well, what now?

ROSMER. How am I to explain Beata's terrible accusation?

REBECCA. [*Vehemently*] Oh, don't speak of Beata! Don't think of Beata any more! You were just beginning to shake off the hold she has upon you, even in the grave.    560

ROSMER. Since I have heard all this, she seems, in a ghastly sort of way, to be alive again.

REBECCA. Oh no — not that, Rosmer! Not that!

ROSMER. Yes, I tell you. We must try to get to the bottom of this. What can possibly have led her to misinterpret things so fatally?

REBECCA. You are surely not beginning to doubt that she was on the very verge of insanity?

ROSMER. Oh yes — that is just what I can't feel quite certain of any longer. And besides — even if she was —

REBECCA. If she was? Well, what then?    570

ROSMER. I mean — where are we to look for the determining cause that drove her morbid spirit over the borderline of madness?

REBECCA. Oh, why brood over problems no one can solve?

ROSMER. I cannot help it, Rebecca. I cannot shake off these gnawing doubts, however much I may wish to.

REBECCA. But it may become dangerous — this eternal dwelling upon one miserable subject.

ROSMER. [*Walks about restlessly, in thought*] I must have betrayed myself in one way or another. She must have noticed how happy I began to feel from the time you came to us.    580

REBECCA. Yes but, dear, even if she did — ?

ROSMER. Be sure it didn't escape her that we read the same books — that the interest of discussing all the new ideas drew us together. Yet I cannot understand it! I was so careful to spare her. As I look back, it seems to me I made it the business of my life to keep her in ignorance of all our interests. Did I not, Rebecca?

REBECCA. Yes, yes; certainly you did.

ROSMER. And you too. And yet — ! Oh, it's terrible to think of ! She must have gone about here — full of her morbid passion — saying never a word — watching us — noting everything — and misinterpreting everything. 590

REBECCA. [*Pressing her hands together*] Oh, I should never have come to Rosmersholm!

ROSMER. To think of all she must have suffered in silence! All the foulness her sick brain must have conjured up around us! Did she never say anything to you to put you at all on the alert?

REBECCA. [*As if startled*] To me! Do you think I should have stayed a day longer if she had?

ROSMER. No, no, of course not. — Oh, what a battle she must have fought! And alone too, Rebecca; desperate and quite alone! — and then, at last, that heart-breaking, accusing victory — in the mill-race. 600

*Throws himself into the chair by the writing-table, with his elbows on the table and his face in his hands.*

REBECCA. [*Approaches him cautiously from behind*] Listen, Rosmer. If it were in your power to call Beata back — to you — to Rosmersholm — would you do it?

ROSMER. Oh, how do I know what I would or would not do? I can think of nothing but this one thing — that cannot be recalled.

REBECCA. You were just beginning to live, Rosmer. You had begun. You had freed yourself — on every side. You felt so buoyant and happy —

ROSMER. Oh yes — I did indeed. — And now this crushing blow falls on me.

REBECCA. [*Behind him, rests her arms on the chair-back*] How beautiful 610 it was when we sat in the twilight, in the room downstairs, helping each other to lay out our new life-plans! You were to set resolutely to work in the world — the living world of to-day, as you said. You were to go as a messenger of emancipation from home to home; to win over minds and wills; to create noble-men around you in wider and wider circles. Noble-men.

ROSMER. Happy noble-men.

REBECCA. Yes — happy.

ROSMER. For it is happiness that ennobles, Rebecca.

REBECCA. Should you not say — sorrow as well? A great sorrow? 620

ROSMER. Yes — if one can get through it — over it — away from it.

REBECCA. That is what you must do.

ROSMER. [*Shakes his head gloomily*] I shall never get over this — wholly. There will always be a doubt — a question left. I can never again know that luxury of the soul which makes life so marvellously sweet to live!

REBECCA. [*Bends over his chair-back, and says more softly*] What is it you mean, Rosmer?

ROSMER. [*Looking up at her*] Peaceful, happy innocence.

REBECCA. [*Recoils a step*] Yes. Innocence.                    [*A short pause.*

ROSMER. [*With his elbow on the table, leaning his head on his hand, and* 630 *looking straight before him*] And what extraordinary penetration she showed! How systematically she put all this together! First she begins to doubt my orthodoxy — How could that occur to her? But it did occur to her; and then it grew to be a certainty. And then — yes, then of course it was easy for her to think all the rest possible. [*Sits up in his chair and runs his hands through his hair*] Oh, all these horrible imaginings! I shall never get rid of them. I feel it. I know it. At any moment they will come rushing in upon me, and bring back the thought of the dead!

REBECCA. Like the White Horse of Rosmersholm.

ROSMER. Yes, like that. Rushing forth in the darkness – in the silence. 640

REBECCA. And because of this miserable figment of the brain, you will let slip the hold you were beginning to take upon the living world?

ROSMER. You may well think it hard. Yes, hard, Rebecca. But I have no choice. How could I ever leave this behind me?

REBECCA. [*Behind his chair*] By entering into new relations.

ROSMER. [*Surprised, looks up*] New relations?

REBECCA. Yes, new relations to the outside world. Live, work, act. Don't sit here brooding and groping among insoluble enigmas.

ROSMER. [*Rises*] New relations? [*Walks across the floor, stops at the door and then comes back*] One question occurs to me. Has it not occurred to 650 you too, Rebecca?

REBECCA. [*Drawing breath with difficulty*] Let me – hear – what it is.

ROSMER. What form do you think our relations will take after to-day?

REBECCA. I believe our friendship will endure – come what may.

ROSMER. That is not exactly what I meant. The thing that first brought us together, and that unites us so closely – our common faith in a pure comradeship between man and woman —

REBECCA. Yes, yes – what of that?

ROSMER. I mean, that such a relation – as this of ours – does it not pre-suppose a quiet, happy, peaceful life — ? 660

REBECCA. What then?

ROSMER. But the life I must now look forward to is one of struggle and unrest and strong agitations. For I will live my life, Rebecca! I will not be crushed to earth by horrible possibilities. I will not have my course of life forced upon me, either by the living or by – any one else.

REBECCA. No, no – do not! Be an absolutely free man, Rosmer!

ROSMER. But can you not guess what is in my mind? Do you not know? Don't you see how I can best shake off all gnawing memories – all the unhappy past?

REBECCA. How? 670

ROSMER. By opposing to it a new, a living reality.

REBECCA. [*Feeling for the chair-back*] A living — What do you mean?

ROSMER. [*Comes nearer*] Rebecca – if I were to ask you – will you be my second wife?

REBECCA. [*For a moment speechless, then cries out with joy*] Your wife! Your — ! I!

ROSMER. Come; let us try it. We two will be one. The place of the dead must stand empty no longer.

REBECCA. I – in Beata's place — !

ROSMER. Then she will be out of the saga – completely – for ever and 680 ever.

REBECCA. [*Softly, trembling*] Do you believe that, Rosmer?

ROSMER. It must be so! It must! I cannot – I will not go through life with a dead body on my back. Help me to cast it off, Rebecca. And let us stifle all memories in freedom, in joy, in passion. You shall be to me the only wife I have ever had.

REBECCA. [*With self-command*] Never speak of this again. I will never be your wife.

ROSMER. What! Never! Do you not think you could come to love me? Is there not already a strain of love in our friendship? 690

REBECCA. [*Puts her hands over her ears as if in terror*] Don't speak so, Rosmer! Don't say such things!

ROSMER. [*Seizes her arm*] Yes, yes — there is a growing promise in our relation. Oh, I can see that you feel it too. Do you not, Rebecca?

REBECCA. [*Once more firm and calm*] Listen to me. I tell you — if you persist in this, I will go away from Rosmersholm.

ROSMER. Go away! You! You cannot. It is impossible.

REBECCA. It is still more impossible that I should be your wife. Never in this world can I marry you.

ROSMER. [*Looks at her in surprise*] You say "can"; and you say it so 700 strangely. Why can you not?

REBECCA. [*Seizes both his hands*] Dear friend — both for your own sake and for mine — do not ask why. [*Lets go his hands*] Do not, Rosmer.

[*Goes towards the door on the left.*

ROSMER. Henceforth I can think of nothing but that one question — why?

REBECCA. [*Turns and looks at him*] Then it is all over.

ROSMER. Between you and me?

REBECCA. Yes.

ROSMER. It will never be all over between us two. You will never leave Rosmersholm.    710

REBECCA. [*With her hand on the door-handle*] No, perhaps I shall not. But if you ask me again — it is all over.

ROSMER. All over? How — ?

REBECCA. For then I will go the way that Beata went. Now you know it, Rosmer.

ROSMER. Rebecca — ?

REBECCA. [*In the doorway, nods slowly*] Now you know it.    [*She goes out.*

ROSMER. [*Stares, thunderstruck, at the door, and says to himself*] What — is — this?


## ACT THIRD

*The sitting-room at Rosmersholm. The window and the entrance door are open. The sun is shining outside. Forenoon.*

REBECCA WEST, *dressed as in the first Act, stands at the window, watering and arranging the flowers. Her crochet-work lies in the arm-chair.* MADAM HELSETH *is moving about, dusting the furniture with a feather-brush.*

REBECCA. [*After a short silence*] I can't understand the Pastor remaining so long upstairs to-day.

MADAM HELSETH. Oh, he often does that. But he'll soon be down now, I should think.

REBECCA. Have you seen anything of him?

MADAM HELSETH. I caught a glimpse of him when I went upstairs with his coffee. He was in his bedroom, dressing.

REBECCA. I asked because he was a little out of sorts yesterday.

MADAM HELSETH. He didn't look well. I wonder if there isn't something amiss between him and his brother-in-law.    10

REBECCA. What do you think it can be?

MADAM HELSETH. I couldn't say. Perhaps it's that Mortensgård that has been setting them against each other.

REBECCA. Likely enough. — Do you know anything of this Peter Mortensgård?

MADAM HELSETH. No indeed. How could you think so, Miss? A fellow like him?

REBECCA. Do you mean because he edits such a low paper?

MADAM HELSETH. Oh, it's not only that. – You must have heard, Miss, that he had a child by a married woman that had been deserted by her 20 husband?

REBECCA. Yes, I have heard of it. But it must have been long before I came here.

MADAM HELSETH. It's true he was very young at the time; and she should have known better. He wanted to marry her too; but of course he couldn't do that. And I don't say he hasn't paid dear for it. – But, good Lord, Mortensgård has got on in the world since those days. There's a many people run after him now.

REBECCA. Yes, most of the poor people bring their affairs to him when they're in any trouble. 30

MADAM HELSETH. Ah, and others too, perhaps, besides the poor folk —

REBECCA. [*Looks at her furtively*] Indeed.

MADAM HELSETH. [*By the sofa, dusting away vigorously*] Perhaps the last people you would think likely to, Miss.

REBECCA. [*Busy with the flowers*] Come, now, that's only an idea of yours, Madam Helseth. You can't be sure of what you're saying.

MADAM HELSETH. You think I can't, Miss? But I can tell you I am. Why – if you must know it – I once took a letter in to Mortensgård myself.

REBECCA. [*Turning*] No – did you? 40

MADAM HELSETH. Yes, indeed I did. And a letter that was written here at Rosmersholm too.

REBECCA. Really, Madam Helseth?

MADAM HELSETH. Yes, that it was. And it was on fine paper, and there was a fine red seal on it too.

REBECCA. And it was given to you to deliver? Then, my dear Madam Helseth, it's not difficult to guess who wrote it.

MADAM HELSETH. Well?

REBECCA. It must have been something that poor Mrs. Rosmer, in her morbid state — 50

MADAM HELSETH. It's you that say that, Miss, not me.

REBECCA. But what was in the letter? Oh, I forgot — you can't know that.

MADAM HELSETH. H'm; what if I did know it, all the same?

REBECCA. Did she tell you what she was writing about?

MADAM HELSETH. No, she didn't exactly do that. But Mortensgård, when he'd read it, he began questioning me backwards and forwards and up and down, so that I soon guessed what was in it.

REBECCA. Then what do you think it was? Oh my dear good Madam Helseth, do tell me. 60

MADAM HELSETH. Oh no, Miss. Not for the whole world.

REBECCA. Oh you can surely tell me. We two are such good friends.

MADAM HELSETH. Lord preserve me from telling you anything about that, Miss. I can only tell you that it was something horrible that they'd got the poor sick lady to believe.

REBECCA. Who had got her to believe it?

MADAM HELSETH. Wicked people, Miss West. Wicked people.

REBECCA. Wicked — ?

MADAM HELSETH. Yes, I say it again. They must have been real wicked people. 70

REBECCA. And who do you think it could have been?

MADAM HELSETH. Oh, I know well enough what to think. But Lord forbid *I* should say anything. To be sure there's a certain lady in the town — h'm!

REBECCA. I can see you mean Mrs. Kroll.

MADAM HELSETH. Ah, she's a fine one, she is. She has always been the great lady with me. And she's never had any too much love for you neither.

REBECCA. Do you think Mrs. Rosmer was in her right mind when she wrote that letter to Mortensgård?                                                  80

MADAM HELSETH. It's a queer thing a person's mind, Miss. Clean out of her mind I don't think she was.

REBECCA. But she seemed to go distracted when she learned that she must always be childless. It was that that unsettled her reason.

MADAM HELSETH. Yes, poor lady, that was a dreadful blow to her.

REBECCA. [*Takes up her crochet and sits in a chair by the window*] But after all — don't you think it was a good thing for the Pastor, Madam Helseth?

MADAM HELSETH. What, Miss?

REBECCA. That there were no children. Don't you think so?            90

MADAM HELSETH. H'm, I'm sure I don't know what to say about that.

REBECCA. Oh yes, believe me, it was fortunate for him. Pastor Rosmer is not the man to have crying children about his house.

MADAM HELSETH. Ah, Miss, little children don't cry at Rosmersholm.

REBECCA. [*Looks at her*] Don't cry?

MADAM HELSETH. No. As long as people can remember, children have never been known to cry in this house.

REBECCA. That's very strange.

MADAM HELSETH. Yes; isn't it? But it runs in the family. And then there's another strange thing. When they grow up, they never laugh. Never,   100 as long as they live.

REBECCA. Why, how extraordinary —

MADAM HELSETH. Have you ever once heard or seen the Pastor laugh, Miss?

REBECCA. No — now that I think of it, I almost believe you are right. But I don't think any one laughs much in this part of the country.

MADAM HELSETH. No, they don't. They say it began at Rosmersholm. And then I suppose it spread round about, as if it was catching-like.

REBECCA. You are a very wise woman, Madam Helseth.

MADAM HELSETH. Oh, Miss, you mustn't sit there and make fun of me.   110 [*Listens*] Hush, hush — here's the Pastor coming down. He doesn't like to see dusting going on.                                   [*She goes out to the right.*

JOHANNES ROSMER, *with his hat and stick in his hand, enters from the hall.*

ROSMER. Good morning, Rebecca.

REBECCA. Good morning, dear. [*A moment after — crocheting*] Are you going out?

ROSMER. Yes.

REBECCA. It's a beautiful day.

ROSMER. You didn't look in on me this morning.

REBECCA. No, I didn't. Not to-day.

ROSMER. Do you not intend to in future?                              120

REBECCA. Oh, I don't know yet, dear.

ROSMER. Has anything come for me?

REBECCA. The "County News" has come.

ROSMER. The "County News"?

REBECCA. There it is on the table.

ROSMER. [*Puts down his hat and stick*] Is there anything — ?

REBECCA. Yes.

ROSMER. And you didn't send it up?

REBECCA. You will read it soon enough.

ROSMER. Oh, indeed? [*Takes the paper and reads, standing by the table*] —    130
What! — "We cannot warn our readers too earnestly against unprincipled
renegades." [*Looks at her*] They call me a renegade, Rebecca.

REBECCA. They mention no names.

ROSMER. That makes no difference. [*Reads on*] "Secret traitors to the
good cause." — "Judas-natures, who make brazen confession of their
apostasy as soon as they think the most convenient and — profitable
moment has arrived." "Ruthless befouling of a name honoured through
generations" — "in the confident hope of a suitable reward from the party
in momentary power." [*Lays down the paper on the table*] And they can
say such things of me! — Men who have known me so long and so well!    140
Things they themselves don't believe. Things they know there is not a
word of truth in — they print them all the same.

REBECCA. That is not all.

ROSMER. [*Takes up the paper again*] "Inexperience and lack of judgment
the only excuse" — "pernicious influence — possibly extending to matters
which, for the present, we do not wish to make subjects of public discussion or accusation." [*Looks at her*] What is this?

REBECCA. It is aimed at me, plainly enough.

ROSMER. [*Lays down the paper*] Rebecca, — this is the conduct of dis-
honourable men.    150

REBECCA. Yes, they need scarcely be so contemptuous of Mortensgård.

ROSMER. [*Walks about the room*] Something must be done. All that is
good in human nature will go to ruin, if this is allowed to go on. But it
shall not go on! Oh, what a joy — what a joy it would be to me to let a
little light into all this gloom and ugliness!

REBECCA. [*Rises*] Ah yes, Rosmer. In that you have a great and glorious
object to live for.

ROSMER. Only think, if I could rouse them to see themselves as they
are; teach them to repent and blush before their better natures; bring
them together in mutual forbearance — in love, Rebecca!    160

REBECCA. Yes, put your whole strength into that, and you must succeed.

ROSMER. I think success must be possible. Oh, what a delight it would be
then to live one's life! No more malignant wrangling; only emulation. All
eyes fixed on the same goal. Every mind, every will pressing forward —
upward — each by the path its nature prescribes for it. Happiness for all —
through all. [*Happens to look out of the window, starts, and says sadly*] Ah!
Not through me.

REBECCA. Not — ? Not through you?

ROSMER. Nor for me.

REBECCA. Oh Rosmer, do not let such doubts take hold of you.    170

ROSMER. Happiness — dear Rebecca — happiness is above all things the
calm, glad certainty of innocence.

REBECCA. [*Looks straight before her*] Yes, innocence ——

ROSMER. Oh, you cannot know what guilt means. But I ——

REBECCA. You least of all!

ROSMER. [*Points out of the window*] The mill-race.

REBECCA. Oh Rosmer —— !

MADAM HELSETH *looks in at the door.*

MADAM HELSETH. Miss West!

REBECCA. Presently, presently. Not now.

MADAM HELSETH. Only a word, Miss. 180

REBECCA *goes to the door.* MADAM HELSETH *tells her something. They whis-*
*per together for a few moments.* MADAM HELSETH *nods and goes out.*

ROSMER. [*Uneasily*] Was it anything for me?

REBECCA. No, only something about the house-work. — You ought to go
out into the fresh air, dear Rosmer. You should take a good long walk.

ROSMER. [*Takes up his hat*] Yes, come. Let us go together.

REBECCA. No, dear, I can't just now. You must go alone. But shake off
all these gloomy thoughts. Promise me.

ROSMER. I am afraid I shall never shake them off.

REBECCA. Oh, that such baseless fancies should take so strong a hold
of you — !

ROSMER. Not so baseless I am afraid, Rebecca. I lay awake all night 190
thinking it over and over. Perhaps Beata saw clearly after all.

REBECCA. In what?

ROSMER. In her belief that I loved you, Rebecca.

REBECCA. Right in that!

ROSMER. [*Lays his hat down on the table*] The question that haunts me
is this: were we two not deceiving ourselves all the time — when we called
our relation friendship?

REBECCA. You mean that it might as well have been called — ?

ROSMER. — love. Yes, Rebecca, that is what I mean. Even while Beata
was alive, all my thoughts were for you. It was you alone I longed for. 200
It was when you were by my side that I felt the calm gladness of utter
content. If you think it over, Rebecca — did we not feel for each other
from the first a sort of sweet, secret child-love — desireless, dreamless?
Was it not so with you? Tell me.

REBECCA. [*Struggling with herself*] Oh — I don't know what to answer.

ROSMER. And it was this close-linked life in and for each other that we
took for friendship. No, Rebecca — our bond has been a spiritual marriage — perhaps from the very first. That is why there is guilt on my soul. I
had no right to such happiness — it was a sin against Beata.

REBECCA. No right to live happily? Do you believe that, Rosmer? 210

ROSMER. She looked at our relation with the eyes of her love — judged
it after the fashion of her love. Inevitably. Beata could not have judged
otherwise than she did.

REBECCA. But how can you accuse yourself because of Beata's delusion?

ROSMER. It was love for me — her kind of love — that drove her into the
mill-race. That is an immovable fact, Rebecca. And that is what I can
never get over.

REBECCA. Oh, think of nothing but the great, beautiful task you have
devoted your life to.

ROSMER. [*Shakes his head*] It can never be accomplished, dear. Not by 220
me. Not after what I have come to know.

REBECCA. Why not by you?

ROSMER. Because no cause ever triumphs that has its origin in sin.

REBECCA. [*Vehemently*] Oh, these are only ancestral doubts — ancestral
fears — ancestral scruples. They say the dead come back to Rosmersholm
in the shape of rushing white horses. I think this shows that it is true.

ROSMER. Be that as it may; what does it matter, so long as I cannot rid
myself of the feeling? And believe me, Rebecca, it is as I tell you. The
cause that is to win a lasting victory must have for its champion a happy,
an innocent man. 230

REBECCA. Is happiness so indispensable to you, Rosmer?

ROSMER. Happiness? Yes, dear, — it is.

REBECCA. To you, who can never laugh?

ROSMER. Yes, in spite of that. Believe me, I have a great capacity for happiness.

REBECCA. Now go for your walk, dear. A good long walk. Do you hear? — See, here is your hat. And your stick too.

ROSMER. [*Takes both*] Thanks. And you won't come with me?

REBECCA. No, no; I can't just now.

ROSMER. Very well, then. You are with me none the less.                    240

*He goes out by the entrance door.* REBECCA *waits a moment, cautiously watching his departure from behind the open door; then she goes to the door on the right.*

REBECCA. [*Opens the door, and says in a low tone*] Now, Madam Helseth. You can show him in now.                    [*Goes towards the window.*

*A moment after,* RECTOR KROLL *enters from the right. He bows silently and formally, and keeps his hat in his hand.*

KROLL. He has gone out?

REBECCA. Yes.

KROLL. Does he usually stay out long?

REBECCA. Yes, he does. But one cannot count on him to-day. So if you don't care to meet him ——

KROLL. No, no. It is you I want to speak to, — quite alone.

REBECCA. Then we had better not lose time. Sit down, Rector.

*She sits in the easy-chair by the window.* RECTOR KROLL *sits on a chair beside her.*

KROLL. Miss West — you can scarcely imagine how deeply and painfully  250 I have taken this to heart — this change in Johannes Rosmer.

REBECCA. We expected it would be so — at first.

KROLL. Only at first?

REBECCA. Rosmer was confident that sooner or later you would join him.

KROLL. I?

REBECCA. You and all his other friends.

KROLL. Ah, there you see! That shows the infirmity of his judgment in all that concerns men and practical life.

REBECCA. But after all — since he feels it is a necessity to emancipate  260 himself on all sides ——

KROLL. Yes, but wait — that is just what I do not believe.

REBECCA. What do you believe then?

KROLL. I believe that you are at the bottom of it all.

REBECCA. It is your wife who has put that in your head, Rector Kroll.

KROLL. No matter who has put it in my head. What is certain is that I feel a strong suspicion — an exceedingly strong suspicion — when I think things over, and piece together all I know of your behaviour ever since you came here.

REBECCA. [*Looks at him*] I seem to recollect a time when you felt an  270 exceedingly strong faith in me, dear Rector. I might almost call it a warm faith.

KROLL. [*In a subdued voice*] Whom could you not bewitch — if you tried?

REBECCA. Did I try — ?

KROLL. Yes, you did. I am no longer such a fool as to believe that there was any feeling in the matter. You simply wanted to get a footing at Rosmersholm — to strike root here — and in that I was to serve you. Now I see it.

REBECCA. You seem utterly to have forgotten that it was Beata who begged and implored me to come out here? 280

KROLL. Yes, when you had bewitched her to. Can the feeling she came to entertain for you be called friendship? It was adoration — almost idolatry. It developed into — what shall I call it? — a sort of desperate passion. — Yes, that is the right word for it.

REBECCA. Be so good as to recollect the state your sister was in. So far as I am concerned, I don't think any one can accuse me of being hysterical.

KROLL. No; that you certainly are not. But that makes you all the more dangerous to the people you want to get into your power. It is easy for you to weigh your acts and calculate consequences — just because your heart is cold. 290

REBECCA. Cold? Are you so sure of that?

KROLL. I am quite certain of it now. Otherwise you could never have lived here year after year without faltering in the pursuit of your object. Well, well — you have gained your end. You have got him and everything into your power. But in order to do so, you have not scrupled to make him unhappy.

REBECCA. That is not true. It is not I — it is you yourself that have made him unhappy.

KROLL. I?

REBECCA. Yes, when you led him to imagine that he was responsible for 300 Beata's terrible end.

KROLL. Does he feel that so deeply, then?

REBECCA. How can you doubt it? A mind so sensitive as his —

KROLL. I thought that an emancipated man, so-called, was above all such scruples. — But there we have it! Oh yes — I admit I knew how it would be. The descendant of the men that look down on us from these walls — how could he hope to cut himself adrift from all that has been handed down without a break from generation to generation?

REBECCA. [*Looks down thoughtfully*] Johannes Rosmer's spirit is deeply rooted in his ancestry. That is very certain. 310

KROLL. Yes, and you should have taken that fact into consideration, if you had felt any affection for him. But that sort of consideration was no doubt beyond you. There is such an immeasurable difference between your antecedents and his.

REBECCA. What antecedents do you mean?

KROLL. I am speaking of your origin — your family antecedents, Miss West.

REBECCA. Oh, indeed! Yes, it is quite true that I come of very humble folk. Nevertheless —

KROLL. I am not thinking of rank and position. I allude to your moral 320 antecedents.

REBECCA. Moral — ? In what sense?

KROLL. The circumstances of your birth.

REBECCA. What do you mean?

KROLL. I only mention the matter because it accounts for your whole conduct.

REBECCA. I do not understand this. You must explain.

KROLL. I really did not suppose you could require an explanation. Otherwise it would have been very odd that you should have let Dr. West adopt you — 330

REBECCA. [*Rises*] Ah! Now I understand.

KROLL. — and that you should have taken his name. Your mother's name was Gamvik.

REBECCA. [*Walks across the room*] My father's name was Gamvik, Rector Kroll.

KROLL. Your mother's business must have brought her very frequently into contact with the parish doctor.

REBECCA. Yes, it did.

KROLL. And then he takes you into his house — as soon as your mother dies. He treats you harshly; and yet you stay with him. You know that he won't leave you a half-penny — as a matter of fact, you only got a case full of books — and yet you stay on; you bear with him; you nurse him to the last.  340

REBECCA. [*Stands by the table, looking scornfully at him*] And you account for all this by assuming that there was something immoral — something criminal about my birth?

KROLL. I attribute your care for him to involuntary filial instinct. Indeed I believe your whole conduct is determined by your origin.

REBECCA. [*Vehemently*] But there is not a single word of truth in what you say! And I can prove it! Dr. West did not come to Finmark till after I was born.  350

KROLL. Excuse me, Miss West. He settled there the year before. I have assured myself of that.

REBECCA. You are mistaken, I say! You are utterly mistaken.

KROLL. You told me the day before yesterday that you were nine-and-twenty — in your thirtieth year.

REBECCA. Indeed! Did I say so?

KROLL. Yes, you did. And I can calculate from that —

REBECCA. Stop! You needn't calculate. I may as well tell you at once: I am a year older than I give myself out to be.  360

KROLL. [*Smiles incredulously*] Really! I am surprised! What can be the reason of that?

REBECCA. When I had passed twenty-five, it seemed to me I was getting altogether too old for an unmarried woman. And so I began to lie about my age.

KROLL. You? An emancipated woman! Have you prejudices about the age for marriage?

REBECCA. Yes, it was idiotic of me — idiotic and absurd. But some folly or other will always cling to us, not to be shaken off. We are made so.

KROLL. Well, so be it; but my calculation may be right, none the less.  370 For Dr. West was up there on a short visit the year before he got the appointment.

REBECCA. [*With a vehement outburst*] It is not true!

KROLL. Is it not true?

REBECCA. No. My mother never spoke of any such visit.

KROLL. Did she not?

REBECCA. No, never. Nor Dr. West either; not a word about it.

KROLL. Might not that be because they both had reasons for suppressing a year? Just as you have done, Miss West. Perhaps it is a family foible.

REBECCA. [*Walks about clenching and wringing her hands*] It is impossible.  380 You want to cheat me into believing it. This can never, never be true. It cannot! Never in this world —

KROLL. [*Rises*] My dear Miss West — why in heaven's name are you so terribly excited? You quite frighten me! What am I to think — to believe — ?

REBECCA. Nothing! You are to think and believe nothing.

KROLL. Then you must really tell me how you can take this affair —

this possibility — so terribly to heart.

REBECCA. [*Controlling herself*] It is perfectly simple, Rector Kroll. I have no wish to be taken for an illegitimate child. 390

KROLL. Indeed! Well well, let us be satisfied with that explanation — in the meantime. But in that case you must still have a certain — prejudice on that point too?

REBECCA. Yes, I suppose I have.

KROLL. Ah, I fancy it is much the same with most of what you call your "emancipation." You have read yourself into a number of new ideas and opinions. You have got a sort of smattering of recent discoveries in various fields — discoveries that seem to overthrow certain principles which have hitherto been held impregnable and unassailable. But all this has only been a matter of the intellect, Miss West — a superficial acquisi- 400 tion. It has not passed into your blood.

REBECCA. [*Thoughtfully*] Perhaps you are right.

KROLL. Yes, look into your own mind, and you will see! And if this is the case with you, one may easily guess how it must be with Johannes Rosmer. It is sheer, unmitigated madness — it is running blindfold to destruction — for him to think of coming openly forward and confessing himself an apostate! Only think — a man of his sensitive nature! Imagine him disowned and persecuted by the circle of which he has always formed a part — exposed to ruthless attacks from all the best people in the community! He is not — he never can be the man to endure all that. 410

REBECCA. He must endure it! It is too late now for him to retreat.

KROLL. Not at all too late. By no means. What has happened can be hushed up — or at least explained away as a mere temporary aberration, however deplorable. But — one measure is certainly indispensable.

REBECCA. And what is that?

KROLL. You must get him to legalise the position, Miss West.

REBECCA. His position towards me?

KROLL. Yes. You must make him do that.

REBECCA. Then you absolutely cannot clear your mind of the idea that our position requires to be — legalised, as you call it? 420

KROLL. I would rather not go into the matter too closely. But I believe I have noticed that it is nowhere easier to break through all so-called prejudices than in — h'm —

REBECCA. In the relation between man and woman, you mean?

KROLL. Yes, — to speak plainly — I think so.

REBECCA. [*Wanders across the room and looks out at the window*] I could almost say — I wish you were right, Rector Kroll.

KROLL. What do you mean by that? You say it so strangely.

REBECCA. Oh well — please let us drop the subject. Ah, — there he comes.

KROLL. Already! Then I will go. 430

REBECCA. [*Goes towards him*] No — please stay. There is something I want you to hear.

KROLL. Not now. I don't feel as if I could bear to see him.

REBECCA. I beg you to stay. Do! If not, you will regret it by-and-by. It is the last time I shall ask you for anything.

KROLL. [*Looks at her in surprise and puts down his hat*] Very well, Miss West — so be it, then.

*A short silence. Then* JOHANNES ROSMER *enters from the hall.*

ROSMER. [*Sees the* RECTOR, *and stops in the doorway*] What! — Are you here?

REBECCA. He did not wish to meet you, dear.*                                            440

KROLL. [*Involuntarily*] "Dear!"

REBECCA. Yes, Rector Kroll, Rosmer and I say "dear" to each other. That is one result of our "position."

KROLL. Was that what you wanted me to hear?

REBECCA. That — and a little more.

ROSMER. [*Comes forward*] What is the object of this visit?

KROLL. I wanted to try once more to stop you and win you back to us.

ROSMER. [*Points to the newspaper*] After what appears in that paper?

KROLL. I did not write it.

ROSMER. Did you make the slightest effort to prevent its appearance?        450

KROLL. That would have been to betray the cause I serve. And, besides, it was not in my power.

REBECCA. [*Tears the paper into shreds, crushes up the pieces and throws them behind the stove*] There! Now it is out of sight. And let it be out of mind too. For there will be nothing more of that sort, Rosmer.

KROLL. Ah, if you could only make sure of that!

REBECCA. Come, let us sit down, dear. All three of us. And then I will tell you everything.

ROSMER. [*Seats himself mechanically*] What has come over you, Rebecca? This unnatural calmness — what is it?                                         460

REBECCA. The calmness of resolution. [*Seats herself*] Pray sit down too, Rector.                    [RECTOR KROLL *seats himself on the sofa.*

ROSMER. Resolution, you say? What resolution?

REBECCA. I am going to give you back what you require in order to live your life. Dear friend, you shall have your happy innocence back again!

ROSMER. What can you mean?

REBECCA. I have only to tell you something. That will be enough.

ROSMER. Well!

REBECCA. When I came down here from Finmark — along with Dr. West — it seemed to me that a great, wide new world was opening up        470 before me. The Doctor had taught me all sorts of things — all the fragmentary knowledge of life that I possessed in those days. [*With a struggle and in a scarcely audible voice*] And then ——

KROLL. And then?

ROSMER. But Rebecca — I know all this.

REBECCA. [*Mastering herself*] Yes, yes — you are right. You know enough about this.

KROLL. [*Looks hard at her*] Perhaps I had better go.

REBECCA. No, please stay where you are, my dear Rector. [*To* ROSMER] Well, you see, this was how it was — I wanted to take my share in the life        480 of the new era that was dawning, with all its new ideas. — Rector Kroll told me one day that Ulric Brendel had had great influence over you while you were still a boy. I thought it must surely be possible for me to carry on his work.

ROSMER. You came here with a secret design —— ?

REBECCA. We two, I thought, should march onward in freedom, side by side. Ever onward. Ever farther and farther to the front. But between you and perfect emancipation there rose that dismal, insurmountable barrier.

ROSMER. What barrier do you mean?                                         490

*In the original, Rebecca here addresses Rosmer as "du" for the first time in Kroll's presence.

REBECCA. I mean this, Rosmer: You could grow into freedom only in the clear, fresh sunshine — and here you were pining, sickening in the gloom of such a marriage.

ROSMER. You have never before spoken to me of my marriage in that tone.

REBECCA. No, I did not dare to, for I should have frightened you.

KROLL. [*Nods to* ROSMER] Do you hear that?

REBECCA. [*Goes on*] But I saw quite well where your deliverance lay — your only deliverance. And then I went to work.

ROSMER. Went to work? In what way?     500

KROLL. Do you mean that — ?

REBECCA. Yes, Rosmer — [*Rises*] Sit still. You too, Rector Kroll. But now it must out. It was not you, Rosmer. You are innocent. It was I that lured — that ended in luring Beata out into the paths of delusion ——

ROSMER. [*Springs up*] Rebecca!

KROLL. [*Rises from the sofa*] The paths of delusion!

REBECCA. The paths — that led to the mill-race. Now you know it both of you.

ROSMER. [*As if stunned*] But I don't understand —— What is it she is saying? I don't understand a word —— !     510

KROLL. Oh yes, Rosmer, I am beginning to understand.

ROSMER. But what did you do? What can you possibly have told her? There was nothing — absolutely nothing to tell!

REBECCA. She came to know that you were working yourself free from all the old prejudices.

ROSMER. Yes, but that was not the case at that time.

REBECCA. I knew that it soon would be.

KROLL. [*Nods to* ROSMER] Aha!

ROSMER. And then? What more? I must know all now.

REBECCA. Some time after — I begged and implored her to let me go  520 away from Rosmersholm.

ROSMER. Why did you want to go — then?

REBECCA. I did not want to go; I wanted to stay here, where I was. But I told her that it would be best for us all — that I should go away in time. I gave her to understand that if I stayed here any longer, I could not — I could not tell — what might happen.

ROSMER. Then this is what you said and did!

REBECCA. Yes, Rosmer.

ROSMER. This is what you call "going to work."

REBECCA. [*In a broken voice*] I called it so, yes.     530

ROSMER. [*After a pause*] Have you confessed all now, Rebecca?

REBECCA. Yes.

KROLL. Not all.

REBECCA. [*Looks at him in fear*] What more should there be?

KROLL. Did you not at last give Beata to understand that it was necessary — not only that it would be wisest, but that it was necessary — both for your own sake and Rosmer's, that you should go away somewhere — as soon as possible? Well?

REBECCA. [*Low and indistinctly*] Perhaps I did say something of the sort.

ROSMER. [*Sinks into the arm-chair by the window*] And this tissue of lies  540 and deceit she — my unhappy, sick wife believed in! Believed in it so firmly! So immovably! [*Looks up at* REBECCA] And she never turned to me. Never said one word to me! Oh, Rebecca, — I can see it in your face — you dissuaded her from it!

REBECCA. She had conceived a fixed idea that she, as a childless wife, had no right to be here. And then she imagined that it was her duty to you to efface herself.

ROSMER. And you — you did nothing to disabuse her of the idea?

REBECCA. No.

KROLL. Perhaps you confirmed her in it? Answer me! Did you not?  550

REBECCA. I believe she may have understood me so.

ROSMER. Yes, yes — and in everything she bowed before your will. And she did efface herself! [*Springs up*] How could you — how could you play this ghastly game!

REBECCA. It seemed to me I had to choose between your life and hers, Rosmer.

KROLL. [*Severely and impressively*] That choice was not for you to make.

REBECCA. [*Vehemently*] You think then that I was cool and calculating and self-possessed all the time! I was not the same woman then that I am now, as I stand here telling it all. Besides, there are two sorts of will 560 in us I believe! I wanted Beata away, by one means or another; but I never really believed that it would come to pass. As I felt my way forward, at each step I ventured, I seemed to hear something within me cry out: No farther! Not a step farther! And yet I could not stop. I had to venture the least little bit farther. Only one hair's-breadth more. And then one more — and always one more. — And then it happened. — That is the way such things come about. [*A short silence.*]

ROSMER. [*To* REBECCA] What do you think lies before you now? After this?

REBECCA. Things must go with me as they will. It doesn't greatly matter. 570

KROLL. Not a word of remorse! Is it possible you feel none?

REBECCA. [*Coldly putting aside his question*] Excuse me, Rector Kroll — that is a matter which concerns no one but me. I must settle it with myself.

KROLL. [*To* ROSMER] And this is the woman you are living under the same roof with — in the closest intimacy! [*Looks round at the pictures*] Oh if those that are gone could see us now!

ROSMER. Are you going back to town?

KROLL. [*Takes up his hat*] Yes. The sooner the better.

ROSMER. [*Does the same*] Then I will go with you.  580

KROLL. Will you? Ah yes, I was sure we had not lost you for good.

ROSMER. Come then, Kroll! Come!

*Both go out through the hall without looking at* REBECCA. *After a moment,* REBECCA *goes cautiously to the window and looks out through the flowers.*

REBECCA. [*Speaks to herself under her breath*] Not over the foot-bridge to-day either. He goes round. Never across the mill-race. Never. [*Leaves window*] Well, well, well!

*Goes and pulls the bell-rope; a moment after,* MADAM HELSETH *enters from the right.*

MADAM HELSETH. What is it, Miss?

REBECCA. Madam Helseth, would you be so good as to have my trunk brought down from the garret?

MADAM HELSETH. Your trunk?

REBECCA. Yes — the brown sealskin trunk, you know.  590

MADAM HELSETH. Yes, yes. But, Lord preserve us — are you going on a journey, Miss?

REBECCA. Yes — now I am going on a journey, Madam Helseth.

MADAM HELSETH. And immediately!

REBECCA. As soon as I have packed up.

MADAM HELSETH. Well, I've never heard the like of that! But you'll come back again soon, Miss, of course?

REBECCA. I shall never come back again.

MADAM HELSETH. Never! Dear Lord, what will things be like at Rosmersholm when you're gone, Miss? And the poor Pastor was just beginning to   600 be so happy and comfortable.

REBECCA. Yes, but I have taken fright to-day, Madam Helseth.

MADAM HELSETH. Taken fright! Dear, dear! how was that?

REBECCA. I thought I saw something like a glimpse of white horses.

MADAM HELSETH. White horses! In broad daylight!

REBECCA. Oh, they are abroad early and late – the white horses of Rosmersholm. [*With a change of tone*] Well, – about the trunk, Madam Helseth.

MADAM HELSETH. Yes, yes. The trunk.        [*Both go out to the right.*

## ACT FOURTH

*The sitting-room at Rosmersholm. Late evening. A lighted lamp, with a shade over it, on the table.*

REBECCA WEST *stands by the table, packing some small articles in a handbag. Her cloak, hat, and the white crocheted shawl are hanging over the back of the sofa.*

MADAM HELSETH *enters from the right.*

MADAM HELSETH. [*Speaks in a low voice and appears ill at ease*] All your things have been taken down, Miss. They are in the kitchen passage.

REBECCA. Very well. You have ordered the carriage?

MADAM HELSETH. Yes. The coachman wants to know what time he ought to be here.

REBECCA. About eleven o'clock, I think. The steamer starts at midnight.

MADAM HELSETH. [*Hesitates a little*] But the Pastor? If he shouldn't be home by that time?

REBECCA. I shall go all the same. If I don't see him, you can tell him that I will write to him – a long letter. Tell him that.   10

MADAM HELSETH. Yes, writing – that may be all very well. But, poor Miss West – I do think you should try to speak to him once more.

REBECCA. Perhaps so. And yet – perhaps not.

MADAM HELSETH. Well – that I should live to see this! I never thought of such a thing.

REBECCA. What did you think then, Madam Helseth?

MADAM HELSETH. Well, I certainly thought Pastor Rosmer was a more dependable man than this.

REBECCA. Dependable?

MADAM HELSETH. Yes, that's what *I* say.   20

REBECCA. Why, my dear Madam Helseth, what do you mean?

MADAM HELSETH. I mean what's right and true, Miss. He shouldn't get out of it in this way, that he shouldn't.

REBECCA. [*Looks at her*] Come now, Madam Helseth, tell me plainly: what do you think is the reason I am going away?

MADAM HELSETH. Well, Heaven forgive us, I suppose it can't be helped, Miss. Ah, well, well, well! But I certainly don't think the Pastor's behaving handsome-like. Mortensgård had some excuse; for her husband was alive, so that they two couldn't marry, however much they wanted to. But as for the Pastor — h'm! 30

REBECCA. [*With a faint smile*] Could you have believed such a thing of Pastor Rosmer and me?

MADAM HELSETH. No, never in this world. At least, I mean — not until to-day.

REBECCA. But to-day, then — ?

MADAM HELSETH. Well, — after all the horrible things that they tell me the papers are saying about the Pastor —

REBECCA. Aha!

MADAM HELSETH. For the man that can go over to Mortensgård's re- ligion — good Lord, I can believe anything of him. 40

REBECCA. Oh yes, I suppose so. But what about me? What have you to say about me?

MADAM HELSETH. Lord preserve us, Miss — I don't see that there's much to be said against you. It's not so easy for a lone woman to be always on her guard, that's certain. — We're all of us human, Miss West.

REBECCA. That's very true, Madam Helseth. We are all of us human. — What are you listening to?

MADAM HELSETH. [*In a low voice*] Oh Lord, — if I don't believe that's him coming.

REBECCA. [*Starts*] After all then — ? [*Resolutely*] Well well, so be it. 50


JOHANNES ROSMER *enters from the hall.*


ROSMER. [*Sees the hand-bag, etc., turns to* REBECCA, *and asks*] What does this mean?

REBECCA. I am going.

ROSMER. At once?

REBECCA. Yes. [*To* MADAM HELSETH] Eleven o'clock then.

MADAM HELSETH. Very well, Miss. [*Goes out to the right.*

ROSMER. [*After a short pause*] Where are you going to, Rebecca?

REBECCA. North, by the steamer.

ROSMER. North? What takes you to the North?

REBECCA. It was there I came from. 60

ROSMER. But you have no ties there now.

REBECCA. I have none here either.

ROSMER. What do you think of doing?

REBECCA. I don't know. I only want to have done with it all.

ROSMER. To have done with it?

REBECCA. Rosmersholm has broken me.

ROSMER. [*His attention aroused*] Do you say that?

REBECCA. Broken me utterly and hopelessly. — I had a free and fearless will when I came here. Now I have bent my neck under a strange law. — From this day forth, I feel as if I had no courage for anything in the 70 world.

ROSMER. Why not? What is the law that you say you have — ?

REBECCA. Dear, don't let us talk of that just now. — What happened be- tween you and the Rector?

ROSMER. We have made peace.

REBECCA. Ah yes; so that was the end.

ROSMER. He gathered all our old friends together at his house. They have made it clear to me that the work of ennobling the minds of men — is not for me. — And besides, it is hopeless in itself, Rebecca. — I shall let it alone.

REBECCA. Yes, yes — perhaps it is best so. 80

ROSMER. Is that what you say now? Do you think so now?

REBECCA. I have come to think so — in the last few days.

ROSMER. You are lying, Rebecca.

REBECCA. Lying — !

ROSMER. Yes, you are lying. You have never believed in me. You have never believed that I was man enough to carry the cause through to victory.

REBECCA. I believed that we two together could do it.

ROSMER. That is not true. You thought that you yourself could do something great in life; and that you could use me to further your ends. I was to be a serviceable instrument to you — that is what you thought.   90

REBECCA. Listen to me, Rosmer —

ROSMER. [*Seats himself listlessly on the sofa*] Oh, what is the use? I see through it all now — I have been like a glove in your hands.

REBECCA. Listen, Rosmer. Hear what I have to say. It will be for the last time. [*Sits in a chair close to the sofa*] I intended to write you all about it — when I was back in the North. But I daresay it is best that you should hear it at once.

ROSMER. Have you more confessions to make?

REBECCA. The greatest of all is to come.   100

ROSMER. The greatest?

REBECCA. What you have never suspected. What gives light and shade to all the rest.

ROSMER. [*Shakes his head*] I don't understand you at all.

REBECCA. It is perfectly true that I once schemed to gain a footing at Rosmersholm. I thought I could not fail to turn things to good account here. In one way or the other — you understand.

ROSMER. Well, you accomplished your ends.

REBECCA. I believe I could have accomplished anything, anything in the world — at that time. For I had still my fearless, free-born will. I knew no   110 scruples — I stood in awe of no human tie. — But then began what has broken my will — and cowed me so pitiably for all my days.

ROSMER. What began? Do not speak in riddles.

REBECCA. It came over me, — this wild, uncontrollable passion —— . Oh, Rosmer — !

ROSMER. Passion? You — ! For what?

REBECCA. For you.

ROSMER. [*Tries to spring up*] What is this?

REBECCA. [*Stops him*] Sit still, dear; there is more to tell.

ROSMER. And you mean to say — that you have loved me — in that way!   120

REBECCA. I thought that it should be called love — then. Yes, I thought it was love. But it was not. It was what I said. It was a wild, uncontrollable passion.

ROSMER. [*With difficulty*] Rebecca, is it really you — you yourself — that you are speaking of?

REBECCA. Yes, would you believe it, Rosmer?

ROSMER. Then it was because of this — under the influence of this — that you — that you "went to work," as you call it?

REBECCA. It came upon me like a storm on the sea. It was like one of the storms we sometimes have in the North in the winter time. It seizes   130 you — and whirls you along with it — wherever it will. There is no resisting it.

ROSMER. And so it swept the unhappy Beata into the mill-race.

REBECCA. Yes; for it was a life-and-death struggle between Beata and me at that time.

ROSMER. Assuredly you were the strongest at Rosmersholm. Stronger than Beata and I together.

REBECCA. I judged you rightly in so far that I was sure I could never reach you until you were a free man, both in circumstances — and in spirit.

ROSMER. But I don't understand you, Rebecca. You — yourself — your 140 whole conduct is an insoluble riddle to me. I am free now — both in spirit and in circumstances. You have reached the very goal you aimed at from the first. And yet —

REBECCA. I have never stood farther from my goal than now.

ROSMER. And yet I say — when I asked you yesterday — begged you to be my wife — you cried out, as if in fear, that it could never be.

REBECCA. I cried out in despair, Rosmer.

ROSMER. Why?

REBECCA. Because Rosmersholm has sapped my strength. My old fearless will has had its wings clipped here. It is crippled! The time is past when 150 I had courage for anything in the world. I have lost the power of action, Rosmer.

ROSMER. Tell me how this has come about.

REBECCA. It has come about through my life with you.

ROSMER. But how? How?

REBECCA. When I was left alone with you here, — and when you had become yourself again —

ROSMER. Yes, yes?

REBECCA. — for you were never quite yourself so long as Beata lived —

ROSMER. I am afraid you are right there. 160

REBECCA. But when I found myself sharing your life here, in quiet — in solitude, — when you showed me all your thoughts without reserve — every tender and delicate feeling, just as it came to you — then the great change came over me. Little by little, you understand. Almost imperceptibly — but at last with such overwhelming force that it reached to the depths of my soul.

ROSMER. Oh, is this true, Rebecca?

REBECCA. All the rest — the horrible sense-intoxicated desire — passed far, far away from me. All the whirling passions settled down into quiet and silence. Rest descended on my soul — a stillness as on one of our northern 170 bird-cliffs under the midnight sun.

ROSMER. Tell me more of this. Tell me all you can.

REBECCA. There is not much more, dear. Only this — it was love that was born in me. The great self-denying love, that is content with life, as we two have lived it together.

ROSMER. Oh, if I had only had the faintest suspicion of all this!

REBECCA. It is best as it is. Yesterday — when you asked me if I would be your wife — I cried out with joy —

ROSMER. Yes, did you not, Rebecca! I thought that was the meaning of your cry. 180

REBECCA. For a moment, yes. I had forgotten myself. It was my old buoyant will that was struggling to be free. But it has no energy left now — no power of endurance.

ROSMER. How do you account for what has happened to you?

REBECCA. It is the Rosmer view of life — or your view of life, at any rate — that has infected my will.

ROSMER. Infected?

REBECCA. And made it sick. Enslaved it to laws that had no power over me before. You — life with you — has ennobled my mind —

ROSMER. Oh that I could believe it! 190

REBECCA. You may safely believe it! The Rosmer view of life ennobles. But — [*Shaking her head*] But – but —

ROSMER. But — ? Well?

REBECCA. — but it kills happiness.

ROSMER. Do you think so, Rebecca?

REBECCA. My happiness, at any rate.

ROSMER. Yes, but are you so certain of that? If I were to ask you again now — ? If I were to beg and entreat you — ?

REBECCA. Dear, – never speak of this again! It is impossible — ! For you must know, Rosmer, I have a – a past behind me.          200

ROSMER. More than what you have told me?

REBECCA. Yes. Something different and something more.

ROSMER. [*With a faint smile*] Is it not strange, Rebecca? Some such idea has crossed my mind now and then.

REBECCA. It has? And yet — ? Even so — ?

ROSMER. I never believed it. I only played with it – in my thoughts, you understand.

REBECCA. If you wish it, I will tell you all, at once.

ROSMER. [*Turning it off*] No, no! I will not hear a word. Whatever it may be – I can forget it.          210

REBECCA. But I cannot.

ROSMER. Oh Rebecca — !

REBECCA. Yes, Rosmer – this is the terrible part of it: that now, when all life's happiness is within my grasp – my heart is changed, and my own past cuts me off from it.

ROSMER. Your past is dead, Rebecca. It has no hold on you any more – it is no part of you – as you are now.

REBECCA. Oh, you know that these are only phrases, dear. And innocence? Where am I to get that from?

ROSMER. [*Sadly*] Ah, – innocence.          220

REBECCA. Yes, innocence. That is the source of peace and happiness. That was the vital truth you were to implant in the coming generation of happy noble-men —

ROSMER. Oh, don't remind me of that. It was only an abortive dream, Rebecca – an immature idea, that I myself no longer believe in. – Ah no, we cannot be ennobled from without, Rebecca.

REBECCA. [*Softly*] Not even by tranquil love, Rosmer?

ROSMER. [*Thoughtfully*] Yes – that would be the great thing – the most glorious in life, almost – if it were so. [*Moves uneasily*] But how can I be certain of that? How convince myself?          230

REBECCA. Do you not believe me, Rosmer?

ROSMER. Oh Rebecca – how can I believe in you, fully? You who have all this while been cloaking, concealing such a multitude of things! – Now you come forward with something new. If you have a secret purpose in all this, tell me plainly what it is. Is there anything you want to gain by it? You know that I will gladly do everything I can for you.

REBECCA. [*Wringing her hands*] Oh this killing doubt — ! Rosmer – Rosmer —!

ROSMER. Yes, is it not terrible, Rebecca? But I cannot help it. I shall never be able to shake off the doubt. I can never be absolutely sure that 240 you are mine in pure and perfect love.

REBECCA. Is there nothing in the depths of your own heart that bears witness to the transformation in me? And tells you that it is due to you – and you alone?

ROSMER. Oh Rebecca – I no longer believe in my power of transforming any one. My faith in myself is utterly dead. I believe neither in myself nor in you.

REBECCA. [*Looks darkly at him*] Then how will you be able to live your life?

ROSMER. That I don't know. I cannot imagine how. I don't think I can 250 live it. — And I know of nothing in the world that is worth living for.

REBECCA. Oh, life — life will renew itself. Let us hold fast to it, Rosmer. — We shall leave it soon enough.

ROSMER. [*Springs up restlessly*] Then give me my faith again! My faith in you, Rebecca! My faith in your love! Proof! I must have proof!

REBECCA. Proof? How can I give you proof — ?

ROSMER. You must! [*Walks across the room*] I cannot bear this desolation — this horrible emptiness — this — this — [*A loud knock at the hall door.*

REBECCA. [*Starts up from her chair*] Ah — did you hear that?

*The door opens.* ULRIC BRENDEL *enters. He has a white shirt on, a black coat and a good pair of boots, with his trousers tucked into them. Otherwise he is dressed as in the first Act. He looks excited.*

ROSMER. Ah, is it you, Mr. Brendel?                                          260

BRENDEL. Johannes, my boy — hail — and farewell!

ROSMER. Where are you going so late?

BRENDEL. Downhill.

ROSMER. How —?

BRENDEL. I am going homewards, my beloved pupil. I am home-sick for the mighty Nothingness.

ROSMER. Something has happened to you, Mr. Brendel! What is it?

BRENDEL. So you observe the transformation? Yes — well you may. When I last set foot in these halls — I stood before you as a man of substance, and slapped my breast-pocket.                                          270

ROSMER. Indeed! I don't quite understand —

BRENDEL. But as you see me this night, I am a deposed monarch on the ash-heap that was my palace.

ROSMER. If there is anything *I* can do for you —

BRENDEL. You have preserved your child-like heart, Johannes. Can you grant me a loan?

ROSMER. Yes, yes, most willingly!

BRENDEL. Can you spare me an ideal or two?

ROSMER. What do you say?

BRENDEL. One or two cast-off ideals. It would be an act of charity. For 280 I'm cleaned out, my boy. Ruined, beggared.

REBECCA. Have you not delivered your lecture?

BRENDEL. No, seductive lady. What do you think? Just as I am standing ready to pour forth the horn of plenty, I make the painful discovery that I am bankrupt.

REBECCA. But all your unwritten works — ?

BRENDEL. For five-and-twenty years I have sat like a miser on his double-locked treasure-chest. And then yesterday — when I open it and want to display the treasure — there's none there! The teeth of time had ground it into dust. There was nix and nothing in the whole concern.          290

ROSMER. But are you so sure of that?

BRENDEL. There's no room for doubt, my dear fellow. The President has convinced me of it.

ROSMER. The President?

BRENDEL. Well well — His Excellency then. *Ganz nach Belieben.*

ROSMER. What do you mean?

BRENDEL. Peter Mortensgård, of course.

ROSMER. What?

BRENDEL. [*Mysteriously*] Hush, hush, hush! Peter Mortensgård is the lord and leader of the future. Never have I stood in a more august presence. 300 Peter Mortensgård has the secret of omnipotence. He can do whatever he will.

ROSMER. Oh, don't believe that.

BRENDEL. Yes, my boy! For Peter Mortensgård never wills more than he can do. Peter Mortensgård is capable of living his life without ideals. And that, do you see — that is just the mighty secret of action and of victory. It is the sum of the whole world's wisdom. *Basta!*

ROSMER. [*In a low voice*] Now I understand — why you leave here poorer than you came.

BRENDEL. *Bien!* Then take a *Beispiel* by your ancient teacher. Rub out 310 all that he once imprinted on your mind. Build not thy house on shifting sand. And look ahead — and feel your way — before you build on this exquisite creature, who here lends sweetness to your life.

REBECCA. Is it me you mean?

BRENDEL. Yes, my fascinating mermaid.

REBECCA. Why am I not to be built on?

BRENDEL. [*Comes a step nearer*] I gather that my former pupil has a great cause to carry forward to victory.

REBECCA. What then — ?

BRENDEL. Victory is assured. But — mark me well — on one indispensable 320 condition.

REBECCA. Which is —?

BRENDEL. [*Taking her gently by the wrist*] That the woman who loves him shall gladly go out into the kitchen and hack off her tender, rosy-white little finger — here — just here at the middle joint. Item, that the aforesaid loving woman — again gladly — shall slice off her incomparably-moulded left ear. [*Lets her go, and turns to* ROSMER] Farewell, my conquering Johannes.

ROSMER. Are you going now? In the dark night?

BRENDEL. The dark night is best. Peace be with you. 330

[*He goes. There is a short silence in the room.*

REBECCA. [*Breathes heavily*] Oh, how close and sultry it is here!

[*Goes to the window, opens it, and remains standing by it.*

ROSMER. [*Sits down in the arm-chair by the stove*] There is nothing else for it after all, Rebecca. I see it. You must go away.

REBECCA. Yes, I see no choice.

ROSMER. Let us make the most of our last hour. Come here and sit by me.

REBECCA. [*Goes and sits on the sofa*] What do you want to say to me, Rosmer? 340

ROSMER. First, I want to tell you that you need not feel any anxiety about your future.

REBECCA. [*Smiles*] H'm, my future.

ROSMER. I have long ago arranged for everything. Whatever may happen, you are provided for.

REBECCA. That too, my dear one?

ROSMER. You might surely have known that.

REBECCA. It is many a long day since I have given a thought to such things.

ROSMER. Yes, yes – you thought things would always remain as they   350
were between us.

REBECCA. Yes, I thought so.

ROSMER. So did I. But if I were to go —

REBECCA. Oh, Rosmer – you will live longer than I.

ROSMER. Surely my worthless life lies in my own hands.

REBECCA. What is this? You are never thinking of — !

ROSMER. Do you think it would be so strange? After this pitiful, lamentable defeat! I, who was to have borne a great cause on to victory – have I
not fled from the battle before it was well begun?

REBECCA. Take up the fight again, Rosmer! Only try – and you shall see,   360
you will conquer. You will ennoble hundreds – thousands of minds. Only
try!

ROSMER. Oh Rebecca – I, who no longer believe in my own mission!

REBECCA. But your mission has stood the test already. You have ennobled
one human being at least – me you have ennobled for the rest of my days.

ROSMER. Oh – if I dared believe you.

REBECCA. [*Pressing her hands together*] Oh Rosmer, – do you know of
nothing – nothing that could make you believe it?

ROSMER. [*Starts as if in fear*] Don't speak of that! Keep away from that,
Rebecca! Not a word more.   370

REBECCA. Yes, this is precisely what we must speak about. Do you know
of anything that would kill the doubt? For *I* know of nothing in the world.

ROSMER. It is well for you that you do not know. – It is well for both
of us.

REBECCA. No, no, no. – I will not be put off in this way! If you know of
anything that would absolve me in your eyes, I claim as my right to be
told of it.

ROSMER. [*As if impelled against his will to speak*] Then let us see. You
say that a great love is in you; that through me your mind has been ennobled. Is it so? Is your reckoning just, Rebecca? Shall we try to prove the   380
sum? Say?

REBECCA. I am ready.

ROSMER. At any time?

REBECCA. Whenever you please. The sooner the better.

ROSMER. Then let me see, Rebecca, – if you for my sake – this very
evening — [*Breaks off*] Oh, no, no, no!

REBECCA. Yes, Rosmer! Yes! Tell me, and you shall see.

ROSMER. Have you the courage – have you the will – gladly, as Ulric
Brendel said – for my sake, to-night – gladly – to go the same way that
Beata went?   390

REBECCA. [*Rises slowly from the sofa; almost voiceless*] Rosmer — !

ROSMER. Yes, Rebecca – that is the question that will for ever haunt me
– when you are gone. Every hour in the day it will return upon me. Oh, I
seem to see you before my very eyes. You are standing out on the foot-
bridge – right in the middle. Now you are bending forward over the railing – drawn dizzily downwards, downwards towards the rushing water! No
– you recoil. You have not the heart to do what she dared.

REBECCA. But if I had the heart to do it? And the will to do it gladly?
What then?

ROSMER. I should have to believe you then. I should recover my faith   400
in my mission. Faith in my power to ennoble human souls. Faith in the
human soul's power to attain nobility.

REBECCA. [*Takes up her shawl slowly, and puts it over her head; says with
composure*] You shall have your faith again.

ROSMER. Have you the will and the courage — for this, Rebecca?

REBECCA. That you shall see to-morrow — or afterwards — when they find my body.

ROSMER. [*Puts his hand to his forehead*] There is a horrible fascination in this — !

REBECCA. For I don't want to remain down there. Not longer than 410 necessary. You must see that they find me.

ROSMER. [*Springs up*] But all this — is nothing but madness. Go — or stay! I will take your bare word this time too.

REBECCA. Phrases, Rosmer! Let us have no more cowardly subterfuges, dear! How can you believe me on my bare word after this day?

ROSMER. I shrink from seeing your defeat, Rebecca!

REBECCA. It will be no defeat.

ROSMER. Yes, it will. You will never bring yourself to go Beata's way.

REBECCA. Do you think not?

ROSMER. Never. You are not like Beata. You are not under the dominion 420 of a distorted view of life.

REBECCA. But I am under the dominion of the Rosmersholm view of life — now. What I have sinned — it is fit that I should expiate.

ROSMER. [*Looks at her fixedly*] Is that your point of view?

REBECCA. Yes.

ROSMER. [*With resolution*] Well then, *I* stand firm in our emancipated view of life, Rebecca. There is no judge over us; and therefore we must do justice upon ourselves.

REBECCA. [*Misunderstanding him*] Yes, that is true — that too. My going away will save what is best in you. 430

ROSMER. Oh, there is nothing left to save in me.

REBECCA. Yes, there is. But I — after to-day, I should only be a sea-troll dragging down the ship that is to carry you forward. I must go over-board. Why should I remain here in the world, trailing after me my own crippled life? Why brood and brood over the happiness that my past has forfeited for ever? I must give up the game, Rosmer.

ROSMER. If you go — I go with you.

REBECCA. [*Smiles almost imperceptibly, looks at him, and says more softly*] Yes, come with me — and see —

ROSMER. I go with you, I say. 440

REBECCA. To the foot-bridge, yes. You know you never dare go out upon it.

ROSMER. Have you noticed that?

REBECCA. [*Sadly and brokenly*] Yes. — It was that that made my love hopeless.

ROSMER. Rebecca, — now I lay my hand on your head — [*Does so*] — and I wed you as my true wife.

REBECCA. [*Takes both his hands, and bows her head towards his breast*] Thanks, Rosmer. [*Lets him go*] And now I will go — gladly.

ROSMER. Man and wife should go together. 450

REBECCA. Only to the bridge, Rosmer.

ROSMER. Out on to it, too. As far as you go — so far shall I go with you. For now I dare.

REBECCA. Are you absolutely certain — that this way is the best for you?

ROSMER. I am certain that it is the only way.

REBECCA. If you were deceiving yourself? If it were only a delusion? One of those white horses of Rosmersholm?

ROSMER. It may be so. For we can never escape from them — we of this house.

REBECCA. Then stay, Rosmer!                                                460
ROSMER. The husband shall go with his wife, as the wife with her
husband.
REBECCA. Yes, but first tell me this: Is it you who follow me? Or is it
I who follow you?
ROSMER. We shall never think that question out.
REBECCA. But I should like to know.
ROSMER. We go with each other, Rebecca — I with you, and you with me.
REBECCA. I almost think that is the truth.
ROSMER. For now we two are one.
REBECCA. Yes. We are one. Come! We go gladly.                              470

*They go out hand in hand through the hall, and are seen to turn to the
left. The door remains open. The room stands empty for a little while.
Then the door to the right is opened by* MADAM HELSETH.

MADAM HELSETH. Miss West — the carriage is — [*Looks round*] Not here?
Out together at this time of night? Well — I must say — ! H'm! [*Goes out
into the hall, looks round, and comes in again*] Not on the garden seat.
Ah, well well. [*Goes to the window and looks out*] Oh, good God! that
white thing there — ! My soul! They're both of them out on the bridge!
God forgive the sinful creatures — if they're not in each other's arms!
[*Shrieks aloud*] Oh — down — both of them! Out into the mill-race! Help!
Help! [*Her knees tremble; she holds on to the chair-back, shaking all over;
she can scarcely get the words out*] No. No help here. — The dead wife has
taken them.                                                               480

---

### FOR DISCUSSION AND WRITING

---

*Rosmer and Rebecca are trapped. They cannot advance, either to leader-
ship or love, since Rosmersholm and its dead do not permit it; and we agree,
as we did not in* Ghosts, *that the dead are right. The argument by which
they work out with remorseless logic that they also must commit suicide may
appear, like Gregers' advice to Hedvig, too abstractedly reasoned, and the
producer and the performers must, by atmosphere, force of personality, and
stage-business, do what they can to give it conviction. The surface dialogue
is really little more than a provisional rationalisation of a deeper necessity
governed by universals. If Beata, product of normality and the simple biological values, could so martyr herself, then the exponents of enlightenment
should, as Julian argued when thinking of his followers and the Christians,
show an equal courage; anything less would be an admission of defeat. They
have been exerting on each other reciprocal influences; after Rebecca has
converted Rosmer to free thought he more subtly affects her; what was, and
is, wanted is high achievement "together" (*IV. 88*). And if the rival powers
of will and conscience which they personify cannot be married in life, there
is nothing for it but either a falling-back to the second-rate, or marriage in
death. It is not simply a matter of expiation, though that is included: rather,
in direct line with the "free necessity" of* Emperor and Galilean (The
Emperor Julian, *IV. i. 394), they must be felt as willing a joint perfection in
any event unrealisable in other terms. So they formally celebrate their union,
and plunge into the mill-race.*

*From G. Wilson Knight,* Ibsen *(London: Oliver and Boyd, 1962), pp. 60-61.*

*... The title of* Rosmersholm *in its first drafts was* White Horses. *The White Horse is the symbol of Rosmersholm: it is linked with dead who cling to the house; the Mill-Race that has drowned Beata, the footbridge which Kroll will cross and Rosmer will not; the portraits that recall the dead burden that lies on Rosmer himself; the white shawl that Rebecca wears: all these point the contrast between the darkness that belongs to the dead wife, Beata, and the new hope and life that Rebecca seeks to bring down from the North.*

*Much of the controversy that surrounds the play becomes redundant if we regard it as the tragedy of Rebecca, defeated by the spirit of Rosmersholm and of the past. Rosmer is too supine to be a hero. But if we focus our interest on Rebecca, she is, in three ways, the victim struggling in the net; the revelation of her illegitimacy (and hence the incest of her relation with Rosmer); the struggle against her own love; the struggle with the house and its drowned mistress. For the cumulative evil generated by a house is very real, and is a complex of physical surroundings, past thoughts and deeds, and, I think, an attempt to arrest the time-stream; an image to which we can relate the Mill-Race and its victims. The action of clinging to a house and its past, of a failure to realize when the stream of history has passed it by, is a deep-rooted and evil instinct, the more insidious because it is so easily rationalized into a belief in aristocracy, pride of race and birth, and so on. The plays of Chekhov show this craving at its worst.*

*As Rebecca's tragedy, the emotional impact is great, Rosmer's accidie, the second-hand sterile philosophy, the catastrophic impinging of the idealist Brendel in his borrowed clothes, the background of small-town scandal and gossip, are set against Ibsen's northern romanticism which is now adequately controlled. The horse is an archetypal image; its part in the play is the more powerful because it is never artificially related (as the* Wild Duck *seems to be) by too large or too explicit a number of connections. The position of Rebecca has been criticized, since it is she who induced Beata's suicide; it is possible in view of Beata's mental illness to condone her action in some measure. But the crimes of both Rosmer and Rebecca are confronted squarely by each; the final suicide of both in the Mill-Race has at least the strength of their love — for Rosmer's is now awakened to respond to and confront hers — to justify their expiation. That expiation is whole and satisfying; for Rosmer's earlier and tentative suggestion, so close to that made to Hedwig in* The Wild Duck, *is now submerged in a knowledge of mutual responsibility.*

From *Thomas Rice Henn*, The Harvest of Tragedy
*(London: Methuen, 1956), pp. 179-180.*

1) To what extent does *Rosmersholm* reflect the theme of the burdens laid by the past on the present? What thematic tie does this play have with *Agamemnon?*

2) The idea of tragedy described by Cornford (p. 24) and by Butcher (p. 9) is apparently not appropriate to Ibsen's story of Rosmer, a middle-class hero. But can it be said that *Rosmersholm* does *not* "represent the destiny of man, the turning wheel of Time and Fate"? Is Ibsen's use of such symbolic devices as the mill-race and the white horses an attempt to give wider significance to the play?

3) In his analysis of Greek tragedy, Alexander seems to reject the conventional notion of *hamartia* — the tragic flaw — as being a vital element in the experience that Aristotle calls *catharsis*. Rather, he feels that virtue — or a

striving for *areté* — and not vice brings the tragic hero to disaster. Can this theory be applied to Rosmer or to Rebecca?

4) Anderson sees as the central factor in tragedy the "discovery by the hero of some element in his environment or in his own soul of which he has not been aware" (p. 32). Does either Rosmer or Rebecca make such a discovery? What are its results?

5) Ellis-Fermor states that in tragedy "something is revealed" that makes possible a reconciliation of the permanence of evil and pain in man's life (p. 35). What is this "something" in *Rosmersholm*?

6) Do Rosmer and the situation in which he finds himself qualify as tragic in terms of Raphael's analysis of sublime opposites (pp. 39-41)?

7) It might be said that the Duchess exerts a beneficent influence on Bosola. Could the same be said of Rebecca's influence on Rosmer, or of his on her?

8) To what extent does Rosmer (or Rebecca) feel and try to overcome "the underlying fear of being displaced, the disaster inherent in being torn away from our chosen image of what and who we are in this world" (Miller, p. 68)?

❈

# AESCHYLUS

## *Agamemnon*

---

Characters:      A WATCHMAN
                 CHORUS of twelve elders of Argos
                 CLYTEMNESTRA, wife of Agamemnon
                 A HERALD
                 AGAMEMNON, king of Argos
                 CASSANDRA, a princess of Troy
                 AEGISTHUS, Clytemnestra's paramour,
                    cousin to Agamemnon
                 Soldiers attending Agamemnon,
                    guards attending Aegisthus

*It is night, a little before sunrise. On the roof of Atreus' palace a* WATCH-
*MAN stands, or rises from a small mattress placed on the hewn stone.
In front of the palace are statues of Zeus, Apollo, and Hermes; each
with an altar before it.*

WATCHMAN. O gods! grant me release from this long weary watch.
Release, O gods! Twelve full months now, night after night
Dog-like I lie here, keeping guard from this high roof
On Atreus' palace. The nightly conference of stars,
Resplendent rulers, bringing heat and cold in turn,
Studding the sky with beauty — I know them all, and watch them
Setting and rising; but the one light I long to see
Is a new star, the promised sign, the beacon-flare
To speak from Troy and utter one word, 'Victory!' —
Great news for Clytemnestra, in whose woman's heart          10
A man's will nurses hope.
                         Now once more, drenched with dew,
I walk about; lie down, but no dreams visit me.

Agamemnon, *tr.* Philip Vellacott, The Oresteian Trilogy *(New York: Penguin Books, rev. ed.,
1959). The play was written* circa *458* B.C.

Sleep's enemy, fear, stands guard beside me, to forbid
My eyes one instant's closing. If I sing some tune —
Since music's the one cure prescribed for heartsickness —
Why, then I weep, to think how changed this house is now
From splendour of old days, ruled by its rightful lord.
So may the gods be kind and grant release from trouble,
And send the fire to cheer this dark night with good news.

*[The beacon shines out.*

O welcome beacon, kindling night to glorious day,                    20
Welcome! You'll set them dancing in every street in Argos
When they hear your message. Ho there! Hullo! Call Clytemnestra!
The Queen must rise at once like Dawn from her bed, and welcome
The fire with pious words and a shout of victory,
For the town of Ilion's ours — that beacon's clear enough!
I'll be the first myself to start the triumphal dance.
Now I can say the gods have blessed my master's hand;
And for me too that beacon-light's a lucky throw.
Now Heaven bring Agamemnon safe to his home! May I
Hold his dear hand in mine! For the rest, I say no more;          30
My tongue's nailed down. This house itself, if walls had words,
Would tell its story plainly. Well, I speak to those
Who understand me; to the rest — my door is shut.

> *He descends. Lights begin to appear in the palace. A cry of triumph is
> heard from* CLYTEMNESTRA *within, and is echoed by other women. Then
> from the palace a messenger hurries out towards the city; attendants
> follow, going in various directions, and carrying jars and bowls with oil
> and incense for sacrifice. Then* CLYTEMNESTRA *enters from the palace,
> with two attendants; she casts incense on the altars, and prays before
> the statue of Zeus.*
>
> *Day begins to break. From the city enter the* ELDERS OF ARGOS. *They
> do not yet see* CLYTEMNESTRA.

CHORUS. Ten years have passed since the strong sons of Atreus,
Menelaus and Agamemnon, both alike
Honoured by Zeus with throned and sceptred power,
Gathered and manned a thousand Argive ships,
And with the youth of Hellas under arms
Sailed from these ports to settle scores with Priam.

Then loud their warlike anger cried,                                     40
As eagles cry, that wild with grief,
On some steep, lonely mountain-side
Above their robbed nest wheel and sail,
Oaring the airy waves, and wail
Their wasted toil, their watchful pride;
Till some celestial deity,
Zeus, Pan, Apollo, hears on high
Their scream of wordless misery;
And pitying their forlorn estate
(Since air is Heaven's protectorate)                                    50
Sends a swift Fury to pursue
Marauding guilt with vengeance due.

So against Paris's guilty boast
Zeus, witness between guest and host,
Sends Atreus' sons for stern redress

Of his and Helen's wantonness.
Now Greece and Troy both pay their equal debt
Of aching limbs and wounds and sweat,
While knees sink low in gory dust,
And spears are shivered at first thrust.                          60
Things are — as they are now; their end
Shall follow Fate's decree, which none can bend.
In vain shall Priam's altars burn,
His rich libations vainly flow
To gods above and powers below:
No gift, no sacrificial flame
Can soothe or turn
The wrath of Heaven from its relentless aim.

We were too old to take our share
With those who joined the army then.                              70
We lean on sticks — in strength not men
But children; so they left us here.
In weakness youth and age are one:
The sap sleeps in the unripe bone
As in the withered. The green stalk
Grows without thorns: so, in the grey
And brittle years, old men must walk
Three-footed, weak as babes, and stray
Like dreams lost in the light of day.

[*Here the* CHORUS-LEADER *sees* CLYTEMNESTRA.

Daughter of Tyndareos, Queen Clytemnestra,                        80
What have you heard? What has happened? Why have you ordered
Sacrifice through the city? Is there news?
Altars of all the gods who guard our State,
Gods of the sky, powers of the lower earth,
Altars of town and country, blaze with offerings;
On every hand heaven-leaping flames implore
Anger to melt in gentleness — a glare
Enriched with holy ointment, balm so rare
As issues only from a royal store!
Why are these things? Be gracious, Queen:                         90
Tell what you can, or what you may;
Be healer of this haunting fear
Which now like an enemy creeps near,
And now again, when hope has seen
These altars bright with promise, slinks away —
Tell us, that hope may lift the load
Which galls our souls by night and day,
Sick with the evil which has been,
The evil which our hearts forebode.

CLYTEMNESTRA *remains silent, her back turned to the* CHORUS. *They
continue, addressing the audience.*

I am the man to speak, if you would hear                         100
The whole tale from its hopeful starting-place —
That portent, which amazed our marching youth.
It was ten years ago — but I was there.
The poet's grace, the singer's fire,
Grow with his years; and I can still speak truth
With the clear ring the gods inspire; —

How those twin monarchs of our warlike race,
Two leaders one in purpose, were sped forth —
Their vengeful spears in thousands pointing North
To Troy — by four wings' furious beat:                     110
Two kings of birds, that seemed to bode
Great fortune to the kings of that great fleet.
Close to the palace, on spear-side of the road,
One tawny-feathered, one white in the tail,
Perched in full view, they ravenously tear
The body of a pregnant hare
Big with her burden, now a living prey
In the last darkness of their unborn day.
*Cry Sorrow, sorrow — yet let good prevail!*

The army's learned Seer saw this, and knew            120
The devourers of the hare
For that relentless pair —
Different in nature, as the birds in hue —
The sons of Atreus; and in council of war
Thus prophesied: 'Your army, it is true,
In time shall make King Priam's town their prey;
Those flocks and herds Troy's priests shall slay
With prayers for safety of her wall
Perish in vain — Troy's violent doom shall swallow all.
Only, see to it, you who go                                130
To bridle Trojan pride, that no
Anger of gods benight your day
And strike before your hulls are under way.
For virgin Artemis, whom all revere,
Hates with a deadly hate
The swift-winged hounds of Zeus who swooped to assail
Their helpless victim wild with fear
Before her ripe hour came;
Who dared to violate
(So warning spoke the priest)                              140
The awe that parenthood must claim,
As for some rite performed in Heaven's name;
Yes, Artemis abominates the eagles' feast!'
*Cry Sorrow, sorrow — yet let good prevail!*

Still spoke on the prophet's tongue:
'Lovely child of Zeus, I pray,
You who love the tender whelp
Of the ravening lion, and care
For the fresh-wild sucking young
Of fox and rat and hind and hare;                         150
If ever by your heavenly help
Hope of good was brought to flower,
Bless the sign we saw today!
Cancel all its presaged ill,
All its promised good fulfil!
Next my anxious prayers entreat
Lord Apollo's healing power,
That his Sister may not plan
Winds to chain the Hellene fleet;
That her grievance may not crave                          160

Blood to drench another grave
From a different sacrifice
Hallowed by no festal joy —
Blood that builds a tower of hate,
Mad blood raging to destroy
Its self-source, a ruthless Fate
Warring with the flesh of man;
Bloodshed bringing in its train
Kindred blood that flows again,
Anger still unreconciled                                              170
Poisoning a house's life
With darkness, treachery and strife,
Wreaking vengeance for a murdered child.'

So Calchas, from that parting prodigy
Auguring the royal house's destiny,
Pronounced his warning of a fatal curse,
With hope of better mingling fear of worse.
Let us too, echoing his uncertain tale,
*Cry Sorrow, sorrow — yet let good prevail!*

Let good prevail!                                                     180
So be it! Yet, what is good? And who
Is God? How name him, and speak true?
If he accept the name that men
Give him, Zeus I name him then.
I, still perplexed in mind,
For long have searched and weighed
Every hope of comfort or of aid:
Still I can find
No creed to lift this heaviness,
This fear that haunts without excuse —                               190
No name inviting faith, no wistful guess,
Save only — Zeus.

The first of gods is gone,
Old Ouranos, once blown
With violence and pride;
His name shall not be known,
Nor that his dynasty once lived, and died.
His strong successor, Cronos, had his hour,
Then went his way, thrice thrown
By a yet stronger power.                                              200
Now Zeus is lord; and he
Who loyally acclaims his victory
Shall by heart's instinct find the universal key:

Zeus, whose will has marked for man
The sole way where wisdom lies;
Ordered one eternal plan:
*Man must suffer to be wise.*
Head-winds heavy with past ill
Stray his course and cloud his heart:
Sorrow takes the blind soul's part —                                 210
Man grows wise against his will.
For powers who rule from thrones above
By ruthlessness commend their love.

So was it then. Agamemnon, mortified,
Dared not, would not, admit to error; thought
Of his great Hellene fleet, and in his pride
Spread sail to the ill wind he should have fought.
Meanwhile his armed men moped along the shores,
And cursed the wind, and ate his dwindling stores;
Stared at white Chalkis' roofs day after day                    220
Across the swell that churned in Aulis Bay.
And still from Strymon came that Northern blast,
While hulks and ropes grew rotten, moorings parted,
Deserters slunk away,
All ground their teeth, bored, helpless, hungry, thwarted.
The days of waiting doubled. More days passed.
The flower of warlike Hellas withered fast.

Then Calchas spoke again. The wind, he said,
Was sent by Artemis; and he revealed
Her remedy — a thought to crush like lead                       230
The hearts of Atreus' sons, who wept, as weep they must,
And speechless ground their sceptres in the dust.

The elder king then spoke: 'What can I say?
Disaster follows if I disobey;
Surely yet worse disaster if I yield
And slaughter my own child, my home's delight,
In her young innocence, and stain my hand
With blasphemous unnatural cruelty,
Bathed in the blood I fathered! Either way,
Ruin! Disband the fleet, sail home, and earn                    240
The deserter's badge — abandon my command,
Betray the alliance — now! The wind must turn,
There must be sacrifice, a maid must bleed —
Their chafing rage demands it — they are right!
May good prevail, and justify my deed!'

Then he put on
The harness of Necessity.
The doubtful tempest of his soul
Veered, and his prayer was turned to blasphemy,
His offering to impiety.                                        250
Hence that repentance late and long
Which, since his madness passed, pays toll
For that one reckless wrong.
Shameless self-willed infatuation
Emboldens men to dare damnation,
And starts the wheels of doom which roll
Relentless to their piteous goal.

So Agamemnon, rather than retreat,
Endured to offer up his daughter's life
To help a war fought for a faithless wife                       260
And pay the ransom for a storm-bound fleet.

Heedless of her tears,
Her cries of 'Father!' and her maiden years,
Her judges valued more
Their glory and their war.

A prayer was said. Her father gave the word.
Limp in her flowing dress
The priest's attendants held her high
Above the altar, as men hold a kid.
Her father spoke again, to bid                                          270
One bring a gag, and press
Her sweet mouth tightly with a cord,
Lest Atreus' house be cursed by some ill-omened cry.

Rough hands tear at her girdle, cast
Her saffron silks to earth. Her eyes
Search for her slaughterers; and each,
Seeing her beauty, that surpassed
A painter's vision, yet denies
The pity her dumb looks beseech,
Struggling for voice; for often in old days,                           280
When brave men feasted in her father's hall,
With simple skill and pious praise
Linked to the flute's pure tone
Her virgin voice would melt the hearts of all,
Honouring the third libation near her father's throne.

The rest I did not see,
Nor do I speak of it . . .
                         But this I know:
What Calchas prophesies will be fulfilled.
The scale of Justice falls in equity:
The killer will be killed.                                             290

But now, farewell foreboding! Time may show,
But cannot alter, what shall be.
What help, then, to bewail
Troubles before they fall?
Events will take their way
Even as the prophet's words foreshadowed all.
For what is next at hand,
Let good prevail!
That is the prayer we pray —
We, who alone now stand                                                300
In Agamemnon's place, to guard this Argive land.

*The day has broken.* THE QUEEN *now turns and stands facing the* ELDERS.

CHORUS. We come obedient to your bidding, Clytemnestra.
Our king and leader absent, and his throne unfilled,
Our duty pays his due observance to his wife.
Have you received some message? Do these sacrifices
Rise for good news, give thanks for long hope re-assured?
I ask in love; and will as loyally receive
Answer or silence.
     CLYTEMNESTRA. Good news, if the proverb's true,
Should break with sunrise from the kindly womb of night.
But here's a richer joy than you dared ever hope:                      310
Our Argive men have captured Priam's town.
     CHORUS.                         Have *what?*
I heard it wrong — I can't believe it!

CLYTEMNESTRA.                    Troy is ours!
Is that clear speaking?
    CHORUS.              Happiness fills my eyes with tears.
    CLYTEMNESTRA. They show your loyalty.
    CHORUS.                        Have you some sure proof of this?
    CLYTEMNESTRA. I have indeed; unless a god has played me false.
    CHORUS. A god! Was it some dream you had, persuaded you?
    CLYTEMNESTRA. Dream! Am I one to air drowsy imaginings?
    CHORUS. Surely you feed yourself on unconfirmed report?
    CLYTEMNESTRA. You choose to criticize me as an ignorant girl!
    CHORUS. Well, then, when was Troy captured?
    CLYTEMNESTRA.                      In this very night          320
That brought to birth this glorious sun.
    CHORUS.                  What messenger
Could fly so fast from Troy to here?
    CLYTEMNESTRA.                The god of fire!
Ida first launched his blazing beam; thence to this palace
Beacon lit beacon in relays of flame. From Ida
To Hermes' crag on Lemnos; from that island, third
To receive the towering torch was Athos, rock of Zeus;
There, as the blaze leapt the dark leagues, the watch in welcome
Leapt too, and a twin tower of brightness speared the sky,
Pointing athwart the former course; and in a stride
Crossing the Aegean, like the whip-lash of lightning, flew          330
The resinous dazzle, molten-gold, till the fish danced,
As at sunrise, enraptured with the beacon's glow,
Which woke reflected sunrise on Makistos' heights.
The watchman there, proof against sleep, surprise or sloth,
Rose faithful to the message; and his faggots' flame
Swept the wide distance to Euripus' channel, where
Its burning word was blazoned to the Messapian guards.
They blazed in turn, kindling their pile of withered heath,
And passed the signal on. The strong beam, still undimmed,
Crossed at one bound Asopus' plain, and like the moon          340
In brilliance, lighted on Cithaeron's crags, and woke
Another watch, to speed the flying token on.
On still the hot gleam hurtled, past Gorgopis' lake;
Made Aegiplanctus, stirred those watching mountaineers
Not to stint boughs and brushwood; generously they fed
Their beacon, and up burst a monstrous beard of fire,
Leapt the proud headland fronting the Saronic Gulf,
To lofty Arachnaeus, neighbour to our streets;
Thence on this Atreid palace the triumphant fire
Flashed, lineal descendant of the flame of Ida.          350

Such, Elders, was the ritual race my torchbearers,
Each at his faithful post succeeding each, fulfilled;
And first and last to run share equal victory.
Such, Elders, is my proof and token offered you,
A message sent to me from Troy by Agamemnon.
    CHORUS. Madam, we will in due course offer thanks to Heaven;
But now we want to savour wonder to the full,
And hear you speak at length: tell us your news again!
    CLYTEMNESTRA. Today the Greeks hold Troy! Her walls echo with cries
That will not blend. Pour oil and vinegar in one vessel,          360

You'll see them part and swirl, and never mix: so, there,
I think, down narrow streets a discord grates the ear —
Screams of the captured, shouts of those who've captured them,
The unhappy and the happy. Women of Troy prostrate
Over dead husbands, brothers; aged grandfathers
Mourning dead sons and grandsons, and remembering
Their very cries are slaves' cries now. . . . And then the victors:
After a night of fighting, roaming, plundering,
Hungry to breakfast, while their hosts lie quiet in dust;
No rules to keep, no order of place; each with the luck               370
That fell to him, quartered in captured homes of Troy,
Tonight, at last, rolled in dry blankets, safe from frost —
No going on guard — blissfully they'll sleep from dusk to dawn.

If in that captured town they are reverencing the gods
Whose home it was, and not profaning holy places,
The victors will avoid being vanquished in their turn.
Only, let no lust of unlawful plunder tempt
Our soldiers' hearts with wealth, to their own harm — there still
Remains the journey home: God grant we see them safe!
If the fleet sails free from the taint of sin, the gods               380
May grant them safely to retrace their outward course —
Those whom no wakeful anger of the forgotten dead
Waits to surprise with vengeance. . . .
                                   These are a woman's words.
May good prevail beyond dispute, in sight of all!
My life holds many blessings; I would enjoy them now.
    CHORUS. Madam, your words are like a man's, both wise and kind.
Now we have heard trustworthy proof from your own lips,
We will prepare ourselves again to praise the gods,
Whose gracious acts call for our most devout response.
                          [CLYTEMNESTRA *goes into the palace.*
    CHORUS. Zeus, supreme of heavenly powers!                         390
        Friendly night, whose fateful hours
        Built for Argos' warlike name
        Bright imperishable fame!
        Night in which a net was laid
        Fast about the Trojan towers
        Such that none of mortal flesh,
        Great or little, could evade
        Grim annihilation's deadly mesh!
    This is the hand of Zeus! Zeus we revere,
        Whose lasting law both host and guest must fear;              400
        Who long since against Paris bent
        His bow with careful aim, and sent
        His vengeance flying not too near
        Nor past the stars, but timed to pay
        The debt of Justice on the appointed day.

        'The hand of Zeus has cast
        The proud from their high place!'
        This we may say, and trace
        That hand from first to last.
        As Zeus foreknowing willed,                                   410
        So was their end fulfilled.

One said, 'The gods disdain
To mark man's wanton way
Who tramples in the dust
Beauty of holy things.'
Impious! The truth shows plain:
Pride now has paid its debt, and they
Who laughed at Right and put their boastful trust
In arms and swollen wealth of kings,
Have gone their destined way.                                420
A middle course is best,
Not poor nor proud; but this,
By no clear rule defined,
Eludes the unstable, undiscerning mind,
Whose aim will surely miss.
Thenceforth there is no way to turn aside;
When man has once transgressed,
And in his wealth and pride
Spurned the high shrine of Justice, nevermore
May his sin hope to hide                                     430
In that safe dimness he enjoyed before.

Retreat cut off, the fiend Temptation
Forces him onward, the unseen
Effectual agent of Damnation;
When his fair freshness once has been
Blotched and defiled with grime, and he,
Like worthless bronze, which testing blows
Have blackened, lies despoiled, and shows
His baseness plain for all to see,
Then every cure renews despair;                              440
A boy chasing a bird on wing,
He on his race and soil must bring
A deeper doom than flesh can bear;
The gods are deaf to every prayer;
If pity lights a human eye,
Pity by Justice' law must share
The sinner's guilt, and with the sinner die.
So, doomed, deluded, Paris came
To sit at his host's table, and seduce
Helen his wife, and shame                                    450
The house of Atreus and the law of Zeus.

Bequeathing us in Argos
Muster of shields and spears,
The din of forge and dockyard,
Lightly she crossed the threshold
And left her palace, fearless
Of what should wake her fears;
And took to Troy as dowry
Destruction, blood, and tears.
Here, in her home deserted,                                  460
The voice of guard and groom
With love and grief lamented:
'O house! O king! O pity!
O pillow softly printed
Where her loved head had rested!'

There lies her husband fasting,
Dumb in his stricken room.
His thought across sea reaches
With longings, not reproaches;
A ghost will rule the palace,                         470
A home become a tomb!
Her statue's sweet perfection
Torments his desolation;
Still his eyes' hunger searches —
That living grace is hardened
And lost that beauty's bloom.

Visions of her beset him
With false and fleeting pleasure
When dreams and dark are deep.
He sees her, runs to hold her;                        480
And, through his fingers slipping,
Lightly departs his treasure,
The dream he cannot keep,
Wafted on wings that follow
The shadowy paths of sleep.

Such are the searching sorrows
This royal palace knows,
While through the streets of Argos
Grief yet more grievous grows,
With all our manhood gathered                         490
So far from earth of Hellas;
As in each home unfathered,
Each widowed bed, the whetted
Sword of despair assails
Hearts where all hope has withered
And angry hate prevails.
They sent forth men to battle,
But no such men return;
And home, to claim their welcome,
Come ashes in an urn.                                 500

For War's a banker, flesh his gold.
There by the furnace of Troy's field,
Where thrust meets thrust, he sits to hold
His scale, and watch the spear-point sway;
And back to waiting homes he sends
Slag from the ore, a little dust
To drain hot tears from hearts of friends;
Good measure, safely stored and sealed
In a convenient jar — the just
Price for the man they sent away.                     510
They praise him through their tears, and say,
'He was a soldier!' or, 'He died
Nobly, with death on every side!'
And fierce resentment mutters low,
'Yes — for another's wife!' And so
From grief springs gall, which fear must hide
Let kings and their revenges go!
But under Ilion's wall the dead,

Heirs of her earth, lie chambered deep;
While she, whose living blood they shed,                    520
Covers her conquerors in sleep.

A nation's voice, enforced with anger,
Strikes deadly as a public curse.
I wait for word of hidden danger,
And fear lest bad give place to worse.
God marks that man with watchful eyes
Who counts his killed by companies;
And when his luck, his proud success,
Forgets the law of righteousness,
Then the dark Furies launch at length                      530
A counter-blow to crush his strength
And cloud his brightness, till the dim
Pit of oblivion swallows him.
In fame unmeasured, praise too high,
Lies danger: God's sharp lightnings fly
To stagger mountains. Then, I choose
Wealth that invites no rankling hate;
Neither to lay towns desolate,
Nor wear the chains of those who lose
Freedom and life to war and Fate.                          540

*The sound of women's voices excitedly shouting and cheering is heard.
One or two* ELDERS *go out, and return immediately to report. The following remarks are made severally by various members of the* CHORUS.

Since the beacon's news was heard
Rumour flies through every street.
Ought we to believe a word?
Is it some inspired deceit?
Childish, crack-brained fantasy!
Wing your hopes with such a tale,
Soon you'll find that fire can lie,
Facts can change, and trust can fail.
Women all are hasty-headed:
Beacons blaze — belief rejoices;                           550
All too easily persuaded.
Rumour fired by women's voices,
As we know, is quickly spread;
— As we know, is quickly dead!

*The* CHORUS *depart; and an interval representing the lapse of several days
now takes place. After the interval the* CHORUS *re-appear in great excitement.*

CHORUS. We shall soon know whether this relay-race of flame,
This midnight torch-parade, this beacon-telegraph,
Told us the truth, or if the fire made fools of us —
All a delightful dream! Look! There's a herald coming
Up from the shore, wearing a crown of olive-leaves!
And, further off, a marching column of armed men,           560
Sheathed in hot dust, tells me this herald won't stand dumb
Or light a pinewood fire to announce the smoke of Troy!
Either his news doubles our happiness, or else —
The gods forbid all else! Good shows at first appearance,

Now may the proof be good! He who prays otherwise
For Argos — let him reap the folly of his soul!

*Enter a* HERALD.

HERALD. Argos! Dear earth my fathers trod! After ten years
Today I have come home! All other hopes were false,
But this proves true! I dared not think my own land would
In death receive me to my due and dearest rest.                                570
Now blest be Argos, and the sun's sweet light, and Zeus,
God of this realm, and Pythian Apollo, who no more
Aims against us the shafts of his immortal bow.
You fought us, Phoebus, by Scamander long enough:
Be Saviour now, be Healer; once, not twice, our death!
Gods of the city's gathering, hear my prayer; and thou,
Hermes, dear Guardian, Herald, every herald's god;
And you, heroes of old, whose blessing sent us forth,
Bless the returning remnant that the sword has spared!
O house of kings! Beloved walls! O august thrones!                             580
You deities who watch the rising sun, watch now!
Welcome with shining eyes the royal architect
Of towering glories to adorn his ancient throne.
To you, and every Argive citizen, Agamemnon
Brings light in darkness; come, then, greet him royally,
As fits one in whose hands Zeus the Avenger's plough
Passed over Troy, to split her towers, scar and subdue
Her fields, and from her fair soil extirpate her seed.
So harsh a halter Atreus' elder son has thrown
Around Troy's neck, and now comes home victorious                              590
To claim supremest honours among mortal men.
For neither Paris now, nor his accomplice town,
Can boast their deed was greater than their punishment.
Found guilty of theft and robbery, he has forfeited
His treasured spoil, destroyed his father's house and throne,
And made his people pay twice over for his sin.
CHORUS. Herald of the Greek army, greeting! Welcome home!
HERALD. Thanks. For ten years I've prayed for life; now I can die.
CHORUS. Longing for Argos, for your home, tormented you?
HERALD. Cruelly; and now my cloak is wet with tears of joy.                    600
CHORUS. Your suffering had its happy side.
HERALD.                                    What do you mean?
CHORUS. Your love and longing were returned. Is that not happy?
HERALD. You mean that Argos longed for us, as we for her?
CHORUS. Our hearts were dark with trouble. We missed and needed you.
HERALD. What caused your trouble? An enemy?
CHORUS.                                    I learnt long ago,
*Least said is soonest mended.*
HERALD.                        But was Argos threatened
In the king's absence?
CHORUS.              Friend, you said just now that death
Was dearly welcome. Our hearts echo what you felt.
HERALD. Yes, I could die, now the war's over, and all well.
Time blurs the memory; some things one recalls as good,                        610
Others as hateful. We're not gods; then why expect
To enjoy a lifetime of unbroken happiness?
To think what we went through! If I described it all,

The holes we camped in, dirt and weariness and sweat;
Or out at sea, with storms all night, trying to sleep
On a narrow board, with half a blanket; and all day,
Miserable and sick, we suffered and put up with it.
Then, when we landed, things were worse. We had to camp
Close by the enemy's wall, in the wet river-meadows,
Soaked with the dew and mist, ill from damp clothes, our hair          620
Matted like savages'. If I described the winter, when
In cruel snow-winds from Ida birds froze on the trees;
Or if I told of the fierce heat, when Ocean dropped
Waveless and windless to his noon-day bed, and slept . . .

Well, it's no time for moaning; all that's over now.
And those who died out there — it's over for them too;
No need to jump to orders; they can take their rest.
Why call the roll of those who were expendable,
And make the living wince from old wounds probed again?
Nor much hurrahing either, if we're sensible.                          630
For us who've come safe home the good weighs heaviest,
And what we've suffered counts for less. The praise that's due,
Proudly inscribed, will show these words to the bright sun:
      *The Argive army conquered Troy,*
      *And brought home over land and sea*
      *These hard-won spoils, the pride and joy*
      *Of ancient palaces, to be*
      *Trophies of victory, and grace*
      *The temples of the Hellene race.*
Let Argos hear this, and receive her general home                      640
With thanks and praise. Let Zeus, who gave us victory,
Be blest for his great mercy, I have no more to say.
      CHORUS. Well, I was wrong, I own it. Old and ready to learn
Is always young. But this great news is for the palace,
And chiefly Clytemnestra, whose wealth of joy we share.

      CLYTEMNESTRA *has appeared at the palace door.*

      CLYTEMNESTRA. I sang for joy to hail this victory long ago,
When the first fiery midnight message told that Troy
Was sacked and shattered. Someone then took me to task:
'Beacons! So you believe them? Troy, you think, is taken?
Typical female hopefulness!' Remarks like these                        650
Exposed my folly. Yet I made thankful sacrifice,
And throughout Argos women gathered to celebrate
Victory with songs of praise in temples of all the gods,
And feed their scented fires with rich flesh-offerings.
I have no need now to hear your detailed narrative;
I'll hear all from the king's own lips. But first, to greet
Fitly and soon my honoured husband's home-coming —
For to a wife what day is sweeter than when she,
Receiving by God's mercy her lord safe home from war,
Flings wide the gates in welcome? — take to him this message:          660
Let him come quickly; Argos longs for him; and he
Will find at home a wife as faithful as he left,
A watch-dog at his door; knowing one loyalty;
To enemies implacable; in all ways unchanged.
No seal of his have I unsealed in these ten years

Of pleasure found with other men, or any breath
Of scandal, I know no more than how to dip hot steel.

       [*Exit* CLYTEMNESTRA *to the palace.*

 HERALD. That's a strange boast — and more strange, as more full of truth.
Is it not scandal that a queen should speak such words?
 CHORUS. Strange? No! Her style eludes you. We interpret her.    670
A very proper statement — unimpeachable!
Now, Herald, tell us of our loved King Menelaus:
Has he come? Did he sail with you? Is he safely home?
 HERALD. That false good news you ask for — I can't give it you,
My friends; delusion would not comfort you for long.
 CHORUS. Telling a fair tale falsely cannot hide the truth;
When truth and good news part, the rift shows plain enough.
 HERALD. Then here it is: Menelaus has vanished, ship and all!
 CHORUS. You mean, he sailed with you from Troy, and then a storm
Fell on the fleet, and parted his ship from the rest?    680
 HERALD. Good marksman! An age of agony pointed in three words.
 CHORUS. But Menelaus — what was it thought had happened to him?
Is he given up for lost? Or may he yet survive?
 HERALD. No one can tell, for no one knows; except, perhaps,
The Sun, who fosters every earthly creature's life.
 CHORUS. You mean, I think, that when this storm had scourged our fleet
Some anger of the heavenly powers was satisfied?
 HERALD. Can it be right to foul this fair and holy day,
Blurting bad news? After our thanksgiving to the gods,
Such speech is out of place. When a man stands recounting    690
With bloodshot stare catastrophe and horror, an army dead,
The body of State staggered and gored, homes emptied, men
Blasted, lashed out of life by fire and sword, War's whips —
If such tales were my wares, this triumph-song of disaster
I bring, would suit well. But my news is victory,
Brought to a jubilant city — how can I countervail
Such good with sorrow, tell of the murderous armed alliance
Fate forged with angry gods to pursue and harass us?
For fire and water, age-old enemies, made league,
And pledged good faith in combined slaughter of Greek men.    700
One night a vicious swell rose with a gale from Thrace;
The sky was a mad shepherd tearing his own flock;
Ship against ship butted like rutting rams; mountains
Of wind and water leapt, surge swallowed and rain threshed.
At dawn, where were the ships? The bright sun beamed — we saw
The Aegean flowering thick with faces of dead Greeks
And scraps of wrecks . . .

      Our hull had held, and we came through.
It was no mortal hand that gripped our helm that night:
Some god, by guile or intercession, saved our lives.
Fortune sat smiling on our prow; we sprang no leak,    710
Nor ran aground on rocks. In the next morning's light,
Stunned, sickened, still incredulous of our own luck,
We brooded, thinking of our maimed and battered fleet.
And they, if any still drew breath, now speak of us
As caught in the same fate we picture theirs. . . . But yet,
May best prove truest! For Menelaus, more than all else
Expect him home. If any searching shaft of sun

Sees him alive and well, by the providence of Zeus
Not yet resolved to exterminate this house — there's hope
That Menelaus will yet come safe to his own home.                    720
And every word you have heard me speak is the plain truth.
        [*The* MESSENGER *goes, in the direction from which he came.*
  CHORUS. Who was the unknown seer whose voice —
    Uttered at venture, but instinct
    With prescience of what Fate decreed —
    Guessing infallibly, made choice
    Of a child's name, and deftly linked
    Symbol with truth, and name with deed,
    Naming, inspired, the glittering bride
    Of spears, for whom men killed and died,
    Helen, the Spoiler? On whose lips                            730
    Was born that fit and fatal name,
    To glut the sea with spoil of ships,
    Spoil souls with swords, a town with flame?
    The curtained softness of her bed
    She left, to hear the Zephyr breathe
    Gigantic in tall sails; and soon
    Comes hue and cry — armed thousands fly
    Tracing her trackless oar, and sheathe
    Their keels in Simois' shingly bank,
    Near fields where grass today grows rank                     740
    In soil by war's rich rain made red.

    And anger — roused, relentless, sure —
    Taught Troy that words have double edge,
    That men and gods use *bond* and *pledge*
    For love past limit, doom past cure:
    Love seals the hearts of bride and groom;
    And seal of love is seal of doom.
    Loud rings the holy marriage-song
    As kinsmen honour prince and bride;
    The hour is theirs — but not for long.                       750
    Wrath, borne on Time's unhurrying tide,
    Claims payment due for double wrong —
    The outraged hearth, the god defied.
    And songs are drowned in tears, and soon
    Must Troy the old learn a new tune;
    On Paris, once her praise and pride,
    She calls reproach, that his proud wooing
    Has won his own and her undoing:
    Her sons beset on every side,
    Her life-blood mercilessly spilt —                           760
    Hers is the loss, and his the guilt.

There was a shepherd once who reared at home
A lion's cub. It shared with sucking lambs
Their milk — gentle, while bone and blood were young.
The children loved it; the old watched and smiled.
Often the shepherd held it like a child
High in his arms; and often it would seek
His hand with soft eyes and caressing tongue,
Tense with the force of hunger. But in time
It showed the nature of its kind. Repaying                           770

Its debt for food and shelter, it prepared
A feast unbidden. Soon the nauseous reek
Of torn flesh filled the house; a bloody slime
Drenched all the ground from that unholy slaying,
While helpless weeping servants stood and stared.
The whelp once reared with lambs, now grown a beast,
Fulfils his nature as Destruction's priest!

And so to Troy there came
One in whose presence shone
Beauty no thought can name:                          780
A still enchantment of sweet summer calm;
A rarity for wealth to dote upon;
Glances whose gentle fire
Bestowed both wound and balm;
A flower to melt man's heart with wonder and desire.
But time grew ripe, and love's fulfilment ran
Aside from that sweet course where it began.
She, once their summer joy,
Transmuted, now like a swift curse descended
On every home, on every life                          790
Whose welcome once befriended
The outlaw wife;
A fiend sent by the god of host and guest,
Whose law her lover had transgressed,
To break his heart, and break the pride of Troy.

When Earth and Time were young,
A simple ancient saw
Phrased on the common tongue
Declared that man's good fortune, once mature,
Does not die childless, but begets its heir;        800
That from life's goodness grows, by Nature's law,
Calamity past cure
And ultimate despair.
I think alone; my mind
Rejects this general belief.
Sin, not prosperity, engenders grief;
For impious acts breed their own kind,
And evil's nature is to multiply.
The house whose ways are just in word and deed
Still as the years go by                             810
Sees lasting wealth and noble sons succeed.

So, by law of consequence,
Pride or Sin the Elder will,
In the man who chooses ill,
Breed a Younger Insolence.
Sin the Younger breeds again
Yet another unseen Power
Like the Powers that gave it birth:
Recklessness, whose force defies
War and violence, heaven and earth;                 820
Whose menace like a black cloud lies
On the doomed house hour by hour,
Fatal with fear, remorse, and pain.

But Justice with her shining eyes
Lights the smoke-begrimed and mean
Dwelling; honours those who prize
Honour; searches far to find
All whose hearts and hands are clean;
Passes with averted gaze
Golden palaces which hide                                    830
Evil armed in insolence;
Power and riches close combined,
Falsely stamped with all men's praise,
Win from her no reverence.
Good and evil she will guide
To their sure end by their appointed ways.

*Enter* AGAMEMNON *in his chariot, followed by another chariot bearing spoils of war and* CASSANDRA.

CHORUS. King! Heir of Atreus! Conqueror of Troy!
    What greeting shall we bring? What shall we say
        To voice our hearts' devotion,
        Observe both truth and measure,                      840
    Be neither scant nor fulsome in our love?
    Many, whose conscience is not innocent,
    Attach high value to a show of praise.
        As ill-luck finds on all sides
        Eyes brimming with condolence
    Where no true sting of sorrow pricks the heart,
    So now some harsh embittered faces, forced
    Into a seemly smile, will welcome you,
        And hide the hearts of traitors
        Beneath their feigned rejoicing.                     850
    Well, a wise shepherd knows his flock by face;
    And a wise king can tell the flatterer's eye —
        Moist, unctuous, adoring —
    The expressive sign of loyalty not felt.
    Now this I will not hide: ten years ago
    When you led Greece to war for Helen's sake
        You were set down as sailing
        Far off the course of wisdom.
    We thought you wrong, misguided, when you tried
        To keep morale from sagging                          860
        In superstitious soldiers
    By offering sacrifice to stop the storm.
    Those times are past; you have come victorious home;
    Now from our open hearts we wish you well.
        Time and your own enquiries
        Will show, among your people,
    Who has been loyal, who has played you false.
    AGAMEMNON. First, Argos, and her native gods, receive from me
The conqueror's greeting on my safe return; for which,
As for the just revenge I wrought on Priam's Troy,          870
Heaven shares my glory. Supplications without end
Won Heaven's ear; Troy stood her trial; unfaltering
The immortals cast their votes into the urn of death,
Dooming Troy's walls to dust, her men to the sword's edge.
The acquitting urn saw hope alone come near, and pass,

Vanishing in each empty hand. Smoke, rising still,
Marks great Troy's fall; flames of destruction's sacrifice
Live yet; and, as they die, stirs from the settled ash
The wind-borne incense of dead wealth and luxury.

Now for this victory let our pious thanksgiving                              880
Tell and re-tell Heaven's favour. We have made Troy pay
For her proud rape a woman's price. The Argive beast,
The lion rampant on all our shields, at dead of night
Sprang from the womb of the horse to grind that city's bones,
A ranked and ravening litter, that over wall and tower
Leaping, licked royal blood till lust was surfeited.

Thus to the gods I pay first my full salutation.
For your advice, I note it; I am of your mind,
And uphold your judgement. There are few whose inborn love
Warms without envy to a friend's prosperity.                                 890
Poison of jealousy laps the disappointed heart,
Doubling its grievance: pangs for its own losses match
With pangs for neighbours' wealth. Life and long observation
Taught me the look of men whose loving show, examined,
Proves but a shadow's shadow: I speak of what I know.
One man, Odysseus, who set sail unwillingly –
At this hour dead or living? – he alone, once yoked,
With good will shared my burden.

                                   For affairs of State,
And this feared disaffection, we will set a day
For assembly and debate among our citizens,                                  900
And take wise counsel; where disease wants remedy,
Fire or the knife shall purge this body for its good.

Now to my home, to stand at my own altar-hearth
And give Heaven my first greeting, whose protecting power
Sent forth, and brought me home again. May Victory,
My guardian hitherto, walk constant at my side!

*Enter* CLYTEMNESTRA *attended by* MAIDS *holding a long drape of crimson
silk.*

CLYTEMNESTRA. Elders and citizens of Argos! In your presence now
I will speak, unashamed, a wife's love for her husband.
With time dies diffidence. What I shall tell I learnt
Untaught, from my own long endurance, these ten years                        910
My husband spent under the walls of Ilion.
First, that a woman should sit forlorn at home, unmanned,
Is a crying grief. Then, travellers, one on other's heels,
Dismay the palace, each with worse news than the last.
Why, if my lord received as many wounds as Rumour,
Plying from Troy to Argos, gave him, he is a net,
All holes! Or had he died each time report repeated
News of his death – see him, a second Geryon,
Boasting his monstrous right, his thrice-spread quilt of earth –
A grave for each death, each body! Many times despair                        920
At a cruel message noosed my throat in a hung cord,
Which force against my will untied.

                                   These fears explain
Why our child is not here to give you fitting welcome,

Our true love's pledge, Orestes. Have no uneasiness.
He is in Phocis, a guest of Strophius your well-tried friend,
Who warned me of peril from two sources: first, the risk
Threatening your life at Troy; then, if conspiracy
Matured to popular revolt in Argos, fear
Of man's instinct to trample on his fallen lord.
Such was his reasoning — surely free from all suspicion.     930

For me — the springing torrents of my tears are all
Drawn dry, no drop left; and my sleepless eyes are sore
With weeping by the lamp long lit for you in vain.
In dreams, the tenuous tremors of the droning gnat
Roused me from dreadful visions of more deaths for you
Than could be compassed in the hour that slept with me.

There is no dearer sight than shelter after storm;
No escape sweeter than from siege of circumstance.
Now, after siege and storm endured, my happy heart
Welcomes my husband, faithful watch-dog of his home,     940
Our ship's firm anchor, towering pillar that upholds
This royal roof; as dear, as to a father's hope
His longed-for son, a spring to thirsty travellers,
Or sight of land unlooked-for to men long at sea.

Such praise I hold his due; and may Heaven's jealousy
Acquit us; our past suffering has been enough.

Now, dearest husband, come, step from your chariot.
But do not set to earth, my lord, the conquering foot
That trod down Troy. Servants, do as you have been bidden;
Make haste, carpet his way with crimson tapestries,     950
Spread silk before your master's feet; Justice herself
Shall lead him to a home he never hoped to see.
All other matters forethought, never lulled by sleep,
Shall order justly as the will of Heaven decrees.
    *Clytemnestra's* MAIDS *spread a path of crimson cloth from the chariot to*
      *the palace door.*
    AGAMEMNON. Daughter of Leda, guardian of my house, your speech
Matches its theme, my absence; for both were prolonged.
Praise fitly spoken should be heard on other lips.
And do not with these soft attentions woman me,
Nor prostrate like a fawning Persian mouth at me
Your loud addresses; not with your spread cloths invite     960
Envy of gods, for honours due to gods alone.
I count it dangerous, being mortal, to set foot
On rich embroidered silks. I would be reverenced
As man, not god. The praise of fame rings clear without
These frills and fancy foot-rugs; and the god's best gift
Is a mind free from folly. Call him fortunate
Whom the end of life finds harboured in tranquillity.
    CLYTEMNESTRA. There is the sea — who shall exhaust the sea? — which
      teems
With purple dye costly as silver, a dark stream
For staining of fine stuffs, unceasingly renewed.     970
This house has store of crimson, by Heaven's grace, enough
For one outpouring; you are no king of beggary!

Had oracles prescribed it, I would have dedicated
Twenty such cloths to trampling, if by care and cost
I might ensure safe journey's end for this one life.
Now you are come to your dear home, your altar-hearth,
The tree, its root refreshed, spreads leaf to the high beams
To veil us from the dog-star's heat. Your loved return
Shines now like Spring warmth after winter; but when Zeus
From the unripe grape presses his wine, then through the house     980
Heat dies, and coolness comes, as through this royal door
Enters its lord, perfected to receive his own.

   AGAMEMNON. I have said how I would enter with an easy mind.
   CLYTEMNESTRA. Tell me — not contrary to your resolve — one thing.
   AGAMEMNON. Be sure I shall do nothing against my resolve.
   CLYTEMNESTRA. Might you have vowed to the gods, in danger, such an act?
   AGAMEMNON. Yes, if someone with knowledge had prescribed it me.
   CLYTEMNESTRA. Imagine Priam conqueror: what would he have done?
   AGAMEMNON. Walked on embroidered satin, I have little doubt.
   CLYTEMNESTRA. Then why humble your heart to men's censorious tongue?  990
   AGAMEMNON. Why indeed? Yet the people's voice speaks with great power.
   CLYTEMNESTRA. Greatness wins hate. Unenvied is unenviable.
   AGAMEMNON. It does not suit a woman to be combative.
   CLYTEMNESTRA. Yet it suits greatness also to accept defeat.
   AGAMEMNON. Why, here's a battle! What would you not give to win?
   CLYTEMNESTRA. Yield! You are victor: give me too my victory.
   AGAMEMNON. Since you're resolved — [*To an attendant*] Come kneel;
      untie my shoes; dismiss
These leathern slaves that smooth my path. And as I tread
This deep-sea treasure, may no watchful envious god
Glance from afar. It offends modesty, that I     1000
Should dare with unwashed feet to soil these costly rugs,
Worth weight for weight of silver, spoiling my own house!
But let that pass.

          Take in this girl and treat her well.
God will reward from heaven a gentle conqueror.
Slavery is a yoke no one bears willingly; and she
Came to me by the army's gift, of all Troy's wealth
The chosen jewel.
Now, since I have been subdued to obedience in this matter,
Treading on purple I will go into my house.
   CLYTEMNESTRA. Eleleleleu!     1010

*A prolonged triumphant cry, which the* CHORUS *accept as a formal celebration of the victor's return, while only* CASSANDRA *understands its true meaning.* AGAMEMNON *walks alone along the purple path and enters the palace.*

   CLYTEMNESTRA. Zeus, Zeus, Fulfiller! Now fulfil these prayers of mine;
And let thy will accomplish all that is thy will!

CLYTEMNESTRA *enters the palace.* AGAMEMNON'S *chariot is taken away by attendants.* CASSANDRA *remains seated in the second chariot.*

   CHORUS. What is this persistent dread
    Haunting, hovering to show
    Signs to my foreboding soul,
    While unbidden and unpaid
    Throbs the prophet in my veins,
    While persuasive confidence

That should rule the heart, and scorn
Fantasies of cloudy dreams,                          1020
Trembles, and resigns her throne?
Once before, though far away,
My heart knew the pregnant hour,
When at Troy our sailors' shouts,
As they coiled their sheets astern,
Chimed with my triumphal song;
And the fleet set sail for home.

Then was guessing; now I see
With these eyes the fleet returned.
Yet my spirit knows again                            1030
The foreboding hour; again
Sings, by untaught instinct, that
Sad, familiar, fatal dirge;
Yields her kingdom in the flesh,
Daunted with surmise, and feels
Pang and pulse of groin and gut,
Blood in riot, brain awhirl,
Nerve and tissue taut, and knows
Truth must prick, where flesh is sore.
Yet I pray, may time and truth                       1040
Shame my fears; may prophecy
Vanish, and fulfilment fail!

When fortune flowers too lushly,
Decay, her envious neighbour,
Stands eager to invade;
Glory's brief hours are numbered,
And what has flowered must fade.
Bold in success, ambition
Sails on, where rocks lie hidden,
Strikes, and her debt is paid.                       1050
Yet, debts may be compounded:
When Thracian storm-winds threaten,
The merchant, for his silver,
With pious prayers devotes
A tithe in ample measure;
Into the sea he slings it,
And safe his vessel floats.
The house that offers to the envious Powers
Its wealthy surplus will not fail and die;
Zeus to their prayers will bounteously reply,        1060
Bless each year's furrowed fields with sun and showers,
Bid harvests teem, and fear of famine fly.

But when, from flesh born mortal,
Man's blood on earth lies fallen,
A dark, unfading stain,
Who then by incantations
Can bid blood live again?
Zeus in pure wisdom ended
That sage's skill who summoned
Dead flesh to rise from darkness                     1070
And live a second time;

Lest murder cheaply mended
Invite men's hands to crime.
Were I not sure that always
Events and causes hold
Sequence divinely ordered,
And next by last controlled,
Speech would forestall reluctance,
Voice thoughts I dare not fathom,
And leave no fear untold.                                    1080
But now my tongue mutters in darkness, sharing
The heart's distress, tormented with desire
To achieve some timely word, and still despairing;
While my dumb spirit smoulders with deep fire.

CLYTEMNESTRA *comes to the palace door.*

CLYTEMNESTRA. You too, Cassandra there, do you hear me? Get indoors.
You may thank Zeus, this palace bears you no ill-will;
You shall stand near our sovereign altar, and partake,
With many other slaves, the cleansing ritual.
Then leave that chariot; do not be proud. They say
Heracles once was sold, and learnt to eat slaves' bread.          1090
If such misfortune falls, and there's no help for it —
A house of long-established wealth is generous;
Where meagre hopes reap opulence, it goes hard with slaves.
Here you shall have your due — what's customary, and more.
CHORUS. It was to you she spoke. She waits. Was it not clear?
Since you're a captive in the toils of destiny
Obey, if you understand. Or do you choose defiance?
CLYTEMNESTRA. If she's not crazed, she will obey; unless she speaks
Some weird unheard-of tongue, like swallows twittering.
CHORUS. Come, now; her bidding is the best that's possible.       1100
Leave sitting in that chariot; obey, go in.
CLYTEMNESTRA. I have no time to spend standing out here. Already
Victims for sacrifice wait at the central hearth.
If you understand what I have said, come in at once;
If not, [*to an attendant*] since she's a foreigner, explain by signs.
            [*An attendant makes signs to* CASSANDRA *to enter the palace.*
CHORUS. It's clear enough the girl needs an interpreter.
She has the look of some wild creature newly trapped.
CLYTEMNESTRA. Why, she is mad, hears only her own frenzied thoughts.
Has she not left her city levelled with the ground? —
Yet has not sense enough to accept her owner's bit               1110
Till she has frothed her rage out from a bloody mouth.
I will spend words no longer, to be thus ignored.
                        [CLYTEMNESTRA *goes into the palace.*
CHORUS. I feel pity, not anger. Come, poor girl, step down;
Yield to this hard necessity; wear your new yoke.
                [CASSANDRA *steps down. She sees the statue of Apollo.*
CASSANDRA. O Apollo! Oh, oh! No, no, no, no! O Earth! O Apollo!
CHORUS. Why name Apollo with this wail of agony?
He is no god of mourning, to be so invoked.
CASSANDRA. Oh, oh! O horror! O Earth! O Apollo, Apollo!
CHORUS. Again she utters blasphemy, to call Apollo,
Whose godhead may not stand in the same house with grief.        1120

CASSANDRA. Apollo, Apollo! Leader of journeys, my destroyer!
All this way you have led me, to destroy me again!
    CHORUS. She is inspired to speak of her own sufferings.
The prophetic power stays with her even in slavery.
    CASSANDRA. Apollo, Apollo! Leader of journeys, my destroyer!
Where have you led me? Oh! what fearful house is this?
    CHORUS. Does not prophecy tell you this is Atreus' palace?
*I* tell you, then; so call it, and you will speak the truth.
    CASSANDRA. No! but a house that hates
      The gods; whose very stones                                              1130
Bear guilty witness to a bloody act;
      That hides within these gates
      Remnants of bodies hacked,
      And murdered children's bones!
    CHORUS. This prophetess goes to it like a keen-scented hound;
We know the trail she follows, and it leads to blood.
    CASSANDRA. To blood — I know. See there,
      The witness that they bear —
Those children weeping for their own blood shed,
      For their own tender flesh,                                              1140
      That cruel, nameless dish
      From which their father fed!
    CHORUS. We had all heard of your prophetic power; but this
Requires no prophecy to tell us of —
    CASSANDRA.                Ah, ah!
      Oh, shame! Conspiracy!
      A heart obsessed with hate
      And lurking to betray
      Pollutes this house anew
      With deadly injury
      Where deepest love was due!                                              1150
Surprised, unarmed, how can he fight with Fate?
      And help is far away.
    CHORUS. The first we understand — all Argos speaks of it;
But to this second prophecy I have no key.
    CASSANDRA. Shame on her! She will stand —
      Would there were room for doubt! —
      To cleanse her lawful lord
      From guilt of war — and then —
      How can I speak the word?
      This cleansing ritual                                              1160
      Shall serve his burial!
      Despairing hands reach out,
      Snared by a stronger hand!
    CHORUS. Still I am baffled by her riddling utterance;
What can one make of prophecy so recondite?
    CASSANDRA. There, there! O terror! What is this new sight?
A hunting-net, Death's weapon of attack!
And she who hunts is she who shared his bed.
Howl, Furies, howl, you bloody ravening pack,
Gorged with this house's blood, yet thirsting still;                                              1170
The victim bleeds: come, Fiends, and drink your fill!
    CHORUS. What fiends are these you call to bay at Death?
Your ghastly hymn has paled your cheek; and pale
The blood shrinks to your heart, as when men die

Sword-struck in battle, pulse and vision fail,
And life's warm colours fly;
See, how her utterance chokes her laboured breath!
   CASSANDRA. Help! Look, a nightmare! What? will cow gore bull,
The black-horned monarch? Save him, drag him away!
The treacherous water's poured, the lustral bath is full;       1180
She holds him in a trap made like a gown —
She strikes! He crashes down!
Listen! It is treachery, treachery, I say!
   CHORUS. Although I claim no special skill in oracles,
Her words, I feel, augur no good. Yet, after all,
What good news ever comes to men through oracles?
Prophets find bad news useful. Why, the primary aim
Of all their wordy wisdom is to make men gape.
   CASSANDRA. O fear, and fear again!
     O pity! Not alone                       1190
     He suffers; with his pain
     Mingled I mourn my own!
     Cruel Apollo! Why,
     Why have you led me here?
     Only that I may share
     The death that he must die!
   CHORUS. She is insane, poor girl, or god-possessed,
And for herself alone she makes this wail,
Unwearied in her tuneless song;
As the shrill nightingale                      1200
Unburdens her distracted breast,
Sobbing *Itun, Itun,* remembering all her wrong.
   CASSANDRA. Bitter was her ordeal;
     Yet by the kind gods' wish
     The lovely robe she wears
     Is feathered wings; and even
     The plaint she pours to heaven,
     Note answering note with tears,
     Rings sweet. But I must feel
     The parting of the flesh                 1210
     Before the whetted steel.
   CHORUS. Whence come these violent miseries, god-inspired
Yet void of meaning? Why with voice like doom
Intone these horrors in heart-searing words?
     Who marked the oracular road
     Whose evil terms you trace?
   CASSANDRA. [*Changing from the shrill declamation of prophecy to the
    quiet sadness of mourning*] O Paris and his passion!
     O marriage-bed that slew
     His family and city!
     O sweet Scamander river                1220
     Our thirsting fathers knew,
     By whose loved banks I grew!
     But soon the dark Cocytus
     And Acheron shall echo
     My prophecies, and witness
     Whether my words are true.
   CHORUS. Paris's marriage! This at last is clear
To any child. Yet in her muttered fear

Lies more than meets the sight:
With stunning pain, like a brute serpent's bite,                              1230
Her whispered cry crashes upon my ear.

    CASSANDRA. O Ilion and her passion!
      O city burnt and razed!
      O fires my father kindled
      To keep his towers defiant!
      O blood of beasts he offered
      From every herd that grazed!
      Yet no propitiation
      Could save her sons from dying
      As I foretold they would;                                        1240
      And I will join my brothers,
      And soon the ground will welcome
      My warm and flowing blood.

    CHORUS. Once more her utterance adds like to like.
      Tell us, what god is he, so merciless,
      Whose grievous hand can strike
      Such deathly music from your mournful soul,
      Arrows of prophecy whose course and goal
      I seek, but cannot guess?

    CASSANDRA. Then listen. Now my prophecy shall no more peep      1250
From under shy veils like a new-made bride, but blow
A bounding gale towards the sunrise, on whose surge
A crime more fearful than my murder shall at once
Sweep into blazing light. Without more mystery
I will instruct you; but first testify how close
I scent the trail of bloody guilt incurred long since.
Under this roof live day and night a ghastly choir
Venting their evil chant in hideous harmony;
Drunk with men's blood, boldly established here, they hold
Unbroken revel, Fiends of the blood royal, whom none               1260
Can exorcize. Drinking they sit, and with their songs
Drive folly first to crime; the crime performed, in turn
They spew out the defiler of his brother's bed!
Do I miss? Or has my arrow found a mark you know?
Or am I 'lying prophet', 'gipsy', 'tale-spinner'?
Come, on your oath, bear witness: the foul history
Of Atreus' palace, sin for sin, is known to me!

    CHORUS. The holiest oath could help but little. Yet I marvel
That you, bred overseas in a foreign tongue, unfold
Our city's past as truly as if you had been here.                     1270

    CASSANDRA. Apollo, god of prophecy, gave me this office.
    CHORUS. Did *he* lust for your mortal body, though a god?
    CASSANDRA. Yes. Until now I was ashamed to speak of it.
    CHORUS. We all are more reserved when we are prosperous.
    CASSANDRA. He urged me hard, made warmest protest of his love.
    CHORUS. And did you lie together? Had you child by him?
    CASSANDRA. I gave my word, and broke it — to the God of Words.
    CHORUS. Already god-possessed with the prophetic art?
    CASSANDRA. I had foretold already the whole doom of Troy.
    CHORUS. Surely the god was angry? Did he punish you?           1280
    CASSANDRA. After my sin, no one believed one word I spoke.
    CHORUS. To us your prophecies seem all too credible.
    CASSANDRA. Oh! Oh!

Horror and sin! Again the anguish of true vision —
Yes, sin and horror! — racks and ravages my brain.
Look! See them sit, there on the wall, like forms in dreams,
Children butchered like lambs by their own kindred. See,
What do they carry in their hands? O piteous sight!
It is their own flesh — limb and rib and heart they hold,
Distinct and horrible, the food their father ate!                    1290
I tell you, for this crime revenge grows hot: there lurks
In the home lair — as regent, say — a cowardly lion
Who plots against his master absent at the war;
While the Commander Lion who uprooted Troy,
Met by the fawning tongue, the bright obsequious ear,
Of the vile plotting she-hound, does not know what wounds
Venomed with hidden vengeance she prepares for him.
Female shall murder male: what kind of brazenness
Is that? What loathsome beast lends apt comparison?
A basilisk? Or Scylla's breed, living in rocks                        1300
To drown men in their ships — a raging shark of hell,
Dreaming of steel thrust at her husband's unarmed flesh?
You heard her superb bluff, that cry of triumph, raised
As if for a hard battle won, disguised as joy
At his safe home-coming? You are incredulous —
No matter — I say, no matter; what will come will come.
Soon you will see with your own eyes, and pity me,
And wish my prophecy had not been half so true.
     CHORUS. Thyestes' feast of children's flesh we understand;
Horror gives place to wonder at your true account;                    1310
The rest outstrips our comprehension; we give up.
     CASSANDRA. I say Agamemnon shall lie dead before your eyes.
     CHORUS. Silence, you wretched outcast — or speak wholesome words!
     CASSANDRA. No wholesome word can purge the poison of that truth.
     CHORUS. None, if it is to be; but may the gods forbid!
     CASSANDRA. You turn to prayer: others meanwhile prepare to kill.
     CHORUS. What man can be the source of such polluting sin?
     CASSANDRA. What man? You miss the main point of my prophecies.
     CHORUS. How could such murder be contrived? This baffles me.
     CASSANDRA. Yet I speak good Greek — all too good.
     CHORUS.                                        The oracles           1320
Of Delphi are good Greek, but hard to understand.
     CASSANDRA. Oh, oh! For pity, Apollo! Where can I escape?
This death you send me is impatient, merciless!
She, this lioness in human form, who when her lord
Was absent paired with a wolf, will take my wretched life.
Like one who mixes medicine for her enemies,
Now, while she whets the dagger for her husband's heart,
She vows to drug his dram with a memory of me,
And make him pledge my safe arrival — in my blood.

     This robe — why should I wear what mocks me? Why still keep        1330
This sceptre, these oracular garlands round my neck?
Before I die I'll make an end of you ... and you ...
Go, with my curse, go! Thus I pay my debt to you!
                              [*Trampling them on the ground.*
Go, make some other woman rich in misery!
And let Apollo see, and witness what I do —

He who once saw me in these same insignia
Scorned, jeered at like some gipsy quack, by enemies
And friends alike, called starveling, beggar, conjuror,
Pitiable wretch — all this I bore; and now Apollo,
Who gave a portion of his own prescience to me,                    1340
Brings me from Ilion here to this death-reeking porch,
Where I shall never court crass unbelief again,
Where not my father's hearthstone but the slaughterer's block
Waits for me, warm already with a victim's blood.

    Yet we shall not die unregarded by the gods.
A third shall come to raise our cause, a son resolved
To kill his mother, honouring his father's blood.
He, now a wandering exile, shall return to set
The apex on this tower of crime his race has built.
A great oath, sealed in sight of gods, binds him to exact          1350
Full penance for his father's corpse stretched dead in dust.

    Why then should I lament? Am I so pitiable?
I have watched Fate unfold her pattern: Troy endured
What she endured; her captor now, by Heaven's decree,
Ends thus. I have done with tears. I will endure my death.
O gates of the dark world, I greet you as I come!
Let me receive, I pray, a single mortal stroke,
Sink without spasm, feel the warm blood's gentle ebb,
Embrace death for my comfort, and so close my eyes.
    CHORUS. O woman deep in wisdom as in suffering,        1360
You have told us much. Yet, if you have true foreknowledge
Of your own death, why, like an ox for sacrifice,
Move thus towards the altar with intrepid step?
    CASSANDRA. Friends, there is no escape, none — once the hour has come.
    CHORUS. Yet last to go gains longest time.
    CASSANDRA.                                   This is the day.
Retreat wins little.
    CHORUS.            Courage and destiny in you
Are proudly matched.
    CASSANDRA.            The happy never hear such praise.
    CHORUS. Yet a brave death lends brightness to mortality.
    CASSANDRA. O father! O my brothers! All your brightness dead! . . .
I go. Now in the land of the defeated I                            1370
Will mourn my end and Agamemnon's. I have lived.
             [*She goes towards the door; then with a cry turns back.*
    CHORUS. What is it? What do you see? What terror turns you back?
             [CASSANDRA *gasps, with a sound of choking.*
    CHORUS. You gasp, as if some nausea choked your very soul.
    CASSANDRA. There is a smell of murder. The walls drip with blood.
    CHORUS. The altar's ready. This is the smell of sacrifice.
    CASSANDRA. It is most like the air that rises from a grave.
    CHORUS. You mean the Syrian perfume sprinkled for the feast?
    CASSANDRA. I am not like a bird scared at an empty bush,
Trembling for nothing. Wait: when you shall see my death
Atoned with death, woman for woman; when in place                  1380
Of him whom marriage cursed another man shall fall:
Then witness for me — these and all my prophecies
Were utter truth. This I request before I die.

CHORUS. To die is sad: sadder, to know death fore-ordained.
CASSANDRA. Yet one word more, a prophecy — or, if a dirge,
At least not mine alone. In this sun's light — my last —
I pray: when the sword's edge requites my captor's blood,
Then may his murderers, dying, with that debt pay too
For her they killed in chains, their unresisting prey!

Alas for human destiny! Man's happiest hours          1390
Are pictures drawn in shadow. Then ill fortune comes,
And with two strokes the wet sponge wipes the drawing out.
And grief itself's hardly more pitiable than joy. [*She goes into the palace.*

   CHORUS. Of fortune no man tastes his fill.
     While pointing envy notes his store,
     And tongues extol his happiness,
     Man surfeited will hunger still.
     For who grows weary of success,
     Or turns good fortune from his door
     Bidding her trouble him no more?          1400

     Our king, whom Fortune loves to bless,
     By the gods' will has taken Troy,
     And honour crowns his safe return.
     If now, for blood shed long ago,
     In penance due his blood must flow,
     And if his murderers must earn
     Death upon death, and Fate stands so,
     I ask, what mortal man can claim
     That he alone was born to enjoy
     A quiet life, and an untarnished name?          1410
          [AGAMEMNON'S *voice is heard from inside the palace.*
AGAMEMNON. Help, help! I am wounded, murdered, here in the inner
   room!
   CHORUS. Hush, listen! Who cried 'Murder'? Do you know that voice?
   AGAMEMNON. Help, help again! Murder — a second, mortal blow!
   CHORUS I. That groan tells me the deed is done. It was the king.
Come, let's decide together on the safest plan.
   2. This is what I advise — to send a herald round
Bidding the citizens assemble here in arms.
   3. Too slow. I say we should burst in at once, and catch
Murder in the act, before the blood dries on the sword.
   4. I share your feeling — that is what we ought to do,          1420
Or something of that kind. Now is the time to act.
   5. It's plain what this beginning points to: the assassins
Mean to establish a tyrannical regime.
   6. Yes — while we talk and talk; but action, spurning sleep,
Tramples the gentle face of caution in the dust.
   7. I can suggest no plan that might prove practical.
I say, let those who took this step propose the next.
   8. I'm of the same opinion. If the king is dead,
I know no way to make him live by argument.
   9. Then shall we patiently drag out our servile years          1430
Governed by these disgraces of our royal house?
   10. No, no! Intolerable! Who would not rather die? —
A milder fate than living under tyranny!
   11. Wait; not too fast. What is our evidence? Those groans?
Are we to prophesy from them that the king's dead?

12. We must be certain; this excitement's premature.
Guessing and certain knowledge are two different things.
    CHORUS. I find this view supported on all sides: that we
Make full enquiry what has happened to the king.
    *The palace doors open, revealing* CLYTEMNESTRA. *At her feet* AGAMEMNON
    *lies dead, in a silver bath, and wrapped in a voluminous purple robe.*
    *On his body lies* CASSANDRA, *also dead.*
    CLYTEMNESTRA. I said, not long since, many things to match the time;   1440
All which, that time past, without shame I here unsay.
How else, when one prepares death for an enemy
Who seems a friend — how else net round the deadly trap
High enough to forestall the victim's highest leap?
A great while I have pondered on this trial of strength.
At long last the pitched battle came, and victory:
Here where I struck I stand and see my task achieved.
Yes, this is my work, and I claim it. To prevent
Flight or resistance foiling death, I cast on him,
As one who catches fish, a vast voluminous net,   1450
That walled him round with endless wealth of woven folds;
And then I struck him, twice. Twice he cried out and groaned;
And then fell limp. And as he lay I gave a third
And final blow, my thanks for prayers fulfilled, to Zeus,
Lord of the lower region, Saviour — of dead men!
So falling he belched forth his life; with cough and retch
There spurted from him bloody foam in a fierce jet,
And spreading, spattered me with drops of crimson rain;
While I exulted as the sown cornfield exults
Drenched with the dew of heaven when buds burst forth in Spring.   1460

    So stands the case, Elders of Argos. You may be
As you choose, glad or sorry; I am jubilant.
And, were it seemly over a *dead* man to pour
Thankoffering for safe journey, surely Justice here
Allows it, here demands it; so enriched a wine
Of wickedness this man stored in his house, and now
Returned, drains his own cursed cup to the last dregs.
    CHORUS. The brute effrontery of your speech amazes us.
To boast so shamelessly over your husband's corpse!
    CLYTEMNESTRA. You speak as to some thoughtless woman: you are wrong. 1470
My pulse beats firm. I tell what you already know:
Approve or censure, as you will; all's one to me.
This is my husband, Agamemnon, now stone dead;
His death the work of my right hand, whose craftsmanship
Justice acknowledges. There lies the simple truth.
    CHORUS. Vile woman! What unnatural food or drink,
      Malignant root, brine from the restless sea,
      Transformed you, that your nature did not shrink
      From foulest guilt? Argos will execrate
      Your nameless murder with one voice of hate,   1480
      Revoke your portion with the just and free,
      And drive you outlawed from our Argive gate.
    CLYTEMNESTRA. Yes! Now you righteously mulct *me* with banishment,
Award me public curses, roars of civic hate.
Why, once before, did you not dare oppose this man?
Who with as slight compunction as men butcher sheep,

When his own fields were white with flocks, must sacrifice
His child, and my own darling, whom my pain brought forth —
He killed her for a charm to stop the Thracian wind!
He was the one you should have driven from Argos; he,      1490
Marked with his daughter's blood, was ripe for punishment.
But *my* act shocks your ears, whets your judicial wrath!
Your threats doubtless rely on force — you have your men
And weapons: try your strength in fair fight against mine.
Win, and you may command me. If — please Heaven — you lose,
Old as you are, you shall be taught some wisdom yet.
    CHORUS. Such boasts show folly in a crafty mind.
      So surely as your robe blazons your crime
      In those red drops, shall your own head bow low
      Under a bloody stroke. Wait but the time:      1500
      Friendless, dishonoured, outcast, you shall find
      Your debt fall due, and suffer blow for blow.
    CLYTEMNESTRA. Is it so? Then you shall hear the righteous oath I swear.
By Justice, guardian of my child, now perfected;
By her avenging Fury, at whose feet I poured
His blood: I have no fear that *his* avenger's tread
Shall shake this house, while my staunch ally now as then,
Aegisthus, kindles on my hearth the ancestral fire.
With such a shield, strength marches boldly on. Meanwhile,
He who was sweet to every Trojan Chryseis,      1510
And soured my life, lies here; with him his prisoner,
His faithful soothsayer, who shared his berth, and knew
Sailors' lasciviousness; their ends both richly earned.
He — as you see him; she first, like the dying swan,
Sang her death-song, and now lies in her lover's clasp.
Brought as a variant to the pleasures of my bed,
She lends an added relish now to victory.
    CHORUS. Come, look on him, and weep.
      O that some merciful swift fate,
      Not wasting-sick nor wry with pain,      1520
      Would bid me share his ever-endless sleep!
      Low lies the kindly guardian of our State,
      Who fought ten years to win
      Redress for woman's sin;
      Now by a woman slain.

      Helen! Infatuate Helen! You who spilt
      Beneath Troy's wall lives without number! You
      Now on your house have fixed a lasting guilt
      Which every age will tell anew.
      Surely, that day you fled beyond recall,      1530
      A curse of grief already grew
      Deep-rooted in this royal hall.
    CLYTEMNESTRA. Is fact so gross a burden?
      Put up no prayers for death;
      Nor turn your spleen on Helen,
      As if her act had ordered
      The fate of fighting thousands
      And robbed their souls of breath;
      Or from her fault alone
      Such cureless grief had grown.      1540

CHORUS. Spirit of hate, whose strong curse weighs
      Hard on the house and heirs of Tantalus,
      Your power it is engenders thus
      In woman's brain such evil art,
      And darkens all my bitter days.
      It is your hateful form I see rejoice,
      Standing like crow on carrion; your voice
      Whose execrable song affronts both ear and heart.
CLYTEMNESTRA. You now speak more in wisdom,
      Naming the thrice-gorged Fury                                1550
      That hates and haunts our race.
      Hers is the thirst of slaughter,
      Still slaked with feud and vengeance,
      Till, with each wrong requited,
      A new thirst takes its place.
CHORUS. This grievous power whose wrath you celebrate
      With cursed truth, no royal house's fall,
      No mad catastrophe, can ever state.
      O piteous mystery! Is Zeus not lord?
      Zeus, Zeus, alas! doer and source of all?                   1560
      Could even this horror be, without his sovereign word?

      Sad, silent king! How shall I mourn your death?
      How find the heart's true word, to prove me friend?
      Here where you spent your dying breath,
      Caught by the ruthless falsehood of a wife,
      In the foul spider's web fast bound you lie.
      Unholy rest, and most ignoble end —
      That man like beast should die
      Pierced with a two-edged knife!
CLYTEMNESTRA. This murder's mine, you clamour.                    1570
      I was his wife; but henceforth
      My name from his be freed!
      Dressed in my form, a phantom
      Of vengeance, old and bitter,
      On that obscene host, Atreus,
      For his abhorrent deed,
      Has poured this blood in payment,
      That here on Justice' altar
      A man for babes should bleed.
CHORUS. And are you guiltless? Some revengeful Power             1580
      Stood, maybe, at your side; but of this blood
      Who will, who could absolve you? Hour by hour
      On his unyielding course the black-robed King,
      Pressing to slaughter, swells the endless flood
      Of crimson life by pride and hate released
      From brothers' veins — till the due reckoning,
      When the dried gore shall melt, and Ares bring
      Justice at last for that unnatural feast.

      Sad, silent king! How shall I mourn your death?
      How find the heart's true word, to prove me friend?         1590
      Here where you spent your dying breath,
      Caught by the ruthless falsehood of a wife,
      In the foul spider's web fast bound you lie.

Unholy rest, and most ignoble end —
That man like beast should die
Pierced with a two-edged knife!
CLYTEMNESTRA. The guile I used to kill him
He used himself the first,
When he by guile uprooted
The tender plant he gave me, 1600
And made this house accurst.
When on my virgin daughter
His savage sword descended,
My tears in rivers ran;
If now by savage sword-thrust
His ageing days are ended,
Let shame and conscience ban
His boasts, where he pays forfeit
For wrong his guile began.
CHORUS. Where, where lies Right? Reason despairs her powers, 1610
Mind numbly gropes, her quick resources spent.
Our throne endangered, and disaster near,
Where can I turn? I fear
Thunder that cracks foundations, blood-red showers;
The light rain slacks — the deluge is in store.
Justice, in harmony with Fate's intent,
Hardens her hold to shake the earth once more.

O earth, O earth! Would that some timely chance
Had laid me in your lap, before my eyes
Had seen him laid so low, 1620
Lord of this silver-walled inheritance!
Who will inter him? Who lament the dead?
Will *you* wear mourning for disguise?
Bewail the husband whom your own hand killed?
For his high glories offer gifts of lies?
Since Justice answers, No!
By whom shall tears of honest love be shed,
His graveside ritual of praise fulfilled?
CLYTEMNESTRA. That question's not your business.
I felled him; I despatched him; 1630
And I will earth his bones.
No troops from house or city
Shall beat their breasts and lay him
In vaults of bronze and marble
With seemly civic groans.
But, as is fit, his daughter
Shall meet him near the porchway
Of those who perished young;
His loved Iphigenia
With loving arms shall greet him, 1640
And gagged and silent tongue.
CHORUS. Reproach answers reproach; truth darkens still.
She strikes the striker; he who dared to kill
Pays the full forfeit. While Zeus holds his throne,
This maxim holds on earth: *the sinner dies.*
That is God's law. Oh, who can exorcize
This breeding curse, this canker that has grown

Into these walls, to plague them at its will?

CLYTEMNESTRA. *The sinner dies:* you have reached the truth at last.
Now to the Powers that persecute                                      1650
Our race I offer a sworn pact:
With this harsh deed and bitter fact
*I* am content; let *them* forget the past,
Leave us for ever, and oppress
Some other house with murderous wickedness.
I ask no weight of wealth;
For me it will suffice
To purchase, at this price,
For our long sickness, health.

*Enter* AEGISTHUS.

AEGISTHUS. O happy day, when Justice comes into her own!            1660
Now I believe that gods, who dwell above the earth,
See what men suffer, and award a recompense:
Here, tangled in a net the avenging Furies wove,
He lies, a sight to warm my heart; and pays his blood
In full atonement for his father's treacherous crime.

Here is the story plain. There was dispute between
Atreus, Agamemnon's father, who ruled Argos then,
And my father Thyestes, his own brother; whom
Atreus drove out from home and city. He came back;
Sat as a piteous suppliant at Atreus' hearth;                        1670
Gained his request — in part: his own blood did not stain
His childhood's home. But Atreus, this man's father, gave
His guest, my father, a host's gift; a gift more full
Of eagerness than love. He feigned a feasting-day,
And amidst lavish meats served him his own sons' flesh.
The feet and the splayed fingers he concealed, putting
The other parts, unrecognizably chopped small,
Above them. Each guest had his table; and this dish
Was set before my father. He, in ignorance,
At once took that which prompted no close scrutiny,                  1680
And tasted food from which, as you now see, our house
Has not recovered. Then he recognized, in all
Its loathsomeness, what had been done. With one deep groan,
Back from his chair, vomiting murdered flesh, he fell;
Cursed Pelops' race with an inexorable curse;
With his foot sent the table crashing wide, and screamed,
'So crash to ruin the whole house of Tantalus!'

That deed gave birth to what you now see here, this death.
I planned his killing, as was just: I was the third
Child of Thyestes, then a brat in baby-clothes;                      1690
Spared, and sent off with my distracted father, till,
Full-grown, Justice restored me to my native land.
I, from a distance, plotted this whole evil snare,
And caught my man. Thus satisfied, I could die now,
Seeing Agamemnon in the trap of Justice, dead.

CHORUS. Aegisthus, we acquit you of insults to the dead.
But since you claim that you alone laid the whole plot,
And thus, though absent, took his blood upon your hands,
I tell you plainly, your own life is forfeited;

Justice will curse you, Argive hands will stone you dead.                    1700
 AEGISTHUS. So, this is how you lecture, from the lower deck,
The master on the bridge? Then you shall learn, though old,
How harsh a thing is discipline, when reverend years
Lack wisdom. Chains and the distress of hunger are
A magic medicine, of great power to school the mind.
Does not this sight bid you reflect? Then do not kick
Against the goad, lest you should stumble, and be hurt.
 CHORUS. You woman! While he went to fight, you stayed at home;
Seduced his wife meanwhile; and then, against a man
Who led an army, *you* could scheme this murder! Pah!                    1710
 AEGISTHUS. You still use words that have in them the seed of tears.
Your voice is most unlike the voice of Orpheus: he
Bound all who heard him with delight; your childish yelps
Annoy us, and will fasten bonds on you yourselves.
With hard control you will prove more amenable.
 CHORUS. Control! Are we to see *you* king of Argos — you,
Who, after plotting the king's murder, did not dare
To lift the sword yourself?
 AEGISTHUS.    To lure him to the trap
Was plainly woman's work; I, an old enemy,
Was suspect. Now, helped by his wealth, I will attempt                    1720
To rule in Argos. The refractory shall not
Be fed fat like show-horses, but shall feel the yoke —
A heavy one. Hunger and darkness joined will soon
Soften resistance.
 CHORUS.  Then, if you're so bold, why not
Yourself with your own hands plunder your enemy?
Instead, a woman, whose life makes this earth unclean
And flouts the gods of Argos, helped you murder him!
Oh, does Orestes live? Kind Fortune, bring him home,
To set against these two his sword invincible!
 AEGISTHUS. Then, since your treason's militant, you shall soon learn     1730
That it is foolish to insult authority.
Ready, there! Forward, guards! [*Armed soldiers rush in.*] Here's work for
 you. Each man
Handle his sword.
 CHORUS.  Our swords are ready. We can die.
 AEGISTHUS. 'Die'! We accept the omen. Fortune hold the stakes!
 CLYTEMNESTRA. Stop, stop, Aegisthus, dearest! No more violence!
When this first harvest ripens we'll reap grief enough.
Crime and despair are fed to bursting; let us not
Plunge deeper still in blood. Elders, I beg of you,
Yield in good time to Destiny; go home, before
You come to harm; what we have done was fore-ordained.                    1740
If our long agony finds here fulfilment, we,
Twice gored by Fate's long talons, welcome it. I speak
With woman's wisdom, if you choose to understand.
 AEGISTHUS. Then are these gross-tongued men to aim their pointed gibes
At random, and bluff out the fate they've richly earned?
 CHORUS. You'll find no Argive grovel at a blackguard's feet.
 AEGISTHUS. Enough! Some later day I'll settle scores with you.
 CHORUS. Not if Fate sets Orestes on the Argos road.
 AEGISTHUS. For men in exile hopes are meat and drink; I know.
 CHORUS. Rule on, grow fat defiling Justice — while you can.                    1750

AEGISTHUS. You are a fool; in time you'll pay me for those words.
CHORUS. Brag blindly on — a cock that struts before his hen!
*During these last lines the* CHORUS *have gone out two by two, the last
man vanishing with the last insult, leaving* CLYTEMNESTRA *and* AEGISTHUS
*alone.*
CLYTEMNESTRA. Pay no heed to this currish howling. You and I,
Joint rulers, will enforce due reverence for our throne.

---

## FOR DISCUSSION AND WRITING

*The idea of tragedy proposed here is not a literary artifact, like the
three unities, but a reality. It is very seldom, of course, that we encounter in
life the completeness and the purity of literature. Perhaps Brunetière is right:
"Of all dramatic forms, tragedy is the least realistic, in a sense the most
symbolic, and, as such, in its masterpieces, the least* contingent *or the closest
neighbor of absolute beauty." In life, all seems at first sight to be made up
of contingencies. The curtain does not fall at a climactic moment, we splutter
occasionally in what should be fine situations, bricks do break our heads at
awkward and ridiculous times, and more than once we are surprised by a*
deus ex machina *who liberates us without regard for artistic nicety. And
yet, for all this, the tragic idea, as it represents the search for happiness by
means or under conditions which themselves defeat that search, is one of the
lasting and important ideas concerning human existence. From Leonidas
in the Thermopylae to Peter renouncing his Lord, from the heresiarch who
burns for a creed to the man who must choose between mother and wife,
the tragic idea reaffirms a particular phase of the stirring platitude that "the
world appears to be so constituted, that the greatness of men leads only too
easily to misery and ruin." But tragedy asserts more than "that men die and
are not happy"; it asserts that they die and are not happy through their own
efforts. And not as a mere outcome of their own efforts, but* necessarily *as a
condition contained in the effort. Tragedy, taken all in all, exposes an original
and fatal defect in the relation between a purpose and a something within or
without. Here we leave Aristotle to name the precise condition of downfall:*
inevitability *impresses us as the kernel of the definition. No work can be
tragic without it. Tragedy is always ironic, but it is not because an action*
eventually *leads to the opposite of its intention, but because that opposite is
grafted into the action from the very beginning. If this austere view of tragedy
seems narrow, the pattern is nevertheless repeated time after time, in work
after work. No other precise concept will bind the literature of so many years
and so many nations together. The ironic idea that man's destruction can be
occasioned by his very aspiration is obviously perennial and perennially
fascinating, and it turns up in the guise of a thousand dramatic situations.
The concrete applications of this idea — the plots which express it — are
inexhaustible.*

From Oscar Mandel, A Definition of Tragedy
*(New York: New York University Press, 1961), pp. 23-24.*

1) In the light of Mandel's statement, discuss the inevitability of Agamemnon's fate.

2) How does Cassandra's mere presence on the stage serve to focus our attention on the hero's inevitable fall?

3) The chorus (ll. 100-301) summarizes the events that lead up to Agamemnon's decision to go to war against Troy, including the prophecy that a bloody curse must be worked out; at the same time, the chorus hopes that good will prevail. In view of the curse and the fateful vengeance that must fall upon Agamemnon, how can he be said to have freedom enough to be a tragic hero?

4) "The hubris of the great tragic hero is active. Fully confident of his powers, the individual hero acts in his cosmos, society, in an excess of pride that causes his own downfall. He feels that his individuality cannot be conquered; therefore like a god he can will the perfection of his own action. But in denying man's limitation, he is brought by excess of egotism to humility, to the overpowering knowledge of his own tragic flaw" (Albert Cook, *The Dark Voyage and the Golden Mean,* Cambridge, Mass., Harvard University Press, 1949, pp. 87-88). Are the terms of this definition applicable to Agamemnon? Why or why not? (You may wish to test this statement against the heroes of other plays.)

5) Can it be said that the character of Agamemnon is a too-simple example of overweening pride — from his determination to avenge the theft of Helen to his striding on the purple carpet? If so, is he capable of exciting Aristotelian pity? In your answer, analyze Aeschylus' handling of the chorus.

6) Prosser Hall Frye argues that the function of tragedy is to resolve doubt about whether there is, after all, a "law of eternal righteousness" (a meaningful moral order) in the world (p. 27). Do Frye's views (consider the entire statement) apply to *Agamemnon*?

7) In *Agamemnon,* what is the nature of the audience's "God's-eye view" alluded to by Raphael (p. 40)? Does possession of this view deprive the audience or reader of a necessary sympathy for the characters as human beings?

8) Is it accurate to say that, in terms of Raphael's analysis of sublime opposites (pp. 39-41), the sublimity of Agamemnon does not surpass that of the forces which defeat him, but rather the reverse happens? If the reverse is true, where in the play is the source of tragic satisfaction — in our "God's-eye view"?

9) Demonstrate the truth of the following statement: "In Aeschylus, the past and the elsewhere dominate present action" (Richmond Lattimore, *The Oresteia,* Chicago, University of Chicago Press, 1953, p. 24).

10) To what extent does Agamemnon reflect the tragic philosophy that in human experience every cause has its effect, which is often far out of proportion to the cause?

❋

J O H N

# WEBSTER

## *The Duchess of Malfi*

---

| Characters: | |
|---|---|
| | FERDINAND, duke of Calabria |
| | CARDINAL, his brother |
| | ANTONIO BOLOGNA, steward of the Duchess' household |
| | DELIO, friend to Antonio |
| | DANIEL DE BOSOLA, gentleman of the horse to the Duchess |
| | CASTRUCCIO, an old lord |
| | MARQUIS OF PESCARA |
| | COUNT MALATESTE |
| | RODERIGO |
| | SILVIO }  lords |
| | GRISOLAN |
| | DOCTOR |
| | MADMEN |
| | DUCHESS OF MALFI |
| | CARIOLA, her woman |
| | JULIA, wife to Castruccio, mistress of the cardinal |
| | OLD LADY |
| | Ladies, three young children, two pilgrims, executioners, court officers, and attendants |

## ACT I

SCENE I: *The* DUCHESS' *palace at Amalfi.*

*Enter* ANTONIO *and* DELIO.

DELIO. You are welcome to your country, dear Antonio;
You have been long in France, and you return

*The Duchess of Malfi was first performed in 1614 and first printed in 1623. The present text has been collated for the student's convenience from the original and from modern editions.*

A very formal Frenchman in your habit.
How do you like the French court?
ANT.                              I admire it.
In seeking to reduce both state and people
To a fix'd order, their judicious king
Begins at home; quits first his royal palace
Of flatt'ring sycophants, of dissolute
And infamous persons, — which he sweetly terms
His Master's masterpiece, the work of heaven;                          10
Considering duly that a prince's court
Is like a common fountain, whence should flow
Pure silver drops in general, but if 't chance
Some curs'd example poison 't near the head,
Death and diseases through the whole land spread.
And what is 't makes this blessed government
But a most provident council, who dare freely
Inform him the corruption of the times?
Though some o' th' court hold it presumption
To instruct princes what they ought to do,                             20
It is a noble duty to inform them
What they ought to foresee. — Here comes Bosola,
The only court-gall; yet I observe his railing
Is not for simple love of piety:
Indeed, he rails at those things which he wants;
Would be as lecherous, covetous, or proud,
Bloody, or envious, as any man,
If he had means to be so. — Here's the cardinal.

*Enter* CARDINAL *and* BOSOLA.

BOS. I do haunt you still.
CARD. So.                                                              30
BOS. I have done you better service than to be slighted thus. Miserable age, where only the reward of doing well is the doing of it!
CARD. You enforce your merit too much.
BOS. I fell into the galleys in your service; where, for two years together, I wore two towels instead of a shirt, with a knot on the shoulder, after the fashion of a Roman mantle. Slighted thus! I will thrive some way. Blackbirds fatten best in hard weather; why not I in these dog-days?
CARD. Would you could become honest!
BOS. With all your divinity do but direct me the way to it. I have known many travel far for it, and yet return as arrant knaves as they went forth,   40
because they carried themselves always along with them. [*Exit* CARDINAL]
Are you gone? Some fellows, they say, are possessed with the devil, but this great fellow were able to possess the greatest devil, and make him worse.
ANT. He hath denied thee some suit?
BOS. He and his brother are like plum-trees that grow crooked over standing-pools; they are rich and o'erladen with fruit, but none but crows, pies, and caterpillars feed on them. Could I be one of their flattering pandars, I would hang on their ears like a horseleech, till I were full, and then drop off. I pray, leave me. Who would rely upon these miserable   50
dependences, in expectation to be advanc'd tomorrow? What creature ever fed worse than hoping Tantalus? Nor ever died any man more fearfully

---

*Act I, Scene i.*   48. **pies,** *magpies.*

than he that hop'd for a pardon. There are rewards for hawks and dogs
when they have done us service; but for a soldier that hazards his limbs
in a battle, nothing but a kind of geometry is his last supportation.

DELIO. Geometry?

BOS. Ay, to hang in a fair pair of slings, take his latter swing in the
world upon an honourable pair of crutches, from hospital to hospital.
Fare ye well, sir: and yet do not you scorn us; for places in the court are
but like beds in the hospital, where this man's head lies at that man's foot,   60
and so lower and lower.                                         [*Exit.*

DEL. I knew this fellow seven years in the galleys
For a notorious murther; and 't was thought
The cardinal suborn'd it: he was releas'd
By the French general, Gaston de Foix,
When he recover'd Naples.

ANT.                          'T is great pity
He should be thus neglected: I have heard
He 's very valiant. This foul melancholy
Will poison all his goodness; for, I 'll tell you,
If too immoderate sleep be truly said                              70
To be an inward rust unto the soul,
It then doth follow want of action
Breeds all black malcontents; and their close rearing,
Like moths in cloth, do hurt for want of wearing.

    *Enter* SILVIO, CASTRUCCIO, RODERIGO, *and* GRISOLAN.

DELIO. The presence 'gins to fill; you promis'd me
To make me the partaker of the natures
Of some of your great courtiers.

ANT.                          The lord cardinal's
And other strangers' that are now in court?
I shall. — Here comes the great Calabrian duke.

    *Enter* FERDINAND *and Attendants.*

FERD. Who took the ring oft'nest?                                 80

SIL. Antonio Bologna, my lord.

FERD. Our sister duchess' great master of her household? Give him the
jewel. — When shall we leave this sportive action, and fall to action indeed?

CAST. Methinks, my lord, you should not desire to go to war in person.

FERD. Now for some gravity. — Why, my lord?

CAST. It is fitting a soldier arise to be a prince, but not necessary a prince
descend to be a captain.

FERD. No?

CAST. No, my lord; he were far better do it by a deputy.

FERD. Why should he not as well sleep or eat by a deputy? This might   90
take idle, offensive, and base office from him, whereas the other deprives
him of honour.

CAST. Believe my experience: that realm is never long in quiet where
the ruler is a soldier.

FERD. Thou told'st me thy wife could not endure fighting.

CAST. True, my lord.

FERD. And of a jest she broke of a captain she met full of wounds: I
have forgot it.

---

80. **took the ring,** *a sport in which a horseman attempted to spear with his lance a ring suspended
in mid-air.*

CAST. She told him, my lord, he was a pitiful fellow, to lie, like the children of Ismael, all in tents. 100

FERD. Why, there 's a wit were able to undo all the chirurgeons o' the city, for although gallants should quarrel, and had drawn their weapons, and were ready to go to it, yet her persuasions would make them put up.

CAST. That she would, my lord. — How do you like my Spanish jennet?

ROD. He is all fire.

FERD. I am of Pliny's opinion: I think he was begot by the wind; he runs as if he were ballass'd with quicksilver.

SIL. True, my lord, he reels from the tilt often.

ROD., GRIS. Ha, ha, ha!

FERD. Why do you laugh? Methinks you that are courtiers should be my 110 touch-wood, take fire when I give fire; that is, laugh when I laugh, were the subject never so witty.

CAST. True, my lord. I myself have heard a very good jest, and have scorn'd to seem to have so silly a wit as to understand it.

FERD. But I can laugh at your fool, my lord.

CAST. He cannot speak, you know, but he makes faces; my lady cannot abide him.

FERD. No?

CAST. Nor endure to be in merry company; for she says too much laugh-ing, and too much company, fills her too full of the wrinkle. 120

FERD. I would, then, have a mathematical instrument made for her face, that she might not laugh out of compass. — I shall shortly visit you at Milan, Lord Silvio.

SIL. Your grace shall arrive most welcome.

FERD. You are a good horseman, Antonio; you have excellent riders in France. What do you think of good horsemanship?

ANT. Nobly, my lord. As out of the Grecian horse issued many famous princes, so out of brave horsemanship arise the first sparks of growing resolution, that raise the mind to noble action.

FERD. You have bespoke it worthily. 130

SIL. Your brother, the lord cardinal, and sister duchess.

*Enter* CARDINAL, *with* DUCHESS, *and* CARIOLA.

CARD. Are the galleys come about?

GRIS.                 They are, my lord.

FERD. Here 's the Lord Silvio is come to take his leave.

DELIO. Now, sir, your promise: what 's that cardinal?
I mean his temper. They say he 's a brave fellow.
Will play his five thousand crowns at tennis, dance,
Court ladies, and one that hath fought single combats.

ANT. Some such flashes superficially hang on him for form; but observe his inward character: he is a melancholy churchman. The spring in his face is nothing but the engend'ring of toads; where he is jealous of any 140 man, he lays worse plots for them than ever was impos'd on Hercules, for he strews in his way flatterers, panders, intelligencers, atheists, and a thousand such political monsters. He should have been Pope; but instead of coming to it by the primitive decency of the church, he did bestow bribes so largely and so impudently as if he would have carried it away without heaven's knowledge. Some good he hath done ——

DELIO. You have given too much of him. What 's his brother?

---

100. **tents,** *a pun on "tent" which also may mean a roll of absorbent lint bandage.*
101. **chirurgeons,** *surgeons.*

ANT. The duke there? A most perverse and turbulent nature.
What appears in him mirth is merely outside;
If he laugh heartily, it is to laugh                           150
All honesty out of fashion.
    DELIO.                    Twins?
    ANT.                         In quality.
He speaks with others' tongues, and hears men's suits
With others' ears; will seem to sleep o' th' bench
Only to entrap offenders in their answers;
Dooms men to death by information;
Rewards by hearsay.
    DELIO.          Then the law to him
Is like a foul, black cobweb to a spider,—
He makes it his dwelling and a prison
To entangle those shall feed him.
    ANT.                    Most true:
He never pays debts unless they be shrewd turns,              160
And those he will confess that he doth owe.
Last, for his brother there, the cardinal,
They that do flatter him most say oracles
Hang at his lips; and verily I believe them,
For the devil speaks in them.
But for their sister, the right noble duchess,
You never fix'd your eye on three fair medals
Cast in one figure, of so different temper.
For her discourse, it is so full of rapture,
You only will begin then to be sorry                          170
When she doth end her speech, and wish, in wonder,
She held it less vain-glory to talk much,
Than your penance to hear her. Whilst she speaks,
She throws upon a man so sweet a look
That it were able raise one to a galliard
That lay in a dead palsy; and to dote
On that sweet countenance: but in that look
There speaketh so divine a continence
As cuts off all lascivious and vain hope.
Her days are practis'd in such noble virtue,                  180
That sure her nights, nay, more, her very sleeps,
Are more in heaven than other ladies' shrifts.
Let all sweet ladies break their flatt'ring glasses,
And dress themselves in her.
    DELIO.                    Fie, Antonio,
You play the wire-drawer with her commendations.
    ANT. I 'll case the picture up, only thus much;
All her particular worth grows to this sum:
She stains the time past, lights the time to come.
    CARI. You must attend my lady in the gallery,
Some half an hour hence.
    ANT.              I shall.        [*Exeunt* ANTONIO *and* DELIO. 190
    FERD. Sister, I have a suit to you.
    DUCH.                    To me, sir?
    FERD. A gentleman here, Daniel de Bosola,

175. **galliard**, *a spirited dance.*
185. **play the wire-drawer with**, *distend.*
188. **stains**, *dims by comparison.*

One that was in the galleys.

DUCH.                         Yes, I know him.

FERD. A worthy fellow he 's: pray, let me entreat for
The provisorship of your horse.

DUCH.                         Your knowledge of him
Commends him and prefers him.

FERD.                         Call him hither.     [*Exit Attendants.*
We are now upon parting. Good Lord Silvio,
Do us commend to all our noble friends
At the leaguer.

SIL.           Sir, I shall.

DUCH.                   You are for Milan?

SIL. I am.

DUCH.     Bring the caroches. We 'll bring you down            200
To the haven.         [*Exeunt* DUCHESS, SILVIO, CASTRUCCIO, RODERIGO,
                              GRISOLAN, CARIOLA, JULIA, *and Attendants.*

CARD.       Be sure you entertain that Bosola
For your intelligence. I would not be seen in 't;
And therefore many times I have slighted him
When he did court our furtherance, as this morning.

FERD. Antonio, the great master of her household,
Had been far fitter.

CARD.               You are deceiv'd in him.
His nature is too honest for such business. —
He comes: I 'll leave you.

*Re-enter* BOSOLA.

BOS.                   I was lur'd to you.

FERD. My brother here, the cardinal, could never
Abide you.

BOS.     Never since he was in my debt.                    210

FERD. May be some oblique character in your face
Made him suspect you.

BOS.                 Doth he study physiognomy?
There 's no more credit to be given to th' face
Than to a sick man's urine, which some call
The physician's whore, because she cozens him.
He did suspect me wrongfully.

FERD.                       For that
You must give great men leave to take their times.
Distrust doth cause us seldom be deceiv'd.
You see, the oft shaking of the cedar-tree
Fastens it more at root.

BOS.                 Yet take heed;                        220
For to suspect a friend unworthily
Instructs him the next way to suspect you,
And prompts him to deceive you.

FERD.                         There 's gold.

BOS.                                     So:
What follows? Never rain'd such showers as these
Without thunderbolts i' th' tail of them. Whose throat must I cut?

FERD. Your inclination to shed blood rides post
Before my occasion to use you. I give you that

___
199. **leaguer,** *military camp.*

To live i' th' court here, and observe the duchess;
To note all the particulars of her haviour,
What suitors do solicit her for marriage,                                    230
„And whom she best affects. She 's a young widow;
I would not have her marry again.
    BOS.                         No, sir?
    FERD. Do not you ask the reason; but be satisfied.
I say I would not.
    BOS.            It seems you would create me
One of your familiars.
    FERD.          Familiar! What 's that?
    BOS. Why, a very quaint invisible devil in flesh:
An intelligencer.
    FERD.        Such a kind of thriving thing
I would wish thee; and ere long thou mayst arrive
At a higher place by 't.
    BOS.            Take your devils,
Which hell calls angels! These curs'd gifts would make           240
You a corrupter, me an impudent traitor;
And should I take these, they 'd take me to hell.
    FERD. Sir, I 'll take nothing from you that I have given.
There is a place that I procur'd for you
This morning, the provisorship o' th' horse.
Have you heard on 't?
    BOS.         No.
    FERD. 'T is yours: is 't not worth thanks?
    BOS. I would have you curse yourself now, that your bounty
(Which makes men truly noble) e'er should make me
A villain. O, that to avoid ingratitude                                       250
For the good deed you have done me, I must do
All the ill man can invent! Thus the devil
Candies all sins o'er: and what heaven terms vild,
That names he complimental.
    FERD.               Be yourself;
Keep your old garb of melancholy; 't will express
You envy those that stand above your reach,
Yet strive not to come near 'em. This will gain
Access to private lodgings, where yourself
May, like a politic dormouse —
    BOS.              As I have seen some
Feed in a lord's dish, half asleep, not seeming                              260
To listen to any talk; and yet these rogues
Have cut his throat in a dream. What 's my place?
The provisorship o' th' horse? Say, then, my corruption
Grew out of horse-dung: I am your creature.
    FERD.                     Away!
    BOS. Let good men, for good deeds, covet good fame,
Since place and riches oft are bribes of shame.
Sometimes the devil doth preach.                [*Exit* BOSOLA.

    *Re-enter* CARDINAL, DUCHESS, *and* CARIOLA.

    CARD. We are to part from you; and your own discretion

---

240. **angels,** *gold coins.*

Must now be your director.

FERD.                             You are a widow:
You know already what man is; and therefore                          270
Let not youth, high promotion, eloquence —

CARD. No,
Nor anything without the addition, honour,
Sway your high blood.

FERD.                             Marry! They are most luxurious
Will wed twice.

CARD.          O, fie!

FERD.                             Their livers are more spotted
Than Laban's sheep.

DUCH.                    Diamonds are of most value,
They say, that have pass'd through most jewellers' hands.

FERD. Whores by that rule are precious.

DUCH.                                   Will you hear me?
I 'll never marry.

CARD.          So most widows say;
But commonly that motion lasts no longer
Than the turning of an hour-glass: the funeral sermon                280
And it end both together.

FERD.                    Now hear me:
You live in a rank pasture, here, i' th' court;
There is a kind of honey-dew that 's deadly;
'T will poison your fame; look to 't. Be not cunning;
For they whose faces do belie their hearts
Are witches ere they arrive at twenty years,
Ay, and give the devil suck.

DUCH. This is terrible good counsel.

FERD. Hypocrisy is woven of a fine small thread,
Subtler than Vulcan's engine: yet, believe 't,                       290
Your darkest actions, nay, your privat'st thoughts,
Will come to light.

CARD.          You may flatter yourself,
And take your own choice; privately be married
Under the eaves of night —

FERD.                             Think 't the best voyage
That e'er you made; like the irregular crab,
Which, though 't goes backward, thinks that it goes right
Because it goes its own way: but observe,
Such weddings may more properly be said
To be executed than celebrated.

CARD.                             The marriage night
Is the entrance into some prison.

FERD.                             And those joys,                     300
Those lustful pleasures, are like heavy sleeps
Which do fore-run man's mischief.

CARD.                             Fare you well.
Wisdom begins at the end: remember it.                      [*Exit.*

DUCH. I think this speech between you both was studied,
It came so roundly off.

---

273. **luxurious,** *lustful.*
290. **Vulcan's engine,** *the net which he used to capture his wife, Venus, and Mars at their love-making.*

FERD.             You are my sister;
This was my father's poniard, do you see?
I 'd be loath to see 't look rusty, 'cause 't was his.
I would have you to give o'er these chargeable revels:
A visor and a mask are whispering-rooms
That were never built for goodness. Fare ye well:         310
And women like that part which, like the lamprey,
Hath never a bone in 't.
     DUCH.           Fie, sir!
     FERD.                  Nay,
I mean the tongue: variety of courtship.
What cannot a neat knave with a smooth tale
Make a woman believe? Farewell, lusty widow.        [*Exit.*
     DUCH. Shall this move me? If all my royal kindred
Lay in my way unto this marriage,
I 'd make them my low footsteps. And even now,
Even in this hate, as men in some great battles,
By apprehending danger, have achiev'd            320
Almost impossible actions (I have heard soldiers say so),
So I through frights and threat'nings will assay
This dangerous venture. Let old wives report
I wink'd and chose a husband. Cariola,
To thy known secrecy I have given up
More than my life, — my fame.
     CARI.                  Both shall be safe;
For I 'll conceal this secret from the world
As warily as those that trade in poison
Keep poison from their children.
     DUCH.                  Thy protestation
Is ingenious and hearty; I believe it.         330
Is Antonio come?
     CARI.        He attends you.
     DUCH.                  Good dear soul,
Leave me; but place thyself behind the arras,
Where thou may'st overhear us. Wish me good speed,
For I am going into a wilderness,
Where I shall find nor path nor friendly clue
To be my guide.           [CARIOLA *goes behind the arras.*

     *Enter* ANTONIO.

               I sent for you: sit down;
Take pen and ink, and write. Are you ready?
     ANT.                 Yes.
     DUCH. What did I say?
     ANT. That I should write somewhat.
     DUCH.             O, I remember.
After these triumphs and this large expense         340
It 's fit, like thrifty husbands, we inquire
What 's laid up for to-morrow.
     ANT. So please your beauteous excellence.
     DUCH.                  Beauteous!
Indeed, I thank you. I look young for your sake;
You have ta'en my cares upon you.
     ANT.                I 'll fetch your grace

The particulars of your revenue and expense.

DUCH. O, you are
An upright treasurer, but you mistook;
For when I said I meant to make inquiry
What 's laid up for to-morrow, I did mean                    350
What 's laid up yonder for me.

ANT.                                    Where?

DUCH.                                                    In heaven.
I am making my will (as 't is fit princes should,
In perfect memory), and, I pray, sir, tell me,
Were not one better make it smiling, thus,
Than in deep groans and terrible ghastly looks,
As if the gifts we parted with procur'd
That violent distraction?

ANT.                            O, much better.

DUCH. If I had a husband now, this care were quit:
But I intend to make you overseer.
What good deed shall we first remember? Say.               360

ANT. Begin with that first good deed began i' th' world.
After man's creation, the sacrament of marriage.
I 'd have you first provide for a good husband;
Give him all.

DUCH.        All!

ANT.              Yes, your excellent self.

DUCH. In a winding-sheet?

ANT.                        In a couple.

DUCH. Saint Winfrid, that were a strange will!

ANT. 'T were stranger if there were no will in you
To marry again.

DUCH.        What do you think of marriage?

ANT. I take 't, as those that deny purgatory,
It locally contains or heaven or hell;                      370
There 's no third place in 't.

DUCH.                        How do you affect it?

ANT. My banishment, feeding my melancholy,
Would often reason thus: —

DUCH.                        Pray, let 's hear it.

ANT. Say a man never marry, nor have children,
What takes that from him? Only the bare name
Of being a father, or the weak delight
To see the little wanton ride a cock-horse
Upon a painted stick, or hear him chatter
Like a taught starling.

DUCH.                    Fie, fie, what 's all this?
One of your eyes is blood-shot; use my ring to 't.         380
They say 't is very sovereign. 'T was my wedding-ring,
And I did vow never to part with it
But to my second husband.

ANT. You have parted with it now.

DUCH. Yes, to help your eye-sight.

ANT. You have made me stark blind.

DUCH.                                How?

ANT. There is a saucy and ambitious devil
Is dancing in this circle.

DUCH.                    Remove him.
ANT.                         How?
DUCH. There needs small conjuration, when your finger
May do it: thus. Is it fit?    [*She puts the ring upon his finger; he kneels.*
ANT.                   What said you?
DUCH.                              Sir,                                390
This goodly roof of yours is too low built;
I cannot stand upright in 't nor discourse,
Without I raise it higher. Raise yourself;
Or, if you please my hand to help you: so!        [*Raises him.*
ANT. Ambition, madam, is a great man's madness,
That is not kept in chains and close-pent rooms,
But in fair lightsome lodgings, and is girt
With the wild noise of prattling visitants,
Which makes it lunatic beyond all cure.
Conceive not I am so stupid but I aim              400
Whereto your favours tend. But he 's a fool
That, being a-cold, would thrust his hands i' th' fire
To warm them.
DUCH.          So, now the ground 's broke,
You may discover what a wealthy mine
I make you lord of.
ANT.              O my unworthiness!
DUCH. You were ill to sell yourself:
This dark'ning of your worth is not like that
Which tradesmen use i' th' city; their false lights
Are to rid bad wares off, and I must tell you,
If you will know where breathes a complete man       410
(I speak it without flattery), turn your eyes,
And progress through yourself.
ANT. Were there nor heaven nor hell,
I should be honest: I have long serv'd virtue,
And never ta'en wages of her.
DUCH.                    Now she pays it.
The misery of us that are born great!
We are forc'd to woo, because none dare woo us;
And as a tyrant doubles with his words
And fearfully equivocates, so we
Are forc'd to express our violent passions       420
In riddles and in dreams, and leave the path
Of simple virtue, which was never made
To seem the thing it is not. Go, go brag
You have left me heartless; mine is in your bosom:
I hope 't will multiply love there. You do tremble:
Make not your heart so dead a piece of flesh
To fear more than to love me. Sir, be confident:
What is 't distracts you? This is flesh and blood, sir;
'T is not the figure cut in alabaster
Kneels at my husband's tomb. Awake, awake, man!       430
I do here put off all vain ceremony,
And only do appear to you a young widow
That claims you for her husband, and, like a widow,
I use but half a blush in 't.
ANT.                    Truth speak for me:

I will remain the constant sanctuary
Of your good name.
  DUCH.     I thank you, gentle love,
And 'cause you shall not come to me in debt,
(Being now my steward) here upon your lips
I sign your *Quietus est*. This you should have begg'd now.
I have seen children oft eat sweetmeats thus,      440
As fearful to devour them too soon.
  ANT. But for your brothers?
  DUCH.       Do not think of them:
All discord without this circumference
Is only to be pitied, and not fear'd;
Yet, should they know it, time will easily
Scatter the tempest.
  ANT.      These words should be mine,
And all the parts you have spoke, if some part of it
Would not have savour'd flattery.
  DUCH.      Kneel. [*Cariola comes from behind the arras.*
  ANT.       Ha!
  DUCH. Be not amaz'd; this woman 's of my counsel.
I have heard lawyers say, a contract in a chamber     450
*Per verba* [*de*] *presenti* is absolute marriage.    [*She and* ANTONIO *kneel.*
Bless, heaven, this sacred Gordian, which let violence
Never untwine.
  ANT. And may our sweet affections, like the spheres,
Be still in motion!
  DUCH.     Quick'ning, and make
The like soft music!
  ANT. That we may imitate the loving palms,
Best emblem of a peaceful marriage,
That never bore fruit, divided!
  DUCH. What can the church force more?       460
  ANT. That fortune may not know an accident,
Either of joy or sorrow, to divide
Our fixed wishes!
  DUCH.     How can the church build faster?
We now are man and wife, and 't is the church
That must but echo this. – Maid, stand apart:
I now am blind.
  ANT.      What 's your conceit in this?
  DUCH. I would have you lead your fortune by the hand
Unto your marriage-bed:
(You speak in me this, for we now are one).
We 'll only lie and talk together, and plot       470
T' appease my humorous kindred; and if you please,
Like the old tale in *Alexander and Lodowick*,
Lay a naked sword between us, keep us chaste.
O, let me shroud my blushes in your bosom,
Since 't is the treasury of all my secrets! [*Exeunt* DUCHESS *and* ANTONIO.
  CARI. Whether the spirit of greatness or of woman
Reign most in her, I know not; but it shows
A fearful madness. I owe her much of pity.       [*Exit.*

443. **without,** *outside.*
451. **Per verba** [**de**] **presenti,** *heard by a third person.*

## ACT II

SCENE I: *An apartment in the* DUCHESS' *palace.*

*Enter* BOSOLA *and* CASTRUCCIO.

BOS. You say you would fain be taken for an eminent courtier?

CAST. 'T is the very main of my ambition.

BOS. Let me see: you have a reasonable good face for 't already, and your night-cap expresses your ears sufficient largely. I would have you learn to twirl the strings of your band with a good grace, and in a set speech, at th' end of every sentence, to hum three or four times, or blow your nose till it smart again, to recover your memory. When you come to be a president in criminal causes, if you smile upon a prisoner, hang him; but if you frown upon him and threaten him, let him be sure to scape the gallows.                                                               10

CAST. I would be a very merry president.

BOS. Do not sup o' nights; 't will beget you an admirable wit.

CAST. Rather it would make me have a good stomach to quarrel; for they say, your roaring boys eat meat seldom, and that makes them so valiant. But how shall I know whether the people take me for an eminent fellow?

BOS. I will teach a trick to know it: give out you lie a-dying, and if you hear the common people curse you, be sure you are taken for one of the prime night-caps.

*Enter an* OLD LADY.

You come from painting now?                                                  20

OLD LADY. From what?

BOS. Why, from your scurvy face-physic. To behold thee not painted inclines somewhat near a miracle. These in thy face here were deep ruts and foul sloughs the last progress. There was a lady in France that, having had the small-pox, flayed the skin off her face to make it more level; and whereas before she looked like a nutmeg-grater, after she resembled an abortive hedgehog.

OLD LADY. Do you call this painting?

BOS. No, no, but I call it careening of an old morphew'd lady, to make her disembogue again; there 's rough-cast phrase to your plastic.          30

OLD LADY. It seems you are well acquainted with my closet.

BOS. One would suspect it for a shop of witchcraft, to find it the fat of serpents, spawn of snakes, Jews' spittle, and their young children's ordure; and all these for the face. I would sooner eat a dead pigeon taken from the soles of the feet of one sick of the plague, than kiss one of you fasting. Here are two of you, whose sin of your youth is the very patrimony of the physician; makes him renew his foot-cloth with the spring, and change his high-pric'd courtesan with the fall of the leaf. I do wonder you do not loathe yourselves. Observe my meditation now:

What thing is in this outward form of man                                    40
To be belov'd? We account it ominous,
If nature do produce a colt, or lamb,
A fawn, or goat, in any limb resembling
A man, and fly from 't as a prodigy.
Man stands amaz'd to see his deformity

*Act II. Scene i.*  2. **main**, *height.*

24. **progress**, *royal journey.*

29-30. **careening . . . disembogue.** *Probably an allusion to the process of cleaning the sides of a vessel to make it seaworthy.*

In any other creature but himself.
But in our own flesh though we bear diseases
Which have their true names only ta'en from beasts, —
As the most ulcerous wolf and swinish measle, —
Though we are eaten up of lice and worms,                                    50
And though continually we bear about us
A rotten and dead body, we delight
To hide it in rich tissue: all our fear,
Nay, all our terror, is, lest our physician
Should put us in the ground to be made sweet. —
Your wife 's gone to Rome: you two couple, and get you to the wells at
Lucca to recover your aches. I have other work on foot.
                                        [*Exeunt* CASTRUCCIO *and* OLD LADY.
I observe our duchess
Is sick a-days, she pukes, her stomach seethes,
The fins of her eye-lids look most teeming blue,                             60
She wanes i' the cheek, and waxes fat i' th' flank,
And, contrary to our Italian fashion,
Wears a loose-bodied gown: there 's somewhat in 't.
I have a trick may chance discover it,
A pretty one: I have bought some apricocks,
The first our spring yields.

*Enter* ANTONIO *and* DELIO, *talking together apart.*

   DELIO. And so long since married? You amaze me.
   ANT. Let me seal your lips forever,
For did I think that anything but the air
Could carry these words from you, I should wish                              70
You had no breath at all. — Now, sir, in your contemplation?
You are studying to become a great wise fellow.
   BOS. O, sir, the opinion of wisdom is a foul tetter that runs all over a
man's body: if simplicity direct us to have no evil, it directs us to a happy
being; for the subtlest folly proceeds from the subtlest wisdom. Let me be
simply honest.
   ANT. I do understand your inside.
   BOS.                              Do you so?
   ANT. Because you would not seem to appear to th' world
Puff'd up with your preferment, you continue
This out-of-fashion melancholy: leave it, leave it.                          80
   BOS. Give me leave to be honest in any phrase, in any compliment
whatsoever. Shall I confess myself to you? I look no higher than I can
reach: they are the gods that must ride on winged horses. A lawyer's
mule of a slow pace will both suit my disposition and business; for, mark
me, when a man's mind rides faster than his horse can gallop, they quickly
both tire.
   ANT. You would look up to heaven, but I think
The devil, that rules i' th' air, stands in your light.
   BOS. O, sir, you are lord of the ascendant, chief man with the duchess:
a duke was your cousin-german remov'd. Say you were lineally descended   90
from King Pepin, or he himself, what of this? Search the heads of the
greatest rivers in the world, you shall find them but bubbles of water.
Some would think the souls of princes were brought forth by some more
weighty cause than those of meaner persons: they are deceiv'd, there 's

49. **wolf,** *sore.*
73. **tetter,** *skin disease.*

the same hand to them; the like passions sway them; the same reason that makes a vicar go to law for a tithe-pig, and undo his neighbours, makes them spoil a whole province, and batter down goodly cities with the cannon.

*Enter* DUCHESS *and Ladies.*

    DUCH. Your arm, Antonio; do I not grow fat? I am exceeding short-
winded. — Bosola,
I would have you, sir, provide for me a litter,                100
Such a one as the Duchess of Florence rode in.
    BOS. The duchess us'd one when she was great with child.
    DUCH. I think she did. — Come hither, mend my ruff!
Here, when? Thou are such a tedious lady; and
Thy breath smells of lemon-pills; would thou hadst done!
Shall I swoon under thy fingers? I am
So troubled with the mother!
    BOS. [*Aside*]              I fear, too much.
    DUCH. I have heard you say that the French courtiers
Wear their hats on 'fore the king.
    ANT. I have seen it.
    DUCH.         In the presence?
    ANT.               Yes.                110
    DUCH. Why should not we bring up that fashion?
'T is ceremony more than duty that consists
In the removing of a piece of felt.
Be you the example to the rest o' th' court;
Put on your hat first.
    ANT.         You must pardon me:
I have seen, in colder countries than in France,
Nobles stand bare to th' prince; and the distinction
Methought show'd reverently.
    BOS. I have a present for your grace.
    DUCH.             For me, sir?
    BOS. Apricocks, madam.
    DUCH.         O, sir, where are they?       120
I have heard of none to-year.
    BOS. [*Aside*]        Good; her colour rises.
    DUCH. Indeed, I thank you: they are wondrous fair ones.
What an unskilful fellow is our gardener!
We shall have none this month.
    BOS. Will not your grace pare them?
    DUCH. No: they taste of musk, methinks; indeed they do.
    BOS. I know not; yet I wish your grace had par'd 'em.
    DUCH. Why?
    BOS. I forgot to tell you, the knave gardener,
(Only to raise his profit by them the sooner)            130
Did ripen them in horse-dung.
    DUCH.         O, you jest. —
You shall judge: pray, taste one.
    ANT.           Indeed, madam,
I do not love the fruit.
    DUCH.       Sir, you are loath
To rob us of our dainties. 'T is a delicate fruit;
They say they are restorative.

---

107. **mother,** *hysteria.*

BOS.                    'T is a pretty art,
This grafting.
DUCH.        'T is so; a bettering of nature.
BOS. To make a pippin grow upon a crab,
A damson on a black-thorn. — [*Aside*] How greedily she eats them!
A whirlwind strike off these bawd-farthingales!
For, but for that and the loose-bodied gown,                                 140
I should have discover'd apparently
The young springal cutting a caper in her belly.
DUCH. I thank you, Bosola: they were right good ones,
If they do not make me sick.
ANT.                          How now, madam!
DUCH. This green fruit and my stomach are not friends:
How they swell me!
BOS. [*Aside*]        Nay, you are too much swell'd already.
DUCH. O, I am in an extreme cold sweat!
BOS.                          I am very sorry.        [*Exit.*
DUCH. Lights to my chamber! — O good Antonio,
I fear I am undone!
DELIO.        Lights there, lights!        [*Exeunt* DUCHESS *with Ladies.*
ANT. O my most trusty Delio, we are lost!                                    150
I fear she 's fall'n in labour; and there 's left
No time for her remove.
DELIO.              Have you prepar'd
Those ladies to attend her; and procur'd
That politic safe conveyance for the midwife
Your duchess plotted?
ANT.              I have.
DELIO. Make use, then, of this forc'd occasion.
Give out that Bosola hath poison'd her
With these apricocks: that will give some colour
For keeping her close.
ANT.              Fie, fie, the physicians
Will then flock to her.                                                      160
DELIO. For that you may pretend
She 'll use some prepar'd antidote of her own,
Lest the physicians should re-poison her.
ANT. I am lost in amazement: I know not what to think on 't. [*Exeunt.*

SCENE II: *A hall in the palace.*

*Enter* BOSOLA.

BOS. So, so, there 's no question but her tetchiness and most vulturous
eating of the apricocks are apparent signs of breeding. — Now?

*Enter* OLD LADY.

OLD LADY. I am in haste, sir.
BOS. There was a young waiting-woman had a monstrous desire to see
the glass-house ——
OLD LADY. Nay, pray, let me go.
BOS. And it was only to know what strange instrument it was should
swell up a glass to the fashion of a woman's belly.

*Scene ii.*   1. **tetchiness,** *peevishness.*

OLD LADY. I will hear no more of the glass-house. You are still abusing
women!                                                                    10

BOS. Who? I? No; only, by the way now and then, mention your frailties.
The orange-tree bears ripe and green fruit and blossoms all together; and
some of you give entertainment for pure love, but more for more precious
reward. The lusty spring smells well; but drooping autumn tastes well. If
we have the same golden showers that rained in the time of Jupiter the
thunderer, you have the same Danaës still, to hold up their laps to receive
them. Didst thou never study the mathematics?

OLD LADY. What 's that, sir?

BOS. Why, to know the trick how to make a many lines meet in one
centre. Go, go, give your foster-daughters good counsel: tell them, that   20
the devil takes delight to hang at a woman's girdle, like a false rusty watch,
that she cannot discern how the time passes.          [*Exit* OLD LADY.

*Enter* ANTONIO, RODERIGO, *and* GRISOLAN.

ANT. Shup up the court-gates.

ROD.                            Why, sir? What 's the danger?

ANT. Shut up the posterns presently, and call
All the officers o' th' court.

GRIS.                I shall instantly.                    [*Exit.*

ANT. Who keeps the key o' th' park-gate?

ROD.                              Forobosco.

ANT. Let him bring 't presently.

*Re-enter* GRISOLAN *with Servants.*

1 SERV. O, gentlemen o' th' court, the foulest treason!

BOS. [*Aside*] If that these apricocks should be poison'd now,
Without my knowledge!                                                     30

1 SERV. There was taken even now a Switzer in the duchess' bed-
chamber —

2 SERV. A Switzer!

1 SERV. With a pistol in his great codpiece.

BOS. Ha, ha, ha!

1 SERV. The codpiece was the case for 't.

2 SERV. There was a cunning traitor. Who would have search'd his
codpiece?

1 SERV. True, if he had kept out of the ladies' chambers. And all the
moulds of his buttons were leaden bullets.                                40

2 SERV. O wicked cannibal! A fire-lock in 's codpiece!

1 SERV. 'T was a French plot, upon my life.

2 SERV. To see what the devil can do!

ANT. All the officers here?

SERVANTS. We are.

ANT. Gentlemen,
We have lost much plate, you know; and but this evening
Jewels, to the value of four thousand ducats,
Are missing in the duchess' cabinet.
Are the gates shut?

SERV.          Yes.

ANT.                    'T is the duchess' pleasure                      50
Each officer be lock'd into his chamber
Till the sun-rising; and to send the keys
Of all their chests and of their outward doors
Into her bed-chamber. She is very sick.

ROD. At her pleasure.

ANT. She entreats you take 't not ill: the innocent
Shall be the more approv'd by it.

BOS. Gentleman o' th' wood-yard, where 's your Switzer now?

1 SERV. By this hand, 't was credibly reported by one o' th' black guard.

                     [*Exeunt all except* ANTONIO *and* DELIO.

DELIO. How fares it with the duchess?

ANT.                   She 's expos'd             60
Unto the worst of torture, pain and fear.

DELIO. Speak to her all happy comfort.

ANT. How I do play the fool with mine own danger!
You are this night, dear friend, to post to Rome:
My life lies in your service.

DELIO.             Do not doubt me.

ANT. O, 't is far from me: and yet fear presents me
Somewhat that looks like danger.

DELIO.            Believe it,
'T is but the shadow of your fear, no more.
How superstitious we mind our evils!
The throwing down salt, or crossing of a hare,        70
Bleeding at nose, the stumbling of a horse,
Or singing of a cricket, are of power
To daunt whole man in us. Sir, fare you well:
I wish you all the joys of a bless'd father;
And, for my faith, lay this unto your breast:
Old friends, like old swords, still are trusted best.      [*Exit.*

*Enter* CARIOLA.

CARI. Sir, you are the happy father of a son:
Your wife commends him to you.

ANT.                  Blessed comfort! —
For heaven's sake, tend her well: I 'll presently
Go set a figure for 's nativity.               [*Exeunt.*   80

SCENE III:    *The inner court of the palace.*

*Enter* BOSOLA, *carrying a dark lantern.*

BOS. Sure I did hear a woman shriek: list, ha!
And the sound came, if I receiv'd it right,
From the duchess' lodgings. There 's some stratagem
In the confining all our courtiers
To their several wards: I must have part of it;
My intelligence will freeze else. List, again!
It may be 't was the melancholy bird,
Best friend of silence and of solitariness,
The owl, that scream'd so. — Ha! Antonio!

*Enter* ANTONIO, *with sword drawn.*

ANT. I heard some noise. — Who 's there? What are thou? Speak.    10

BOS. Antonio? put not your face nor body
To such a forc'd expression of fear;
I am Bosola, your friend.

---

80. **set a figure for 's nativity,** *cast a horoscope.*

ANT.                           Bosola! —
[*Aside*] This mole does undermine me. — Heard you not
A noise even now?
    BOS.                From whence?
    ANT.                                       From the duchess' lodging.
    BOS. Not I: did you?
    ANT.                     I did, or else I dream'd.
    BOS. Let 's walk toward it.
    ANT.                          No: it may be 't was
But the rising of the wind.
    BOS.                     Very likely.
Methinks 't is very cold, and yet you sweat:
You look wildly.
    ANT.              I have been setting a figure                    20
For the duchess' jewels.
    BOS.                     Ah, and how falls your question?
Do you find it radical?
    ANT.                     What 's that to you?
'T is rather to be question'd what design,
When all men are commanded to their lodgings,
Makes you a night-walker.
    BOS.                     In sooth, I 'll tell you:
Now all the court 's asleep, I thought the devil
Had least to do here. I came to say my prayers;
And if it do offend you, I do so.
You are a fine courtier.
    ANT. [*Aside*] This fellow will undo me! —                    30
You gave the duchess apricocks today:
Pray heaven they were not poison'd!
    BOS. Poison'd! a Spanish fig
For the imputation!
    ANT.              Traitors are ever confident
Till they are discover'd. There were jewels stol'n too;
In my conceit, none are to be suspected
More than yourself.
    BOS.                     You are a false steward.
    ANT. Saucy slave, I 'll pull thee up by the roots.
    BOS. May be the ruin will crush you to pieces.
    ANT. You are an impudent snake indeed, sir:                    40
Are you scarce warm, and do you show your sting?
You libel well, sir.
    BOS.              No, sir: copy it out,
And I will set my hand to 't.
    ANT. [*Aside*]                 My nose bleeds.
One that were superstitious would count
This ominous, when it merely comes by chance.
Two letters, that are wrought here for my name,
Are drown'd in blood!
Mere accident. — For you, sir, I 'll take order
I' th' morn you shall be safe. — [*Aside*] 'T is that must colour
Her lying-in. — Sir, this door you pass not:                    50
I do not hold it fit that you come near
The duchess' lodgings, till you have quit yourself. —

---

*Scene iii.*   22. **radical,** *basically revealing.*

[*Aside*] The great are like the base; nay, they are the same,
When they seek shameful ways to avoid shame.          [*Exit.*
   BOS. Antonio hereabout did drop a paper: —
Some of your help, false friend. O, here it is.
What 's here? A child's nativity calculated!          [*Reads.*
'The duchess was deliver'd of a son 'tween the hours twelve and one in the
night, Anno Dom. 1504.' — that 's this year — 'decimo nono Decembris,' —
that 's this night — 'taken according to the meridian of Malfi,' — that 's   60
our duchess: happy discovery! — 'The lord of the first house being combust
in the ascendant signifies short life; and Mars being in a human sign, joined
to the tail of the Dragon, in the eighth house, doth threaten a violent death.
Cætera non scrutantur.'
Why now 't is most apparent; this precise fellow
Is the duchess' bawd: — I have it to my wish!
This is a parcel of intelligency
Our courtiers were cas'd up for. It needs must follow
That I must be committed on pretence
Of poisoning her; which I 'll endure, and laugh at.          70
If one could find the father now! but that
Time will discover. Old Castruccio
I' th' morning posts to Rome; by him I 'll send
A letter that shall make her brothers' galls
O'erflow their livers. This was a thrifty way!
Though Lust do mask in ne'er so strange disguise,
She 's oft found witty, but is never wise.          [*Exit.*

   SCENE IV: *Rome. A room in the* CARDINAL'S *palace.*

   *Enter* CARDINAL *and* JULIA.

   CARD. Sit: thou art my best of wishes. Prithee, tell me
What trick didst thou invent to come to Rome
Without thy husband?
   JULIA.          Why, my lord, I told him
I came to visit an old anchorite
Here for devotion.
   CARD.          Thou art a witty false one, —
I mean, to him.
   JULIA.          You have prevail'd with me
Beyond my strongest thoughts; I would not now
Find you inconstant.
   CARD.          Do not put thyself
To such a voluntary torture, which proceeds
Out of your own guilt.
   JULIA.          How, my lord!
   CARD.          You fear          10
My constancy, because you have approv'd
Those giddy and wild turnings in yourself.
   JULIA. Did you e'er find them?
   CARD.          Sooth, generally for women,
A man might strive to make glass malleable,
Ere he should make them fixed.
   JULIA.          So, my lord.

56. **false friend,** *i.e., his lantern.*
64. **Cætera non scrutantur.** *The rest is not scrutinized.*

CARD. We had need go borrow that fantastic glass
Invented by Galileo, the Florentine,
To view another spacious world i' the moon,
And look to find a constant woman there.
    JULIA. This is very well, my lord.
    CARD.                     Why do you weep?        20
Are tears your justification? The self-same tears
Will fall into your husband's bosom, lady,
With a loud protestation that you love him
Above the world. Come, I 'll love you wisely:
That 's jealously, since I am very certain
You cannot me make cuckold.
    JULIA.                I 'll go home
To my husband.
    CARD.        You may thank me, lady.
I have taken you off your melancholy perch,
Bore you upon my fist, and show'd you game,
And let you fly at it. I pray thee, kiss me.          30
When thou wast with thy husband, thou wast watch'd
Like a tame elephant: — still you are to thank me: —
Thou hadst only kisses from him and high feeding;
But what delight was that? 'T was just like one
That hath a little fing'ring on the lute,
Yet cannot tune it: — still you are to thank me.
    JULIA. You told me of a piteous wound i' th' heart,
And a sick liver, when you woo'd me first,
And spake like one in physic.
    CARD.              Who 's that? —

*Enter* SERVANT.

Rest firm! for my affection to thee,         40
Lightning moves slow to 't.
    SERV.            Madam, a gentleman
That 's come post from Malfi, desires to see you.
    CARD. Let him enter: I 'll withdraw.        [*Exit.*
    SERV.            He says
Your husband, old Castruccio, is come to Rome,
Most pitifully tir'd with riding post.        [*Exit.*

*Enter* DELIO.

    JULIA. [*Aside*] Signior Delio! 't is one of my old suitors.
    DELIO. I was bold to come and see you.
    JULIA.                 Sir, you are welcome.
    DELIO. Do you lie here?
    JULIA.             Sure, your own experience
Will satisfy you no: our Roman prelates
Do not keep lodging for ladies.
    DELIO.           Very well:        50
I have brought you no commendations from your husband,
For I know none by him.
    JULIA.          I hear he 's come to Rome.
    DELIO. I never knew man and beast, of a horse and a knight,
So weary of each other. If he had had a good back,
He would have undertook to have borne his horse,
His breech was so pitifully sore.

JULIA.                    Your laughter
Is my pity.
    DELIO.   Lady, I know not whether
You want money, but I have brought some.
    JULIA. From my husband?
    DELIO.                      No, from mine own allowance.
    JULIA. I must hear the condition, ere I be bound to take it.          60
    DELIO. Look on 't, 't is gold; hath it not a fine colour?
    JULIA. I have a bird more beautiful.
    DELIO.                    Try the sound on 't.
    JULIA. A lute-string far exceeds it.
It hath no smell, like cassia or civet;
Nor is it physical, though some fond doctors
Persuade us seethe 't in cullises. I 'll tell you,
This is a creature bred by —

    *Re-enter* SERVANT.

    SERV.                    Your husband 's come,
Hath deliver'd a letter to the Duke of Calabria
That, to my thinking, hath put him out of his wits.          [*Exit.*
    JULIA. Sir, you hear:                                                 70
Pray, let me know your business and your suit
As briefly as can be.
    DELIO. With good speed: I would wish you,
At such time as you are non-resident
With your husband, my mistress.
    JULIA. Sir, I 'll go ask my husband if I shall,
And straight return your answer.                            [*Exit.*
    DELIO.                    Very fine!
Is this her wit, or honesty, that speaks thus?
I heard one say the duke was highly mov'd
With a letter sent from Malfi. I do fear                                 80
Antonio is betray'd. How fearfully
Shows his ambition now! Unfortunate fortune!
They pass through whirl-pools, and deep woes do shun,
Who the event weigh ere the action 's done.                 [*Exit.*


SCENE V: *Another room in the* CARDINAL'S *palace.*

*Enter* CARDINAL *and* FERDINAND, *with a letter.*

    FERD. I have this night digg'd up a mandrake.
    CARD.                          Say you?
    FERD. And I am grown mad with 't.
    CARD.                       What 's the prodigy?
    FERD. Read there, — a sister damn'd! She 's loose i' th' hilts;
Grown a notorious strumpet!
    CARD.               Speak lower.
    FERD.                       Lower!
Rogues do not whisper 't now, but seek to publish 't
(As servants do the bounty of their lords)
Aloud; and with a covetous searching eye,
To mark who note them. O, confusion seize her!

    *Scene iv.   65.* **physical,** *medicinal.*
*66.* **cullises,** *broths.*
    *Scene v.   1.* **mandrake,** *a plant superstitiously believed to shriek when dug up, causing any hearer to go mad.*

She hath had most cunning bawds to serve her turn,
And more secure conveyances for lust                                    10
Than towns of garrison for service.
    CARD.                              Is 't possible?
Can this be certain?
    FERD.                   Rhubarb! O, for rhubarb
To purge this choler! Here 's the cursed day
To prompt my memory; and here 't shall stick
Till of her bleeding heart I make a sponge
To wipe it out.
    CARD.          Why do you make yourself
So wild a tempest?
    FERD.               Would I could be one,
That I might toss her palace 'bout her ears,
Root up her goodly forests, blast her meads,
And lay her general territory as waste                                  20
As she hath done her honours.
    CARD.                    Shall our blood,
The royal blood of Arragon and Castile,
Be thus attainted?
    FERD.              Apply desperate physic:
We must not now use balsamum, but fire,
The smarting cupping-glass, for that 's the mean
To purge infected blood, such blood as hers.
There is a kind of pity in mine eye, —
I 'll give it to my handkercher; and now 't is here,
I 'll bequeath this to her bastard.
    CARD.                            What to do?
    FERD. Why, to make soft lint for his mother's wounds,     30
When I have hew'd her to pieces.
    CARD.                        Curs'd creature!
Unequal nature, to place women's hearts
So far upon the left side!
    FERD.                     Foolish men,
That e'er will trust their honour in a bark
Made of so slight weak bulrush as is woman,
Apt every minute to sink it!
    CARD. Thus ignorance, when it hath purchas'd honour,
It cannot wield it.
    FERD.            Methinks I see her laughing, —
Excellent hyena! Talk to me somewhat, quickly,
Or my imagination will carry me                                         40
To see her in the shameful act of sin.
    CARD. With whom?
    FERD. Happily with some strong-thigh'd bargeman,
Or one o' th' wood-yard that can quoit the sledge
Or toss the bar, or else some lovely squire
That carries coals up to her privy lodgings.
    CARD. You fly beyond your reason.
    FERD.                          Go to, mistress!
'T is not your whore's milk that shall quench my wild-fire,
But your whore's blood.
    CARD. How idly shows this rage, which carries you,      50

---

44. **quoit the sledge,** *throw the hammer.*

As men convey'd by witches through the air
On violent whirlwinds! This intemperate noise
Fitly resembles deaf men's shrill discourse,
Who talk aloud, thinking all other men
To have their imperfection.
    FERD.               Have not you
My palsy?
    CARD.   Yes, but I can be angry
Without this rupture. There is not in nature
A thing that makes man so deform'd, so beastly,
As doth intemperate anger. Chide yourself.
You have divers men who never yet express'd 60
Their strong desire of rest but by unrest,
By vexing of themselves. Come, put yourself
In tune.
    FERD. So I will only study to seem
The thing I am not. I could kill her now,
In you, or in myself; for I do think
It is some sin in us heaven doth revenge
By her.
    CARD. Are you stark mad?
    FERD.            I would have their bodies
Burnt in a coal-pit with the ventage stopp'd,
That their curs'd smoke might not ascend to heaven;
Or dip the sheets they lie in in pitch or sulphur, 70
Wrap them in 't, and then light them like a match;
Or else to boil their bastard to a cullis,
And give 't his lecherous father to renew
The sin of his back.
    CARD.       I 'll leave you.
    FERD.           Nay, I have done.
I am confident, had I been damn'd in hell,
And should have heard of this, it would have put me
Into a cold sweat. In, in; I 'll go sleep.
Till I know who leaps my sister, I 'll not stir:
That known, I 'll find scorpions to string my whips,
And fix her in a general eclipse.     [*Exeunt.* 80

# ACT III

SCENE I: *Amalfi. A room in the* DUCHESS' *palace.*

*Enter* ANTONIO *and* DELIO.

    ANT. Our noble friend, my most beloved Delio!
O, you have been a stranger long at court.
Came you along with the Lord Ferdinand?
    DELIO. I did, sir: and how fares your noble duchess?
    ANT. Right fortunately well: she 's an excellent
Feeder of pedigrees; since you last saw her,
She hath had two children more, a son and daughter.
    DELIO. Methinks 't was yesterday. Let me but wink,
And not behold your face, which to mine eye
Is somewhat leaner, verily I should dream 10
It were within this half hour.

ANT. You have not been in law, friend Delio,
Nor in prison, nor a suitor at the court,
Nor begg'd the reversion of some great man's place,
Nor troubled with an old wife, which doth make
Your time so insensibly hasten.
    DELIO.             Pray, sir, tell me,
Hath not this news arriv'd yet to the ear
Of the lord cardinal?
    ANT.         I fear it hath;
The Lord Ferdinand, that 's newly come to court,
Doth bear himself right dangerously.
    DELIO.            Pray, why?        20
    ANT. He is so quiet that he seems to sleep
The tempest out, as dormice do in winter.
Those houses that are haunted are most still,
Till the devil be up.
    DELIO.        What say the common people?
    ANT. The common rabble do directly say
She is a strumpet.
    DELIO.       And your graver heads
Which would be politic, what censure they?
    ANT. They do observe I grow to infinite purchase
The left-hand way, and all suppose the duchess
Would amend it, if she could; for, say they,        30
Great princes, though they grudge their officers
Should have such large and unconfined means
To get wealth under them, will not complain,
Lest thereby they should make them odious
Unto the people. For other obligation,
Of love or marriage between her and me,
They never dream of.
    DELIO.       The Lord Ferdinand
Is going to bed.

    *Enter* DUCHESS, FERDINAND, *and Attendants.*

    FERD.      I 'll instantly to bed,
For I am weary. — I am to bespeak
A husband for you.
    DUCH.        For me, sir? Pray, who is 't?        40
    FERD. The great Count Malateste.
    DUCH.              Fie upon him!
A count! He 's a mere stick of sugar-candy;
You may look quite through him. When I choose
A husband, I will marry for your honour.
    FERD. You shall do well in 't. — How is 't, worthy Antonio?
    DUCH. But, sir, I am to have private conference with you
About a scandalous report is spread
Touching mine honour.
    FERD.        Let me be ever deaf to 't:
One of Pasquil's paper-bullets, court-calumny,
A pestilent air, which princes' palaces        50
Are seldom purg'd of. Yet, say that it were true,
I pour it in your bosom, my fix'd love

---

*Act III, Scene i.*  **49. Pasquil,** *a statue in Rome on which lampoons were often posted.*

Would strongly excuse, extenuate, nay, deny
Faults, were they apparent in you. Go, be safe
In your own innocency.
    DUCH. [*Aside*]        O bless'd comfort!
This deadly air is purg'd.
                [*Exeunt* DUCHESS, ANTONIO, DELIO, *and Attendants.*
    FERD.             Her guilt treads on
Hot-burning coulters.

    *Enter* BOSOLA.

                        Now, Bosola,
How thrives our intelligence?
    BOS.             Sir, uncertainly:
'T is rumour'd she hath had three bastards, but
By whom we may go read i' th' stars.
    FERD.              Why, some      60
Hold opinion all things are written there.
    BOS. Yes, if we could find spectacles to read them.
I do suspect there hath been some sorcery
Us'd on the duchess.
    FERD.          Sorcery! To what purpose?
    BOS. To make her dote on some desertless fellow
She shames to acknowledge.
    FERD.             Can your faith give way
To think there 's power in potions or in charms,
To make us love whether we will or no?
    BOS. Most certainly.
    FERD. Away! These are mere gulleries, horrid things,    70
Invented by some cheating mountebanks
To abuse us. Do you think that herbs or charms
Can force the will? Some trials have been made
In this foolish practice, but the ingredients
Were lenitive poisons, such as are of force
To make the patient mad; and straight the witch
Swears by equivocation they are in love.
The witchcraft lies in her rank blood. This night
I will force confession from her. You told me
You had got, within these two days, a false key    80
Into her bed-chamber.
    BOS.          I have.
    FERD.             As I would wish.
    BOS. What do you intend to do?
    FERD.             Can you guess?
    BOS.                  No.
    FERD.                      Do not ask, then:
He that can compass me, and know my drifts,
May say he hath put a girdle 'bout the world,
And sounded all her quick-sands.
    BOS.             I do not
Think so.
    FERD. What do you think, then, pray?
    BOS.                That you
Are your own chronicle too much, and grossly
Flatter yourself.
    FERD.        Give me thy hand; I thank thee:

I never gave pension but to flatterers,
Till I entertained thee. Farewell.                                            90
That friend a great man's ruin strongly checks,
Who rails into his belief all his defects.                    [*Exeunt.*

SCENE II: *The* DUCHESS' *bed-chamber.*

*Enter* DUCHESS, ANTONIO, *and* CARIOLA.

DUCH. Bring me the casket hither, and the glass. —
You get no lodging here to-night, my lord.
ANT. Indeed, I must persuade one.
DUCH.                                  Very good:
I hope in time 't will grow into a custom,
That noblemen shall come with cap and knee
To purchase a night's lodging of their wives.
ANT. I must lie here.
DUCH. Must! You are a lord of mis-rule.
ANT. Indeed, my rule is only in the night.
DUCH. To what use will you put me?
ANT.                              We 'll sleep together.          10
DUCH. Alas, what pleasure can two lovers find in sleep?
CARI. My lord, I lie with her often, and I know
She 'll much disquiet you.
ANT.                  See, you are complain'd of.
CARI. For she 's the sprawling'st bedfellow.
ANT. I shall like her the better for that.
CARI. Sir, shall I ask you a question?
ANT. I pray thee, Cariola.
CARI. Wherefore still when you lie with my lady
Do you rise so early?
ANT.            Labouring men
Count the clock oft'nest, Cariola,                                20
Are glad when their task 's ended.
DUCH. I 'll stop your mouth.                        [*Kisses him.*
ANT. Nay, that 's but one; Venus had two soft doves
To draw her chariot: I must have another. —     [*She kisses him again.*
When wilt thou marry, Cariola?
CARI.                    Never, my lord.
ANT. O, fie upon this single life! Forgo it.
We read how Daphne, for her peevish slight,
Became a fruitless bay-tree; Syrinx turn'd
To the pale empty reed; Anaxarete
Was frozen into marble: whereas those                          30
Which married, or prov'd kind unto their friends,
Were by a gracious influence trans-shap'd
Into the olive, pomegranate, mulberry,
Became flowers, precious stones, or eminent stars.
CARI. This is a vain poetry: but I pray you, tell me,
If there were propos'd me wisdom, riches, and beauty,
In three several young men, which should I choose?
ANT. 'T is a hard question. This was Paris' case,
And he was blind in 't, and there was great cause;
For how was 't possible he could judge right,                  40
Having three amorous goddesses in view,
And they stark naked? 'T was a motion

Were able to benight the apprehension
Of the severest counsellor of Europe.
Now I look on both your faces so well form'd,
It puts me in mind of a question I would ask.
   CARI. What is 't?
   ANT. I do wonder why hard-favour'd ladies,
For the most part, keep worse-favour'd waiting-women
To attend them, and cannot endure fair ones.        50
   DUCH. O, that 's soon answer'd.
Did you ever in your life know an ill painter
Desire to have his dwelling next door to the shop
Of an excellent picture-maker? 'T would disgrace
His face-making, and undo him. I prithee,
When were we so merry? My hair tangles.
   ANT. Pray thee, Cariola, let 's steal forth the room,
And let her talk to herself. I have divers times
Serv'd her the like, when she hath chaf'd extremely.
I love to see her angry. Softly, Cariola,    [*Exeunt* ANTONIO *and* CARIOLA.   60
   DUCH. Doth not the colour of my hair 'gin to change?
When I wax gray, I shall have all the court
Powder their hair with arras, to be like me.
You have cause to love me; I ent'red you into my heart

   *Enter* FERDINAND *unseen.*

Before you would vouchsafe to call for the keys.
We shall one day have my brothers take you napping.
Methinks his presence, being now in court,
Should make you keep your own bed; but you 'll say
Love mix'd with fear is sweetest. I 'll assure you,
You shall get no more children till my brothers      70
Consent to be your gossips. Have you lost your tongue?
'T is welcome:
For know, whether I am doom'd to live or die,
I can do both like a prince.
   FERD.              Die, then, quickly.
                      [FERDINAND *gives her a poniard.*
Virtue, where art thou hid? What hideous thing
Is it that doth eclipse thee?
   DUCH.           Pray, sir, hear me.
   FERD. Or is it true thou art but a bare name,
And no essential thing?
   DUCH.         Sir——
   FERD.             Do not speak.
   DUCH. No, sir:
I will plant my soul in mine ears, to hear you.      80
   FERD. O most imperfect light of human reason,
That mak'st us so unhappy to foresee
What we can least prevent! Pursue thy wishes,
And glory in them: there 's in shame no comfort
But to be past all bounds and sense of shame.
   DUCH. I pray, sir, hear me: I am married.
   FERD.                  So!
   DUCH. Happily, not to your liking: but for that,

*Scene ii.*   71. **gossips,** *godfathers.*

Alas, your shears do come untimely now
To clip the bird's wings that 's already flown!
Will you see my husband?

    FERD.                 Yes, if I could change         90
Eyes with a basilisk.

    DUCH.             Sure, you came hither
By his confederacy.

    FERD.            The howling of a wolf
Is music to thee, screech-owl: prithee, peace. —
Whate'er thou art that hast enjoy'd my sister,
For I am sure thou hear'st me, for thine own sake
Let me not know thee. I came hither prepar'd
To work thy discovery; yet am now persuaded
It would beget such violent effects
As would damn us both. I would not for ten millions
I had beheld thee: therefore use all means         100
I never may have knowledge of thy name.
Enjoy thy lust still, and a wretched life,
On that condition. — And for thee, vild woman,
If thou do wish thy lecher may grow old
In thy embracements, I would have thee build
Such a room for him as our anchorites
To holier use inhabit. Let not the sun
Shine on him till he 's dead; let dogs and monkeys
Only converse with him, and such dumb things
To whom nature denies use to sound his name;       110
Do not keep a paraquito, lest she learn it;
If thou do love him, cut out thine own tongue,
Lest it betray him.

    DUCH.            Why might not I marry?
I have not gone about in this to create
Any new world or custom.

    FERD.               Thou art undone;
And thou hast ta'en that massy sheet of lead
That hid thy husband's bones, and folded it
About my heart.

    DUCH.        Mine bleeds for 't.

    FERD.                    Thine! thy heart!
What should I name 't, unless a hollow bullet
Fill'd with unquenchable wild-fire?

    DUCH.                  You are in this      120
Too strict; and were you not my princely brother,
I would say, too wilful: my reputation
Is safe.

    FERD. Dost thou know what reputation is?
I 'll tell thee, — to small purpose, since th' instruction
Comes now too late.
Upon a time Reputation, Love, and Death
Would travel o'er the world; and it was concluded
That they should part, and take three several ways.
Death told them, they should find him in great battles,     130
Or cities plagu'd with plagues; Love gave them counsel
To inquire for him 'mongst unambitious shepherds,
Where dowries were not talk'd of, and sometimes
'Mongst quiet kindred that had nothing left

By their dead parents. "Stay," quoth Reputation,
"Do not forsake me; for it is my nature,
If once I part from any man I meet,
I am never found again." And so for you:
You have shook hands with Reputation,
And made him invisible. So, fare you well.     140
I will never see you more.
    DUCH.                Why should only I,
Of all the other princes of the world,
Be cas'd up, like a holy relic? I have youth
And a little beauty.
    FERD.           So you have some virgins
That are witches. I will never see thee more.         [*Exit.*

    *Enter* ANTONIO *with a pistol, and* CARIOLA.

    DUCH. You saw this apparition?
    ANT.                Yes: we are
Betray'd. How came he hither? I should turn
This to thee, for that.
    CARI.          Pray, sir, do; and when
That you have cleft my heart, you shall read there
Mine innocence.
    DUCH.        That gallery gave him entrance.      150
    ANT. I would this terrible thing would come again,
That, standing on guard, I might relate
My warrantable love. —         [*She shows the poniard.*
           Ha! what means this?
    DUCH. He left this with me.
    ANT.             And it seems did wish
You would use it on yourself?
    DUCH.           His action seem'd
To intend so much.
    ANT.         This hath a handle to 't,
As well as a point. Turn it towards him, and
So fasten the keen edge in his rank gall.     [*Knocking within.*
How now! Who knocks? More earthquakes?
    DUCH.            I stand
As if a mine beneath my feet were ready      160
To be blown up.
    CARI.     'T is Bosola.
    DUCH.        Away!
O misery! methinks unjust actions
Should wear these masks and curtains, and not we.
You must instantly part hence: I have fashion'd it already.
           [*Exit* ANTONIO.

    *Enter* BOSOLA.

    BOS. The duke your brother is ta'en up in a whirlwind;
Hath took horse, and 's rid post to Rome.
    DUCH.           So late?
    BOS. He told me, as he mounted into th' saddle,
You were undone.
    DUCH.        Indeed, I am very near it.
    BOS. What 's the matter?
    DUCH. Antonio, the master of our household,     170

Hath dealt so falsely with me in 's accounts.
My brother stood engag'd with me for money
Ta'en up of certain Neapolitan Jews,
And Antonio lets the bonds be forfeit.
   BOS. Strange! — [*Aside*] This is cunning.
   DUCH.                    And hereupon
My brother's bills at Naples are protested
Against. — Call up our officers.
   BOS.             I shall.                           [*Exit.*

   *Re-enter* ANTONIO.

   DUCH. The place that you must fly to is Ancona:
Hire a house there. I 'll send after you
My treasure and my jewels. Our weak safety             180
Runs upon enginous wheels: short syllables
Must stand for periods. I must now accuse you
Of such a feigned crime as Tasso calls
*Magnanima menzogna,* a noble lie.
'Cause it must shield our honours. — Hark! they are coming.

   *Re-enter* BOSOLA *and Officers.*

   ANT. Will your grace hear me?
   DUCH. I have got well by you: you have yielded me
A million of loss; I am like to inherit
The people's curses for your stewardship.
You had the trick in audit-time to be sick,            190
Till I had sign'd your quietus; and that cur'd you
Without help of a doctor. — Gentlemen,
I would have this man be an example to you all:
So shall you hold my favour; I pray, let him;
For h'as done that, alas, you would not think of,
And, because I intend to be rid of him,
I mean not to publish. — Use your fortune elsewhere.
   ANT. I am strongly arm'd to brook my overthrow,
As commonly men bear with a hard year.
I will not blame the cause on 't; but do think         200
The necessity of my malevolent star
Procures this, not her humour. O, the inconstant
And rotten ground of service! You may see,
'T is e'en like him, that in a winter night,
Takes a long slumber o'er a dying fire,
As loath to part from 't; yet parts thence as cold
As when he first sat down.
   DUCH.              We do confiscate,
Towards the satisfying of your accounts,
All that you have.
   ANT. I am all yours; and 't is very fit         210
All mine should be so.
   DUCH.         So, sir, you have your pass.
   ANT. You may see, gentlemen, what 't is to serve
A prince with body and soul.                    [*Exit.*
   BOS. Here 's an example for extortion: what moisture is drawn out of
the sea, when foul weather comes, pours down, and runs into the sea
again.

182. **periods,** *periodic sentences.*
191. **sign'd your quietus,** *settled your account.*

DUCH. I would know what are your opinions
Of this Antonio.

2 OFF. He could not abide to see a pig's head gaping: I thought your
grace would find him a Jew.                                                    220

3 OFF. I would you had been his officer, for your own sake.

4 OFF. You would have had more money.

1 OFF. He stopp'd his ears with black wool, and to those came to him
for money said he was thick of hearing.

2 OFF. Some said he was an hermaphrodite, for he could not abide a
woman.

4 OFF. How scurvy proud he would look when the treasury was full!
Well, let him go.

1 OFF. Yes, and the chippings of the buttery fly after him, to scour his
gold chain.                                                                    230

DUCH. Leave us.                                            [*Exeunt Officers.*
What do you think of these?

BOS. That these are rogues that in 's prosperity,
But to have waited on his fortune, could have wish'd
His dirty stirrup riveted through their noses,
And follow'd after 's mule, like a bear in a ring;
Would have prostituted their daughters to his lust;
Made their first-born intelligencers; thought none happy
But such as were born under his blest planet,
And wore his livery: and do these lice drop off now?                           240
Well, never look to have the like again;
He hath left a sort of flatt'ring rogues behind him:
Their doom must follow. Princes pay flatterers
In their own money: flatterers dissemble their vices,
And they dissemble their lies; that 's justice.
Alas, poor gentleman!

DUCH. Poor! He hath amply fill'd his coffers.

BOS. Sure, he was too honest. Pluto, the god of riches,
When he 's sent by Jupiter to any man,
He goes limping, to signify that wealth                                        250
That comes on God's name comes slowly; but when he 's sent
On the devil's errand, he rides post and comes in by scuttles.
Let me show you what a most unvalu'd jewel
You have in a wanton humour thrown away,
To bless the man shall find him. He was an excellent
Courtier and most faithful; a soldier that thought it
As beastly to know his own value too little
As devilish to acknowledge it too much.
Both his virtue and form deserv'd a far better fortune;
His discourse rather delighted to judge itself than show itself.               260
His breast was fill'd with all perfection,
And yet it seem'd a private whisp'ring-room,
It made so little noise of 't.

DUCH. But he was basely descended.

BOS. Will you make yourself a mercenary herald,
Rather to examine men's pedigrees than virtues?
You shall want him,
For know, an honest statesman to a prince
Is like a cedar planted by a spring;

---

230. **gold chain,** *steward's badge.*

The spring bathes the tree's root, the grateful tree        270
Rewards it with his shadow: you have not done so.
I would sooner swim to the Bermooths on
Two politicians' rotten bladders, tied
Together with an intelligencer's heart-string,
Than depend on so changeable a prince's favour.
Fare thee well, Antonio! Since the malice of the world
Would needs down with thee, it cannot be said yet
That any ill happen'd unto thee, considering thy fall
Was accompanied with virtue.
    DUCH. O, you render me excellent music!
    BOS.                         Say you?        280
    DUCH. This good one that you speak of is my husband.
    BOS. Do I not dream? Can this ambitious age
Have so much goodness in 't as to prefer
A man merely for worth, without these shadows
Of wealth and painted honours? Possible?
    DUCH. I have had three children by him.
    BOS.                      Fortunate lady!
For you have made your private nuptial bed
The humble and fair seminary of peace.
No question but many an unbenefic'd scholar
Shall pray for you for this deed, and rejoice        290
That some preferment in the world can yet
Arise from merit. The virgins of your land
That have no dowries shall hope your example
Will raise them to rich husbands. Should you want
Soldiers, 't would make the very Turks and Moors
Turn Christians, and serve you for this act.
Last, the neglected poets of your time,
In honour of this trophy of a man,
Rais'd by that curious engine, your white hand,
Shall thank you in your grave for 't, and make that        300
More reverend than all the cabinets
Of living princes. For Antonio,
His fame shall likewise flow from many a pen,
When heralds shall want coats to sell to men.
    DUCH. As I taste comfort in this friendly speech,
So would I find concealment.
    BOS. O, the secret of my prince,
Which I will wear on th' inside of my heart!
    DUCH. You shall take charge of all my coin and jewels,
And follow him, for he retires himself        310
To Ancona.
    BOS.      So.
    DUCH.        Whither, within few days,
I mean to follow thee.
    BOS.           Let me think:
I would wish your grace to feign a pilgrimage
To our Lady of Loretto, scarce seven leagues
From fair Ancona; so may you depart
Your country with more honour, and your flight
Will seem a princely progress, retaining
Your usual train about you.
    DUCH.             Sir, your direction

Shall lead me by the hand.

CARI. In my opinion,
She were better progress to the baths at Lucca,                          320
Or go visit the Spa
In Germany; for, if you will believe me,
I do not like this jesting with religion,
This feigned pilgrimage.

DUCH. Thou art a superstitious fool!
Prepare us instantly for our departure.
Past sorrows, let us moderately lament them,
For those to come, seek wisely to prevent them.

[*Exeunt* DUCHESS *and* CARIOLA.

BOS. A politician is the devil's quilted anvil;                          330
He fashions all sins on him, and the blows
Are never heard: he may work in a lady's chamber,
As here for proof. What rests but I reveal
All to my lord? O, this base quality
Of intelligencer! Why, every quality i' th' world
Prefers but gain or commendation:
Now, for this act I am certain to be rais'd,
And men that paint weeds to the life are prais'd.

[*Exit.*

SCENE III: *Rome. A room in the* CARDINAL'S *palace.*

*Enter* CARDINAL, FERDINAND, MALATESTE, PESCARA, SILVIO, *and* DELIO.

CARD. Must we turn soldier, then?

MAL. The emperor,
Hearing your worth that way (ere you attain'd
This reverend garment), joins you in commission
With the right fortunate soldier, the Marquis of Pescara,
And the famous Lannoy.

CARD. He that had the honour
Of taking the French king prisoner?

MAL. The same.
Here 's a plot drawn for a new fortification
At Naples.

FERD. This great Count Malateste, I perceive,
Hath got employment?

DELIO. No employment, my lord,                          10
A marginal note in the muster-book that he is
A voluntary lord.

FERD. He 's no soldier?

DELIO. He has worn gun-powder in 's hollow tooth for the tooth-ache.

SIL. He comes to the leaguer with a full intent
To eat fresh beef and garlic, means to stay
Till the scent be gone, and straight return to court.

DELIO. He hath read all the late service
As the City Chronicle relates it,
And keeps two pewterers going, only to express
Battles in model.

SIL. Then he 'll fight by the book.                          20

DELIO. By the same almanac, I think,
To choose good days and shun the critical.
That 's his mistress' scarf.

SIL.                    Yes, he protests
He would do much for that taffeta.

DELIO. I think he would run away from a battle,
To save it from taking prisoner.

SIL.                   He is horribly afraid
Gun-powder will spoil the perfume on 't.

DELIO. I saw a Dutchman break his pate once
For calling him a pot-gun; he made his head
Have a bore in 't like a musket.                  30

SIL. I would he had made a touch-hole to 't.
He is indeed a guarded sumpter-cloth,
Only for the remove of the court.

*Enter* BOSOLA.

PES. Bosola arriv'd! What should be the business?
Some falling-out amongst the cardinals.
These factions amongst great men, they are like
Foxes: when their heads are divided,
They carry fire in their tails, and all the country
About them goes to wrack for 't.

SIL.                 What 's that Bosola?

DELIO. I knew him in Padua, — a fantastical scholar, like such who study    40
to know how many knots was in Hercules' club, of what colour Achilles'
beard was, or whether Hector were not troubled with the tooth-ache. He
hath studied himself half blear-ey'd to know the true symmetry of Cæsar's
nose by a shoeing-horn; and this he did to gain the name of a speculative
man.

PES. Mark Prince Ferdinand:
A very salamander lives in 's eye,
To mock the eager violence of fire.

SIL. That cardinal hath made more bad faces with his oppression than
ever Michael Angelo made good ones. He lifts up 's nose, like a foul por-    50
poise before a storm.

PES. The Lord Ferdinand laughs.

DELIO.                Like a deadly cannon
That lightens ere it smokes.

PES. These are your true pangs of death,
The pangs of life, that struggle with great statesmen.

DELIO. In such a deformed silence, witches whisper their charms.

CARD. Doth she make religion her riding-hood
To keep her from the sun and tempest?

FERD. That, that damns her. Methinks her fault and beauty,
Blended together, show like leprosy,                  60
The whiter the fouler. I make it a question
Whether her beggarly brats were ever christ'n'd.

CARD. I will instantly solicit the state of Ancona
To have them banish'd.

FERD.             You are for Loretto?
I shall not be at your ceremony; fare you well. —
Write to the Duke of Malfi, my young nephew
She had by her first husband, and acquaint him
With 's mother's honesty.

BOS.              I will.

---

*Scene iii.*    32. **guarded sumpter-cloth,** *decorated saddle blanket.*

FERD.                          Antonio!
A slave that only smell'd of ink and counters,
And nev'r in 's life look'd like a gentleman,                    70
But in the audit-time. — Go, go presently,
Draw me out an hundreth and fifty of our horse,
And meet me at the fort-bridge.                    [*Exeunt.*

SCENE IV: *The shrine of our Lady of Loretto.*

*Enter Two Pilgrims.*

1 PIL. I have not seen a goodlier shrine than this;
Yet I have visited many.
    2 PIL.                    The cardinal of Arragon
Is this day to resign his cardinal's hat;
His sister duchess likewise is arriv'd
To pay her vow of pilgrimage. I expect
A noble ceremony.
    1 PIL.            No question. — They come.

*Here the ceremony of the* CARDINAL'S *instalment in the habit of a soldier:
    perform'd in delivering up his cross, hat, robes and ring at the shrine,
    and investing him with sword, helmet, shield, and spurs. Then* ANTONIO,
    *the* DUCHESS *and their children, having presented themselves at the
    shrine, are, by a form of banishment in dumb show expressed towards
    them by the* CARDINAL *and the state of Ancona, banished. During all
    which ceremony, this ditty is sung, to very solemn music, by divers
    churchmen; and then exeunt, all except the Two Pilgrims.*

Arms and honours deck thy story,
To thy fame's eternal glory!
Adverse fortune ever fly thee;
No disastrous fate come nigh thee!                    10
I alone will sing thy praises,
Whom to honour virtue raises,
And thy study, that divine is,
Bent to martial discipline is.
Lay aside all those robes lie by thee;
Crown thy arts with arms, they 'll beautify thee.

O worthy of worthiest name, adorn'd in this manner,
Lead bravely thy forces on under war's warlike banner!
O, mayst thou prove fortunate in all martial courses!
Guide thou still by skill in arts and forces!                    20
Victory attend thee nigh, whilst fame sings loud thy powers;
Triumphant conquest crown thy head, and blessings pour down showers!

    1 PIL. Here 's a strange turn of state! Who would have thought
So great a lady would have match'd herself
Unto so mean a person? Yet the Cardinal
Bears himself much too cruel.
    2 PIL.                    They are banish'd.
    1 PIL. But I would ask what power hath this state
Of Ancona to determine of a free prince?
    2 PIL. They are a free state, sir, and her brother show'd
How that the Pope, fore-hearing of her looseness,                    30
Hath seiz'd into th' protection of the church
The dukedom which she held as dowager.

1 PIL. But by what justice?

2 PIL.                    Sure, I think by none,
Only her brother's instigation.

1 PIL. What was it with such violence he took
Off from her finger?

2 PIL.                    'T was her wedding-ring;
Which he vow'd shortly he would sacrifice
To his revenge.

1 PIL.          Alas, Antonio!
If that a man be thrust into a well,
No matter who sets hand to 't, his own weight          40
Will bring him sooner to th' bottom. Come, let 's hence.
Fortune makes this conclusion general:
All things do help th' unhappy man to fall.          [*Exeunt.*

SCENE V: *Near Loretto.*

*Enter* DUCHESS, ANTONIO, *Children,* CARIOLA, *and Servants.*

DUCH. Banish'd Ancona!

ANT.                    Yes, you see what power
Lightens in great men's breath.

DUCH.                    Is all our train
Shrunk to this poor remainder?

ANT.                    These poor men,
Which have got little in your service, vow
To take your fortune; but your wiser buntings,
Now they are fledg'd, are gone.

DUCH.                    They have done wisely.
This puts me in mind of death: physicians thus,
With their hands full of money, use to give o'er
Their patients.

ANT.          Right the fashion of the world:
From decay'd fortunes every flatterer shrinks;          10
Men cease to build where the foundation sinks.

DUCH. I had a very strange dream to-night.

ANT.                              What was 't?

DUCH. Methought I wore my coronet of state,
And on a sudden all the diamonds
Were chang'd to pearls.

ANT.                    My interpretation
Is, you'll weep shortly; for to me the pearls
Do signify your tears.

DUCH.                The birds, that live i' th' field
On the wild benefit of nature, live
Happier than we: for they may choose their mates,
And carol their sweet pleasures to the spring.          20

*Enter* BOSOLA *with a letter.*

BOS. You are happily o'erta'en.

DUCH.                    From my brother?

BOS. Yes, from the Lord Ferdinand, your brother,
All love and safety.

DUCH.                Thou dost blanch mischief,
Would'st make it white. See, see, like to calm weather
At sea before a tempest, false hearts speak fair

To those they intend most mischief.                                        [*Reads.*
"Send Antonio to me; I want his head in a business."
A political equivocation!
He doth not want your counsel, but your head;
That is, he cannot sleep till you be dead.                                      30
And here 's another pitfall that 's strew'd o'er
With roses; mark, 't is a cunning one:                          [*Reads.*
"I stand engaged for your husband for several debts at Naples: let not
that trouble him; I had rather have his heart than his money." —
And I believe so too.
    BOS.                What do you believe?
    DUCH. That he so much distrusts my husband's love,
He will by no means believe his heart is with him
Until he see it. The devil is not cunning enough
To circumvent us in riddles.
    BOS. Will you reject that noble and free league                      40
Of amity and love which I present you?
    DUCH. Their league is like that of some politic kings,
Only to make themselves of strength and power
To be our after-ruin: tell them so.
    BOS. And what from you?
    ANT.            Thus tell him: I will not come.
    BOS. And what of this?
    ANT.            My brothers have dispers'd
Bloodhounds abroad; which till I hear are muzzl'd,
No truce, though hatch'd with ne'er such politic skill,
Is safe, that hangs upon our enemies' will.
I 'll not come at them.
    BOS.          This proclaims your breeding.                      50
Every small thing draws a base mind to fear
As the adamant draws iron. Fare you well, sir;
You shall shortly hear from 's.                                        [*Exit.*
    DUCH.          I suspect some ambush;
Therefore by all my love I do conjure you
To take your eldest son, and fly towards Milan,
Let us not venture all this poor remainder
In one unlucky bottom.
    ANT.          You counsel safely.
Best of my life, farewell. Since we must part,
Heaven hath a hand in 't; but no otherwise
Than as some curious artist takes in sunder                           60
A clock or watch, when it is out of frame,
To bring 't in better order.
    DUCH. I know not which is best,
To see you dead, or part with you. Farewell, boy:
Thou art happy that thou hast not understanding
To know thy misery; for all our wit
And reading brings us to a truer sense
Of sorrow. — In the eternal church, sir,
I do hope we shall not part thus.
    ANT.         O, be of comfort!
Make patience a noble fortitude,                                        70
And think not how unkindly we are us'd:
Man, like to cassia, is prov'd best, being bruis'd.
    DUCH. Must I, like to a slave-born Russian,

Account it praise to suffer tyranny?
And yet, O heaven, thy heavy hand is in 't!
I have seen my little boy oft scourge his top,
And compar'd myself to 't: naught made me e'er
Go right but heaven's scourge-stick.

    ANT.                     Do not weep:
Heaven fashion'd us of nothing; and we strive
To bring ourselves to nothing. — Farewell, Cariola,      80
And thy sweet armful. — If I do never see thee more,
Be a good mother to your little ones,
And save them from the tiger: fare you well.

    DUCH. Let me look upon you once more, for that speech
Came from a dying father. Your kiss is colder
Than that I have seen an holy anchorite
Give to a dead man's skull.

    ANT. My heart is turn'd to a heavy lump of lead,
With which I sound my danger: fare you well.

                           [*Exeunt* ANTONIO *and his son.*

    DUCH. My laurel is all withered.                90

    CARI. Look, madam, what a troop of armed men
Make towards us!

    *Re-enter* BOSOLA, *vizarded, with a Guard.*

    DUCH.          O, they are very welcome:
When Fortune's wheel is over-charg'd with princes,
The weight makes it move swift: I would have my ruin
Be sudden. — I am your adventure, am I not?

    BOS. You are: you must see your husband no more.

    DUCH. What devil are thou that counterfeits heaven's thunder?

    BOS. Is that terrible? I would have you tell me whether
Is that note worse that frights the silly birds
Out of the corn, or that which doth allure them      100
To the nets? You have heark'ned to the last too much.

    DUCH. O misery! Like to a rusty o'ercharg'd cannon,
Shall I never fly in pieces? Come, to what prison?

    BOS. To none.

    DUCH.          Whither, then?

    BOS.                 To your palace.

    DUCH.                      I have heard
That Charon's boat serves to convey all o'er
The dismal lake, but brings none back again.

    BOS. Your brothers mean you safety and pity.

    DUCH.                       Pity!
With such a pity men preserve alive
Pheasants and quails, when they are not fat enough
To be eaten.

    BOS.     These are your children?

    DUCH.                 Yes.

    BOS.                   Can they prattle?     110

    DUCH. No:
But I intend, since they were born accurs'd,
Curses shall be their first language.

    BOS.                 Fie, madam!
Forget this base, low fellow.

    DUCH.                 Were I a man,

I 'd beat that counterfeit face into thy other.
   BOS. One of no birth.
   DUCH.               Say that he was born mean.
Man is most happy when 's own actions
Be arguments and examples of his virtue.
   BOS. A barren, beggarly virtue.
   DUCH. I prithee, who is greatest? Can you tell?      120
Sad tales befit my woe: I 'll tell you one.
A salmon, as she swam unto the sea,
Met with a dog-fish, who encounters her
With this rough language: "Why art thou so bold
To mix thyself with our high state of floods,
Being no eminent courtier, but one
That for the calmest and fresh time o' th' year
Dost live in shallow rivers, rank'st thyself
With silly smelts and shrimps? And darest thou
Pass by our dog-ship without reverence?"           130
"O," quoth the salmon, "sister, be at peace:
Thank Jupiter we both have pass'd the net!
Our value never can be truly known,
Till in the fisher's basket we be shown;
I' th' market then my price may be the higher,
Even when I am nearest to the cook and fire."
So to great men the moral may be stretched:
Men oft are valu'd high, when th' are most wretched. —
But come, whither you please. I am arm'd 'gainst misery,
Bent to all sways of the oppressor's will.          140
There's no deep valley but near some great hill.      [*Exeunt.*

## ACT IV

SCENE I: *A room in the* DUCHESS' *palace at Malfi.*

*Enter* FERDINAND *and* BOSOLA.

   FERD. How doth our sister duchess bear herself
In her imprisonment?
   BOS.           Nobly: I 'll describe her.
She 's sad as one long us'd to 't, and she seems
Rather to welcome the end of misery
Than shun it; a behaviour so noble
As gives a majesty to adversity.
You may discern the shape of loveliness
More perfect in her tears than in her smiles;
She will muse four hours together, and her silence,
Methinks, expresseth more than if she spake.      10
   FERD. Her melancholy seems to be fortified
With a strange disdain.
   BOS.          'T is so; and this restraint,
(Like English mastiffs that grow fierce with tying)
Makes her too passionately apprehend
Those pleasures she 's kept from.
   FERD.              Curse upon her!

---

115. **counterfeit face,** *his mask.*

I will no longer study in the book
Of another's heart. Inform her what I told you.          [*Exit.*

 *Enter* DUCHESS *and Attendants.*

 BOS. All comfort to your grace!
 DUCH.      I will have none.
Pray thee, why dost thou wrap thy poison'd pills
In gold and sugar?          20
 BOS. Your elder brother, the Lord Ferdinand,
Is come to visit you, and sends you word,
'Cause once he rashly made a solemn vow
Never to see you more, he comes i' th' night;
And prays you gently neither torch nor taper
Shine in your chamber. He will kiss your hand,
And reconcile himself; but for his vow
He dares not see you.
 DUCH.   At his pleasure. —
Take hence the lights. — He 's come.     [*Exeunt Attendants with lights.*

 *Enter* FERDINAND.

 FERD.   Where are you?
 DUCH.      Here, sir.          30
 FERD. This darkness suits you well.
 DUCH.     I would ask you pardon.
 FERD. You have it;
For I account it the honourabl'st revenge,
Where I may kill, to pardon. — Where are your cubs?
 DUCH. Whom?
 FERD.   Call them your children;
For though our national law distinguish bastards
From true legitimate issue, compassionate nature
Makes them all equal.
 DUCH.   Do you visit me for this?
You violate a sacrament o' th' church
Shall make you howl in hell for 't.
 FERD.    It had been well,          40
Could you have liv'd thus always; for, indeed,
You were too much i' th' light. — But no more;
I come to seal my peace with you. Here 's a hand
     [*Gives her a dead man's hand.*
To which you have vow'd much love; the ring upon 't
You gave.
 DUCH. I affectionately kiss it.
 FERD. Pray, do, and bury the print of it in your heart.
I will leave this ring with you for a love-token;
And the hand as sure as the ring: and do not doubt          50
But you shall have the heart too. When you need a friend,
Send it to him that owned it; you shall see
Whether he can aid you.
 DUCH.   You are very cold:
I fear you are not well after your travel. —
Ha! lights! — O, horrible!
 FERD. Let her have lights enough.          [*Exit.*
 DUCH. What witchcraft doth he practise, that he hath left
A dead man's hand here?

*Here is discover'd, behind a traverse,*
   *the artificial figures of* ANTONIO *and*               60
   *his children, appearing as if they*
   *were dead.*

BOS. Look you, here 's the piece from which 't was ta'en.
He doth present you this sad spectacle,
That, now you know directly they are dead,
Hereafter you may wisely cease to grieve
For that which cannot be recovered.
   DUCH. There is not between heaven and earth one wish
I stay for after this. It wastes me more
Than were 't my picture, fashion'd out of wax,            70
Stuck with a magical needle, and then buried
In some foul dung-hill; and yond 's an excellent property
For a tyrant, which I would account mercy.
   BOS.                     What 's that?
   DUCH. If they would bind me to that lifeless trunk,
And let me freeze to death.
   BOS.              Come, you must live.
   DUCH. That 's the greatest torture souls feel in hell:
In hell that they must live, and cannot die.
Portia, I 'll new-kindle thy coals again,
And revive the rare and almost dead example
Of a loving wife.
   BOS.        O, fie! despair? Remember          80
You are a Christian.
   DUCH.        The church enjoins fasting:
I 'll starve myself to death.
   BOS.           Leave this vain sorrow.
Things being at the worst begin to mend: the bee
When he hath shot his sting into your hand,
May then play with your eye-lid.
   DUCH.             Good comfortable fellow!
Persuade a wretch that 's broke upon the wheel
To have all his bones new set; entreat him live
To be executed again. Who must despatch me?
I account this world a tedious theatre,
For I do play a part in 't 'gainst my will.          90
   BOS. Come, be of comfort: I will save your life.
   DUCH. Indeed, I have not leisure to tend so small a business.
   BOS. Now, by my life, I pity you.
   DUCH.            Thou art a fool, then,
To waste thy pity on a thing so wretched
As cannot pity itself. I am full of daggers.
Puff, let me blow these vipers from me.

*Enter Servant.*

What are you?
   SERV.       One that wishes you long life.
   DUCH. I would thou wert hang'd for the horrible curse
Thou hast given me: I shall shortly grow one
Of the miracles of pity. I 'll go pray; —            [*Exit Serv.* 100
No, I 'll go curse!

---

*Act IV, Scene i.*    78. **Portia,** *wife of the Roman Brutus; she committed suicide by swallowing fire.*

BOS.                O, fie!

DUCH.                     I could curse the stars —

BOS.                          O, fearful!

DUCH. And those three smiling seasons of the year
Into a Russian winter; nay, the world
To its first chaos.

BOS.              Look you, the stars shine still.

DUCH. O, but you must
Remember, my curse hath a great way to go. —
Plagues, that make lanes through largest families,
Consume them! —

BOS.           Fie, lady!

DUCH.                     Let them, like tyrants,
Never be remember'd but for the ill they have done;
Let all the zealous prayers of mortified                        110
Churchmen forget them! —

BOS.                     O, uncharitable!

DUCH. Let heaven a little while cease crowning martyrs,
To punish them! —
Go, howl them this, and say, I long to bleed:
It is some mercy when men kill with speed.                 [*Exit.*

     *Re-enter* FERDINAND.

FERD. Excellent, as I would wish; she 's plagu'd in art.
These presentations are but fram'd in wax
By the curious master in that quality,
Vincentio Lauriola, and she takes them
For true substantial bodies.

BOS.                     Why do you do this?            120

FERD. To bring her to despair.

BOS.                     Faith, end here,
And go no farther in your cruelty.
Send her a penitential garment to put on
Next to her delicate skin, and furnish her
With beads and prayer-books.

FERD.                     Damn her! that body of hers,
While that my blood ran pure in 't, was more worth
Than that which thou wouldst comfort, call'd a soul.
I will send her masques of common courtesans,
Have her meat serv'd up by bawds and ruffians,
And, 'cause she 'll needs be mad, I am resolv'd       130
To remove forth the common hospital
All the mad-folk, and place them near her lodging;
There let them practise together, sing and dance,
And act their gambols to the full o' th' moon:
If she can sleep the better for it, let her.
Your work is almost ended.

BOS.                     Must I see her again?

FERD. Yes.

BOS.      Never.

FERD.      You must.

BOS.                     Never in mine own shape;
That 's forfeited by my intelligence
And this last cruel lie: when you send me next,
The business shall be comfort.

FERD.                    Very likely!                                                        140
Thy pity is nothing of kin to thee. Antonio
Lurks about Milan; thou shalt shortly thither,
To feed a fire as great as my revenge,
Which never will slack till it hath spent his fuel:
Intemperate agues make physicians cruel.                    [*Exeunt.*


SCENE II: *Another room in the palace.*

*Enter* DUCHESS *and* CARIOLA.

DUCH. What hideous noise was that?
CARI.                                                    'T is the wild consort
Of madmen, lady, which your tyrant brother
Hath plac'd about your lodging. This tyranny,
I think, was never practis'd till this hour.
DUCH. Indeed, I thank him. Nothing but noise and folly
Can keep me in my right wits; whereas reason
And silence make me stark mad. Sit down;
Discourse to me some dismal tragedy.
CARI. O, 't will increase your melancholy!
DUCH.                                                    Thou art deceiv'd:
To hear of greater grief would lessen mine.                                        10
This is a prison?
CARI.                    Yes, but you shall live
To shake this durance off.
DUCH.                                    Thou art a fool:
The robin-red-breast and the nightingale
Never live long in cages.
CARI.                                    Pray, dry your eyes.
What think you of, madam?
DUCH.                                    Of nothing;
When I muse thus, I sleep.
CARI. Like a madman, with your eyes open?
DUCH. Dost thou think we shall know one another
In th' other world?
CARI.                    Yes, out of question.
DUCH. O, that it were possible we might                                        20
But hold some two days' conference with the dead!
From them I should learn somewhat, I am sure,
I never shall know here. I 'll tell thee a miracle:
I am not mad yet, to my cause of sorrow:
The' heaven o'er my head seems made of molten brass,
The earth of flaming sulphur, yet I am not mad.
I am acquainted with sad misery
As the tann'd galley-slave is with his oar;
Necessity makes me suffer constantly,
And custom makes it easy. Who do I look like now?                                30
CARI. Like to your picture in the gallery,
A deal of life in show, but none in practice;
Or rather like some reverend monument
Whose ruins are even pitied.
DUCH.                                    Very proper;
And Fortune seems only to have her eye-sight

To behold my tragedy. — How now!
What noise is that?

*Enter Servant.*

SERV.                    I am come to tell you,
Your brother hath intended you some sport.
A great physician, when the Pope was sick
Of a deep melancholy, presented him                              40
With several sorts of madmen, which wild object
Being full of change and sport forc'd him to laugh,
And so th' imposthume broke: the self-same cure
The duke intends on you.
DUCH.                    Let them come in.
SERV. There's a mad lawyer; and a secular priest;
A doctor that hath forfeited his wits
By jealousy; an astrologian
That in his works said such a day o' th' month
Should be the day of doom, and, failing of 't,
Ran mad; an English tailor, craz'd i' th' brain                   50
With the study of new fashion; a gentleman-usher
Quite beside himself with care to keep in mind
The number of his lady's salutations,
Or 'How do you,' she employ'd him in each morning;
A farmer, too, an excellent knave in grain,
Mad 'cause he was hinder'd transportation:
And let one broker that 's mad loose to these,
You 'd think the devil were among them.
DUCH. Sit, Cariola. — Let them loose when you please,
For I am chain'd to endure all your tyranny.                       60

*Enter* MADMEN.

*Here by a* MADMAN *this song is sung to a dismal kind of music.*

> *O, let us howl some heavy note,*
>   *Some deadly dogged howl,*
> *Sounding as from the threat'ning throat*
>   *Of beasts and fatal fowl!*
> *As ravens, screech-owls, bulls, and bears,*
>   *We 'll bell, and bawl our parts,*
> *Till irksome noise have cloy'd your ears*
>   *And corrosiv'd your hearts.*
> *At last, when as our choir wants breath,*
>   *Our bodies being blest,*                                       70
> *We 'll sing, like swans, to welcome death,*
>   *And die in love and rest.*

1 MADMAN. Doom's-day not come yet! I 'll draw it nearer by a perspective, or make a glass that shall set all the world on fire upon an instant. I
cannot sleep; my pillow is stuff'd with a litter of porcupines.
2 MADMAN. Hell is a mere glass-house, where the devils are continually
blowing up women's souls on hollow irons, and the fire never goes out.
3 MADMAN. I will lie with every woman in my parish the tenth night. I
will tithe them over like hay-cocks.
4 MADMAN. Shall my 'pothecary out-go me, because I am a cuckold? I    80

*Scene ii.*   43. **imposthume,** *abscess.*

have found out his roguery: he makes alum of his wife's urine, and sells it to Puritans that have sore throats with over-straining.

1 MADMAN. I have skill in heraldry.

2 MADMAN. Hast?

1 MADMAN. You do give for your crest a woodcock's head with the brains pick'd out on 't; you are a very ancient gentleman.

3 MADMAN. Greek is turn'd Turk: we are only to be sav'd by the Helvetian translation.

1 MADMAN. Come on, sir, I will lay the law to you.

2 MADMAN. O, rather lay a corrosive: the law will eat to the bone.          90

3 MADMAN. He that drinks but to satisfy nature is damn'd.

4 MADMAN. If I had my glass here, I would show a sight should make all the women here call me mad doctor.

1 MADMAN. What 's he? A rope-maker?

2 MADMAN. No, no, no; a snuffling knave that while he shows the tombs, will have his hand in a wench's placket.

3 MADMAN. Woe to the caroche that brought home my wife from the masque at three o'clock in the morning! It had a large feather-bed in it.

4 MADMAN. I have pared the devil's nails forty times, roasted them in raven's eggs, and cur'd agues with them.          100

3 MADMAN. Get me three hundred milchbats, to make possets to procure sleep.

4 MADMAN. All the college may throw their caps at me: I have made a soap-boiler costive; it was my masterpiece.

*Here the dance, consisting of eight* MADMEN, *with music answerable thereunto; after which,* BOSOLA, *like an old man, enters.*

DUCH. Is he mad too?

SERV.                    Pray, question him. I 'll leave you.

                         [*Exeunt Servant and* MADMEN.

BOS. I am come to make thy tomb.

DUCH.                    Ha! my tomb!
Thou speak'st as if I lay upon my death-bed,
Gasping for breath. Dost thou perceive me sick?

BOS. Yes, and the more dangerously, since thy sickness is insensible.

DUCH. Thou art not mad, sure; dost know me?          110

BOS. Yes.

DUCH. Who am I?

BOS. Thou art a box of worm-seed, at best but a salvatory of green mummy. What 's this flesh? A little crudded milk, fantastical puff-paste. Our bodies are weaker than those paper-prisons boys use to keep flies in; more contemptible, since ours is to preserve earth-worms. Didst thou ever see a lark in a cage? Such is the soul in the body: this world is like her little turf of grass, and the heaven o'er our heads, like her looking-glass, only gives us a miserable knowledge of the small compass of our prison.

DUCH. Am not I thy duchess?          120

BOS. Thou are some great woman, sure, for riot begins to sit on thy forehead, clad in gray hairs, twenty years sooner than on a merry milkmaid's. Thou sleep'st worse than if a mouse should be forc'd to take up her lodging in a cat's ear: a little infant that breeds its teeth, should it lie with thee, would cry out, as if thou wert the more unquiet bedfellow.

---

87. **Helvetian translation,** *a Calvinist edition of the Bible, produced in 1560 at Geneva.*
104. **costive,** *constipated.*
113. **green mummy,** *a drug partly composed of powdered parts of human or animal bodies.*

DUCH. I am Duchess of Malfi still.

BOS. That makes thy sleeps so broken:
Glories, like glow-worms, afar off shine bright,
But, look'd to near, have neither heat nor light.

DUCH. Thou art very plain.                                              130

BOS. My trade is to flatter the dead, not the living; I am a tomb-maker.

DUCH. And thou com'st to make my tomb?

BOS. Yes.

DUCH. Let me be a little merry: — of what stuff wilt thou make it?

BOS. Nay, resolve me first of what fashion?

DUCH. Why, do we grow fantastical in our deathbed?
Do we affect fashion in the grave?

BOS. Most ambitiously. Princes' images on their tombs do not lie, as
they were wont, seeming to pray up to heaven; but with their hands under
their cheeks, as if they died of the tooth-ache. They are not carved with   140
their eyes fix'd upon the stars; but, as their minds were wholly bent upon
the world, the selfsame way they seem to turn their faces.

DUCH. Let me know fully therefore the effect
Of this thy dismal preparation,
This talk fit for a charnel.

BOS.                          Now I shall: —

*Enter Executioners, with a coffin, cords, and a bell.*

Here is a present from your princely brothers;
And may it arrive welcome, for it brings
Last benefit, last sorrow.

DUCH.                       Let me see it;
I have so much obedience in my blood,
I wish it in their veins to do them good.                              150

BOS. This is your last presence-chamber.

CARI. O my sweet lady!

DUCH.                    Peace; it affrights not me.

BOS. I am the common bellman
That usually is sent to condemn'd persons
The night before they suffer.

DUCH.                          Even now thou said'st
Thou wast a tomb-maker.

BOS.                     'T was to bring you
By degrees to mortification. Listen.

> *Hark, now everything is still,*
> *The screech-owl and the whistler shrill*
> *Call upon our dame aloud,*                                          160
> *And bid her quickly don her shroud!*
> *Much you had of land and rent;*
> *Your length in clay 's now competent.*
> *A long war disturb'd your mind;*
> *Here your perfect peace is sign'd.*
> *Of what is 't fools make such vain keeping?*
> *Sin their conception, their birth weeping,*
> *Their life a general mist of error,*
> *Their death a hideous storm of terror.*
> *Strew your hair with powders sweet,*
> *Don clean linen, bathe your feet,*                                  170
> *And (the foul fiend more to check)*

> *A crucifix let bless your neck.*
> *'T is now full tide 'tween night and day;*
> *End your groan, and come away.*

CARI. Hence, villains, tyrants, murderers! Alas!
What will you do with my lady? — Call for help!
DUCH. To whom? To our next neighbours? They are mad-folks.
BOS. Remove that noise.
DUCH.                              Farewell, Cariola.
In my last will I have not much to give:                                        180
A many hungry guests have fed upon me;
Thine will be a poor reversion.
CARI.                              I will die with her.
DUCH. I pray thee, look thou giv'st my little boy
Some syrup for his cold, and let the girl
Say her prayers ere she sleep.
Now what you please:          [CARIOLA *is forced out by the Executioners.*
What death?
BOS. Strangling: here are your executioners.
DUCH. I forgive them:
The apoplexy, catarrh, or cough o' th' lungs,                                    190
Would do as much as they do.
BOS. Doth not death fright you?
DUCH.                              Who would be afraid on 't,
Knowing to meet such excellent company
In th' other world?
BOS. Yet, methinks,
The manner of your death should much afflict you:
This cord should terrify you.
DUCH.                    Not a whit.
What would it pleasure me to have my throat cut
With diamonds? Or to be smothered
With cassia? Or to be shot to death with pearls?                                200
I know death hath ten thousand several doors
For men to take their exits; and 't is found
They go on such strange geometrical hinges,
You may open them both ways: any way, for heaven-sake,
So I were out of your whispering. Tell my brothers
That I perceive death, now I am well awake,
Best gift is they can give or I can take.
I would fain put off my last woman's-fault:
I 'd not be tedious to you.
EXECUT.                    We are ready.
DUCH. Dispose my breath how please you; but my body                             210
Bestow upon my women, will you?
EXECUT.                    Yes.
DUCH. Pull, and pull strongly, for your able strength
Must pull down heaven upon me: —
Yet stay; heaven-gates are not so highly arch'd
As princes' palaces; they that enter there
Must go upon their knees [*kneels*]. — Come violent death,
Serve for mandragora to make me sleep! —
Go tell my brothers, when I am laid out,
They then may feed in quiet.          [*They strangle her.*
BOS. Where 's the waiting-woman?                                                220
Fetch her: some other strangle the children.

*Enter* CARIOLA.

Look you, there sleeps your mistress.

CARI.                              O, you are damn'd
Perpetually for this! My turn is next;
Is 't not so order'd?

BOS.                    Yes, and I am glad
You are so well prepared for 't.

CARI.                         You are deceiv'd, sir,
I am not prepar'd for 't, I will not die;
I will first come to my answer, and know
How I have offended.

BOS.                      Come, despatch her. —
You kept her counsel; now you shall keep ours.

CARI. I will not die, I must not; I am contracted                    230
To a young gentleman.

EXECUT.                  Here 's your wedding-ring.

CARI. Let me but speak with the duke, I 'll discover
Treason to his person.

BOS.                    Delays! — Throttle her!

EXECUT. She bites and scratches.

CARI.                           If you kill me now,
I am damn'd; I have not been at confession
This two years.

BOS. [*To Executioners*] When!

CARI.                     I am quick with child.

BOS.                                   Why, then,
Your credit 's saved.          [*Executioners strangle* CARIOLA.
               Bear her into th' next room;
Let this lie still.          [*Exeunt Executioners with body of* CARIOLA.

*Enter* FERDINAND.

FERD. Is she dead?

BOS.           She is what                                          240
You 'd have her. But here begin your pity:
                              [*Shows the Children strangled.*
Alas, how have these offended?

FERD.                   The death
Of young wolves is never to be pitied.

BOS. Fix your eye here.

FERD.           Constantly.

BOS.                    Do you not weep?
Other sins only speak; murder shrieks out.
The element of water moistens the earth,
But blood flies upwards and bedews the heavens.

FERD. Cover her face; mine eyes dazzle: she died young.

BOS. I think not so; her infelicity                                250
Seem 'd to have years too many.

FERD. She and I were twins;
And should I die this instant, I had liv'd
Her time to a minute.

BOS.           It seems she was born first:
You have bloodily approv'd the ancient truth,
That kindred commonly do worse agree
Than remote strangers.

FERD.                 Let me see her face

Again. Why didst not thou pity her? What
An excellent honest man mightst thou have been,
If thou hadst borne her to some sanctuary! 260
Or, bold in a good cause, oppos'd thyself,
With thy advanced sword above thy head,
Between her innocence and my revenge!
I bade thee, when I was distracted of my wits,
Go kill my dearest friend, and thou hast done 't.
For let me but examine well the cause:
What was the meanness of her match to me?
Only I must confess I had a hope,
Had she continu'd widow, to have gain'd
An infinite mass of treasure by her death. 270
And that was the main cause, — her marriage,
That drew a stream of gall quite through my heart.
For thee, as we observe in tragedies
That a good actor many times is curs'd
For playing a villain's part, I hate thee for 't.
And, for my sake, say, thou hast done much ill well.

    BOS. Let me quicken your memory, for I perceive
You are falling into ingratitude: I challenge
The reward due to my service.

     FERD.             I 'll tell thee
What I 'll give thee.

    BOS.         Do.

    FERD.            I 'll give thee a pardon 280
For this murder.

    BOS.        Ha!

    FERD.          Yes, and 't is
The largest bounty I can study to do thee.
By what authority didst thou execute
This bloody sentence?

    BOS.           By yours.

    FERD. Mine! Was I her judge?
Did any ceremonial form of law
Doom her to not-being? Did a complete jury
Deliver her conviction up i' th' court?
Where shalt thou find this judgment register'd,
Unless in hell? See, like a bloody fool, 290
Thou 'st forfeited thy life, and thou shalt die for 't.

    BOS. The office of justice is perverted quite
When one thief hangs another. Who shall dare
To reveal this?

    FERD.       O, I 'll tell thee;
The wolf shall find her grave, and scrape it up,
Not to devour the corpse, but to discover
The horrid murder.

    BOS.          You, not I, shall quake for 't.

    FERD. Leave me.

    BOS.         I will first receive my pension.

    FERD. You are a villain.

    BOS.           When your ingratitude
Is judge, I am so.

    FERD.      O horror! 300
That not the fear of him which binds the devils

Can prescribe man obedience! —
Never look upon me more.
    BOS.                Why, fare thee well.
Your brother and yourself are worthy men!
You have a pair of hearts are hollow graves,
Rotten, and rotting others; and your vengeance,
Like two chain'd bullets, still goes arm in arm.
You may be brothers; for treason, like the plague,
Doth take much in a blood. I stand like one
That long hath ta'en a sweet and golden dream:         310
I am angry with myself, now that I wake.
    FERD. Get thee into some unknown part o' th' world,
That I may never see thee.
    BOS.             Let me know
Wherefore I should be thus neglected. Sir,
I serv'd your tyranny, and rather strove
To satisfy yourself than all the world;
And though I loath'd the evil, yet I lov'd
You that did counsel it and rather sought
To appear a true servant than an honest man.
    FERD. I 'll go hunt the badger by owl-light:         320
'T is a deed for darkness.                            [*Exit.*
    BOS. He 's much distracted. Off, my painted honour!
While with vain hopes our faculties we tire,
We seem to sweat in ice and freeze in fire.
What would I do, were this to do again?
I would not change my peace of conscience
For all the wealth of Europe. — She stirs; here 's life: —
Return, fair soul, from darkness, and lead mine
Out of this sensible hell! — she 's warm, she breathes: —
Upon thy pale lips I will melt my heart,         330
To store them with fresh colour. — Who 's there?
Some cordial drink! — Alas! I dare not call:
So pity would destroy pity. — Her eye opes,
And heaven in it seems to ope, that late was shut,
To take me up to mercy.
    DUCH. Antonio!
    BOS.           Yes, madam, he is living;
The dead bodies you saw were but feign'd statues.
He 's reconciled to your brothers; the Pope hath wrought
The atonement.
    DUCH.       Mercy!                      [*She dies.*
    BOS. O, she 's gone again! There the cords of life broke.    340
O sacred innocence, that sweetly sleeps
On turtles' feathers, whilst a guilty conscience
Is a black register wherein is writ
All our good deeds and bad, a perspective
That shows us hell! That we cannot be suffer'd
To do good when we have a mind to it!
This is manly sorrow!
These tears, I am very certain, never grew
In my mother's milk. My estate is sunk
Below the degree of fear: where were         350
These penitent fountains while she was living?
O, they were frozen up! Here is a sight

As direful to my soul as is the sword
Unto a wretch hath slain his father.
Come, I 'll bear thee hence,
And execute thy last will; that 's deliver
Thy body to the reverend dispose
Of some good women: that the cruel tyrant
Shall not deny me. Then I 'll post to Milan,
Where somewhat I will speedily enact                          360
Worth my dejection.                          [*Exit with the body.*


## ACT V

SCENE I:   *Milan. A public place.*

*Enter* ANTONIO *and* DELIO.

ANT. What think you of my hope of reconcilement
To the Arragonian brethren?
      DELIO.                      I misdoubt it;
For though they have sent their letters of safe-conduct
For your repair to Milan, they appear
But nets to entrap you. The Marquis of Pescara,
Under whom you hold certain land in cheat,
Much 'gainst his noble nature hath been mov'd
To seize those lands; and some of his dependants
Are at this instant making it their suit
To be invested in your revenues.                          10
I cannot think they mean well to your life
That do deprive you of your means of life,
Your living.
      ANT.      You are still an heretic
To any safety I can shape myself.
      DELIO. Here comes the marquis: I will make myself
Petitioner for some part of your land,
To know whither it is flying.
      ANT.                      I pray, do.                          [*Withdraws.*

*Enter* PESCARA.

DELIO. Sir, I have a suit to you.
PES.                      To me?
DELIO.                              An easy one:
There is the Citadel of Saint Bennet,
With some demesnes, of late in the possession                          20
Of Antonio Bologna; — please you bestow them on me.
      PES. You are my friend; but this is such a suit,
Nor fit for me to give, nor you to take.
      DELIO. No, sir?
      PES. I will give you ample reason for 't
Soon in private. Here 's the cardinal's mistress.

*Enter* JULIA.

JULIA. My lord, I am grown your poor petitioner,
And should be an ill beggar, had I not

---

*Act V, Scene i.*   6. **cheat,** *escheat: subject to forfeit.*

A great man's letter here (the cardinal's)
To court you in my favour.                                    [*Gives a letter.*
    PES.               He entreats for you    30
The Citadel of Saint Bennet, that belong'd
To the banish'd Bologna.
    JULIA.             Yes.
    PES. I could not have thought of a friend I could rather
Pleasure with it: 't is yours.
    JULIA.           Sir, I thank you;
And he shall know how doubly I am engag'd,
Both in your gift, and speediness of giving,
Which makes your grant the greater.                           [*Exit.*
    ANT. [*Aside*]            How they fortify
Themselves with my ruin!
    DELIO.           Sir, I am
Little bound to you.
    PES.        Why?
    DELIO. Because you denied this suit to me, and gave 't    40
To such a creature.
    PES.           Do you know what it was?
It was Antonio's land: not forfeited
By course of law, but ravish'd from his throat
By the cardinal's entreaty. It were not fit
I should bestow so main a piece of wrong
Upon my friend: 't is a gratification
Only due to a strumpet, for it is injustice.
Shall I sprinkle the pure blood of innocents
To make those followers I call my friends
Look ruddier upon me? I am glad    50
This land, ta'en from the owner by such wrong,
Returns again unto so foul an use
As salary for his lust. Learn, good Delio,
To ask noble things of me, and you shall find
I 'll be a noble giver.
    DELIO.          You instruct me well.
    ANT. [*Aside*] Why, here 's a man now would fright impudence
From sauciest beggars.
    PES.          Prince Ferdinand's come to Milan,
Sick, as they give out, of an apoplexy;
But some say 't is a frenzy. I am going
To visit him.                                                 [*Exit.*
    ANT.     'T is a noble old fellow.    60
    DELIO. What course do you mean to take, Antonio?
    ANT. This night I mean to venture all my fortune,
Which is no more than a poor ling'ring life,
To the cardinal's worst of malice. I have got
Private access to his chamber; and intend
To visit him about the mid of night,
As once his brother did our noble duchess.
It may be that the sudden apprehension
Of danger, — for I 'll go in mine own shape, —
When he shall see it fraught with love and duty,    70
May draw the poison out of him, and work
A friendly reconcilement. If it fail,

Yet it shall rid me of this infamous calling;
For better fall once than be ever falling.
    DELIO. I 'll second you in all danger; and, howe'er,
My life keeps rank with yours.
    ANT. You are still my lov'd and best friend.       [*Exeunt.*

    SCENE II: *The* CARDINAL'S *palace at Milan.*

    *Enter* PESCARA *and* DOCTOR.

    PES. Now, doctor, may I visit your patient?
    DOC. If 't please your lordship; but he 's instantly
To take the air here in the gallery
By my direction.
    PES.         Pray thee, what 's his disease?
    DOC. A very pestilent disease, my lord,
They call lycanthropia.
    PES.         What 's that?
I need a dictionary to 't.
    DOC.         I 'll tell you.
In those that are possess'd with 't there o'erflows
Such melancholy humour they imagine
Themselves to be transformed into wolves;       10
Steal forth to church-yards in the dead of night,
And dig dead bodies up: as two nights since
One met the duke 'bout midnight in a lane
Behind Saint Mark's church, with the leg of a man
Upon his shoulder; and he howl'd fearfully;
Said he was a wolf, only the difference
Was, a wolf's skin was hairy on the outside,
His on the inside; bade them take their swords,
Rip up his flesh, and try. Straight I was sent for,
And, having minister'd to him, found his grace       20
Very well recovered.
    PES. I am glad on 't.
    DOC.         Yet not without some fear
Of a relapse. If he grow to his fit again,
I 'll go a nearer way to work with him
Than ever Paracelsus dream'd of; if
They 'll give me leave. I 'll buffet his madness out of him.
Stand aside; he comes.

    *Enter* FERDINAND, CARDINAL, MALATESTE, *and* BOSOLA.

    FERD. Leave me.
    MAL. Why doth your lordship love this solitariness?
    FERD. Eagles commonly fly alone: they are crows, daws, and starlings   30
that flock together. Look, what 's that follows me?
    MAL. Nothing, my lord.
    FERD. Yes.
    MAL. 'T is your shadow.
    FERD. Stay it; let it not haunt me.
    MAL. Impossible, if you moved, and the sun shine.
    FERD. I will throttle it.       [*Throws himself down on his shadow.*
    MAL. O, my lord, you are angry with nothing.

*Scene ii.*   25. **Paracelsus,** *famous Swiss physician and alchemist.*

FERD. You are a fool: how is 't possible I should catch my shadow, un-   40
less I fall upon 't? When I go to hell, I mean to carry a bribe; for, look
you, good gifts evermore make way for the worst persons.

PES. Rise, good my lord.

FERD. I am studying the art of patience.

PES. 'T is a noble virtue.

FERD. To drive six snails before me from this town to Moscow; neither
use goad nor whip to them, but let them take their own time; — the patient'st man i' the world match me for an experiment; and I 'll crawl after
like a sheepbiter.

CARD. Force him up.                           [*They raise him.*

FERD. Use me well, you were best. What I have done, I have done:   50
I 'll confess nothing.

DOC. Now let me come to him. — Are you mad, my lord?
Are you out of your princely wits?

FERD.                          What 's he?

PES.                                   Your doctor.

FERD. Let me have his beard saw'd off, and his eye-brows fil'd more
civil.

DOC. I must do mad tricks with him, for that 's the only way on 't. —
I have brought your grace a salamander's skin to keep you from sunburn-
ing.

FERD. I have cruel sore eyes.

DOC. The white of a cockatrix's egg is present remedy.             60

FERD. Let it be a new-laid one, you were best. Hide me from him:
physicians are like kings, — they brook no contradiction.

DOC. Now he begins to fear me: now let me alone with him.

CARD. How now! put off your gown?

DOC. Let me have some forty urinals filled with rose-water: he and I 'll
go pelt one another with them. — Now he begins to fear me. — Can you
fetch a frisk, sir? — Let him go, let him go, upon my peril. I find by his
eye he stands in awe of me; I 'll make him as tame as a dormouse.

FERD. Can you fetch your frisks, sir? — I will stamp him into a cullis,
flay off his skin to cover one of the anatomies this rogue hath set i' th'   70
cold yonder in Barber-Chirurgeons's-hall. — Hence, hence! you are all of
you like beasts for sacrifice. [*Throws the* DOCTOR *down and beats him*]
There 's nothing left of you but tongue and belly, flattery and lechery.
                                                          [*Exit.*

PES. Doctor, he did not fear you thoroughly.

DOC. True; I was somewhat too forward.

BOS. Mercy upon me, what a fatal judgment
Hath fall'n upon this Ferdinand!

PES.                          Knows your grace
What accident hath brought unto the prince
This strange distraction?                                  80

CARD. [*Aside*] I must feign somewhat. — Thus they say it grew.
You have heard it rumour'd, for these many years,
None of our family dies but there is seen
The shape of an old woman, which is given
By tradition to us to have been murder'd
By her nephews for her riches. Such a figure
One night, as the prince sat up late at 's book,

60. **cockatrix,** *a fabulous serpent with deadly powers.*
67. **fetch a frisk,** *cut a caper.*
70. **anatomies,** *skeleton.*

Appear'd to him; when crying out for help,
The gentleman of 's chamber found his grace
All on a cold sweat, alter'd much in face                                    90
And language: since which apparition,
He hath grown worse and worse, and I much fear
He cannot live.
    BOS.        Sir, I would speak with you.
    PES. We 'll leave your grace,
Wishing to the sick prince, our noble lord,
All health of mind and body.
    CARD.        You are most welcome.
            [*Exeunt* PESCARA, MALATESTE, *and* DOCTOR.
Are you come? so. — [*Aside*] This fellow must not know
By any means I had intelligence
In our duchess' death; for, though I counsell'd it,                           100
The full of all th' engagement seem'd to grow
From Ferdinand. — Now, sir, how fares our sister?
I do not think but sorrow makes her look
Like to an oft-dy'd garment: she shall now
Take comfort from me. Why do you look so wildly?
O, the fortune of your master here, the prince,
Dejects you; but be you of happy comfort:
If you 'll do one thing for me I 'll entreat,
Though he had a cold tomb-stone o'er his bones,
I 'd make you what you would be.                                              110
    BOS.            Anything!
Give it me in a breath, and let me fly to 't.
They that think long small expedition win,
For musing much o' th' end cannot begin.

    *Enter* JULIA.

    JULIA. Sir, will you come in to supper?
    CARD.            I am busy; leave me.
    JULIA. [*Aside*] What an excellent shape hath that fellow!    [*Exit.*
    CARD. 'T is thus. Antonio lurks here in Milan:
Inquire him out, and kill him. While he lives,
Our sister cannot marry; and I have thought
Of an excellent match for her. Do this, and style me
Thy advancement.                                                              120
    BOS. But by what means shall I find him out?
    CARD. There is a gentleman call'd Delio
Here in the camp, that hath been long approv'd
His loyal friend. Set eye upon that fellow;
Follow him to mass; may be Antonio,
Although he do account religion
But a school-name, for fashion of the world
May accompany him; or else go inquire out
Delio's confessor, and see if you can bribe
Him to reveal it. There are a thousand ways                                   130
A man might find to trace him: as to know
What fellows haunt the Jews for taking up
Great sums of money, for sure he 's in want;
Or else to go to th' picture-makers, and learn
Who bought her picture lately: some of these
Happily may take —

BOS.                    Well, I 'll not freeze i' th' business:
I would see that wretched thing, Antonio,
Above all sights i' th' world.
    CARD.                    Do, and be happy.                    [*Exit.*
    BOS. This fellow doth breed basilisks in 's eyes,
He 's nothing else but murder; yet he seems                    140
Not to have notice of the duchess' death.
'T is his cunning: I must follow his example;
There cannot be a surer way to trace
Than that of an old fox.

    *Re-enter* JULIA, *with a pistol.*

    JULIA. So, sir, you are well met.
    BOS.                    How now!
    JULIA. Nay, the doors are fast enough:
Now, sir, I will make you confess your treachery.
    BOS. Treachery!
    JULIA.                    Yes, confess to me
Which of my women 't was you hir'd to put
Love-powder into my drink?                    150
    BOS. Love-powder!
    JULIA.                    Yes, when I was at Malfi.
Why should I fall in love with such a face else?
I have already suffer'd for thee so much pain,
The only remedy to do me good
Is to kill my longing.
    BOS.                    Sure, your pistol holds
Nothing but perfumes or kissing-comfits.
Excellent lady!
You have a pretty way on 't to discover
Your longing. Come, come, I 'll disarm you,
And arm you thus: yet this is wondrous strange.                    160
    JULIA. Compare thy form and my eyes together,
You 'll find my love no such great miracle.
Now you 'll say
I am wanton. This nice modesty in ladies
Is but a troublesome familiar
That haunts them.
    BOS. Know you me: I am a blunt soldier.
    JULIA.                    The better:
Sure, there wants fire where there are no lively sparks
Of roughness.
    BOS.          And I want compliment.
    JULIA.                    Why, ignorance
In courtship cannot make you do amiss,                    170
If you have a heart to do well.
    BOS.                    You are very fair.
    JULIA. Nay, if you lay beauty to my charge,
I must plead unguilty.
    BOS.                    Your bright eyes
Carry a quiver of darts in them, sharper
Than sun-beams.
    JULIA.          You will mar me with commendation,
Put yourself to the charge of courting me,
Whereas now I woo you.

BOS. [*Aside*] I have it, I will work upon this creature. —
Let us grow most amorously familiar.
If the great cardinal now should see me thus,                              180
Would he not count me a villain?
    JULIA. No; he might count me a wanton,
Not lay a scruple of offence on you;
For if I see and steal a diamond,
The fault is not i' th' stone, but in me the thief
That purloins it. I am sudden with you.
We that are great women of pleasure use to cut off
These uncertain wishes and unquiet longings,
And in an instant join the sweet delight
And the pretty excuse together. Had you been i' th' street,     190
Under my chamber-window, even there
I should have courted you.
    BOS. O, you are an excellent lady!
    JULIA. Bid me do somewhat for you presently
To express I love you.
    BOS.                    I will; and if you love me,
Fail not to effect it.
The cardinal is grown wondrous melancholy:
Demand the cause, let him not put you off
With feign'd excuse; discover the main ground on 't.
    JULIA. Why would you know this?
    BOS.                    I have depended on him,            200
And I hear that he is fall'n in some disgrace
With the emperor: if he be, like the mice
That forsake falling houses, I would shift
To other dependance.
    JULIA.            You shall not need
Follow the wars: I 'll be your maintenance.
    BOS. And I your loyal servant: but I cannot
Leave my calling.
    JULIA.            Not leave an ungrateful
General for the love of a sweet lady?
You are like some cannot sleep in feather-beds,
But must have blocks for their pillows.
    BOS.                    Will you do this?            210
    JULIA. Cunningly.
    BOS. To-morrow I 'll expect th' intelligence.
    JULIA. To-morrow! Get you into my cabinet;
You shall have it with you. Do not delay me,
No more than I do you: I am like one
That is condemn'd; I have my pardon promis'd,
But I would see it seal'd. Go, get you in:
You shall see me wind my tongue about his heart
Like a skein of silk.                    [*Exit* BOSOLA.

*Re-enter* CARDINAL.

CARD.            Where are you?

*Enter Servants.*

SERVANTS.                    Here.
    CARD. Let none, upon your lives, have conference            220
With the Prince Ferdinand, unless I know it. —

[*Aside*] In this distraction he may reveal
The murder.                                   [*Exeunt Servants.*
                Yond 's my lingering consumption:
I am weary of her, and by any means
Would be quit of.
    JULIA.          How now, my lord! what ails you?
    CARD. Nothing.
    JULIA.          O, you are much alter'd:
Come, I must be your secretary, and remove
This lead from off your bosom; what 's the matter?
    CARD. I may not tell you.
    JULIA. Are you so far in love with sorrow                     230
You cannot part with part of it? Or think you
I cannot love your grace when you are sad
As well as merry? Or do you suspect
I, that have been a secret to your heart
These many winters, cannot be the same
Unto your tongue?
    CARD.         Satisfy thy longing. —
The only way to make thee keep my counsel
Is, not to tell thee.
    JULIA.         Tell your echo this,
Or flatterers, that like echoes still report
What they hear, though most imperfect, and not me;            240
For if that you be true unto yourself,
I 'll know.
    CARD. Will you rack me?
    JULIA.              No, judgment shall
Draw it from you: it is an equal fault,
To tell one's secrets unto all or none.
    CARD. The first argues folly.
    JULIA. But the last tyranny.
    CARD. Very well; why, imagine I have committed
Some secret deed which I desire the world
May never hear of.
    JULIA.        Therefore may not I know it?            250
You have conceal'd for me as great a sin
As adultery. Sir, never was occasion
For perfect trial of my constancy
Till now; sir, I beseech you —
    CARD.           You 'll repent it.
    JULIA. Never.
    CARD. It hurries thee to ruin: I 'll not tell thee.
Be well advis'd, and think what danger 't is
To receive a prince's secrets. They that do,
Had need have their breasts hoop'd with adamant
To contain them. I pray thee, yet be satisfied;              260
Examine thine own frailty; 't is more easy
To tie knots than unloose them. 'T is a secret
That, like a ling'ring poison, many chance lie
Spread in thy veins, and kill thee seven year hence.
    JULIA. Now you dally with me.
    CARD.           No more; thou shalt know it.
By my appointment, the great Duchess of Malfi

And two of her young children, four nights since,
Were strangled.
    JULIA. O heaven! Sir, what have you done!
    CARD. How now? How settles this? Think you your bosom    270
Will be a grave dark and obscure enough
For such a secret?
    JULIA.        You have undone yourself, sir.
    CARD. Why?
    JULIA.        It lies not in me to conceal it.
    CARD.                No?
Come, I will swear you 't upon this book.
    JULIA. Most religiously.
    CARD.        Kiss it.            *[She kisses the book.*
Now you shall never utter it; thy curiosity
Hath undone thee: thou 'rt poison'd with that book.
Because I knew thou couldst not keep my counsel,
I have bound thee to 't by death.

    *Re-enter* BOSOLA.

    BOS. For pity sake, hold!
    CARD.        Ha, Bosola!
    JULIA.                I forgive you    280
This equal piece of justice you have done,
For I betray'd your counsel to that fellow.
He overheard it: that was the cause I said
It lay not in me to conceal it.
    BOS. O foolish woman,
Couldst not thou have poison'd him?
    JULIA.                'T is weakness
Too much to think what should have been done. I go,
I know not whither.               *[Dies.*
    CARD.        Wherefore com'st thou hither?
    BOS. That I might find a great man like yourself,
Not out of his wits, as the Lord Ferdinand,    290
To remember my service.
    CARD. I 'll have thee hew'd in pieces.
    BOS. Make not yourself such a promise of that life
Which is not yours to dispose of.
    CARD.            Who plac'd thee here?
    BOS. Her lust, as she intended.
    CARD.           Very well:
Now you know me for your fellow-murderer.
    BOS. And wherefore should you lay fair marble colours
Upon your rotten purposes to me?
Unless you imitate some that do plot great treasons,
And when they have done, go hide themselves i' th' graves    300
Of those were actors in 't?
    CARD.        No more; there is
A fortune attends thee.
    BOS. Shall I go sue to Fortune any longer?
'T is the fool's pilgrimage.
    CARD. I have honours in store for thee.
    BOS. There are a many ways that conduct to seeming
Honour, and some of them very dirty ones.

CARD. Throw to the devil
Thy melancholy. The fire burns well;
What need we keep a-stirring of 't, and make                            310
A greater smother? Thou wilt kill Antonio?
BOS. Yes.
CARD.    Take up that body.
BOS.                            I think I shall
Shortly grow the common bier for church-yards.
CARD. I will allow thee some dozen of attendants
To aid thee in the murder.
BOS. O, by no means. Physicians that apply horse-leeches to any rank
swelling use to cut off their tails, that the blood may run through them the
faster: let me have no train when I go to shed blood, lest it make me have
a greater when I ride to the gallows.                                   320
CARD. Come to me after midnight, to help to remove
That body to her own lodging. I 'll give out
She died o' th' plague; 't will breed the less inquiry
After her death.
BOS. Where 's Castruccio her husband?
CARD. He 's rode to Naples, to take possession
Of Antonio's citadel.
BOS. Believe me, you have done a very happy turn.
CARD. Fail not to come. There is the master-key
Of our lodgings; and by that you may conceive                          330
What trust I plant in you.                                      [*Exit.*
BOS.                            You shall find me ready.
O poor Antonio, though nothing be so needful
To thy estate as pity, yet I find
Nothing so dangerous! I must look to my footing;
In such slippery ice-pavements men had need
To be frost-nail'd well: they may break their necks else.
The precedent 's here afore me. How this man
Bears up in blood! seems fearless! Why, 't is well:
Security some men call the suburbs of hell,
Only a dead wall between. Well, good Antonio,                          340
I 'll seek thee out; and all my care shall be
To put thee into safety from the reach
Of these most cruel biters that have got
Some of thy blood already. It may be,
I 'll join with thee in a most just revenge.
The weakest arm is strong enough that strikes
With the sword of justice. Still methinks the duchess
Haunts me: there, there! — 'T is nothing but my melancholy.
O Penitence, let me truly taste thy cup,
That throws men down only to raise them up!                   [*Exit.* 350

SCENE III: *Milan. A fortification.*

*Enter* ANTONIO *and* DELIO.

DELIO. Yond 's the cardinal's window. This fortification
Grew from the ruins of an ancient abbey;
And to yond side o' th' river lies a wall,
Piece of a cloister, which in my opinion
Gives the best echo that you ever heard,
So hollow and so dismal, and withal

So plain in the distinction of our words,
That many have suppos'd it is a spirit
That answers.
    ANT.       I do love these ancient ruins.
We never tread upon them but we set            10
Our foot upon some reverend history;
And, questionless, here in this open court,
Which now lies naked to the injuries
Of stormy weather, some men lie interr'd
Lov'd the church so well, and gave so largely to 't,
They thought it should have canopied their bones
Till dooms-day. But all things have their end;
Churches and cities, which have diseases like to men,
Must have like death that we have.
    ECHO.                *Like death that we have.*
    DELIO. Now the echo hath caught you.        20
    ANT. It groan'd, methought, and gave
A very deadly accent.
    ECHO.        *Deadly accent.*
    DELIO. I told you 't was a pretty one. You may make it
A huntsman, or a falconer, a musician,
Or a thing of sorrow.
    ECHO.        *A thing of sorrow.*
    ANT. Ay, sure, that suits it best.
    ECHO.          *That suits it best.*
    ANT. 'T is very like my wife's voice.
    ECHO.           *Ay, wife's voice.*
    DELIO. Come, let 's us walk farther from 't.
I would not have you go to th' cardinal's tonight:
Do not.                 30
    ECHO. *Do not.*
    DELIO. Wisdom doth not more moderate wasting sorrow
Than time. Take time for 't; be mindful of thy safety.
    ECHO. *Be mindful of thy safety.*
    ANT. Necessity compels me.
Make scrutiny throughout the passages
Of your own life; you 'll find it impossible
To fly your fate.
    ECHO.       *O, fly your fate.*
    DELIO. Hark! the dead stones seem to have pity on you,
And give you good counsel.
    ANT. Echo, I will not talk with thee,       40
For thou art a dead thing.
    ECHO.          *Thou art a dead thing.*
    ANT. My duchess is asleep now,
And her little ones, I hope sweetly. O heaven,
Shall I never see her more?
    ECHO.         *Never see her more.*
    ANT. I mark'd not one repetition of the echo
But that; and on the sudden a clear light
Presented me a face folded in sorrow.
    DELIO. Your fancy merely.
    ANT.             Come, I 'll be out of this ague,
For to live thus is not indeed to live;
It is a mockery and abuse of life.        50

I will not henceforth save myself by halves;
Lose all, or nothing.
    DELIO.        Your own virtue save you!
I 'll fetch your eldest son, and second you.
It may be that the sight of his own blood,
Spread in so sweet a figure, may beget
The more compassion. However, fare you well.
Though in our miseries Fortune have a part,
Yet in our noble suff'rings she hath none.
Contempt of pain, that we may call our own.        [*Exeunt.*


SCENE IV: *A room in the* CARDINAL'S *palace at Milan.*

*Enter* CARDINAL, PESCARA, MALATESTE, RODERIGO, *and* GRISOLAN.

    CARD. You shall not watch to-night by the sick prince;
His grace is very well recover'd.
    MAL. Good my lord, suffer us.
    CARD.        O, by no means;
The noise, and change of object in his eye,
Doth more distract him. I pray, all to bed;
And though you hear him in his violent fit,
Do not rise, I entreat you.
    PES. So, sir; we shall not.
    CARD.        Nay, I must have you promise
Upon your honours, for I was enjoin'd to 't
By himself; and he seem'd to urge it sensibly.        10
    PES. Let our honours bind this trifle.
    CARD. Nor any of your followers.
    MAL. Neither.
    CARD. It may be, to make trial of your promise,
When he 's asleep, myself will rise and feign
Some of his mad tricks, and cry out for help,
And feign myself in danger.
    MAL. If your throat were cutting,
I 'd not come at you, now I have protested against it.
    CARD. Why, I thank you.
    GRIS.        'T was a foul storm to-night.        20
    ROD. The Lord Ferdinand's chamber shook like an osier.
    MAL. 'T was nothing but pure kindness in the devil
To rock his own child.    [*Exeunt all except the* CARDINAL.
    CARD. The reason why I would not suffer these
About my brother, is, because at midnight
I may with better privacy convey
Julia's body to her own lodging. O, my conscience!
I would pray now, but the devil takes away my heart
For having any confidence in prayer.
About this hour I appointed Bosola        30
To fetch the body. When he hath serv'd my turn,
He dies.        [*Exit.*

*Enter* BOSOLA.

    BOS. Ha! 't was the cardinal's voice; I heard him name Bosola and my
death. Listen; I hear one's footing.

*Enter* FERDINAND.

FERD. Strangling is a very quiet death.

BOS. [*Aside*] Nay, then, I see I must stand upon my guard.

FERD. What say to that? Whisper softly: do you agree to 't?
So; it must be done i' th' dark: the cardinal would not for a thousand
pounds the doctor should see it.      [*Exit.*

BOS. My death is plotted; here 's the consequence of murder.    40
We value not desert nor Christian breath,
When we know black deeds must be cured with death.

*Enter* ANTONIO *and Servant.*

SERV. Here stay, Sir, and be confident, I pray;
I 'll fetch you a dark lantern.      [*Exit.*

ANT. Could I take him at his prayers,
There were hope of pardon.

BOS. Fall right, my sword! —      [*Stabs him.*
I 'll not give thee so much leisure as to pray!

ANT. O, I am gone! Thou hast ended a long suit
In a minute.

BOS.      What art thou?

ANT.                 A most wretched thing,    50
That only have thy benefit in death,
To appear myself.

*Re-enter Servant with a lantern.*

SERV. Where are you, sir?

ANT. Very near my home. — Bosola!

SERV. O, misfortune!

BOS. Smother thy pity, thou art dead else. — Antonio!
The man I would have sav'd 'bove mine own life!
We are merely the stars' tennis-balls, struck and bandied
Which way please them. — O good Antonio,
I 'll whisper one thing in thy dying ear    60
Shall make thy heart break quickly! Thy fair duchess
And two sweet children ——

ANT.              Their very names
Kindle a little life in me.

BOS.             Are murder'd.

ANT. Some men have wish'd to die
At the hearing of sad tidings; I am glad
That I shall do 't in sadness. I would not now
Wish my wounds balm'd nor heal'd, for I have no use
To put my life to. In all our quest of greatness,
Like wanton boys whose pastimes is their care,
We follow after bubbles blown in th' air.    70
Pleasure of life, what is 't? Only the good hours
Of an ague, merely a preparative to rest,
To endure vexation. I do not ask
The process of my death; only commend me
To Delio.

BOS. Break, heart!

ANT. And let my son fly the courts of princes.      [*Dies.*

BOS. Thou seem'st to have lov'd Antonio.

SERV. I brought him hither,
To have reconcil'd him to the cardinal.    80

BOS. I do not ask thee that.

Take him up, if thou tender thine own life,
And bear him where the lady Julia
Was wont to lodge. — O, my fate moves swift!
I have this cardinal in the forge already;
Now I 'll bring him to th' hammer. O direful misprision!
I will not imitate things glorious,
No more than base: I 'll be mine own example. —
On, on, and look thou represent, for silence,
The thing thou bear'st.                                    [*Exeunt.*   90

SCENE V: *Another room in the* CARDINAL'S *palace.*

*Enter* CARDINAL, *with a book.*

CARD. I am puzzl'd in a question about hell;
He says, in hell there 's one material fire,
And yet it shall not burn all men alike.
Lay him by. How tedious is a guilty conscience!
When I look into the fish-ponds in my garden,
Methinks I see a thing arm'd with a rake,
That seems to strike at me.

*Enter* BOSOLA *and Servant bearing* ANTONIO'S *body.*

                         Now, art thou come?
Thou look'st ghastly;
There sits in thy face some great determination
Mixed with some fear.
    BOS.                Thus it lightens into action:          10
I am come to kill thee.
    CARD. Ha! — Help! Our guard!
    BOS.                        Thou art deceived;
They are out of thy howling.
    CARD. Hold; and I will faithfully divide
Revenues with thee.
    BOS.            Thy prayers and proffers
Are both unseasonable.
    CARD.            Raise the watch!
We are betray'd!
    BOS.         I have confin'd your flight:
I 'll suffer your retreat to Julia's chamber,
But no further.
    CARD.      Help! We are betray'd!

*Enter, above,* PESCARA, MALATESTE, RODERIGO, *and* GRISOLAN.

    MAL. Listen.                                             20
    CARD. My dukedom for rescue!
    ROD. Fie upon his counterfeiting!
    MAL. Why, 't is not the cardinal.
    ROD. Yes, yes, 't is he:
But I 'll see him hang'd ere I 'll go down to him.
    CARD. Here 's a plot upon me; I am assaulted! I am lost,
Unless some rescue!
    GRIS.         He doth this pretty well;
But it will not serve to laugh me out of mine honour.

Scene iv.   86. **misprision**, *error.*

CARD. The sword 's at my throat!

ROD.                      You would not bawl so loud then.

MAL. Come, come, let 's go to bed: he told us thus much aforehand.    30

PES. He wish'd you should not come at him; but, believe 't,

The accent of the voice sounds not in jest.

I 'll down to him, howsoever, and with engines

Force ope the doors.                          [*Exit above.*

ROD.          Let 's follow him aloof,

And note how the cardinal will laugh at him.

         *Exeunt, above,* MALATESTE, RODERIGO, *and* GRISOLAN.

BOS. There 's for you first,

'Cause you shall not unbarricade the door

To let in rescue.                       [*He kills the Servant.*

CARD.       What cause hast thou to pursue my life?

BOS.                              Look there.

CARD. Antonio!

BOS.          Slain by my hand unwittingly.

Pray, and be sudden. When thou kill'd'st thy sister,          40

Thou took'st from Justice her most equal balance,

And left her naught but her sword.

CARD.                 O, mercy!

BOS. Now it seems thy greatness was only outward;

For thou fall'st faster of thyself than calamity

Can drive thee. I 'll not waste longer time; there!       [*Stabs him.*

CARD. Thou hast hurt me.

BOS.          Again!

CARD.              Shall I die like a leveret,

Without any resistance? — Help, help, help!

I am slain!

*Enter* FERDINAND.

FERD. Th' alarum! Give me a fresh horse!

Rally the vaunt-guard, or the day is lost!          50

Yield, yield! I give you the honour of arms,

Shake my sword over you; will you yield?

CARD. Help me; I am your brother!

FERD.                  The devil!

My brother fight upon the adverse party!

             [*He wounds the* CARDINAL, *and (in the*

             *scuffle) gives* BOSOLA *his death-wound.*

There flies your ransom.

CARD. O justice!

I suffer now for what hath former been:

Sorrow is held the eldest child of sin.          60

FERD. Now you 're brave fellows. Cæsar's fortune was harder than Pompey's: Cæsar died in the arms of prosperity, Pompey at the feet of disgrace. You both died in the field. The pain 's nothing; pain many times is taken away with the apprehension of greater, as the tooth-ache with the sight of a barber that comes to pull it out. There 's philosophy for you.

BOS. Now my revenge is perfect. — Sink, thou main cause

                     [*He kills* FERDINAND.

Of my undoing! — The last part of my life

Hath done me best service.

*Scene v.*   46. **leveret,** *young hare.*

FERD. Give me some wet hay; I am broken-winded.      70
I do account this world but a dog-kennel:
I will vault credit and affect high pleasures
Beyond death.
     BOS.      He seems to come to himself,
Now he 's so near the bottom.
     FERD. My sister, O my sister! There 's the cause on 't.
Whether we fall by ambition, blood, or lust,
Like diamonds, we are cut with our own dust.      [*Dies.*
     CARD. Thou hast thy payment too.
     BOS. Yes, I hold my weary soul in my teeth;
'T is ready to part from me. I do glory      80
That thou, which stood'st like a huge pyramid
Begun upon a large and ample base,
Shalt end in a little point, a kind of nothing.

     *Enter, below,* PESCARA, MALATESTE, RODERIGO, *and* GRISOLAN.

     PES. How now, my lord!
     MAL.           O sad disaster!
     ROD.              How comes this?
     BOS. Revenge for the Duchess of Malfi murdered
By th' Arragonian brethren; for Antonio
Slain by this hand; for lustful Julia
Poison'd by this man; and lastly for myself,
That was an actor in the main of all
Much 'gainst mine own good nature, yet i' th' end      90
Neglected.
     PES.      How now, my lord!
     CARD.           Look to my brother:
He gave us these large wounds, as we were struggling
Here i' th' rushes. And now, I pray, let me
Be laid by and never thought of.      [*Dies.*
     PES. How fatally, it seems, he did withstand
His own rescue!
     MAL.      Thou wretched thing of blood,
How came Antonio by his death?
     BOS. In a mist; I know not how.
Such a mistake as I have often seen
In a play. O, I am gone!      100
We are only like dead walls or vaulted graves,
That, ruin'd, yields no echo. Fare you well!
It may be pain, but no harm, to me to die
In so good a quarrel. O, this gloomy world!
In what a shadow, or deep pit of darkness,
Doth womanish and fearful mankind live!
Let worthy minds ne'er stagger in distrust
To suffer death or shame for what is just:
Mine is another voyage.      [*Dies.*
     PES. The noble Delio, as I came to th' palace,      110
Told me of Antonio's being here, and show'd me
A pretty gentleman, his son and heir.

     *Enter* DELIO, *and* ANTONIO'S SON.

---

72. **vault credit,** *transcend belief.*

MAL. O sir, you come too late!
DELIO.                            I heard so, and
Was arm'd for 't, ere I came. Let us make noble use
Of this great ruin; and join all our force
To establish this young hopeful gentleman
In 's mother's right. These wretched eminent things
Leave no more fame behind 'em, than should one
Fall in a frost, and leave his print in snow:
As soon as the sun shines, it ever melts,                         120
Both form and matter. I have ever thought
Nature doth nothing so great for great men
As when she 's pleas'd to make them lords of truth:
Integrity of life is fame's best friend,
Which nobly, beyond death, shall crown the end.                  [*Exeunt.*

---

## FOR DISCUSSION AND WRITING

>     ... *Webster's world is inhabited by people driven, like animals, and perhaps like men, only by their instincts, but more blindly and ruinously. Life there seems to flow into its forms and shapes with an irregular abnormal and horrible volume. That is ultimately the most sickly, distressing feature of Webster's characters, their foul and indestructible vitality. It fills one with the repulsion one feels at the unending soulless energy that heaves and pulses through the lowest forms of life. They kill, love, torture one another blindly and without ceasing. A play of Webster's is full of the feverish and ghastly turmoil of a nest of maggots. Maggots are what the inhabitants of this universe most suggest and resemble. The sight of their fever is only alleviated by the permanent calm, unfriendly summits and darknesses of the background of death and doom. For that is equally a part of Webster's universe. Human beings are writhing grubs in an immense night. And the night is without stars or moon. But it has sometimes a certain quietude in its darkness; but not very much.*

> From *Rupert Brooke,* John Webster and the Elizabethan Drama
> *(New York: John Lane, 1916), pp. 161-162.*

1) Assess the validity of Brooke's comments by applying them to *The Duchess of Malfi.*

2) Both Aristotle and Cornford speak of a tragedy as an action in which each episode is felt to be inevitable, to spring from "the movement of life, the workings of destiny." Is this sense of inevitability apparent in *The Duchess of Malfi*? At what point does one first become aware of the tragic potentialities of the situation?

3) To what extent is the Duchess, like Oedipus and Lear, a figure who gradually assumes a position of spiritual isolation? In this connection, what is the significance of the following lines:

>          *Wish me good speed;*
> *For I am going into a wilderness,*

> *Where I shall find nor path nor friendly clue*
> *To be my guide.*            *(I. ii. 400-403)*

4) Does the fact that the titular figure dies in Act IV indicate a serious structural flaw in the play? Or is the "redemption" of Bosola — the effect on him of his experience with the Duchess — a dominant enough theme to justify the structure? What is the "sweet and golden dream" (IV. ii. 372) from which Bosola says he awakens following the Duchess' death?

5) According to Butcher, the private life of an individual can become tragic only if the higher laws that rule the world are perceived behind the dramatic action in which that life is presented (pp. 9-15). Is it possible to conceive the life of the Duchess in terms of such significance?

6) Lucas states that tragedy embodies the "eternal contradiction" between man's strength and weakness (p. 29). Which character exemplifies most clearly this duality — the Duchess, Bosola, or Ferdinand?

7) In attempting to explain the meaning of Aristotle's analysis of the effects of tragedy, Frye says that the function of a tragedy is to resolve the "contradiction [that] life is perpetually opposing to our human values and standards" (p. 27). Is this statement consistent with Gassner's belief (p. 60) that tragedy should produce in us a sense of "enlightenment"? In view of Bosola's pessimistic statements that conclude the play, do you feel that *The Duchess of Malfi* fulfills the function of tragedy as stated by Frye and Gassner?

8) Compare the effect of Bosola's final judgment of mankind (V. v. 126-128) with that spoken by the chorus at the close of *King Oedipus.*

9) Clifford Leech (*Webster: The Duchess of Malfi,* London, Edward Arnold, 1963, p. 39) compares the presence of the murdered Duchess in Act V to that of the murdered Julius Caesar in the last acts of Shakespeare's play. Discuss the accuracy of his further statement concerning Webster's drama: "And the effect of this is to reduce the stature of those still alive in the fifth act: they are haunted men who cannot escape the disembodied judgment that hangs in the air."

✳

ANTON

# CHEKHOV

## *Uncle Vanya*

---

*Characters:*   ALEXANDER SEREBRAKOFF, a retired professor

HELENA, his wife, twenty-seven years old

SONIA, his daughter by a former marriage

MME. VOITSKAYA, widow of a privy councilor,
and mother of Serebrakoff's first wife

IVAN (VANYA) VOITSKI, her son

MICHAEL ASTROFF, a doctor

ILIA (WAFFLES) TELEGIN, an impoverished
landowner

MARINA, an old nurse

A WORKMAN

*Scene:* SEREBRAKOFF's country place.

## ACT FIRST

*A country house on a terrace. In front of it a garden. In an avenue of trees under an old poplar, stands a table set for tea, with a samovar, etc. Some benches and chairs stand near the table. On one of them is lying a guitar. A hammock is swung near the table. It is three o'clock in the afternoon of a cloudy day.*

MARINA, *a quiet, gray-haired, little old woman, is sitting at the table knitting a stocking.* ASTROFF *is walking up and down near her.*

MARINA. [*Pouring some tea into a glass*] Take a little tea, my son.

ASTROFF. [*Takes the glass from her unwillingly*] Somehow, I don't seem to want any.

MARINA. Then will you have a little vodka instead?

ASTROFF. No, I don't drink vodka every day, and besides, it is too hot now. [*A pause*] Tell me, nurse, how long have we known each other?

*Uncle Vanya, tr. Marian Fell (New York: Charles Scribner's Sons, 1912). The play was written in 1897.*

MARINA. [*Thoughtfully*] Let me see, how long is it? Lord — help me to remember. You first came here, into our parts — let me think — when was it? Sonia's mother was still alive — it was two winters before she died; that was eleven years ago — [*Thoughtfully*] perhaps more.    10

ASTROFF. Have I changed much since then?

MARINA. Oh, yes. You were handsome and young then, and now you are an old man and not handsome any more. You drink, too.

ASTROFF. Yes, ten years have made me another man. And why? Because I am overworked. Nurse, I am on my feet from dawn till dusk. I know no rest; at night I tremble under my blankets for fear of being dragged out to visit some one who is sick; I have toiled without repose or a day's freedom since I have known you; could I help growing old? And then, existence is tedious, anyway; it is a senseless, dirty business, this life, and goes heavily. Every one about here is silly, and after living with them for two    20 or three years one grows silly oneself. It is inevitable. [*Twisting his mustache*] See what a long mustache I have grown. A foolish, long mustache. Yes, I am as silly as the rest, nurse, but not as stupid; no, I have not grown stupid. Thank God, my brain is not addled yet, though my feelings have grown numb. I ask nothing, I need nothing, I love no one, unless it is yourself alone. [*He kisses her head.*] I had a nurse just like you when I was a child.

MARINA. Don't you want a bite of something to eat?

ASTROFF. No. During the third week of Lent I went to the epidemic at Malitskoi. It was eruptive typhoid. The peasants were all lying side by    30 side in their huts, and the calves and pigs were running about the floor among the sick. Such dirt there was, and smoke! Unspeakable! I slaved among those people all day, not a crumb passed my lips, but when I got home there was still no rest for me; a switchman was carried in from the railroad; I laid him on the operating table and he went and died in my arms under chloroform, and then my feelings that should have been deadened awoke again, my conscience tortured me as if I had killed the man. I sat down and closed my eyes — like this — and thought: will our descendants two hundred years from now, for whom we are breaking the road, remember to give us a kind word? No, nurse, they will forget.    40

MARINA. Man is forgetful, but God remembers.

ASTROFF. Thank you for that. You have spoken the truth.

*Enter* VOITSKI *from the house. He has been asleep after dinner and looks rather disheveled. He sits down on the bench and straightens his collar.*

VOITSKI. H'm. Yes. [*A pause*] Yes.

ASTROFF. Have you been asleep?

VOITSKI. Yes, very much so. [*He yawns.*] Ever since the Professor and his wife have come, our daily life seems to have jumped the track. I sleep at the wrong time, drink wine, and eat all sorts of messes for luncheon and dinner. It isn't wholesome. Sonia and I used to work together and never had an idle moment, but now Sonia works alone and I only eat and drink and sleep. Something is wrong.    50

MARINA. [*Shaking her head*] Such a confusion in the house! The Professor gets up at twelve, the samovar is kept boiling all the morning, and everything has to wait for him. Before they came we used to have dinner at one o'clock, like everybody else, but now we have it at seven. The Professor sits up all night writing and reading, and suddenly, at two o'clock, there goes the bell! Heavens, what is that? The Professor wants some tea! Wake the servants, light the samovar! Lord, what disorder!

ASTROFF. Will they be here long?

VOITSKI. A hundred years! The Professor has decided to make his home
here.                                                                    60

MARINA. Look at this now! The samovar has been on the table for two
hours, and they are all out walking!

VOITSKI. All right, don't get excited; here they come.

*Voices are heard approaching.* SEREBRAKOFF, HELENA, SONIA, *and* TELE-
GIN *come in from the depths of the garden, returning from their walk.*

SEREBRAKOFF. Superb! Superb! What beautiful views!

TELEGIN. They are wonderful, your Excellency.

SONIA. To-morrow we shall go into the woods, shall we, papa?

VOITSKI. Ladies and gentlemen, tea is ready.

SEREBRAKOFF. Won't you please be good enough to send my tea into the
library? I still have some work to finish.

SONIA. I am sure you will love the woods.                                70

HELENA, SEREBRAKOFF, *and* SONIA *go into the house.* TELEGIN *sits down
at the table beside* MARINA.

VOITSKI. There goes our learned scholar on a hot, sultry day like this,
in his overcoat and goloshes and carrying an umbrella!

ASTROFF. He is trying to take good care of his health.

VOITSKI. How lovely she is! How lovely! I have never in my life seen a
more beautiful woman.

TELEGIN. Do you know, Marina, that as I walk in the fields or in the
shady garden, as I look at this table here, my heart swells with unbounded
happiness. The weather is enchanting, the birds are singing, we are all
living in peace and contentment — what more could the soul desire?

[*Takes a glass of tea.*   80

VOITSKI. [*Dreaming*] Such eyes — a glorious woman!

ASTROFF. Come, Ivan, tell us something.

VOITSKI. [*Indolently*] What shall I tell you?

ASTROFF. Haven't you any news for us?

VOITSKI. No, it is all stale. I am just the same as usual, or perhaps worse,
because I have become lazy. I don't do anything now but croak like an old
raven. My mother, the old magpie, is still chattering about the emancipation
of woman, with one eye on her grave and the other on her learned books,
in which she is always looking for the dawn of a new life.

ASTROFF. And the Professor?                                              90

VOITSKI. The Professor sits in his library from morning till night, as
usual —

> "Straining the mind, wrinkling the brow,
>     We write, write, write,
>     Without respite
>     Or hope of praise in the future or now."

Poor paper! He ought to write his autobiography; he would make a really
splendid subject for a book! Imagine it, the life of a retired professor, as
stale as a piece of hardtack, tortured by gout, headaches, and rheumatism,
his liver bursting with jealousy and envy, living on the estate of his first   100
wife, although he hates it, because he can't afford to live in town. He is
everlastingly whining about his hard lot, though, as a matter of fact, he is
extraordinarily lucky. He is the son of a common deacon and has attained
the professor's chair, become the son-in-law of a senator, is called "your
Excellency," and so on. But I'll tell you something; the man has been
writing on art for twenty-five years, and he doesn't know the very first

thing about it. For twenty-five years he has been chewing on other men's thoughts about realism, naturalism, and all such foolishness; for twenty-five years he has been reading and writing things that clever men have long known and stupid ones are not interested in; for twenty-five years he 110 has been making his imaginary mountains out of molehills. And just think of the man's self-conceit and presumption all this time! For twenty-five years he has been masquerading in false clothes and has now retired, absolutely unknown to any living soul; and yet see him! stalking across the earth like a demi-god!

ASTROFF. I believe you envy him.

VOITSKI. Yes, I do. Look at the success he has had with women! Don Juan himself was not more favored. His first wife, who was my sister, was a beautiful, gentle being, as pure as the blue heaven there above us, noble, great-hearted, with more admirers than he has pupils, and she loved him 120 as only beings of angelic purity can love those who are as pure and beautiful as themselves. His mother-in-law, my mother, adores him to this day, and he still inspires a sort of worshipful awe in her. His second wife is, as you see, a brilliant beauty; she married him in his old age and has surrendered all the glory of her beauty and freedom to him. Why? What for?

ASTROFF. Is she faithful to him?

VOITSKI. Yes, unfortunately she is.

ASTROFF. Why "unfortunately"?

VOITSKI. Because such fidelity is false and unnatural, root and branch. 130 It sounds well, but there is no logic in it. It is thought immoral for a woman to deceive an old husband whom she hates, but quite moral for her to strangle her poor youth in her breast and banish every vital desire from her heart.

TELEGIN. [*In a tearful voice*] Vanya, I don't like to hear you talk so. Listen, Vanya; every one who betrays husband or wife is faithless, and could also betray his country.

VOITSKI. [*Crossly*] Turn off the tap, Waffles.

TELEGIN. No, allow me, Vanya. My wife ran away with a lover on the day after our wedding, because my exterior was unprepossessing. I have 140 never failed in my duty since then. I love her and am true to her to this day. I help her all I can and have given my fortune to educate the daughter of herself and her lover. I have forfeited my happiness, but I have kept my pride. And she? Her youth has fled, her beauty has faded according to the laws of nature, and her lover is dead. What has she kept?

HELENA *and* SONIA *come in; after them comes* MME. VOITSKAYA *carrying a book. She sits down and begins to read. Some one hands her a glass of tea which she drinks without looking up.*

SONIA. [*Hurriedly, to the nurse*] There are some peasants waiting out there. Go and see what they want. I shall pour the tea.

[*Pours out some glasses of tea.*

MARINA *goes out.* HELENA *takes a glass and sits drinking in the hammock.*

ASTROFF. I have come to see your husband. You wrote me that he had rheumatism and I know not what else, and that he was very ill, but he 150 appears to be as lively as a cricket.

HELENA. He had a fit of the blues yesterday evening and complained of pains in his legs, but he seems all right again to-day.

ASTROFF. And I galloped over here twenty miles at breakneck speed! No matter, though, it is not the first time. Once here, however, I am going to stay until to-morrow, and at any rate sleep *quantum satis*.

SONIA. Oh, splendid! You so seldom spend the night with us. Have you had dinner yet?

ASTROFF. No.

SONIA. Good. So you will have it with us. We dine at seven now. [*Drinks her tea*] This tea is cold! 160

TELEGIN. Yes, the samovar has grown cold.

HELENA. Don't mind, Monsieur Ivan, we will drink cold tea, then.

TELEGIN. I beg your pardon, my name is not Ivan, but Ilia, ma'am — Ilia Telegin, or Waffles, as I am sometimes called on account of my pock-marked face. I am Sonia's godfather, and his Excellency, your husband, knows me very well. I now live with you, ma'am, on this estate, and per-haps you will be so good as to notice that I dine with you every day.

SONIA. He is our great help, our right-hand man. [*Tenderly*] Dear god-father, let me pour you some tea. 170

MME. VOITSKAYA. Oh! Oh!

SONIA. What is it, grandmother?

MME. VOITSKAYA. I forgot to tell Alexander — I have lost my memory — I received a letter to-day from Paul Alexevitch in Kharkoff. He has sent me a new pamphlet.

ASTROFF. Is it interesting?

MME. VOITSKAYA. Yes, but strange. He refutes the very theories which he defended seven years ago. It is appalling!

VOITSKI. There is nothing appalling about it. Drink your tea, mamma.

MME. VOITSKAYA. It seems you never want to listen to what I have to 180 say. Pardon me, Jean, but you have changed so in the last year that I hardly know you. You used to be a man of settled convictions and had an illuminating personality —

VOITSKI. Oh, yes. I had an illuminating personality, which illuminated no one. [*A pause*] I had an illuminating personality! You couldn't say any-thing more biting. I am forty-seven years old. Until last year I endeavored, as you do now, to blind my eyes by your pedantry to the truths of life. But now — Oh, if you only knew! If you knew how I lie awake at night, heartsick and angry, to think how stupidly I have wasted my time when I might have been winning from life everything which my old age now 190 forbids.

SONIA. Uncle Vanya, how dreary!

MME. VOITSKAYA. [*To her son*] You speak as if your former convictions were somehow to blame, but you yourself, not they, were at fault. You have forgotten that a conviction, in itself, is nothing but a dead letter. You should have done something.

VOITSKI. Done something! Not every man is capable of being a writer *perpetuum mobile* like your Herr Professor.

MME. VOITSKAYA. What do you mean by that?

SONIA. [*Imploringly*] Mother! Uncle Vanya! I entreat you! 200

VOITSKI. I am silent. I apologize and am silent. [*A pause.*

HELENA. What a fine day! Not too hot. [*A pause.*

VOITSKI. A fine day to hang oneself.

TELEGIN *tunes the guitar.* MARINA *appears near the house, calling the chickens.*

MARINA. Chick, chick, chick!

SONIA. What did the peasants want, nurse?

MARINA. The same old thing, the same old nonsense. Chick, chick, chick!

SONIA. Why are you calling the chickens?

MARINA. The speckled hen has disappeared with her chicks. I am afraid 210 the crows have got her. [TELEGIN *plays a polka. All listen in silence.*

*Enter* WORKMAN.

WORKMAN. Is the doctor here? [*To* ASTROFF] Excuse me, sir, but I have been sent to fetch you.

ASTROFF. Where are you from?

WORKMAN. The factory.

ASTROFF. [*Annoyed*] Thank you. There is nothing for it, then, but to go. [*Looking around him for his cap*] Damn it, this is annoying!

SONIA. Yes, it is too bad, really. You must come back to dinner from the factory.                                                                            220

ASTROFF. No, I won't be able to do that. It will be too late. Now where, where — [*To the* WORKMAN] Look here, my man, get me a glass of vodka, will you? [*The* WORKMAN *goes out.*] Where – where — [*Finds his cap*] One of the characters in Ostroff's plays is a man with a long mustache and short wits, like me. However, let me bid you good-bye, ladies and gentlemen. [*To* HELENA] I should be really delighted if you would come to see me some day with Miss Sonia. My estate is small, but if you are interested in such things I should like to show you a nursery and seed-bed whose like you will not find within a thousand miles of here. My place is surrounded by government forests. The forester is old and always ailing,  230 so I superintend almost all the work myself.

HELENA. I have always heard that you were very fond of the woods. Of course one can do a great deal of good by helping to preserve them, but does not that work interfere with your real calling?

ASTROFF. God alone knows what a man's real calling is.

HELENA. And do you find it interesting?

ASTROFF. Yes, very.

VOITSKI. [*Sarcastically*] Oh, extremely!

HELENA. You are still young, not over thirty-six or seven, I should say, and I suspect that the woods do not interest you as much as you say they  240 do. I should think you would find them monotonous.

SONIA. No, the work is thrilling. Dr. Astroff watches over the old woods and sets out new plantations every year, and he has already received a diploma and a bronze medal. If you will listen to what he can tell you, you will agree with him entirely. He says that forests are the ornaments of the earth, that they teach mankind to understand beauty and attune his mind to lofty sentiments. Forests temper a stern climate, and in countries where the climate is milder, less strength is wasted in the battle with nature, and the people are kind and gentle. The inhabitants of such countries are handsome, tractable, sensitive, graceful in speech and gesture. Their phi-  250 losophy is joyous, art and science blossom among them, their treatment of women is full of exquisite nobility —

VOITSKI. [*Laughing*] Bravo! Bravo! All that is very pretty, but it is also unconvincing. So, my friend [*To* ASTROFF], you must let me go on burning firewood in my stoves and building my sheds of planks.

ASTROFF. You can burn peat in your stoves and build your sheds of stone. Oh, I don't object, of course, to cutting wood from necessity, but why destroy the forests? The woods of Russia are trembling under the blows of the axe. Millions of trees have perished. The homes of the wild animals and birds have been desolated; the rivers are shrinking, and many  260 beautiful landscapes are gone forever. And why? Because men are too lazy and stupid to stoop down and pick up their fuel from the ground. [*To* HELENA] Am I not right, Madame? Who but a stupid barbarian could burn so much beauty in his stove and destroy that which he cannot make? Man is endowed with reason and the power to create, so that he may increase that which has been given him, but until now he has not created, but demolished. The forests are disappearing, the rivers are running dry, the game is exterminated, the climate is spoiled, and the earth becomes poorer and uglier every day. [*To* VOITSKI] I read irony in your eye; you do not take what I am saying seriously, and — and — after all, it may very 270 well be nonsense. But when I pass peasant-forests that I have preserved from the axe, or hear the rustling of the young plantations set out with my own hands, I feel as if I had had some small share in improving the climate, and that if mankind is happy a thousand years from now I will have been a little bit responsible for their happiness. When I plant a little birch tree and then see it budding into young green and swaying in the wind, my heart swells with pride and I — [*Sees the* WORKMAN, *who is bringing him a glass of vodka on a tray*] However — [*He drinks*] I must be off. Probably it is all nonsense, anyway. Good-bye.

[*He goes toward the house.* SONIA *takes his arm and goes with him.* 280
SONIA. When are you coming to see us again?
ASTROFF. I can't say.
SONIA. In a month?
ASTROFF *and* SONIA *go into the house.* HELENA *and* VOITSKI *walk over to the terrace.*
HELENA. You have behaved shockingly again. Ivan, what sense was there in teasing your mother and talking about *perpetuum mobile*? And at breakfast you quarreled with Alexander again. Really, your behavior is too petty.
VOITSKI. But if I hate him? 290
HELENA. You hate Alexander without reason; he is like every one else, and no worse than you are.
VOITSKI. If you could only see your face, your gestures! Oh, how tedious your life must be.
HELENA. It is tedious, yes, and dreary! You all abuse my husband and look on me with compassion; you think, "Poor woman, she is married to an old man." How well I understand your compassion! As Astroff said just now, see how you thoughtlessly destroy the forests, so that there will soon be none left. So you also destroy mankind, and soon fidelity and purity and self-sacrifice will have vanished with the woods. Why cannot 300 you look calmly at a woman unless she is yours? Because, the doctor was right, you are all possessed by a devil of destruction; you have no mercy on the woods or the birds or on women or on one another.
VOITSKI. I don't like your philosophy.
HELENA. That doctor has a sensitive, weary face — an interesting face. Sonia evidently likes him, and she is in love with him, and I can understand it. This is the third time he has been here since I have come, and I have not had a real talk with him yet or made much of him. He thinks I am disagreeable. Do you know, Ivan, the reason you and I are such friends? I think it is because we are both lonely and unfortunate. Yes, unfortunate. 310 Don't look at me in that way, I don't like it.
VOITSKI. How can I look at you otherwise when I love you? You are my joy, my life, and my youth. I know that my chances of being loved in return are infinitely small, do not exist, but I ask nothing of you. Only let me look at you, listen to your voice —
HELENA. Hush, some one will overhear you.
[*They go toward the house.*
VOITSKI. [*Following her*] Let me speak to you of my love, do not drive me away, and this alone will be my greatest happiness!

HELENA. Ah! This is agony!                                           320

TELEGIN *strikes the strings of his guitar and plays a polka.* MME. VOIT-
SKAYA *writes something on the leaves of her pamphlet.*


## ACT SECOND

*The dining-room of* SEREBRAKOFF'S *house. It is night. The tapping of the*
WATCHMAN'S *rattle is heard in the garden.* SEREBRAKOFF *is dozing in an*
*armchair by an open window and* HELENA *is sitting beside him, also half*
*asleep.*

SEREBRAKOFF. [*Rousing himself*] Who is here? Is it you, Sonia?

HELENA. It is I.

SEREBRAKOFF. Oh, it is you, Nelly. This pain is intolerable.

HELENA. Your shawl has slipped down. [*She wraps up his legs in the shawl.*]
Let me shut the window.

SEREBRAKOFF. No, leave it open; I am suffocating; I dreamt just now that
my left leg belonged to some one else, and it hurt so that I woke. I don't
believe this is gout, it is more like rheumatism. What time is it?

HELENA. Half-past twelve.                                   [*A pause.*

SEREBRAKOFF. I want you to look for Batushka's works in the library    10
to-morrow. I think we have him.

HELENA. What is that?

SEREBRAKOFF. Look for Batushka to-morrow morning; we used to have
him, I remember. Why do I find it so hard to breathe?

HELENA. You are tired; this is the second night you have had no sleep.

SEREBRAKOFF. They say that Turgenieff got angina of the heart from
gout. I am afraid I am getting angina too. Oh, damn this horrible, accursed
old age! Ever since I have been old I have been hateful to myself, and I
am sure, hateful to you all as well.

HELENA. You speak as if we were to blame for your being old.          20

SEREBRAKOFF. I am more hateful to you than to any one.

[HELENA *gets up and walks away from him, sitting down at a distance.*

SEREBRAKOFF. You are quite right, of course. I am not an idiot; I can
understand you. You are young and healthy and beautiful, and longing
for life, and I am an old dotard, almost a dead man already. Don't I know
it? Of course I see that it is foolish for me to live so long, but wait! I
shall soon set you all free. My life cannot drag on much longer.

HELENA. You are overtaxing my powers of endurance. Be quiet, for God's
sake!

SEREBRAKOFF. It appears that, thanks to me, everybody's power of endur-   30
ance is being overtaxed; everybody is miserable, only I am blissfully
triumphant. Oh, yes, of course!

HELENA. Be quiet! You are torturing me.

SEREBRAKOFF. I torture everybody. Of course.

HELENA. [*Weeping*] This is unbearable! Tell me, what is it you want me
to do?

SEREBRAKOFF. Nothing.

HELENA. Then be quiet, please.

SEREBRAKOFF. It is funny that everybody listens to Ivan and his old idiot
of a mother, but the moment I open my lips you all begin to feel ill-treated.   40
You can't even stand the sound of my voice. Even if I am hateful, even if
I am a selfish tyrant, haven't I the right to be one at my age? Haven't
I deserved it? Haven't I, I ask you, the right to be respected, now that I
am old?

HELENA. No one is disputing your rights. [*The window slams in the wind.*] The wind is rising, I must shut the window. [*She shuts it.*] We shall have rain in a moment. Your rights have never been questioned by any-body. [*The* WATCHMAN *in the garden sounds his rattle.*

SEREBRAKOFF. I have spent my life working in the interests of learning. I am used to my library and the lecture hall and to the esteem and admiration of my colleagues. Now I suddenly find myself plunged in this wilderness, condemned to see the same stupid people from morning till night and listen to their futile conversation. I want to live; I long for success and fame and the stir of the world, and here I am in exile! Oh, it is dreadful to spend every moment grieving for the lost past, to see the success of others and sit here with nothing to do but to fear death. I cannot stand it! It is more than I can bear. And you will not even forgive me for being old!

HELENA. Wait, have patience; I shall be old myself in four or five years.

SONIA *comes in.*

SONIA. Father, you sent for Dr. Astroff, and now when he comes you refuse to see him. It is not nice to give a man so much trouble for nothing.

SEREBRAKOFF. What do I care about your Astroff? He understands medicine about as well as I understand astronomy.

SONIA. We can't send for the whole medical faculty, can we, to treat your gout?

SEREBRAKOFF. I won't talk to that madman!

SONIA. Do as you please. It's all the same to me. [*She sits down.*

SEREBRAKOFF. What time is it?

HELENA. One o'clock.

SEREBRAKOFF. It is stifling in here. Sonia, hand me that bottle on the table.

SONIA. Here it is. [*She hands him a bottle of medicine.*

SEREBRAKOFF. [*Crossly*] No, not that one! Can't you understand me? Can't I ask you to do a thing?

SONIA. Please don't be captious with me. Some people may like it, but you must spare me, if you please, because I don't. Besides, I haven't the time; we are cutting the hay to-morrow and I must get up early.

VOITSKI *comes in dressed in a long gown and carrying a candle.*

VOITSKI. A thunderstorm is coming up. [*The lightning flashes.*] There it is! Go to bed, Helena and Sonia. I have come to take your place.

SEREBRAKOFF. [*Frightened*] No, no, no! Don't leave me alone with him! Oh, don't. He will begin to lecture me.

VOITSKI. But you must give them a little rest. They have not slept for two nights.

SEREBRAKOFF. Then let them go to bed, but you go away too! Thank you. I implore you to go. For the sake of our former friendship do not protest against going. We will talk some other time —

VOITSKI. Our former friendship! Our former —

SONIA. Hush, Uncle Vanya!

SEREBRAKOFF. [*To his wife*] My darling, don't leave me alone with him. He will begin to lecture me.

VOITSKI. This is ridiculous.

MARINA *comes in carrying a candle.*

SONIA. You must go to bed, nurse, it is late.

MARINA. I haven't cleared away the tea things. Can't go to bed yet.

SEREBRAKOFF. No one can go to bed. They are all worn out, only I enjoy perfect happiness.

MARINA. [*Goes up to* SEREBRAKOFF *and speaks tenderly*] What's the matter, master? Does it hurt? My own legs are aching too, oh, so badly. [*Arranges his shawl about his legs*] You have had this illness such a long time. Sonia's dead mother used to stay awake with you too, and wear herself out for you. She loved you dearly. [*A pause*] Old people want to be pitied as    100 much as young ones, but nobody cares about them somehow. [*She kisses* SEREBRAKOFF'S *shoulder.*] Come, master, let me give you some linden-tea and warm your poor feet for you. I shall pray to God for you.

SEREBRAKOFF. [*Touched*] Let us go, Marina.

MARINA. My own feet are aching so badly, oh, so badly! [*She and* SONIA *lead* SEREBRAKOFF *out.*] Sonia's mother used to wear herself out with sorrow and weeping. You were still little and foolish then, Sonia. Come, come, master.                              [SEREBRAKOFF, SONIA, *and* MARINA *go out.*

HELENA. I am absolutely exhausted by him, and can hardly stand.

VOITSKI. You are exhausted by him, and I am exhausted by my own    110 self. I have not slept for three nights.

HELENA. Something is wrong in this house. Your mother hates everything but her pamphlets and the professor; the professor is vexed, he won't trust me, and fears you; Sonia is angry with her father, and with me, and hasn't spoken to me for two weeks! I am at the end of my strength, and have come near bursting into tears at least twenty times to-day. Something is wrong in this house.

VOITSKI. Leave speculating alone.

HELENA. You are cultured and intelligent, Ivan, and you surely understand that the world is not destroyed by villains and conflagrations, but    120 by hate and malice and all this spiteful tattling. It is your duty to make peace, and not to growl at everything.

VOITSKI. Help me first to make peace with myself. My darling!
[*Seizes her hand.*

HELENA. Let go! [*She drags her hand away.*] Go away!

VOITSKI. Soon the rain will be over, and all nature will sigh and awake refreshed. Only I am not refreshed by the storm. Day and night the thought haunts me like a fiend, that my life is lost forever. My past does not count, because I frittered it away on trifles, and the present has so terribly miscarried! What shall I do with my life and my love? What is to become of    130 them? This wonderful feeling of mine will be wasted and lost as a ray of sunlight is lost that falls into a dark chasm, and my life will go with it.

HELENA. I am as it were benumbed when you speak to me of your love, and I don't know how to answer you. Forgive me, I have nothing to say to you. [*She tries to go out.*] Good-night!

VOITSKI. [*Barring the way*] If you only knew how I am tortured by the thought that beside me in this house is another life that is being lost forever — it is yours! What are you waiting for? What accursed philosophy stands in your way? Oh, understand, understand —

HELENA. [*Looking at him intently*] Ivan, you are drunk!    140

VOITSKI. Perhaps. Perhaps.

HELENA. Where is the doctor?

VOITSKI. In there, spending the night with me. Perhaps I am drunk, perhaps I am; nothing is impossible.

HELENA. Have you just been drinking together? Why do you do that?

VOITSKI. Because in that way I get a taste of life. Let me do it, Helena!

HELENA. You never used to drink, and you never used to talk so much. Go to bed, I am tired of you.

VOITSKI. [*Falling on his knees before her*] My sweetheart, my beautiful one —— 150

HELENA. [*Angrily*] Leave me alone! Really, this has become too disagreeable. [HELENA *goes out. A pause.*

VOITSKI. [*Alone*] She is gone! I met her first ten years ago, at her sister's house, when she was seventeen and I was thirty-seven. Why did I not fall in love with her then and propose to her? It would have been so easy! And now she would have been my wife. Yes, we would both have been waked to-night by the thunderstorm, and she would have been frightened, but I would have held her in my arms and whispered: "Don't be afraid! I am here." Oh, enchanting dream, so sweet that I laugh to think of it. [*He laughs.*] But my God! My head reels! Why am I so old? Why won't 160 she understand me? I hate all that rhetoric of hers, that morality of indolence, that absurd talk about the destruction of the world — [*A pause*] Oh, how I have been deceived! For years I have worshipped that miserable gout-ridden professor. Sonia and I have squeezed this estate dry for his sake. We have bartered our butter and curds and peas like misers, and have never kept a morsel for ourselves, so that we could scrape enough pennies together to send to him. I was proud of him and of his learning; I received all his words and writings as inspired, and now? Now he has retired, and what is the total of his life? A blank! He is absolutely unknown, and his fame has burst like a soap-bubble. I have been deceived; 170 I see that now, basely deceived.

ASTROFF *comes in. He has his coat on, but is without his waistcoat or collar, and is slightly drunk.* TELEGIN *follows him, carrying a guitar.*

ASTROFF. Play!

TELEGIN. But every one is asleep.

ASTROFF. Play! [TELEGIN *begins to play softly.*

ASTROFF. Are you alone here? No women about? [*Sings with his arms akimbo.*

"The hut is cold, the fire is dead;
Where shall the master lay his head?"

The thunderstorm woke me. It was a heavy shower. What time is it?

VOITSKI. The devil only knows. 180

ASTROFF. I thought I heard Helena's voice.

VOITSKI. She was here a moment ago.

ASTROFF. What a beautiful woman! [*Looking at the medicine bottles on the table*] Medicine, is it? What a variety we have; prescriptions from Moscow, from Kharkoff, from Tula! Why, he has been pestering all the towns of Russia with his gout! Is he ill, or simply shamming?

VOITSKI. He is really ill.

ASTROFF. What is the matter with you to-night? You seem sad. Is it because you are sorry for the professor?

VOITSKI. Leave me alone. 190

ASTROFF. Or in love with the professor's wife?

VOITSKI. She is my friend.

ASTROFF. Already?

VOITSKI. What do you mean by "already"?

ASTROFF. A woman can only become a man's friend after having first been his acquaintance and then his beloved — then she becomes his friend.

VOITSKI. What vulgar philosophy!

ASTROFF. What do you mean? Yes, I must confess I am getting vulgar, but then, you see, I am drunk. I usually only drink like this once a month.

At such times my audacity and temerity know no bounds. I feel capable    200
of anything. I attempt the most difficult operations and do them magnifi-
cently. The most brilliant plans for the future take shape in my head. I
am no longer a poor fool of a doctor, but mankind's greatest benefactor.
I evolve my own system of philosophy and all of you seem to crawl at my
feet like so many insects or microbes. [*To* TELEGIN] Play, Waffles!

TELEGIN. My dear boy, I would with all my heart, but do listen to
reason; everybody in the house is asleep.

ASTROFF. Play!                                    [TELEGIN *plays softly.*

ASTROFF. I want a drink. Come, we still have some brandy left. And
then, as soon as it is day, you will come home with me.                  210

*He sees* SONIA, *who comes in at that moment.*

ASTROFF. I beg your pardon, I have no collar on.
                        [*He goes out quickly, followed by* TELEGIN.

SONIA. Uncle Vanya, you and the doctor have been drinking! The good
fellows have been getting together! It is all very well for him, he has always
done it, but why do you follow his example? It looks dreadfully at your
age.

VOITSKI. Age has nothing to do with it. When real life is wanting one
must create an illusion. It is better than nothing.

SONIA. Our hay is all cut and rotting in these daily rains, and here you
are busy creating illusions! You have given up the farm altogether. I have  220
done all the work alone until I am at the end of my strength — [*Frightened*] Uncle! Your eyes are full of tears!

VOITSKI. *Tears?* Nonsense, there are no tears in my eyes. You looked at
me then just as your dead mother used to, my darling — [*He eagerly kisses
her face and hands*] My sister, my dearest sister, where are you now? Ah,
if you only knew, if you only knew!

SONIA. If she only knew what, Uncle?

VOITSKI. My heart is bursting. It is awful. No matter, though. I must go.
                                                    [*He goes out.*

SONIA. [*Knocks at the door*] Dr. Astroff! Are you awake? Please come   230
here a minute.

ASTROFF. [*Behind the door*] In a moment.

*He appears in a few seconds. He has put on his collar and waistcoat.*

ASTROFF. What do you want?

SONIA. Drink as much as you please yourself, if you don't find it revolting, but I implore you not to let my uncle do it. It is bad for him.

ASTROFF. Very well; we won't drink any more. I am going home at once.
That is settled. It will be dawn by the time the horses are harnessed.

SONIA. It is still raining; wait till morning.

ASTROFF. The storm is blowing over. This is only the edge of it. I must
go. And please don't ask me to come and see your father any more. I tell   240
him he has gout, and he says it is rheumatism. I tell him to lie down, and
he sits up. To-day he refused to see me at all.

SONIA. He has been spoilt. [*She looks in the sideboard.*] Won't you have a
bite to eat?

ASTROFF. Yes, please. I believe I will.

SONIA. I love to eat at night. I am sure we shall find something in here.
They say that he has made a great many conquests in his life, and that the
women have spoiled him. Here is some cheese for you.

                                    [*They stand eating by the sideboard.*

ASTROFF. I haven't eaten anything to-day. Your father has a very difficult 250
nature. [*He takes a bottle out of the sideboard.*] May I? [*He pours himself a
glass of vodka.*] We are alone here, and I can speak frankly. Do you know,
I could not stand living in this house for even a month? This atmosphere
would stifle me. There is your father, entirely absorbed in his books, and
his gout; there is your Uncle Vanya with his hypochondria, your grandmother, and finally, your stepmother —

SONIA. What about her?

ASTROFF. A human being should be entirely beautiful: the face, the
clothes, the mind, the thoughts. Your step-mother is, of course, beautiful
to look at, but don't you see? She does nothing but sleep and eat and walk 260
and bewitch us, and that is all. She has no responsibilities, everything is
done for her – am I not right? And an idle life can never be a pure one.
[*A pause*] However, I may be judging her too severely. Like your Uncle
Vanya, I am discontented, and so we are both grumblers.

SONIA. Aren't you satisfied with life?

ASTROFF. I like life as life, but I hate and despise it in a little Russian
country village, and as far as my own personal life goes, by heaven! there
is absolutely no redeeming feature about it. Haven't you noticed if you are
riding through a dark wood at night and see a little light shining ahead,
how you forget your fatigue and the darkness and the sharp twigs that 270
whip your face? I work, that you know – as no one else in the country
works. Fate beats me on without rest; at times I suffer unendurably and I
see no light ahead. I have no hope; I do not like people. It is long since
I have loved any one.

SONIA. You love no one?

ASTROFF. Not a soul. I only feel a sort of tenderness for your old nurse
for old-times' sake. The peasants are all alike; they are stupid and live in
dirt, and the educated people are hard to get along with. One gets tired of
them. All our good friends are petty and shallow and see no farther than
their own noses; in one word, they are dull. Those that have brains are 280
hysterical, devoured with a mania for self-analysis. They whine, they hate,
they pick faults everywhere with unhealthy sharpness. They sneak up to me
sideways, look at me out of a corner of the eye, and say: "That man is a
lunatic," "That man is a wind-bag." Or, if they don't know what else to
label me with, they say I am strange. I like the woods; that is strange. I
don't eat meat; that is strange, too. Simple, natural relations between man
and man or man and nature do not exist.

[*He tries to go out;* SONIA *prevents him.*

SONIA. I beg you, I implore you, not to drink any more!

ASTROFF. Why not? 290

SONIA. It is so unworthy of you. You are well-bred, your voice is sweet,
you are even – more than any one I know – handsome. Why do you want
to resemble the common people that drink and play cards? Oh, don't, I
beg you! You always say that people do not create anything, but only
destroy what heaven has given them. Why, oh, why, do you destroy yourself? Oh, don't, I implore you not to! I entreat you!

ASTROFF. [*Gives her his hand*] I won't drink any more.

SONIA. Promise me.

ASTROFF. I give you my word of honor.

SONIA. [*Squeezing his hand*] Thank you. 300

ASTROFF. I have done with it. You see, I am perfectly sober again, and
so I shall stay till the end of my life. [*He looks at his watch.*] But, as I was
saying, life holds nothing for me; my race is run. I am old, I am tired, I

am trivial; my sensibilities are dead. I could never attach myself to any one again. I love no one, and — never shall! Beauty alone has the power to touch me still. I am deeply moved by it. Helena could turn my head in a day if she wanted to, but that is not love, that is not affection —

[*He shudders and covers his face with his hands.*

SONIA. What is it?

ASTROFF. Nothing. During Lent one of my patients died under chloro-   310
form.

SONIA. It is time to forget that. [*A pause*] Tell me, doctor, if I had a friend or a younger sister, and if you knew that she, well — loved you, what would you do?

ASTROFF. [*Shrugging his shoulders*] I don't know. I don't think I should do anything. I should make her understand that I could not return her love — however, my mind is not bothered about those things now. I must start at once if I am ever to get off. Good-bye, my dear girl. At this rate we shall stand here talking till morning. [*He shakes hands with her.*] I shall go out through the sitting-room, because I am afraid your uncle might   320
detain me.                                                        [*He goes out.*

SONIA. [*Alone*] Not a word! His heart and soul are still locked from me, and yet for some reason I am strangely happy. I wonder why? [*She laughs with pleasure.*] I told him that he was well-bred and handsome and that his voice was sweet. Was that a mistake? I can still feel his voice vibrating in the air; it caresses me. [*Wringing her hands*] Oh! how terrible it is to be plain! I am plain, I know it. As I came out of church last Sunday I over-heard a woman say, "She is a dear, noble girl, but what a pity she is so ugly!" So ugly!

HELENA *comes in and throws open the window.*

HELENA. The storm is over. What delicious air! [*A pause*] Where is the   330
doctor?

SONIA. He has gone.                                                [*A pause.*

HELENA. Sonia!

SONIA. Yes?

HELENA. How much longer are you going to sulk at me? We have not hurt each other. Why not be friends? We have had enough of this.

SONIA. I myself — [*She embraces* HELENA.] Let us make peace.

HELENA. With all my heart.                          [*They are both moved.*

SONIA. Has papa gone to bed?

HELENA. No, he is sitting up in the drawing-room. Heavens knows what   340
reason you and I had for not speaking to each other for weeks. [*Sees the open sideboard*] Who left the sideboard open?

SONIA. Dr. Astroff has just had supper.

HELENA. There is some wine. Let us seal our friendship.

SONIA. Yes, let us.

HELENA. Out of one glass. [*She fills a wine-glass.*] So, we are friends, are we?

SONIA. Yes. [*They drink and kiss each other.*] I have long wanted to make friends, but somehow, I was ashamed to.                         [*She weeps.*

HELENA. Why are you crying?                                                350

SONIA. I don't know. It is nothing.

HELENA. There, there, don't cry. [*She weeps.*] Silly! Now I am crying too. [*A pause*] You are angry with me because I seem to have married your father for his money, but don't believe the gossip you hear. I swear to you I married him for love. I was fascinated by his fame and learning. I know now that it was not real love, but it seemed real at the time. I am innocent,

and yet your clever, suspicious eyes have been punishing me for an imaginary crime ever since my marriage.

SONIA. Peace, peace! Let us forget the past.

HELENA. You must not look so at people. It is not becoming to you. You 360
must trust people, or life becomes impossible.

SONIA. Tell me truly, as a friend, are you happy?

HELENA. Truly, no.

SONIA. I knew it. One more question: do you wish your husband were
young?

HELENA. What a child you are! Of course I do. Go on, ask something
else.

SONIA. Do you like the doctor?

HELENA. Yes, very much indeed.

SONIA. [*Laughing*] I have a stupid face, haven't I? He has just gone out, 370
and his voice is still in my ears; I hear his step; I see his face in the dark
window. Let me say all I have in my heart! But no, I cannot speak of it
so loudly. I am ashamed. Come to my room and let me tell you there. I
seem foolish to you, don't I? Talk to me of him.

HELENA. What can I say?

SONIA. He is clever. He can do everything. He can cure the sick, and
plant woods.

HELENA. It is not a question of medicine and woods, my dear, he is a
man of genius. Do you know what that means? It means he is brave, profound, and of clear insight. He plants a tree and his mind travels a thousand 380
years into the future, and he sees visions of the happiness of the human
race. People like him are rare and should be loved. What if he does drink
and act roughly at times? A man of genius cannot be a saint in Russia.
There he lives, cut off from the world by cold and storm and endless roads
of bottomless mud, surrounded by a rough people who are crushed by
poverty and disease, his life one continuous struggle, with never a day's
respite; how can a man live like that for forty years and keep himself sober
and unspotted? [*Kissing* SONIA] I wish you happiness with all my heart;
you deserve it. [*She gets up.*] As for me, I am a worthless, futile woman. I
have always been futile; in music, in love, in my husband's house — in a 390
word, in everything. When you come to think of it, Sonia, I am really very,
very unhappy. [*Walks excitedly up and down*] Happiness can never exist
for me in this world. Never. Why do you laugh?

SONIA. [*Laughing and covering her face with her hands*] I am so happy,
so happy!

HELENA. I want to hear music. I might play a little.

SONIA. Oh, do, do! [*She embraces her.*] I could not possibly go to sleep
now. Do play!

HELENA. Yes, I will. Your father is still awake. Music irritates him when
he is ill, but if he says I may, then I shall play a little. Go, Sonia, and ask 400
him.

SONIA. Very well.

       [*She goes out. The* WATCHMAN's *rattle is heard in the garden.*

HELENA. It is long since I have heard music. And now, I shall sit and
play, and weep like a fool. [*Speaking out of the window*] Is that you rattling
out there, Ephim?

VOICE OF THE WATCHMAN. It is I.

HELENA. Don't make such a noise. Your master is ill.

VOICE OF THE WATCHMAN. I am going away this minute.

       [*Whistles a tune.* 410

SONIA. [*Comes back*] He says, no.

## ACT THIRD

*The drawing-room of* SEREBRAKOFF'S *house. There are three doors: one to the right, one to the left, and one in the center of the room.* VOITSKI *and* SONIA *are sitting down.* HELENA *is walking up and down, absorbed in thought.*

VOITSKI. We were asked by the professor to be here at one o'clock. [*Looks at his watch*] It is now a quarter to one. It seems he has some communication to make to the world.

HELENA. Probably a matter of business.

VOITSKI. He never had any business. He writes twaddle, grumbles, and eats his heart out with jealousy; that's all he does.

SONIA. [*Reproachfully*] Uncle!

VOITSKI. All right. I beg your pardon. [*He points to* HELENA.] Look at her. Wandering up and down from sheer idleness. A sweet picture, really.

HELENA. I wonder you are not bored, droning on in the same key from morning till night. [*Despairingly*] I am dying of this tedium. What shall I do?

SONIA. [*Shrugging her shoulders*] There is plenty to do if you would.

HELENA. For instance?

SONIA. You could help run this place, teach the children, care for the sick — isn't that enough? Before you and papa came, Uncle Vanya and I used to go to market ourselves to deal in flour.

HELENA. I don't know anything about such things, and besides, they don't interest me. It is only in novels that women go out and teach and heal the peasants; how can I suddenly begin to do it?

SONIA. How can you live here and not do it? Wait awhile, you will get used to it all. [*Embraces her*] Don't be sad, dearest. [*Laughing*] You feel miserable and restless, and can't seem to fit into this life, and your restlessness is catching. Look at Uncle Vanya, he does nothing now but haunt you like a shadow, and I have left my work to-day to come here and talk with you. I am getting lazy, and don't want to go on with it. Dr. Astroff hardly ever used to come here; it was all we could do to persuade him to visit us once a month, and now he has abandoned his forestry and his practice, and comes every day. You must be a witch.

VOITSKI. Why should you languish here? Come, my dearest, my beauty, be sensible! The blood of a Nixey runs in your veins. Oh, won't you let yourself be one? Give your nature the reins for once in your life; fall head over ears in love with some other water sprite and plunge down head first into a deep pool, so that the Herr Professor and all of us may have our hands free again.

HELENA. [*Angrily*] Leave me alone! How cruel you are!

[*She tries to go out.*

VOITSKI. [*Preventing her*] There, there, my beauty, I apologize. [*He kisses her hand.*] Forgive me.

HELENA. Confess that you would try the patience of an angel.

VOITSKI. As a peace offering I am going to fetch some flowers which I picked for you this morning: some autumn roses, beautiful, sorrowful roses.

[*He goes out.*

SONIA. Autumn roses, beautiful, sorrowful roses!

[*She and* HELENA *stand looking out of the window.*

HELENA. September already! How shall we live through the long winter here? [*A pause*] Where is the doctor?

SONIA. He is writing in Uncle Vanya's room. I am glad Uncle Vanya has gone out, I want to talk to you about something.

HELENA. About what?                                                      50
SONIA. About what?

[*She lays her head on* HELENA'S *breast.*
HELENA. [*Stroking her hair*] There, there, that will do. Don't, Sonia.
SONIA. I am ugly!
HELENA. You have lovely hair.
SONIA. Don't say that! [*She turns to look at herself in the glass.*] No,
when a woman is ugly they always say she has beautiful hair or eyes. I
have loved him now for six years; I have loved him more than one loves
one's mother. I seem to hear him beside me every moment of the day. I
feel the pressure of his hand on mine. If I look up, I seem to see him     60
coming, and as you see, I run to you to talk of him. He is here every day
now, but he never looks at me, he does not notice my presence. It is agony.
I have absolutely no hope, no, no hope. Oh, my God! Give me strength
to endure. I prayed all last night. I often go up to him and speak to him
and look into his eyes. My pride is gone. I am not mistress of myself.
Yesterday I told Uncle Vanya. I couldn't control myself, and all the servants
know it. Every one knows that I love him.
HELENA. Does he?
SONIA. No, he never notices me.
HELENA. [*Thoughtfully*] He is a strange man. Listen, Sonia, will you      70
allow me to speak to him? I shall be careful, only hint. [*A pause*] Really,
to be in uncertainty all these years! Let me do it!

[SONIA *nods an affirmative.*
HELENA. Splendid! It will be easy to find out whether he loves you or
not. Don't be ashamed, sweetheart, don't worry. I shall be careful; he will
not notice a thing. We only want to find out whether it is yes or no, don't
we? [*A pause*] And if it is no, then he must keep away from here, is that so?

[SONIA *nods.*
HELENA. It will be easier not to see him any more. We won't put off the
examination an instant. He said he had a sketch to show me. Go and tell    80
him at once that I want to see him.
SONIA. [*In great excitement*] Will you tell me the whole truth?
HELENA. Of course I will. I am sure that no matter what it is, it will be
easier for you to bear than this uncertainty. Trust to me, dearest.
SONIA. Yes, yes. I shall say that you want to see his sketch. [*She starts
out, but stops near the door and looks back.*] No, it is better not to know —
and yet — there may be hope.
HELENA. What do you say?
SONIA. Nothing.                                           [*She goes out.*
HELENA. [*Alone*] There is no greater sorrow than to know another's      90
secret when you cannot help them. [*In deep thought*] He is obviously not in
love with her, but why shouldn't he marry her? She is not pretty, but she
is so clever and pure and good, she would make a splendid wife for a
country doctor of his years. [*A pause*] I can understand how the poor child
feels. She lives here in this desperate loneliness with no one around her
except these colorless shadows that go mooning about talking nonsense and
knowing nothing except that they eat, drink, and sleep. Among them
appears from time to time this Dr. Astroff, so different, so handsome, so
interesting, so charming. It is like seeing the moon rise on a dark night.
Oh, to surrender oneself to his embrace! To lose oneself in his arms! I     100
am a little in love with him myself! Yes, I am lonely without him, and when
I think of him I smile. That Uncle Vanya says I have the blood of a Nixey
in my veins: "Give rein to your nature for once in your life!" Perhaps it
is right that I should. Oh, to be free as a bird, to fly away from all your

sleepy faces and your talk and forget that you have existed at all! But I am a coward, I am afraid; my conscience torments me. He comes here every day now. I can guess why, and feel guilty already; I should like to fall on my knees at Sonia's feet and beg her forgiveness, and weep.

ASTROFF *comes in carrying a portfolio.*

ASTROFF. How do you do? [*Shakes hands with her*] Do you want to see my sketch?                                                                                        110
HELENA. Yes, you promised to show me what you had been doing. Have you time now?
ASTROFF. Of course I have!

> [*He lays the portfolio on the table, takes out the sketch and fastens it to the table with thumbtacks.*

ASTROFF. Where were you born?
HELENA. [*Helping him*] In St. Petersburg.
ASTROFF. And educated?
HELENA. At the Conservatory there.
ASTROFF. You don't find this life very interesting, I dare say?                        120
HELENA. Oh, why not? It is true I don't know the country very well, but I have read a great deal about it.
ASTROFF. I have my own desk there in Ivan's room. When I am absolutely too exhausted to go on I drop everything and rush over here to forget myself in this work for an hour or two. Ivan and Miss Sonia sit rattling at their counting-boards, the cricket chirps, and I sit beside them and paint, feeling warm and peaceful. But I don't permit myself this luxury very often, only once a month. [*Pointing to the picture*] Look there! That is a map of our country as it was fifty years ago. The green tints, both dark and light, represent forests. Half the map, as you see, is covered with it.   130
Where the green is striped with red the forests were inhabited by elk and wild goats. Here on this lake lived great flocks of swans and geese and ducks; as the old men say, there was a power of birds of every kind. Now, they have vanished like a cloud. Beside the hamlets and villages, you see, I have dotted down here and there the various settlements, farms, hermit's caves, and water-mills. This country carried a great many cattle and horses, as you can see by the quantity of blue paint. For instance, see how thickly it lies in this part; there were great herds of them here, an average of three horses to every house. [*A pause*] Now, look lower down. This is the country as it was twenty-five years ago. Only a third of the map is green now with   140
forests. There are no goats left and no elk. The blue paint is lighter, and so on, and so on. Now we come to the third part; our country as it appears to-day. We still see spots of green, but not much. The elk, the swans, the black-cock have disappeared. It is, on the whole, the picture of a regular and slow decline which it will evidently only take about ten or fifteen more years to complete. You may perhaps object that it is the march of progress, that the old order must give place to the new, and you might be right if roads had been run through these ruined woods, or if factories and schools had taken their place. The people then would have become better educated and healthier and richer, but as it is, we have nothing of the sort. We have   150
the same swamps and mosquitoes; the same disease and want; the typhoid, the diphtheria, the burning villages. We are confronted by the degradation of our country, brought on by the fierce struggle for existence of the human race. It is the consequence of the ignorance and unconsciousness of starving, shivering, sick humanity that, to save its children, instinctively snatches at everything that can warm it and still its hunger. So it destroys everything

it can lay its hands on, without a thought for the morrow. And almost everything has gone, and nothing has been created to take its place. [*Coldly*] But I see by your face that I am not interesting you.

HELENA. I know so little about such things!                    160

ASTROFF. There is nothing to know. It simply isn't interesting, that's all.

HELENA. Frankly, my thoughts were elsewhere. Forgive me! I want to submit you to a little examination, but I am embarrassed and don't know how to begin.

ASTROFF. An examination?

HELENA. Yes, but quite an innocent one. Sit down. [*They sit down.*] It is about a certain young girl I know. Let us discuss it like honest people, like friends, and then forget what has passed between us, shall we?

ASTROFF. Very well.

HELENA. It is about my step-daughter, Sonia. Do you like her?      170

ASTROFF. Yes, I respect her.

HELENA. Do you like her — as a woman?

ASTROFF. [*Slowly*] No.

HELENA. One more word, and that will be the last. You have not noticed anything?

ASTROFF. No, nothing.

HELENA. [*Taking his hand*] You do not love her. I see that in your eyes. She is suffering. You must realize that, and not come here any more.

ASTROFF. My sun has set, yes, and then I haven't the time. [*Shrugging his shoulders*] Where shall I find time for such things?     [*He is embarrassed.*   180

HELENA. Bah! What an unpleasant conversation! I am as out of breath as if I had been running three miles uphill. Thank heaven, that is over! Now let us forget everything as if nothing had been said. You are sensible. You understand. [*A pause*] I am actually blushing.

ASTROFF. If you had spoken a month ago I might perhaps have considered it, but now — [*He shrugs his shoulders.*] Of course, if she is suffering — but I cannot understand why you had to put me through this examination. [*He searches her face with his eyes, and shakes his finger at her.*] Oho, you are wily!

HELENA. What does this mean?                      190

ASTROFF. [*Laughing*] You are a wily one! I admit that Sonia is suffering, but what does this examination of yours mean? [*He prevents her from retorting, and goes on quickly.*] Please don't put on such a look of surprise; you know perfectly well why I come here every day. Yes, you know perfectly why and for whose sake I come! Oh, my sweet tigress! don't look at me in that way; I am an old bird!

HELENA. [*Perplexed*] A tigress? I don't understand you.

ASTROFF. Beautiful, sleek tigress, you must have your victims! For a whole month I have done nothing but seek you eagerly. I have thrown over everything for you, and you love to see it. Now then, I am sure you   200 knew all this without putting me through your examination. [*Crossing his arms and bowing his head*] I surrender. Here you have me—now, eat me.

HELENA. You have gone mad!

ASTROFF. You are afraid!

HELENA. I am a better and stronger woman than you think me. Goodbye.                                [*She tries to leave the room.*

ASTROFF. Why good-bye? Don't say good-bye, don't waste words. Oh, how lovely you are — what hands!                [*He kisses her hands.*

HELENA. Enough of this! [*She frees her hands.*] Leave the room! You have forgotten yourself.                        210

ASTROFF. Tell me, tell me, where can we meet to-morrow? [*He puts his arm around her.*] Don't you see that we must meet, that it is inevitable?

[*He kisses her.*

VOITSKI *comes in carrying a bunch of roses, and stops in the doorway.*

HELENA. [*Without seeing* VOITSKI] Have pity! Leave me. [*Lays her head on* ASTROFF's *shoulder*] Don't!          [*She tries to break away from him.*

ASTROFF. [*Holding her by the waist*] Be in the forest to-morrow at two o'clock. Will you? Will you?

HELENA. [*Sees* VOITSKI] Let me go! [*Goes to the window deeply embarrassed*] This is appalling!

VOITSKI. [*Throws the flowers on a chair, and speaks in great excitement,*   220
*wiping his face with his handkerchief*] Nothing — yes, yes, nothing.

ASTROFF. The weather is fine to-day, my dear Ivan; the morning was overcast and looked like rain, but now the sun is shining again. Honestly, we have had a very fine autumn, and the wheat is looking fairly well. [*Puts his map back into the portfolio*] But the days are growing short.

[*Exit.*

HELENA. [*Goes quickly up to* VOITSKI] You must do your best; you must use all your power to get my husband and myself away from here to-day! Do you hear? I say, this very day!

VOITSKI. [*Wiping his face*] Oh! Ah! Oh! All right! I — Helena, I saw   230
everything!

HELENA. [*In great agitation*] Do you hear me? I must leave here this very day!

SEREBRAKOFF, SONIA, MARINA, *and* TELEGIN *come in.*

TELEGIN. I am not very well myself, your Excellency. I have been limping for two days, and my head —

SEREBRAKOFF. Where are the others? I hate this house. It is a regular labyrinth. Every one is always scattered through the twenty-six enormous rooms; one never can find a soul. [*Rings*] Ask my wife and Madame Voitskaya to come here!

HELENA. I am here already.   240

SEREBRAKOFF. Please, all of you, sit down.

SONIA. [*Goes up to* HELENA *and asks anxiously*] What did he say?

HELENA. I'll tell you later.

SONIA. You are moved. [*Looking quickly and inquiringly into her face*] I understand; he said he would not come here any more. [*A pause*] Tell me, did he?          [HELENA *nods.*

SEREBRAKOFF. [*To* TELEGIN] One can, after all, become reconciled to being an invalid, but not to this country life. The ways of it stick in my throat and I feel exactly as if I had been whirled off the earth and landed on a strange planet. Please be seated, ladies and gentlemen. Sonia! [SONIA *does*   250
*not hear. She is standing with her head bowed sadly forward on her breast.*] Sonia! [*A pause*] She does not hear me. [*To* MARINA] Sit down too, nurse. [MARINA *sits down and begins to knit her stocking.*] I crave your indulgence, ladies and gentlemen; hang your ears, if I may say so, on the peg of attention.          [*He laughs.*

VOITSKI. [*Agitated*] Perhaps you do not need me — may I be excused?

SEREBRAKOFF. No, you are needed now more than any one.

VOITSKI. What is it you want of me?

SEREBRAKOFF. You — but what are you angry about? If it is anything I have done, I ask you to forgive me.   260

VOITSKI. Oh, drop that and come to business; what do you want?

MME. VOITSKAYA *comes in.*

SEREBRAKOFF. Here is mother. Ladies and gentlemen, I shall begin. I have asked you to assemble here, my friends, in order to discuss a very important matter. I want to ask you for your assistance and advice, and knowing your unfailing amiability I think I can count on both. I am a book-worm and a scholar, and am unfamiliar with practical affairs. I cannot, I find, dispense with the help of well-informed people such as you, Ivan, and you, Telegin, and you, mother. The truth is, *manct omnes una nox*, that is to say, our lives are in the hands of God, and as I am old and ill, I realize that the time has come for me to dispose of my property in regard to the interests of my family. My life is nearly over, and I am not thinking of myself, but I have a young wife and daughter. [*A pause*] I cannot continue to live in the country; we were not made for country life, and yet we cannot afford to live in town on the income derived from this estate. We might sell the woods, but that would be an expedient we could not resort to every year. We must find some means of guaranteeing to ourselves a certain more or less fixed yearly income. With this object in view, a plan has occurred to me which I now have the honor of presenting to you for your consideration. I shall only give you a rough outline, avoiding all details. Our estate does not pay on an average more than two per cent on the money invested in it. I propose to sell it. If we then invest our capital in bonds, it will earn us four to five per cent, and we should probably have a surplus over of several thousand roubles, with which we could buy a summer cottage in Finland —

VOITSKI. Hold on! Repeat what you just said; I don't think I heard you quite right.

SEREBRAKOFF. I said we would invest the money in bonds and buy a cottage in Finland with the surplus.

VOITSKI. No, not Finland — you said something else.

SEREBRAKOFF. I propose to sell this place.

VOITSKI. Aha! That was it! So you are going to sell the place? Splendid. The idea is a rich one. And what do you propose to do with my old mother and me and with Sonia here?

SEREBRAKOFF. That will be decided in due time. We can't do everything at once.

VOITSKI. Wait! It is clear that until this moment I have never had a grain of sense in my head. I have always been stupid enough to think that the estate belonged to Sonia. My father bought it as a wedding present for my sister, and I foolishly imagined that as our laws were made for Russians and not Turks, my sister's estate would come down to her child.

SEREBRAKOFF. Of course it is Sonia's. Has any one denied it? I don't want to sell it without Sonia's consent; on the contrary, what I am doing is for Sonia's good.

VOITSKI. This is absolutely incomprehensible. Either I have gone mad or — or —

MME. VOITSKAYA. Jean, don't contradict Alexander. Trust to him; he knows better than we do what is right and what is wrong.

VOITSKI. I shan't. Give me some water. [*He drinks.*] Go ahead! Say anything you please — anything!

SEREBRAKOFF. I can't imagine why you are so upset. I don't pretend that my scheme is an ideal one, and if you all object to it I shall not insist.

[*A pause.*

TELEGIN. [*With embarrassment*] I not only nourish feelings of respect toward learning, your Excellency, but I am also drawn to it by family ties.

My brother Gregory's wife's brother, whom you may know; his name is Constantine Lakedemonoff, and he used to be a magistrate —

VOITSKI. Stop, Waffles. This is business; wait a bit, we will talk of that later. [*To* SEREBRAKOFF] There now, ask him what he thinks; this estate was bought from his uncle.

SEREBRAKOFF. Ah! Why should I ask questions? What good would it do?  320

VOITSKI. The price was ninety-five thousand roubles. My father paid seventy and left a debt of twenty-five. Now listen! This place could never have been bought had I not renounced my inheritance in favor of my sister, whom I deeply loved — and what is more, I worked for ten years like an ox, and paid off the debt.

SEREBRAKOFF. I regret ever having started this conversation.

VOITSKI. Thanks entirely to my own personal efforts, the place is entirely clear of debts, and now, when I have grown old, you want to throw me out, neck and crop!

SEREBRAKOFF. I can't imagine what you are driving at.  330

VOITSKI. For twenty-five years I have managed this place, and have sent you the returns from it like the most honest of servants, and you have never given me one single word of thanks for my work, not one — neither in my youth nor now. You allowed me a meager salary of five hundred roubles a year, a beggar's pittance, and have never even thought of adding a rouble to it.

SEREBRAKOFF. What did I know about such things, Ivan? I am not a practical man and don't understand them. You might have helped yourself to all you wanted.

VOITSKI. Yes, why did I not steal? Don't you all despise me for not  340 stealing, when it would have been only justice? And I should not now have been a beggar!

MME. VOITSKAYA. [*Sternly*] Jean!

TELEGIN. [*Agitated*] Vanya, old man, don't talk in that way. Why spoil such pleasant relations? [*He embraces him.*] Do stop!

VOITSKI. For twenty-five years I have been sitting here with my mother like a mole in a burrow. Our every thought and hope was yours and yours only. By day we talked with pride of you and your work, and spoke your name with veneration; our nights we wasted reading the books and papers which my soul now loathes.  350

TELEGIN. Don't, Vanya, don't. I can't stand it.

SEREBRAKOFF. [*Wrathfully*] What under heaven do you want, anyway?

VOITSKI. We used to think of you as almost superhuman, but now the scales have fallen from my eyes and I see you as you are! You write on art without knowing anything about it. Those books of yours which I used to admire are not worth one copper kopeck. You are a hoax!

SEREBRAKOFF. Can't any one make him stop? I am going!

HELENA. Ivan, I command you to stop this instant! Do you hear me?

VOITSKI. I refuse! [SEREBRAKOFF *tries to get out of the room, but* VOITSKI *bars the door.*] Wait! I have not done yet! You have wrecked my life. I  360 have never lived. My best years have gone for nothing, have been ruined, thanks to you. You are my most bitter enemy!

TELEGIN. I can't stand it; I can't stand it. I am going.

[*He goes out in great excitement.*

SEREBRAKOFF. But what do you want? What earthly right have you to use such language to me? Ruination! If this estate is yours, then take it, and let me be ruined!

HELENA. I am going away out of this hell this minute. [*Shrieks*] This is too much!

VOITSKI. My life has been a failure. I am clever and brave and strong. If 370
I had lived a normal life I might have become another Schopenhauer or
Dostoieffski. I am losing my head! I am going crazy! Mother, I am in
despair! Oh, mother!

MME. VOITSKAYA. [*Sternly*] Listen, Alexander!

[SONIA *falls on her knees beside the nurse and nestles against her.*

SONIA. Oh, nurse, nurse!

VOITSKI. Mother! What shall I do? But no, don't speak! I know what
to do. [*To* SEREBRAKOFF] And you will understand me!

> [*He goes out through the door in the center of the
> room and* MME. VOITSKAYA *follows him.* 380

SEREBRAKOFF. Tell me, what on earth is the matter? Take this lunatic
out of my sight! I cannot possibly live under the same roof with him. His
room [*He points to the center door*] is almost next door to mine. Let him
take himself off into the village or into the wing of the house, or I shall
leave here at once. I cannot stay in the same house with him.

HELENA. [*To her husband*] We are leaving to-day; we must get ready
at once for our departure.

SEREBRAKOFF. What a perfectly dreadful man!

SONIA. [*On her knees beside the nurse and turning to her father. She speaks
with emotion.*] You must be kind to us, papa. Uncle Vanya and I are so 390
unhappy! [*Controlling her despair*] Have pity on us. Remember how Uncle
Vanya and Granny used to copy and translate your books for you every
night — every, every night. Uncle Vanya has toiled without rest; he would
never spend a penny on us, we sent it all to you. We have not eaten the
bread of idleness. I am not saying this as I should like to, but you must
understand us, papa, you must be merciful to us.

HELENA. [*Very excited, to her husband*] For heaven's sake, Alexander, go
and have a talk with him — explain!

SEREBRAKOFF. Very well, I shall have a talk with him, but I won't apologize for a thing. I am not angry with him, but you must confess that his 400
behavior has been strange, to say the least. Excuse me, I shall go to him.

> [*He goes out through the center door.*

HELENA. Be gentle with him; try to quiet him.

> [*She follows him out.*

SONIA. [*Nestling nearer to* MARINA] Nurse, oh, nurse!

MARINA. It's all right, my baby. When the geese have cackled they will
be still again. First they cackle and then they stop.

SONIA. Nurse!

MARINA. You are trembling all over, as if you were freezing. There, there,
little orphan baby, God is merciful. A little linden-tea, and it will all pass 410
away. Don't cry, my sweetest. [*Looking angrily at the door in the center of
the room*] See, the geese have all gone now. The devil take them!

> [*A shot is heard.* HELENA *screams behind the
> scenes.* SONIA *shudders.*

MARINA. Bang! What's that?

SEREBRAKOFF. [*Comes in reeling with terror*] Hold him! hold him! He
has gone mad!

> [HELENA *and* VOITSKI *are seen struggling in the doorway.*

HELENA. [*Trying to wrest the revolver from him*] Give it to me; give it to
me, I tell you. 420

VOITSKI. Let me go, Helena, let me go! [*He frees himself and rushes in,
looking everywhere for* SEREBRAKOFF.] Where is he? Ah, there he is! [*He
shoots at him. A pause*] I didn't get him? I missed again? [*Furiously*] Damnation! Damnation! To hell with him!

*He flings the revolver on the floor, and drops helpless into a chair.* SERE-
BRAKOFF *stands as if stupefied.* HELENA *leans against the wall, almost
fainting.*

HELENA. Take me away! Take me away! I can't stay here — I can't!

VOITSKI. [*In despair*] Oh, what shall I do? What shall I do?

SONIA. [*Softly*] Oh, nurse, nurse!


## ACT FOURTH

VOITSKI'S *bedroom, which is also his office. A table stands near the window; on it are ledgers, letter scales, and papers of every description. Near
by stands a smaller table belonging to* ASTROFF, *with his paints and
drawing materials. On the wall hangs a cage containing a starling. There
is also a map of Africa on the wall, obviously of no use to anybody.
There is a large sofa covered with buckram. A door to the left leads into
an inner room; one to the right leads into the front hall, and before this
door lies a mat for the peasants with their muddy boots to stand on. It
is an autumn evening. The silence is profound.* TELEGIN *and* MARINA *are
sitting facing one another, winding wool.*

TELEGIN. Be quick, Marina, or we shall be called away to say good-bye
before you have finished. The carriage has already been ordered.

MARINA. [*Trying to wind more quickly*] I am a little tired.

TELEGIN. They are going to Kharkoff to live.

MARINA. They do well to go.

TELEGIN. They have been frightened. The professor's wife won't stay
here an hour longer. "If we are going at all, let's be off," says she, "we
shall go to Kharkoff and look about us, and then we can send for our
things." They are traveling light. It seems, Marina, that fate has decreed
for them not to live here.                                                           10

MARINA. And quite rightly. What a storm they have just raised! It was
shameful!

TELEGIN. It was indeed. The scene was worthy of the brush of Aibazofski.

MARINA. I wish I'd never laid eyes on them. [*A pause*] Now we shall
have things as they were again: tea at eight, dinner at one, and supper in
the evening; everything in order as decent folks, as Christians like to have
it. [*Sighs*] It is a long time since I have eaten noodles.

TELEGIN. Yes, we haven't had noodles for ages. [*A pause*] Not for ages.
As I was going through the village this morning, Marina, one of the shop-
keepers called after me, "Hi! you hanger-on!" I felt it bitterly.              20

MARINA. Don't pay the least attention to them, master; we are all de-
pendents on God. You and Sonia and all of us. Every one must work, no
one can sit idle. Where is Sonia?

TELEGIN. In the garden with the doctor, looking for Ivan. They fear he
may lay violent hands on himself.

MARINA. Where is his pistol?

TELEGIN. [*Whispers*] I hid it in the cellar.

VOITSKI *and* ASTROFF *come in.*

VOITSKI. Leave me alone! [*To* MARINA *and* TELEGIN] Go away! Go away
and leave me to myself, if but for an hour. I won't have you watching me
like this!                                                                            30

TELEGIN. Yes, yes, Vanya.                                    [*He goes out on tiptoe.*

MARINA. The gander cackles; ho! ho! ho!

[*She gathers up her wool and goes out.*

VOITSKI. Leave me by myself!

ASTROFF. I would, with the greatest pleasure. I ought to have gone long ago, but I shan't leave you until you have returned what you took from me.

VOITSKI. I took nothing from you.

ASTROFF. I am not jesting, don't detain me, I really must go.

VOITSKI. I took nothing of yours.

ASTROFF. You didn't? Very well, I shall have to wait a little longer, and then you will have to forgive me if I resort to force. We shall have to bind you and search you. I mean what I say.

VOITSKI. Do as you please. [*A pause*] Oh, to make such a fool of myself! To shoot twice and miss him both times! I shall never forgive myself.

ASTROFF. When the impulse came to shoot, it would have been as well had you put a bullet through your own head.

VOITSKI. [*Shrugging his shoulders*] Strange! I attempted murder, and am not going to be arrested or brought to trial. That means they think me mad. [*With a bitter laugh*] Me! I am mad, and those who hide their worthlessness, their dullness, their crying heartlessness behind a professor's mask, are sane! Those who marry old men and then deceive them under the noses of all, are sane! I saw you kiss her; I saw you in each other's arms!

ASTROFF. Yes, sir, I did kiss her; so there.

[*He puts his thumb to his nose.*]

VOITSKI. [*His eyes on the door*] No, it is the earth that is mad, because she still bears us on her breast.

ASTROFF. That is nonsense.

VOITSKI. Well? Am I not a madman, and therefore irresponsible? Haven't I the right to talk nonsense?

ASTROFF. This is a farce! You are not mad; you are simply a ridiculous fool. I used to think every fool was out of his senses, but now I see that lack of sense is a man's normal state, and you are perfectly normal.

VOITSKI. [*Covers his face with his hands*] Oh! If you knew how ashamed I am! These piercing pangs of shame are like nothing on earth. [*In an agonized voice*] I can't endure them! [*He leans against the table.*] What can I do? What can I do?

ASTROFF. Nothing.

VOITSKI. You must tell me something! Oh, my God! I am forty-seven years old. I may live to sixty; I still have thirteen years before me; an eternity! How shall I be able to endure life for thirteen years? What shall I do? How can I fill them? Oh, don't you see? [*He presses* ASTROFF's *hand convulsively.*] Don't you see, if only I could live the rest of my life in some new way! If I could only wake some still, bright morning and feel that life had begun again; that the past was forgotten and had vanished like smoke. [*He weeps*] Oh, to begin life anew! Tell me, tell me how to begin.

ASTROFF. [*Crossly*] What nonsense! What sort of a new life can you and I look forward to? We can have no hope.

VOITSKI. None?

ASTROFF. None. Of that I am convinced.

VOITSKI. Tell me what to do. [*He puts his hand to his heart.*] I feel such a burning pain here.

ASTROFF. [*Shouts angrily*] Stop! [*Then, more gently*] It may be that posterity, which will despise us for our blind and stupid lives, will find some road to happiness; but we — you and I — have but one hope, the hope that we may be visited by visions, perhaps by pleasant ones, as we lie resting in our graves. [*Sighing*] Yes, brother, there were only two respectable, intelligent men in this county, you and I. Ten years or so of this life of

ours, this miserable life, have sucked us under, and we have become as
contemptible and petty as the rest. But don't try to talk me out of my 90
purpose! Give me what you took from me, will you?

VOITSKI. I took nothing from you.

ASTROFF. You took a little bottle of morphine out of my medicine-case.
[*A pause*] Listen! If you are positively determined to make an end to yourself, go into the woods and shoot yourself there. Give up the morphine, or
there will be a lot of talk and guesswork; people will think I gave it to
you. I don't fancy having to perform a post-mortem on you. Do you think
I should find it interesting?

SONIA *comes in.*

VOITSKI. Leave me alone.

ASTROFF. [*To* SONIA] Sonia, your uncle has stolen a bottle of morphine 100
out of my medicine-case and won't give it up. Tell him that his behavior
is — well, unwise. I haven't time, I must be going.

SONIA. Uncle Vanya, did you take the morphine?

ASTROFF. Yes, he took it. [*A pause*] I am absolutely sure.

SONIA. Give it up! Why do you want to frighten us? [*Tenderly*] Give it
up, Uncle Vanya! My misfortune is perhaps even greater than yours, but
I am not plunged in despair. I endure my sorrow, and shall endure it until
my life comes to a natural end. You must endure yours, too. [*A pause*]
Give it up! Dear, darling Uncle Vanya. Give it up! [*She weeps*] You are so
good, I am sure you will have pity on us and give it up. You must endure 110
your sorrow, Uncle Vanya; you must endure it.

[VOITSKI *takes a bottle from the drawer of the
table and hands it to* ASTROFF.

VOITSKI. There it is! [*To* SONIA] And now, we must get to work at once;
we must do something, or else I shall not be able to endure it.

SONIA. Yes, yes, to work! As soon as we have seen them off we shall go
to work. [*She nervously straightens out the papers on the table.*] Everything
is in a muddle!

ASTROFF. [*Putting the bottle in his case, which he straps together*] Now I
can be off. 120

HELENA *comes in.*

HELENA. Are you here, Ivan? We are starting in a moment. Go to Alexander, he wants to speak to you.

SONIA. Go, Uncle Vanya. [*She takes* VOITSKI's *arm.*] Come, you and papa
must make peace; that is absolutely necessary.

[SONIA *and* VOITSKI *go out.*

HELENA. I am going away. [*She gives* ASTROFF *her hand.*] Good-bye.

ASTROFF. So soon?

HELENA. The carriage is waiting.

ASTROFF. Good-bye.

HELENA. You promised me you would go away yourself to-day. 130

ASTROFF. I have not forgotten. I am going at once. [*A pause*] Were you
frightened? Was it so terrible?

HELENA. Yes.

ASTROFF. Couldn't you stay? Couldn't you? To-morrow — in the forest —

HELENA. No. It is all settled, and that is why I can look you so bravely
in the face. Our departure is fixed. One thing I must ask of you: don't
think too badly of me; I should like you to respect me.

ASTROFF. Ah! [*With an impatient gesture*] Stay, I implore you! Confess
that there is nothing for you to do in this world. You have no object in

life; there is nothing to occupy your attention, and sooner or later your 140
feelings must master you. It is inevitable. It would be better if it happened
not in Kharkoff or in Kursk, but here, in nature's lap. It would then at
least be poetical, even beautiful. Here you have the forests, the houses half
in ruins that Turgenieff writes of.

HELENA. How comical you are! I am angry with you and yet I shall
always remember you with pleasure. You are interesting and original. You
and I will never meet again, and so I shall tell you — why should I conceal
it? — that I am just a little in love with you. Come, one more last pressure
of our hands, and then let us part good friends. Let us not bear each other
any ill will. 150

ASTROFF. [*Pressing her hand*] Yes, go. [*Thoughtfully*] You seem to be
sincere and good, and yet there is something strangely disquieting about
all your personality. No sooner did you arrive here with your husband
than every one whom you found busy and actively creating something
was forced to drop his work and give himself up for the whole summer to
your husband's gout and yourself. You and he have infected us with your
idleness. I have been swept off my feet; I have not put my hand to a thing
for weeks, during which sickness has been running its course unchecked
among the people, and the peasants have been pasturing their cattle in
my woods and young plantations. Go where you will, you and your husband 160
will always carry destruction in your train. I am joking of course, and yet
I am strangely sure that had you stayed here we should have been overtaken by the most immense desolation. I would have gone to my ruin, and
you — you would not have prospered. So to! É finita la commèdia!

HELENA. [*Snatching a pencil off* ASTROFF's *table, and hiding it with a quick
movement*] I shall take this pencil for memory!

ASTROFF. How strange it is. We meet, and then suddenly it seems that
we must part forever. That is the way in this world. As long as we are
alone, before Uncle Vanya comes in with a bouquet — allow me — to kiss
you good-bye — may I? [*He kisses her on the cheek.*] So! Splendid! 170

HELENA. I wish you every happiness. [*She glances about her.*] For once
in my life, I shall! and scorn the consequences! [*She kisses him impetuously,
and they quickly part.*] I must go.

ASTROFF. Yes, go. If the carriage is there, then start at once.

[*They stand listening.*

ASTROFF. É finita!

VOITSKI, SEREBRAKOFF, MME. VOITSKAYA *with her book,* TELEGIN, *and*
SONIA *come in.*

SEREBRAKOFF. [*To* VOITSKI] Shame on him who bears malice for the past.
I have gone through so much in the last few hours that I feel capable of
writing a whole treatise on the conduct of life for the instruction of posterity. I gladly accept your apology, and myself ask your forgiveness. 180

[*He kisses* VOITSKI *three times.* HELENA *embraces* SONIA.

SEREBRAKOFF. [*Kissing* MME. VOITSKAYA's *hand*] Mother!

MME. VOITSKAYA. [*Kissing him*] Have your picture taken, Alexander, and
send me one. You know how dear you are to me.

TELEGIN. Good-bye, your Excellency. Don't forget us.

SEREBRAKOFF. [*Kissing his daughter*] Good-bye, good-bye all. [*Shaking
hands with* ASTROFF] Many thanks for your pleasant company. I have a
deep regard for your opinions and your enthusiasm, but let me, as an old
man, give one word of advice at parting: do something, my friend! Work!
Do something! [*They all bow.*] Good luck to you all. 190

[*He goes out followed by* MME. VOITSKAYA *and* SONIA.

VOITSKI. [*Kissing* HELENA'S *hand fervently*] Good-bye — forgive me. I shall never see you again!

HELENA. [*Touched*] Good-bye, dear boy.

[*She lightly kisses his head as he bends over
her hand, and goes out.*

ASTROFF. Tell them to bring my carriage around too, Waffles.

TELEGIN. All right, old man.

ASTROFF *and* VOITSKI *are left behind alone.* ASTROFF *collects his paints and
drawing materials on the table and packs them away in a box.*                    200

ASTROFF. Why don't you go to see them off?

VOITSKI. Let them go! I — I can't go out there. I feel too sad. I must go to work on something at once. To work! To work!

*He rummages through his papers on the table. A pause. The tinkling of
bells is heard as the horses trot away.*

ASTROFF. They have gone! The professor, I suppose, is glad to go. He couldn't be tempted back now by a fortune.

MARINA *comes in.*

MARINA. They have gone.

[*She sits down in an arm-chair and knits her stocking.*

SONIA *comes in wiping her eyes.*

SONIA. They have gone. God be with them. [*To her uncle*] And now,   210
Uncle Vanya, let us do something!

VOITSKI. To work! To work!

SONIA. It is long, long, since you and I have sat together at this table. [*She lights a lamp on the table.*] No ink! [*She takes the inkstand to the cup-board and fills it from an inkbottle.*] How sad it is to see them go!

MME. VOITSKAYA *comes slowly in.*

MME. VOITSKAYA. They have gone.

*She sits down and at once becomes absorbed in her book.* SONIA *sits down
at the table and looks through an account book.*

SONIA. First, Uncle Vanya, let us write up the accounts. They are in a dreadful state. Come, begin. You take one and I will take the other.   220

VOITSKI. In account with —                    [*They sit silently writing.*

MARINA. [*Yawning*] The sand-man has come.

ASTROFF. How still it is. Their pens scratch, the cricket sings; it is so warm and comfortable. I hate to go.          [*The tinkling of bells is heard.*

ASTROFF. My carriage has come. There now remains but to say good-bye to you, my friends, and to my table here, and then — away!

[*He puts the map into the portfolio.*

MARINA. Don't hurry away; sit a little longer with us.

ASTROFF. Impossible.

VOITSKI. [*Writing*] And carry forward from the old debt two seventy-   230
five —

WORKMAN *comes in.*

WORKMAN. Your carriage is waiting, sir.

ASTROFF. All right. [*He hands the* WORKMAN *his medicine-case, portfolio,
and box.*] Look out, don't crush the portfolio!

WORKMAN. Very well, sir.

SONIA. When shall we see you again?

ASTROFF. Hardly before next summer. Probably not this winter, though, of course, if anything should happen you will let me know. [*He shakes*

*hands with them.*] Thank you for your kindness, for your hospitality, for
everything! [*He goes up to* MARINA *and kisses her head.*] Good-bye, old   240
nurse!

MARINA. Are you going without your tea?

ASTROFF. I don't want any, nurse.

MARINA. Won't you have a drop of vodka?

ASTROFF. [*Hesitatingly*] Yes, I might.                              [MARINA *goes out.*

ASTROFF. [*After a pause*] My off-wheeler has gone lame for some reason.
I noticed it yesterday when Peter was taking him to water.

VOITSKI. You should have him re-shod.

ASTROFF. I shall have to go around by the blacksmith's on my way home.
It can't be avoided. [*He stands looking up at the map of Africa hanging on*   250
*the wall.*] I suppose it is roasting hot in Africa now.

VOITSKI. Yes, I suppose it is.

MARINA *comes back carrying a tray on which are a glass of vodka and a*
*piece of bread.*

MARINA. Help yourself.                                          [ASTROFF *drinks.*

MARINA. To your good health! [*She bows deeply.*] Eat your bread with it.

ASTROFF. No, I like it so. And now, good-bye. [*To* MARINA] You needn't
come out to see me off, nurse.

*He goes out.* SONIA *follows him with a candle to light him to the carriage.*
MARINA *sits down in her arm-chair.*

VOITSKI. [*Writing*] On the 2d of February, twenty pounds of butter; on
the 16th, twenty pounds of butter again. Buckwheat flour ——          260

[*A pause. Bells are heard tinkling.*

MARINA. He has gone.                                             [*A pause.*

SONIA *comes in and sets the candle-stick on the table.*

SONIA. He has gone.

VOITSKI. [*Adding and writing*] Total, fifteen — twenty-five ——

[SONIA *sits down and begins to write.*

MARINA. [*Yawning*] Oh, ho! The Lord have mercy.

TELEGIN *comes in on tiptoe, sits down near the door, and begins to tune*
*his guitar.*

VOITSKI. [*To* SONIA, *stroking her hair*] Oh, my child, I am so miserable;
if you only knew how miserable I am!

SONIA. What can we do? We must live our lives. [*A pause*] Yes, we shall
live, Uncle Vanya. We shall live through the long procession of days before   270
us, and through the long evenings; we shall patiently bear the trials that
fate imposes on us; we shall work for others without rest, both now and
when we are old; and when our last hour comes we shall meet it humbly,
and there, beyond the grave, we shall say that we have suffered and wept,
that our life was bitter, and God will have pity on us. Ah, then, dear,
dear Uncle, we shall see that bright and beautiful life; we shall rejoice
and look back upon our sorrow here; a tender smile — and — we shall
rest. I have faith, Uncle, fervent, passionate faith. [SONIA *kneels down*
*before her uncle and lays her head on his hands. She speaks in a weary*
*voice.*] We shall rest. [TELEGIN *plays softly on the guitar.*] We shall rest.   280
We shall hear the angels. We shall see heaven shining like a jewel. We
shall see all evil and all our pain sink away in the great compassion that
shall enfold the world. Our life will be as peaceful and tender and sweet
as a caress. I have faith; I have faith. [*She wipes away her tears.*] My poor,
poor Uncle Vanya, you are crying! [*Weeping*] You have never known what

happiness was, but wait, Uncle Vanya, wait! We shall rest. [*She embraces him.*] We shall rest. [*The* WATCHMAN'S *rattle is heard in the garden;* TELEGIN *plays softly;* MME. VOITSKAYA *writes something on the margin of her pamphlet;* MARINA *knits her stocking.*] We shall rest.

---

#### FOR DISCUSSION AND WRITING

---

The Might-Have-Been is Chekhov's idée fixe. *His people do not dream only of what could never be, or what could come only after thousands of years; they dream of what their lives actually could have been. They spring from a conviction of human potentiality — which is what separates Chekhov from the real misanthropes of modern literature. Astrov moves us because we can readily feel how fully human he might have been, how he has dwindled, under the influence of "country life," from a thinker to a crank, from a man of feeling to a philanderer. "It is strange somehow," he says to Yelena in the last scene, "we have got to know each other, and all at once for some reason — we shall never meet again. So it is with everything in this world." Such lines might be found in any piece of sentimental theater. But why is it that Chekhov's famous "elegiac note" is, in the full context, deeply moving? Is it not because the sense of death is accompanied with so rich a sense of life and the possible worth of living?*

From Eric Bentley, In Search of Theater
(New York: Alfred A. Knopf, Inc., 1953), p. 350.

1) Chekhov himself thought of his plays as comedies, but are there any definitions of tragedy that might reasonably be applied to *Uncle Vanya*? Consider the last part of Lucas' view of the essence of tragedy (p. 31). Is the fact that Chekhov "never paltered or cheated in his picture of men as they are" sufficient to make *Uncle Vanya* tragic? Or must we say that since Sonya, Astroff, Vanya, and the others are for the most part passive sufferers, the play falls short of tragedy?

2) Aristotle clearly considers plot or fable the main concern of the tragedian (p. 2). Would he think there is enough action in *Uncle Vanya* for it to qualify as tragedy? Might he argue that this play takes up the story at the moment of *discovery* and that Chekhov's rather naturalistic exposition by means of flashback is not a satisfactory substitute for the development of action?

3) In *The Wood Demon*, Chekhov's first version of *Uncle Vanya*, Vanya commits suicide after the professor tells him of plans to sell the estate. What effect does Chekhov achieve in the later play by transforming the suicide into Vanya's unsuccessful attempt to shoot the professor? Does the change from a positive action to an unresolved one suggest a change in Chekhov's concept of human destiny that is implicit throughout *Uncle Vanya*?

4) To what extent is *endurance* with little hope vs. the will to die because of a misspent life the central issue of the play? Is it finally resolved?

5) Robert Corrigan, a recent translator of Chekhov's plays (*Six Plays of Chekhov*, New York, Holt, Rinehart & Winston, 1962), feels that though they were first produced more than sixty years ago, they nevertheless are essentially modern in that they "reflect the mood of spiritual discouragement" so common

in mid-twentieth-century life. Does this seem to be an accurate judgment of *Uncle Vanya?* Explain.

6) "In Ibsen the terrible thing is that the surface of everyday life is a smooth deception. In Chekhov the terrible thing is that the surface of everyday life is itself a kind of tragedy." Do these sentences, from another part of the Bentley essay quoted above, suggest that in Chekhov the normal routines of everyday existence tend to preclude man's attempts to make his life meaningful?

7) Lucas, in his comments on Chekhov's *Three Sisters* (pp. 29-31), states that the tragic feeling implicit in the play proceeds in part from its truthful presentation of hope and despair, the "paradox of life." Can the same judgment be applied to *Uncle Vanya?*

8) Krutch says that in tragedy we are "glad" that the hero suffers, that Lear is turned out into the storm, and that Juliet dies, because such figures illustrate that man has "splendors of his own" which make the calamities of the world seem unimportant (p. 64). In considering *Uncle Vanya*, might a capacity for suffering be construed as such a splendor?

9) In his attempt to justify the common man as tragic hero, Miller implies that any man can participate in the battle to "achieve his humanity" or secure his rightful place in the world, but he also says that "the possibility of victory must be there in tragedy" (p. 69). Would the application of these ideas allow the situation in *Uncle Vanya* to be seen as tragic?

10) How does the fact that Astroff plants trees in an attempt to save or resuscitate the land affect the play? Is this a portion of Chekhov's "larger hope" that, though contemporary men and women may destroy themselves by a brooding and pitiful incapacity to realize themselves, the Russia of the future may find active and meaningful life possible? If so, is this more or less extraneous hope for the future related to whether *Uncle Vanya* may be considered tragic? Is it related to Sonia's last speech?

❋

# Questions for Discussion and Writing
## on Modern Drama

The following questions are intended to assist the teacher and the student in bringing the discussion of the idea of tragedy up to date. Needless to say, there are many recent dramatists whose work might fall somewhere in the spectrum of tragedy, but we have tried to focus on works of such merit and interest that they have already begun to be seriously discussed as representative of modern tragic drama. One late-nineteenth-century play, *The Father*, has been included because Strindberg's particular combination of naturalism and psychological and pathological motivations has had a tremendous influence on dramatists who followed him — especially on Eugene O'Neill.

In our selection of plays and questions, we have attempted to remind the student of the aspects of tragedy and tragic theory considered earlier in the text. Thus the Atreus myth is continued from Greek drama in the plays of O'Neill and Sartre; the topic of tragedy as ritual can be continued with Lorca; the human problem of a father's responsibilities and duties, raised in connection with the Greeks and Shakespeare, can be reconsidered with Strindberg and Miller. With these questions as suggestive guides, the student may extend into the modern theatre his interest in the abiding questions about the nature of tragedy.

All of the plays considered here may be obtained in relatively inexpensive paperback editions, either in the collected works of individual writers or in collections of modern drama.

---

### AUGUST STRINDBERG: *The Father*

1) Are we, the *audience*, expected to perceive the tragic significance of Strindberg's characters, which the characters themselves cannot perceive because of their isolation or hopeless alienation? Apply this question also to O'Neill's *Mourning Becomes Electra* and to other modern plays. If this is the case, can we say that modern dramatists are adding a new dimension to tragedy, or must we say that recognition of tragic experience by the characters is essential?

2) Do the ultimate motivations of the chief characters — the Father's assumptions about the necessity for war between the sexes, his mixed love and hate for his mother and for his wife, and the wife's revulsion for him when he approaches her as a lover — so dominate the play that we feel the characters are deprived of freedom? Does an understanding of these motivations modify your view of *The Father* as tragedy?

3) Does the plight of the Father, in a household cursed with feminine powers — the tigerish wife, the motherly old nurse, the daughter, and the subservient pastor and doctor — induce in the reader a tragic pity for the Father, or is his plight merely pathetic?

4) Can the Father's firmly defined stand against the Mother in Act III be seen as tragically heroic?

5) If this play is tragic, is it so because it presents with a searing conviction the antithetical forces of outraged, though warped and pathological, masculinity and femininity? Can such forces add up to tragedy?

6) Do the Father's references to the *Odyssey*, Pushkin, Hercules, Omphale — all tending to suggest that the mightiest men are felled by women — have the effect of universalizing the war between the sexes? Do they add to the tragic quality of the play?

---

EUGENE O'NEILL: *Mourning Becomes Electra*

*Mourning Becomes Electra* is O'Neill's modern version of the *Oresteia* of Aeschylus. Your appreciation of it and of concepts of tragedy will be enhanced if you read the whole of Aeschylus' trilogy, in addition to the *Electra* of Sophocles and the *Electra* of Euripides, which are available in a variety of translations.

1) O'Neill substitutes for the Greek Fate a psychological determinism, doubtless feeling that modern audiences could not accept supernatural motivations seriously. Thus Mannon is driven by a domineering masculinity that fights for supremacy between love and lust. Christine is driven by a feminine need to triumph over Mannon in any way possible, after Mannon's lust has at first rendered her a servile instrument. Lavinia, a child reared in hate, is driven to seek her vengeance. (Note that Strindberg's notions of inescapable war between the sexes lurks behind O'Neill's thinking and dramatic practice.) Can such determinism result in serious tragedy? Can there be *hamartia* in such a context?

2) Does the fact that O'Neill explains the background for the action of the play by reviewing the history of the Mannon family (in various scattered expository passages) enable us to accept the determinism? Does it increase the tragic, or near-tragic, quality of the play?

3) What are the chief significant differences between the function of O'Neill's exposition and that of Aeschylus' or Sophocles' analogous exposition in the choruses of *Agamemnon* and *King Oedipus*? Is O'Neill's method more like that of Ibsen? Explain.

4) Does Lavinia's last statement, after her attempt to break out of the Mannon mold — "I've got to punish myself. . . . It takes the Mannons to punish themselves for being born" — increase her tragic stature?

5) Edwin A. Engel, in *The Haunted Heroes of Eugene O'Neill* (Cambridge, Mass.: Harvard University Press, 1953, p. 249) says:

> With the mother myth O'Neill tried to find "something to lay hold on," to fill up the moral void, to discover a rationale for his tragedy of family guilt. If Freud could trace the beginning of religion and morality to the slaying by the sons of the primordial father, O'Neill could seek it in the murder of the primordial mother. He continued to make his male characters, at least, have strange feelings of guilt as a result of their transgressions and expiate their "sins" for violating the moral order which they had created. Neither traditional nor transcendent, it is a moral order which takes no heed of impersonal justice or of objective truth.

Does this seem to be a fair summary statement of O'Neill's attitudes and practice in *Mourning Becomes Electra*? Can such a moral order as Engel defines sustain tragedy?

#### JEAN PAUL SARTRE: *The Flies*

1) Does Sartre's Orestes become a tragic hero when in Act III he assumes responsibility for his freedom and action — the killing of Aegisthus and Clytemnestra? Contrast his attitude with that of Electra.

2) In addition to assuming full responsibility for his own acts, Orestes also takes as his burden the guilt of all the citizens of Argos. Is the assumption of this burden analogous to Greek pride? Does it render Orestes more heroic?

3) Aeschylus' Orestes is bound by the order of the Oracle to kill Aegisthus and Clytemnestra — this is his fate. Note that Sartre's hero freely chooses his successive acts. Such choice may be characteristic of a tragic hero, but, in addition, Sartre causes the choice to result in Orestes' realization of his inescapable solitude and alienation. Is this realization tragic in quality? Is it characteristic of modern experience and writing?

4) Orestes attains a sort of nobility by asserting his unsponsored freedom, but he then does not stay to make himself socially effective in Argos. Is his freedom therefore selfish? How does his attitude toward his human responsibility differ from that of Oedipus? of Lear? of Rosmer?

5) Contrast the Orin of O'Neill's play with Sartre's Orestes, who says of men (Act III): "They are free, and human life begins on the other side of despair." Contrast Sartre's notion of the necessity of freedom with Strindberg's determinism.

6) Zeus, in this play by an atheistic existentialist, has no power beyond what human beings attribute to him. When Orestes knows himself free, he knows that he is independent of all authoritarian forces and sanctions including gods, though, of course, he still lives in a world in which most men believe in Zeus. Do such metaphysical and ethical ideas and implications increase or diminish Orestes as tragic hero? Explain.

#### FEDERICO GARCÍA LORCA: *Blood Wedding*

1) As in *Agamemnon*, the past in *Blood Wedding* is filled with violence and meaning. Is the connection between past and present the same in the Spanish play as in the Greek?

2) What is the ironic implication of the title, *Blood Wedding*? How is the fulfillment of this irony affected, or determined, by the conceptions of marriage and honor set forth in the play?

3) To what extent is the feeling of inevitability quickened by poetic figures that suggest the presence of a dark dualism in human life, i.e., the description of the Bride in II. i: "Ah, the white maid!/ Dark winds are the lace/ of her mantilla"? How do such figures carry the import of the play beyond the strong national feelings implicit in the action?

4) The woodcutters that appear in III.i are often identified allegorically with the three Fates. How do their judgments on the lovers' action widen or universalize the essential domestic situation of passion, infidelity, and violence? Does this help to make the play *tragic*?

5) Does the lovers' fateful acceptance of destructive passion and the Mother's final resignation to the fact of death necessarily assign a pessimistic meaning to human destiny?

6) The elemental passion of the lovers is opposed to the traditional and

ceremonial order of Spanish life. The climax of this opposition occurs when passion disrupts part of that order: the wedding festivity. Does the funeral lament at the close of the play in any way resolve this opposition? What significance should be attached to the poetic identification in the lament of the sharp knife of violence with the "sweet nails" that held Christ on the cross?

---

TENNESSEE WILLIAMS: *The Glass Menagerie*

1) Defend or reject the following statement: The human situation in *The Glass Menagerie* lacks universal import.

2) Consider the Narrator's opening description of the Gentleman Caller as a symbol of "the long delayed but always expected something that we live for." In view of the results of the Caller's visit to the Wingfield family, does this description appear to be an ironic judgment on the relationship between illusion and reality in their lives?

3) All four of the characters are affected by illusion in varying ways. Why does the play take its title from Laura's situation?

4) It is not easy to understand the nature of the antagonistic force in plays like *King Oedipus* (the mysterious curse of the gods) and *King Lear* ("Is there any cause in nature that makes these hard hearts?"), but it is not difficult to identify what the hero must struggle against in these plays. Does an antagonistic force exist in Williams' play? If so, to what extent does it produce a *tragic* action?

5) To what extent is a primary meaning of the play involved in the conflict between Tom's dramatic relationship to his father and his relationship to Laura? In this connection, what is the significance of Tom's last speech in the play?

6) The last stage direction concerning Amanda states that she has "dignity and tragic beauty." Can the word "tragic" legitimately be applied to her? Does the description of her in this last paragraph seem to indicate her acceptance of failure and of lost illusions?

---

ARTHUR MILLER: *Death of a Salesman*

1) If Krutch's thesis — that tragic feeling is not possible in modern drama — can be refuted by this play, the burden of the refutation must lie not with the theory that there is a uniqueness about man's dilemma in the modern world but with the assumption that the human implications of Willy Loman's situation and his participation in it are indeed comparable to those of the great tragedies of the past. To what extent, then, if at all, will Miller's play bear comparison with *King Lear* — which is also a dramatic account of an erring, suffering father and his quest for salvation?

2) Analyses of the tragic hero commonly state that an essential stage in his progress must be an understanding of himself and an attendant acceptance of moral responsibility for his actions. Does Willy ever reach this stage?

3) Is our acceptance of Willy as tragic hero prevented by our recognition of the shallow ideals to which he has devoted his life?

4) A key idea in Miller's essay "Tragedy and the Common Man" is that tragedy springs from "the underlying fear of being displaced, the disaster inherent in being torn from our chosen image of what and who we are in this

world." Is Biff's final judgment of his father — "He never knew who he was" — correct? Does it imply that Willy fell short of heroic stature because he did *not* give up his chosen image of himself?

5) Does the fact that Biff ultimately rejects his father's values make it impossible for Willy's suicide to be considered heroic and redemptive?

6) Is it possible to regard Willy's suicide and the final resurrection of Biff's character in terms of the ritual pattern in ancient tragedy outlined by Gilbert Murray and others?